D0734577

NATURAL ORGANIC MACROMOLECULES

NATURAL ORGANIC MACROMOLECULES

BRUNO JIRGENSONS Dr. chem.

University of Texas M. D.
Anderson Hospital and Tumor Institute
Texas Medical Center

PERGAMON PRESS

NEW YORK · OXFORD · LONDON · PARIS

1962

PERGAMON PRESS INC.
122 East 55th Street, New York 22, N.Y.
1404 New York Avenue N.W.,
Washington 5 D.C.
PERGAMON PRESS LTD.
Headington Hill Hall, Oxford
4 & 5 Fitzroy Square, London W.1
PERGAMON PRESS S.A.R.L.
24 Rue des Écoles, Paris Ve
PERGAMON PRESS G.m.b.H.
Kaiserstrasse 75, Frankfurt am Main

Library of Congress Card Number 61-10647

MADE IN ENGLAND
(IV/5/1)

CONTENTS

PAGE

PREFACE IX

PART I

1. THE SCOPE. HIGHLIGHTS ON THE HISTORICAL DEVELOPMENT 3
   Some Important Properties of Large Molecules 6
   Globular and Fibrous Macromolecules 7
   Historical Developments 8
2. ISOLATION OF NATURAL MACROMOLECULES. CRITERIA OF PURITY AND NATIVITY 12
   Factors to be Considered in the Isolation of Native Macromolecules 12
   General Methods of Isolation 15
   Criteria of Purity and Nativity 28
3. THE SIZE, SHAPE, AND HYDRATION OF MACROMOLECULES 41
   Chemical and Physical Molecular Weights 41
   Molecular Weight Averages 43
   Molecular Weight Determination by Osmotic Pressure Measurement 45
   The Size, Shape, and Homogeneity of Macromolecules from Sedimentation and Diffusion Data 50
   Molecular Size and Shape Determination by the Method of Light Scattering 57
   Double Refraction of Flow and Molecular Shape 64
   Direct Observation of Macromolecules in the Electron Microscope 66
   Molecular Weight Determination by X-rays 69
   Hydration of Macromolecules 70
   Thermodynamics of Solution and Solvation Effects 73
4. VISCOSITY OF SOLUTIONS OF MACROMOLECULAR SUBSTANCES 75
   General Terms 75
   Viscosity Measurement 76
   The Viscosity Effects of Globular and Linear Macromolecules 80
   Relationship Between the Intrinsic Viscosity and Molecular Weight of Linear High Polymers 83
   The Viscosity of Ionized High Polymers 87
   Systems Exhibiting Anomalous Flow Properties 90
5. THE CHEMICAL STRUCTURE OF MACROMOLECULES 92
   Chemical Modification of Large Molecules 92
   General Chemical Methods for the Solution of Structural Problems 94
   Structural Analysis from X-ray Diffraction Patterns 96
   Structural Studies by Spectroscopic Methods 105
   The Optical Rotation of Natural Organic Macromolecules 106

PART II

6. RUBBER AND SIMILAR POLYISOPRENES 115
   Rubber in Plant Tissues 116
   Isolation and Properties of Rubber and Gutta 118
   The Macromolecules of Rubber in Solution 121
   Cross-Linking of Rubber (Vulcanization) 122

PAGE

7. POLYSACCHARIDES. CELLULOSE AND ITS DERATIVES 125
Cellulose in Nature 125
Molecular Structure, Size, and Configuration of Cellulose 129
Cellulose Derivatives 132
Enzymic Degradation of Cellulose 137
The Hemicelluloses 138
Lignin 140

8. STARCH AND GLYCOGEN 142
Occurrence and Isolation of Starch and Glycogen 142
Molecular Weight and Structure of Amylose, Amylopectin, and Glycogen 145
Enzymic Breakdown and Synthesis of Amylose, Amylopectin, and Glycogen 150

9. THE PECTINS 155
Occurrence, Molecular Structure, and Size 155
Gelation of Pectin 158
Enzymic Modification of Pectins 160
Araban and Galactan 160

10. GUMS AND MUCILAGES. SEAWEED POLYSACCHARIDES 162
Gum Arabic 162
Tragacanth, Karaya, and other Gums 164
Mucilages 165
Agar and other Seaweed Polysaccharides 167
Dextrans 169

11. LINEAR POLYSACCHARIDES OF ANIMAL ORIGIN 171
Chitin 171
The Chondroitin Sulfates 173
Hyaluronic Acid and other Mucopolysaccharides 177
Heparin 179
Blood Group Polysaccharides 181

12. THE STRUCTURE AND CONFIGURATION OF NATIVE AND DENATURES PROTEINS 183
Classification 183
Terminal Groups and Amino Acid Sequence in the Polypeptide Chain 184
The Number of Polypeptide Chains in the Macromolecules of Proteins 189
Intra- and Inter-chain Bonding and Configuration of Proteins 190
Denaturation of Proteins 194
Optical Rotation and Configuration of Proteins 199

13. ALBUMINS AND GLOBULINS IN ANIMALS AND PLANTS 204
Serum Albumin 204
The γ-Globulins of Serum 215
The Albumins and Globulins of Birds'Eggs 220
Albumins and Globulins in Plants 223

14. THE HEMOGLOBINS AND OTHER RESPIRATORY PROTEINS 226
The Hemoglobins 226
The Myoglobins 231
The Variety of Respiratory Proteins in the Lower Species 233

PAGE

15. ENZYMES, AND ENZYMIC ACTIVITY 236
    - Proteolytic Enzymes 238
    - Ribonuclease 246
    - The Redox Enzymes 251

16. PROTEIN HORMONES 254
    - The Structure of Insulin 254
    - The Adrenocorticotropic Hormone (ACTH) 260
    - The Lactogenic Hormone 261
    - The Growth Hormones 263

17. THE FIBROUS STRUCTURAL PROTEINS 265
    - General Structural Principles 266
    - The Fibrous Proteins in Silk 269
    - Keratin and Epidermin 272
    - The Collagens and Elastins 275
    - The Fibrous Proteins of Muscle 283

18. NUCLEOPROTEINS, HISTONES, PROTAMINES, AND RESIDUAL PROTEINS 288
    - The Nucleoproteins 289
    - The Protamines 291
    - The Histones 294
    - Residual Protein 296

19. THE NUCLEIC ACIDS 299
    - The Composition and Structure of Deoxyribonucleic Acids 301
    - The Size and Configuration of the Macromolecules of DNA 304
    - The Ribonucleic Acids (RNA's) 310
    - Some Uncommon Nucleic Acids and Nucleoproteins 313

PART III

20. VIRUSES AND PHAGES 317
    - Some Simple Nucleoprotein Viruses 319
    - Simple Animal Viruses 327
    - Complex Organized Animal Viruses 329
    - The Phages 331
    - Some Concluding Remarks 334

21. CELLULAR INGREDIENTS 335
    - The Cell Nucleus 336
    - The Mitochondrion 339
    - The Microsome, and Protein Synthesis 344
    - The Fibrous Framework and Organization of the Cell 348

22. RECENT IDEAS ON BIOLOGICAL REPLICATION 351
    - Macromolecules and their Functional Relationships in the Cell 351
    - The Replication of Cellular Macromolecules 353
    - Biosynthesis of DNA 360
    - Concluding Remarks 362

23. MACROMOLECULES IN BLOOD 365
    - Plasma Proteins 368
    - Antibodies and their Reactions 374
    - Macromolecules in Blood Clotting 377

PAGE

24. ABNORMAL PROTEINS IN DISEASES 382
    The Cryoglobulin Problem 384
    The Macroglobulins 385
    Abnormal Serum Globulins in Multiple Myeloma 389
    The Urinary Bence-Jones Proteins 391

25. THE PROBLEM OF MALIGNANT GROWTH 394
    Facts and Ideas Relative to the Origin of the Malignancy 394
    Serum Proteins in Cancer 400
    Antimetabolites in the Biosynthesis of Macromolecules 406

26. MACROMOLECULES IN CONNECTIVE TISSUE 410
    Collagen Fibers and their Functions 410
    Elastic Fibers of Connective Tissue 418
    The Role of Polysaccharides 419

27. MACROMOLECULAR REACTIONS IN MUSCLE AND NERVE TISSUES 421
    Macromolecules and their Motions in Muscle 422
    Macromolecular Structures of Nervous Tissue 430

28. CONCLUDING REMARKS ABOUT THE SYNTHESIS OF MACROMOLECULES AND ORIGIN OF LIFE 434

AUTHOR-INDEX 442

SUBJECT-INDEX 456

PREFACE

THIS TREATISE is an introduction to the chemistry of large molecules. It does not attempt to cover the whole polymer science but only the *natural organic polymers*. This limitation is necessitated by the enormous growth of this new branch of chemistry during the last decades. Since purely *chemical* viewpoints instead of physical chemistry are emphasized, these "Natural Organic Macromolecules" can be regarded as special chapters of organic chemistry. One of the chief purposes of this outline is to present a unifying synthetic picture of this new branch of chemistry showing its growth, present status, and future perspectives, especially in solving the complex biological problems. Since the scope is wide, including the vast domains of proteins, polysaccharides, and nucleic acids, not all aspects could be treated equally thoroughly, but the most important literature is indicated whenever little is said on some topic.

The book is divided into three parts. The shorter first part outlines the methods of study, including isolation and determination of chemical structure and configuration of macromolecules. The second part presents a condensed survey of the most important natural organic polymers, including recent advances up to about the middle of 1959. The third part shows the applications of fundamental principles and facts of macromolecular chemistry chiefly in the fields of biology and medicine. The subject matter is presented in a language understandable for a non-chemist.

At this point the author feels the need also to justify his factual treatment of the subject. Science should not be regarded as an assembly of everchanging more or less useful theories and hypotheses. Science is a system of rationally interconnected facts and relations. Fundamental discoveries and principles do not change. These fundamental facts and quantitative relations are reflections of the objective reality, and they represent the permanent truth, the core of science. Theoretical concepts are tied around this stable core, and they change in accord with new discoveries. A hypothesis must be able to predict undiscovered facts, and a theoretical endeavor earns the name of theory only after it has proved its ability to predict phenomena that are confirmed by experiment. An enthusiastic explorer in science is searching for truth, for the permanent truth which we approach, perhaps asymptotically, by both experimental and theoretical means.

The completion of this work would not be possible without the generous aid of many friends and colleagues who were kind enough to read several chapters and point out imperfections and omissions. The author is indebted in the first place to Dr. A. Clark Griffin, Head of the Department of Biochemistry of The University of Texas M. D. Anderson Hospital and Tumor Institute, and to Dr. Felix L. Haas, Head of the Biology Department of same institute for checking some chapters in the third part. Drs. T. Ikenaka, Marge O'Neal, K. Yunoki, R. W. Cumley, D. H. Ezekiel, Robert B. Hurlbert, Saul Kit, and Darrell N. Ward were helpful in many ways. Also I am indebted to the many colleagues who provided material for illustrations, and to the Publisher for his interest in this undertaking.

PART I

CHAPTER 1

THE SCOPE. HIGHLIGHTS ON THE HISTORICAL DEVELOPMENT

The bewildering variety of living forms conceals an underlying unity in the molecules that nature uses for the process of reproduction, multiplication, growth, movement, metabolism, secretion, and nervous response.

M. F. PERUTZ (*Endeavour*, 17, 190, 1958)

THE REALM of macromolecules or large molecules includes a wide variety of natural and synthetic organic and inorganic substances. In this treatise only the natural organic macromolecular substances will be considered. In spite of this restriction, the scope is wide and the subject is scarcely excelled in importance by anything. The whole magnificence and variety of plant and animal kingdom, including the human body, is built of large molecules. Our food and clothing, footwear, furniture, etc., are composed to a great extent of macromolecules.

There is no sharp borderline between the realm of the *macro-* and *micro-*molecular compounds (macros in Greek means large, micros—small). According to the now generally accepted convention, a macromolecule contains 1000 or more atoms, and there is no upper limit to the size of these large molecules. A macromolecule is a structural unit of definite size and structure, and all atoms in it are linked by primary valency bonds.

There is another familiar term, a close relative to macromolecule — the *polymer*. Poly in Greek means many, and meros means part, hence polymeric molecules are composed of many equal or similar parts. There is a difference in polymeric and macromolecular substances, although the terms often are used as synonyms. The polymers may be micro- or macromolecular, for example paraldehyde $(CH_3CHO)_3$ is a small, micromolecular polymer of aldehyde. Macromolecular polymers, such as rubber, are called *high-polymers.* [1]

Natural organic macromolecules belong to the domain of organic chemistry the chemistry of carbon compounds. There are more than half a million more or less completely investigated carbon compounds, but the number of possible

[1] See for example: K. H. MEYER, *Natural and Synthetic High Polymers* 2nd ed. Interscience, New York, 1950; P. J. FLORY, *Principles of Polymer Chemistry,* Cornell University Press, Ithaca, N. Y., 1953.

isomers is unlimited. It is surprising how many isomers are possible, even of relatively simple hydrocarbons. For instance, there must be 75 decanes ($C_{10}H_{22}$), 2513 pentadecanes ($C_{15}H_{32}$), and not less than 21,500 eicosanes ($C_{20}H_{42}$). This is due to the unique tendency of carbon atoms to combine in a large variety of ways. Furthermore, the number of isomers increases with unsaturation and with addition of atoms other than H to the carbon skeleton. Generally, the number of isomers of carbon compounds increases with the number of carbon atoms in the molecule, and it increases also with increasing variety of elements combined with the carbon. It has been calculated that a polypeptide composed of 20 different residues of amino acids (containing C, H, O, N, and S) and having a molecular weight of approximately 2400, could have $2{\cdot}4 \cdot 10^{18}$ isomers.[(2)] Yet, this compound still is micromolecular. The incomprehensible number of 10^{1268} is obtained when such calculation is extended to a macromolecular protein of molecular weight 120,000. Even if the combinations of the amino acid residues in the macromolecule were restricted, the possibilities of variation remain practically unlimited.

Considering this infinite multitude and variety of possible carbon compounds, one may wonder why Nature has selected only a few major pathways of making them. For example, only the unsaturated polyprenes, such as natural rubber, are synthesized by certain plants, but many other possibilities, e.g., the synthesis of polystyrene, Nature does not accomplish. (Graphite, asphalt, and petroleum hydrocarbons are decomposition products of more complex organic molecules). A few thousand C, H, and O atoms could be combined into uncountable billions of macromolecules which would differ profoundly in their composition and structure, yet the *cells synthesize only a few general types of macromolecules*. Our task in dealing with these natural organic macromolecules thus is greatly alleviated. If Nature were to produce thousands of greatly differing structural types, a macromolecular chemistry would be virtually impossible. There are only *four* general structural types which are of major importance:

(1) the polyprenes, e.g. rubber,

(2) polysaccharides, e.g. cellulose, starch, pectins,

(3) proteins (albumins, hemoglobins, the enzymes), and

(4) nucleic acids and nucleoproteins.

The structural features of these are presented in the following chart. This classification, of course, is not quite complete, as we have not included there such substances as the lignins, tannic acids, and similar compounds. However,

(2) H. STAUDINGER, *Organische Kolloidchemie*, 3rd ed., chap. 3, Vieweg, Braunschweig, 1950.

first, these substances seem to be not truly macromolecular, and, second, they are of secondary importance.

$$\cdots -CH{=}\underset{\displaystyle CH_3}{\underset{|}{C}}-CH_2-CH_2-CH{=}\underset{\displaystyle CH_3}{\underset{|}{C}}-CH_2-CH_2-CH{=}\underset{\displaystyle CH_3}{\underset{|}{C}}-CH_2-CH_2-CH{=}$$

$$={\underset{\displaystyle CH_3}{\underset{|}{C}}}-CH_2-CH_2-\cdots$$

polyprene chain

$$\cdots -O-HC\langle\begin{matrix} | \quad\; | \\ CH-CH \\ CH - O \\ | \end{matrix}\rangle CH-O-HC\langle\begin{matrix} | \quad\; | \\ CH-CH \\ CH - O \\ | \end{matrix}\rangle CH-O-HC\langle\begin{matrix} | \quad\; | \\ CH-CH \\ CH - O \\ | \end{matrix}\rangle CH-\cdots$$

polysaccharide chain

$$NH_2-\underset{\displaystyle R_1}{\underset{|}{CH}}-CO-NH-\underset{\displaystyle R_2}{\underset{|}{CH}}-CO-NH-\underset{\displaystyle R_3}{\underset{|}{CH}}-CO-NH-\underset{\displaystyle R_4}{\underset{|}{CH}}-CO-\cdots-NH-$$

$$-\underset{\displaystyle R_n}{\underset{|}{CH}}-COOH$$

polypeptide chain in proteins

$R_1, R_2, R_3 \ldots$ are the amino acid side groups.

$$\cdots-O-\overset{\displaystyle OH}{\overset{|}{\underset{\displaystyle O}{\underset{\|}{P}}}}-O-HC\begin{matrix}\\ | \\ -HC\end{matrix}\!\!\underset{\underset{\displaystyle R_1}{\underset{|}{CH}}}{\searrow\swarrow}\!\!\begin{matrix}CH-CH_2-O-\\ | \\ O\end{matrix}\overset{\displaystyle OH}{\overset{|}{\underset{\displaystyle O}{\underset{\|}{P}}}}-O-HC\begin{matrix}\\ | \\ -HC\end{matrix}\!\!\underset{\underset{\displaystyle R_2}{\underset{|}{CH}}}{\searrow\swarrow}\!\!\begin{matrix}CH-CH_2-O-\\ | \\ O\end{matrix}\overset{\displaystyle OH}{\overset{|}{\underset{\displaystyle O}{\underset{\|}{P}}}}-O-HC\begin{matrix}\\ | \\ -HC\end{matrix}\!\!\underset{\underset{\displaystyle R_3}{\underset{|}{CH}}}{\searrow\swarrow}\!\!\begin{matrix}CH-\cdots\\ | \\ O\end{matrix}$$

The nucleic acid chain

$R_1, R_2 \ldots$ are the purine and pyrimidine heterocycles.

The long polyprene chains are built entirely of carbon atoms. The polysaccharide chains are more complex, they are composed of linearly arranged rings containing oxygen atoms. There is, however, more of variety, since these linear arrangements may be branched. Furthermore, at the free carbon bonds can be attached various atoms and residues, most commonly the alcoholic OH-groups, sometimes also a CH_2-OH residue, a carboxyl group, etc. In spite of these (and other) diversities, all of the most important natural polysaccharides contain arrays of the pyranoid hexagons, a remarkable feature of uniformity. Next in the chart, the proteins, all have in common the polypeptide chain structure, and most of the variety is introduced by the diversity of the amino acid side groups $R_1, R_2 \ldots$ Moreover, the chains may be of different length, and they may be folded in various ways. This variety of folding and secondary linking of the segments of the chain results in the variety of *configuration*. The mentioned multitude of structural isomers is due to the different *order* of the R_1, R_2,... — containing residues. A similar feature is characteristic for the last major class of natural polymers — the nucleic acids, the important constituents of cell nuclei. The presence of the phosphoric acid residues as chain constituents, beside the furanoid ribose or deoxyribose rings, is a peculiar feature of these macromolecules. The variety of these structures is based on the variety of distribution of the purine and pyrimidine residues (R_1, R_2...) along the chain, as well as on several other possible differences.

We may conclude then this section with the following classification:

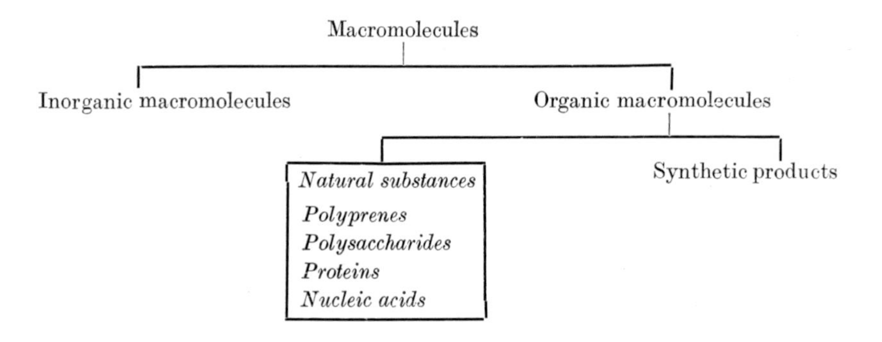

Some Important Properties of Large Molecules

All macromolecular substances are non-volatile solids, they do not possess definite melting points, and most of the organic macromolecules decompose when heated over 300 °C. The solubility of high polymers depends on their composition and structure. When the macromolecular chains are crosslinked by strong primary bonds, the substance cannot be dissolved in any solvent without being decomposed. Otherwise, the polar macromolecules, such as the proteins, can be dissolved in polar solvents, such as water or aqueous salt solutions, and non-polar polymers are miscible with non-polar solvents (e.g. rubber with octane). The solutions of all macromolecular substances possess the properties of *colloids*, i.e. the diffusion rate of the solute is low and the macromolecules do not pass through semipermeable membranes, such as the intestinal wall.[3] The largest macromolecules can be seen in the electron microscope, and they undergo sedimentation in the strong gravitational field as caused in the ultracentrifuge.

[3] B. JIRGENSONS and M. STRAUMANIS, *A Short Textbook of Colloid Chemistry* 2nd ed., Pergamon Press, London, 1961; A. E. ALEXANDER and P. JOHNSON, *Colloid Science*, Clarendon Press, Oxford, 1949; B. JIRGENSONS, *Organic Colloids*, Elsevier Publ., Amsterdam, 1958.

An essential difference between the very small and large molecules is that in the case of small molecules the properties of the substance change profoundly when but one atom in the molecule is replaced or added, whereas in macromolecular substances this usually is not the case. For example, the attachment of 2H atoms to a molecule of ethylene changes this hydrocarbon to ethane, while the attachment of one isoprene residue to the long polyprene chain of rubber does not change the properties of the polymer perceptibly. The larger the molecules, the less their properties depend on small variations in their size and chemical composition. Furthermore, the macromolecular substances differ from simple micromolecular compounds in that the former are almost always polymolecular, whereas the latter are homogeneous. The macromolecules of even the purest natural or synthetic high polymers are not of exactly the same size but they differ more or less markedly. Although the natural organic macromolecules, especially the proteins, are more homogeneous than the synthetic polymers, some heterogeneity has been found also in proteins. It must be borne in mind that even at the lower size limit of the macromolecules it is impossible to distinguish and separate components differing only in, say, 15 atoms. Any preparations of substances like starch, glycogen, or rubber are polymolecular mixtures of similar but not identical macromolecules. Such systems are denoted as polymer-homologous mixtures, and they are characterized by their mean degree of polymerization, and mean or average molecular weight (obtained by multiplying the degree of polymerization by the weight of the reappearing residue or mer).

The larger a molecule, the less important become the *terminal groups* in the chains. For example, it is relatively easy to detect the terminal residues in the relatively small hydrolytic cleavage products of cellulose, but it is difficult to find any end groups in such macromolecules as undegraded cellulose or rubber. This is merely because these groups comprise only a vanishingly small portion of the whole preparation. Consequently, there is not much mistake if we write chain formulae without end groups, as was done on p. 5.

Globular and Fibrous Macromolecules

With respect to their molecular shape, all natural organic high polymers can be classified into two large classes: the globular (sphero-) and fibrous (linear) macromolecules. The usefulness of this classification was impressively exposed by Staudinger.[(4)] The globular macromolecules are built of strongly branched or tightly folded chains, while the fibrous macromolecules are highly extended in one dimension. Such linear macromolecules are long and very thin, like hair or wool fibers. Representatives of these classes differ strongly

(4) H. Staudinger, *Naturwiss.* **42**, 221 (1955); *Organische Kolloidchemie* 3rd ed., Vieweg, Braunschweig, 1950; *Die hochmolekularen organischen Verbindungen, Kautschuk und Cellulose*, Springer, Berlin, 1932; H. Batzer, *Einführung in die makromolekulare Chemie*, A. Hüthig, Heidelberg, 1958.

in the mechanical properties, also in solubility, in flow properties of their solutions, etc. The fibrous macromolecules serve as structural materials: cellulose in plants, the fibrous proteins in animals. No durable fabrics can be made from globular units. They have a different purpose — they are vehicles and active participants in all sorts of physiological reactions. Examples of globular and fibrous macromolecules are mentioned in the following chart:

Natural organic macromolecules

Globular	*Fibrous*
glycogen	cellulose
albumin	rubber
hemoglobin	collagen
pepsin	nucleic acids

There are some quite interesting differences in the chemical stability between the globular and fibrous macromolecules. While the former are relatively stable, the latter can be cleaved readily, for example by traces of oxygen. This is due simply to the geometry of these structures: a thread is much easier to tear than a tight coil. It is important also to consider the stability of configuration. It appears that the fibrous macromolecules are flexible, and can be coiled and extended to various degrees depending on the conditions. When a rubber band is stretched, the macromolecules become stretched and oriented. In various solvents the linear macromolecules are looped and coiled to various degrees. Moreover, the molecular configuration is changed by the thermal motion of the segments, as well as under the influence of flow gradient. The properties of a particular macromolecular system depend strongly on the configuration of the units.

The configuration of the globular macromolecules is more stable than that of the fibrous macromolecules. However, in comparison with small molecules of similar composition, the large molecules, especially those of the proteins, do not possess very stable configuration. The unique folding and secondary bonding of the chains in a macromolecule can be damaged and distorted readily, for example by heating, irradiation with ultrasonic waves, or even by spreading on surfaces or strong shaking. The uniquely folded globular macromolecule may even unfold under these effects and become a linear unit. Sometimes the activated globular units do not unfold but combine into large linear or branched superstructures. Disorganization of the unique native configuration of macromolecules is called denaturation.

Historical Developments

The chemistry of macromolecular substances is one of the most recent developments in modern science. Although the existence of large molecules was surmized by quite a few chemists about a hundred years ago, definite experimental proofs began to accumulate only around 1900–1910. The German chemist Emil Fischer was one of the first pioneers in this field, as he envisaged the macromolecular nature and correct structure of the polysaccharides and proteins. Striving for an unequivocal solution of structural problems, he advocated and partially accomplished step by step syntheses of relatively large polypeptides and similar complicated compounds. However, these syntheses were so complicated, expensive and time-consuming that chemists looked for a simpler, more convenient solution of the problem. The endeavor of E. Fischer remains as one of the most ambitious and daring enterprises in the history of modern chemistry.

Spontaneous or induced polymerization reactions would be another way to try to build large molecules. Many resinous polymers were known in the nineteenth century, but the organic chemists of that time shied from dealing with them, because of the difficulties involved in such work. First of all, it was impossible to crystallize them and to obtain them in a reasonably pure state. The resinous polymers, whenever they appeared, were discarded down the drain. Moreover, there was no clear idea of what polymerization meant. Several investigators regarded these resinous substances as micromolecular association colloids (see ref. 3 and 4). The important fact that a large amount of heat is evolved in spontaneous polymerization was disregarded.

The rise of the new colloid chemistry during 1910–20 had a tremendous impact on the dominating views in this field. The colloid chemists pointed out the fact that every substance can be prepared in a colloidal state, a certain state of aggregation of the small molecules. For example, it is possible to prepare not only colloidal soap solutions and colloidal emulsions of oils, but even colloidal barium sulfate or calcium carbonate are possible. The colloidal particles of soap or barium sulfate are aggregates of many small molecules. These aggregates were called micelles, and the micellar concept was widely generalized to include all the synthetic and natural high polymers, such as gums, starch, rubber, etc. In 1915–30 the micellar concept of the structure of high polymers became very popular, and some prominent organic chemists like P. Karrer and W. N. Haworth advocated it. The micellar hypothesis seemed to be supported also by molecular weight determinations on substances like rubber. Although it was shown later that these experiments were incorrectly interpreted (and that solutions of degraded macromolecules often were used), the micellar concept prevailed in the literature up to the late forties.

The first organic chemist who took an opposite view was H. Staudinger. He expressed clearly the presently prevailing idea that substances like rubber, starch, and cellulose are macromolecular substances, not micellar aggregates.[5] The entities which go into solution upon dissolving rubber in benzene are not aggregated small molecules but they are macromolecules in which all atoms are linked by primary covalent bonds. One of the first major experimental proofs which supported this contention was the fact that rubber can be hydro-

[5] H. Staudinger and J. Fritschi, *Helv. Chim. Acta* **5**, 785 (1922).

genated and converted into saturated hydro-rubber without losing its colloidal properties. Thus in the reaction

$$(C_5H_8)_n + n\,H_2 = (C_5H_{10})_n$$

the macromolecular carbon skeleton remains the same. If the entities were micelles instead of macromolecules it would be very unlikely that the hydro-rubber would form micelles which have the same number of isoprene residues as rubber. Numerous so called polymer-analogous conversions were accomplished later by Staudinger and his associates;[6] for example, it has been shown that the macromolecular backbone remains the same when starch or glycogen is converted into various derivatives (see chapt. 5 and 8). Starch, for example, was converted into the triacetate, and it could be shown that the degree of polymerization did not change in this treatment. Moreover, the triacetates were reconverted into starch, and it was proven by various criteria that the recovered starch has the same structure, configuration, and degree of polymerization as the original native product!

After this and similar evidence, the tide began to turn in favor of the macromolecular concept. The polymerization studies of Carothers [7] also had a strong effect, since he convincingly proved that covalent bonds are involved in these reactions and that the resinous polymers are macromolecular substances.

K. H. Meyer and H. Mark in 1928–35 took a cautious "middle of the road" view, assuming that cellulose is built of relatively large and elongated micelles, each composed of 40–60 anhydroglucose chains and each chain containing 30–50 pyranoid glucose residues.[8] These are the popular "packets of sheaves" as illustrated in many books even in the forties. However, Meyer and Mark later abandoned this view in favour of Staudinger's concept.

The course of developments concerning protein structure is quite interesting. High molecular weights were found by osmotic pressure measurements in various laboratories [9], but it was not altogether clear if those values of 35,000 or more represented true molecular weights. They could have been the relative weights of micellar aggregates as well. A new encouragement to the macromolecular concept was given by the important discoveries of Svedberg and his school in 1923–1938 on the sedimentation of proteins in the ultracentrifuge.[10] Not only were the high molecular weights ascertained, but it was also shown that many proteins are homogeneous. Sedimentation ana-

(6) H. Staudinger and E. Husemann, *Ann.* **527**, 195 (1937); H. Staudinger and R. Mohr, *Ber. dtsch. chem. Ges.* **70**, 2303 (1937); H. Staudinger, *Z. angew. Ch.* **64**, 149 (1952).

(7) W. H. Carothers, *Chem. Rev.* **8**, 353 (1931).

(8) K. H. Meyer and H. Mark, *Ber. dtsch. chem. Ges.* **61**, 609 (1928).

(9) S. P. L. Sørensen, *Hoppe-Seylers Z. physiol. Ch.* **106**, 1 (1919); G. S. Adair, *Proc. Roy. Soc. London* **108**, 627 (1925); **109**, 292 (1925); **120**, 573 (1928); **126**, 16 (1929); N. F. Burk and D. M. Greenberg, *J. biol. Chem.* **87**, 197 (1930).

(10) T. Svedberg and K. O. Pedersen, *The Ultracentrifuge* Clarendon Press, Oxford, 1940; T. Svedberg, *Chem. Rev.* **20**, 81 (1937).

lysis of hemoglobin, for example, showed that all sedimenting entities are of the same weight. A protein solution thus appears more like the homogeneous micromolecular solutions, such as those of sugar, and differs strongly from the polydisperse soaps and similar micellar colloids. Although some inhomogeneity was found later in most of these apparently homogeneous proteins, the work of Svedberg generally supported the macromolecular concept. The ultracentrifuge revealed several other curious facts. For example, the macromolecules of several proteins may reversibly dissociate into subunits which represent 1/2, 1/4, or 1/8 of the original macromolecule.

Although the macromolecular concept is now an established truth, the structure and configuration of many organic natural macromolecules is not completely solved. In the first place, there are the problems concerning on the structure of proteins, nucleic acids, and nucleoproteins. Solutions to these problems are essential for such difficult assignments as the unsolved biological problems of reduplication and differentiation. Thus far, the complete chemical structure of only one small protein is unraveled — the insulin, and this brilliant achievement is now internationally recognized by che award of the Nobel Prize to the young British chemist F. Sanger who has the greatest merit in this grand task. However, the insulin molecule is hardly a macromolecule, since it is composed of "only" a few hundred atoms, and the molecular weight is "only" 5733. Insulin cannot be synthesized as yet, and even if this will one day be achieved, the biological synthesis will not be fully solved. Sanger himself writes: "Clearly the present results can provide little information about the mechanism of protein syntheses, but they do provide certain limitations on those who are speculating on the subject".[11] A long, long road is still ahead of us. The molecular weight of serum albumin is about 70,000, and very little is known thus far about the sequence of the amino acid residues in this middle-size protein. With the proteins, and especially with the still more complex nucleoproteins, we are still at the very beginning.*

(11) F. SANGER, The Structure of Insulin, in *Currents in Biochemical Research* pp. 434–459; quotation from p. 457 (D. E. GREEN, ed.), Interscience, New York, London, 1956.

* During the last years, the complete chemical structure of several other proteins has been worked out.

CHAPTER 2

ISOLATION OF NATURAL MACROMOLECULES. CRITERIA OF PURITY AND NATIVITY*

> Now, let us ask a very silly question. Can we be sure that the substances we isolate from the cell exist in the living cell?
>
> E. CHARGAFF

THIS TREATISE is so much aimed at biological problems that I would like to continue this illuminating quotation of Chargaff [1]: "I should say, the answer will have to be: they do and they do not. A simple monomer — a fatty acid, a sugar, etc. — which we find in a cell probably has not been produced *de novo* in the course of the devastating process known as careful isolation. Even in such cases, to decide whether these substances occurred in the free state is a difficult matter. It becomes immensely more so when we come to high polymers often endowed, as in the case of proteins or nucleic acids, with a multiplicity of charges. I have little doubt that the physical description of the molecular arrangement of such complicated compounds, which must be drawn, quartered, pickled, or embalmed in order to be studied, defines the pleasing shape into which they can be put rather than the form in which they exist in life".

The difficulties encountered in isolation and purification of natural organic macromolecules are indeed enormous, and the nativity of the most thoroughly purified specimens is often questionable. However, in spite of these difficulties, considerable progress has been made in the last decades in the elaboration of mild methods. We have also some evidence, again delivered by recently developed new methods, that the isolated macromolecules do exist in living cells, although in not exactly the same condition as in our test tubes.

Factors to be considered in the Isolation of Native Macromolecules

The purpose of this section is to outline the basic principles of isolation including the precautions to be considered in order to avoid any damage to these tender structures. Detailed descriptions of the various isolation procedures will be given in the Second Part of the book, since the methods differ from case to case.

* The term "nativity" denotes here "existing in the native state".

(1) E. CHARGAFF, from *The Harvey Lectures* p. 58, 1956–57, Academic Press, New York, 1958.

Organic macromolecules exist in plant and animal tissues as complicated organized systems of many chemical constituents of various sizes and shapes. The classical methods of organic chemistry, such as precipitation with non-solvents, crystallization, distillation, etc. are hardly applicable. The macromolecules decompose when distilled, and they may change their configuration when precipitated with organic nonsolvents at room temperatures. Some breakdown of the macromolecular structures can occur even on mincing and grinding of the cellular material. Furthermore, since the molecules are large and often fibrous, they adsorb various small, micromolecular impurities when one succeeds in crystallizing them. These are some of the reasons why some of the natural high polymers which were isolated by the pioneers of polymer chemistry some 70 years ago were either denatured or impure, or both impure and denatured.

Again, at this point it becomes essential to distinguish the globular from the fibrous macromolecules. The former are more stable and much more easy to purify than the long and thin linear macromolecules. While relatively pure glycogen or albumin was prepared long ago, the fibrous myosins or nucleic acids are relatively recent products. It is true that some natural products which are built of fibrous macromolecules, such as cellulose fabrics and leather, man has learned to process and apply since prehistoric times, yet a scientific understanding of this subject began to develop but recently. The reason why fibrous high polymers are so difficult to handle chemically rests simply in their molecular shape. In plant or animal tissues the fibrous macromolecules lay side by side in bundles which form a fabric. The long and thin units in the bundles have numerous points of contact. In these numerous points the fibrous macromolecules become linked by various types of bonds, most often by the relatively weak secondary hydrogen bonds, e.g. between the hydrogen atom of the —NH— group in a protein and an oxygen atom of the —CO— group of adjacent chain. Although any single hydrogen bond is weak, the bond strength being in the order of 4–8 kcal/mole (in comparison to the bond energy of 80–150 kcal/mole of the primary valency bonds), the large number of such bonds along the chains makes the fibrous macromolecules stick together very tenaciously. Two globular macromolecules, on the contrary, have only a few contact points, and such arrangement makes it possible to separate the units readily. Consequently, the fibrous high polymers are much less easily soluble than be globular polymers. Especially difficult are the cases of the polar linear macromolecules, such as cellulose, silk and the keratins, since the hydrogen bonds, and sometimes even the stronger primary bonds, may interlink the chains; the non-polar rubber is more easy to handle (see Fig. 1).

In addition to this difficulty of bringing the fibrous high polymers into solution, they are liable to destructive cleavage. It has been proved by Staudinger and others that traces of oxygen readily degrade rubber, even at room temperatures. Substances like cellulose or rubber are strongly degraded (i.e.

the linear chains broken and shortened) even on intense grinding and milling, procedures often applied as a pretreatment of organic solids in order to facilitate dissolution. Hence the polymer chemist encounters the seemingly unsolvable problem: the fibrous material is resistant to solvents, and the macromolecules are degraded whenever more drastic methods are applied. Furthermore, the fibrous tissues contain a multitude of other fibrous and globular macromolecules, and also a variety of small molecules absorbed in the motley fabric of the tissue. Some of these impurities may be catalysts which promote hydrolytic cleavage of some of the fibrous ingredients, even at a mild treatment. Whenever one wants to avoid drastic treatment and plans a moderate treatment under physiological conditions, enzymic degradation must be considered. (Such cleavage, for example may occur in some of the nucleic acid isolation procedures.) In spite of these difficulties, a considerable progress has been achieved even with such macromolecular systems as cellulose fibers, silk, and the nucleic acids.

One of the most essential factors involved in successful undamaged isolation is temperature. The macromolecular chemist often has to work in cold rooms, a rather unpleasant condition which one tries to avoid in various ways. One of the best practical solutions of this problem is to use a horizontal freezer. Small samples can be readily precipitated, washed, filtered, etc. this way. Large size instruments, such as centrifuges, are now provided with refrigeration, another essential technical improvement the early polymer chemist did not have. Other more complicated devices, such as chromatography columns, also can be handled outside a cold room simply by using jacketed columns and cold water circulation from special cooling machines. Frozen solutions of labile natural polymers are freed from water by freeze-drying or lyophilization, another ingenuous method which facilitated the development of modern macromolecular chemistry considerably. The refrigerating unit and high-vacuum pump are the simple machines without which the modern chemistry of natural high polymers would be helpless.

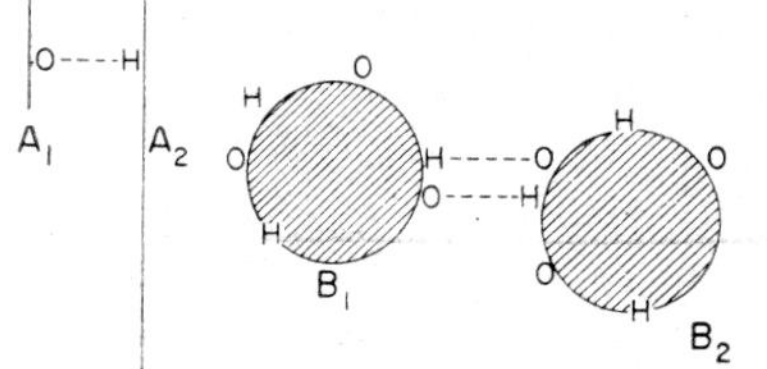

FIG. 1. Attraction (hydrogen bonding) between two linear (A_1 and A_2) and two spherical macromolecules (B_1 and B_2) of approximately equal mass

If the starting material is a tough solid, one of the first steps in isolation involves *grinding* and *milling*. These procedures can do some harm to the large molecules, but the damage can be more or less completely avoided by grinding frozen material under refrigeration. Moreover, it is established in many cases that exclusion of oxygen is beneficial for the preservation of the macromolecular structure of a native material. Let us remember at this point the primitive methods of making fire by rubbing dry wood: the mechanical energy of rubbing is converted into heat, and the presence of oxygen initiates a vigorous oxidation. Again, the linear macromolecules of cellulose, rubber, or the nucleic acids are more liable to destructive oxidation on mechanical treatment than the globular macromolecules. For example, Staudinger has calculated that only 1 mg of oxygen is needed to split the long molecules of 7·5 g of cellulose from an average degree of polymerization 3000 to that of 1500.[2] This can be avoided by working at possibly low temperatures in an inert gas, such as nitrogen or helium. In certain industrial areas, such as rubber tire production, the combined destructive effects of mechanical rubbing and oxidation are supressed by including certain antioxidants in the rubber mixes.[3] Various radiations, such as intense sunlight, ultraviolet radiations, ultrasonic waves etc. also may produce changes in certain macromolecular systems. For example, the long macromolecules of collagen [4] or nucleic acids [5] are chopped into shorter pieces by sonic irradiation; and in order to avoid any uncontrollable side reactions, the irradiation was performed in a nitrogen atmosphere under refrigeration.

Finally, a general precaution to be considered in the work with natural organic high polymers is protection of the solutions from invasion by molds and other microbes. Working at low temperatures (near the freezing point) usually takes care of this danger. When certain long procedures require room temperatures, certain additives, such as toluene, thymol, mercurials, or antibiotics sometimes must be used. The possible interactions of these additives with the macromolecules, however, always must be considered.

General Methods of Isolation

Centrifugation. This is one of the simplest and most important approaches in separation of small particles and large molecules.[6] This is based on Stokes' law for spheres that the rate of settling V is directly proportional to the second power of the particle radius r^2, and to the difference of density $d_p - d_m$ between the sedimenting particles (d_p) and the medium (d_m) and indirectly proportional to the viscosity of the medium η:

$$V = h/t = K r^2 g (d_p - d_m)/\eta ,$$

where h is the distance through which the particle settles in time t, g is the acceleration of gravity (980 cm/sec^2), and K the particle shape factor, which for a sphere is 0.222. (If calculations are made, all of the factors must be expressed in the c. g. s. system.)

(2) H. Mark and A. V. Tobolsky, *Physical Chemistry of High Polymeric Systems* 2nd ed., p. 477ff., Interscience, New York, 1950.

(3) H. Staudinger and J. Jurisch, *Ber. dtsch. chem. Ges.* **71**, 2283 (1938).

(4) T. Nishihara and P. Doty, *Proc. nat. Acad. Sci. USA*. **44**, 411 (1958).

(5) P. Doty, B. Bunce McGill and S. A. Rice, *ibid.* **44**, 432 (1958).

(6) H. B. Golding in Weissberger's *Technique of Organic Chemistry* Vol. III, p. 143ff., 1950.

It appears, however, that natural gravitational force is insufficient for the separation of such small particles as cell fragments or macromolecules, even if the particle radii r of the various components differ widely. A certain separation can be expected only in very coarse systems, and the smaller the particles the less they will be affected by the gravitational force. This is due to the Brownian movement caused by the irregular molecular impacts. Moreover, in biological fluids the density differences between the particles and the medium are small, and the viscosity often is high. If the density of the particles is lower than that of the medium, as it is in the case of fat droplets in milk, the latter move to the opposite direction (creaming).

For these reasons, natural sedimentation (or creaming) is of little importance in the isolation of natural macromolecules. This approach, however, becomes very important when the gravitational force is replaced by a centrifugal force. Again, it is self-evident that the separation will be more efficient the greater the difference in particle sizes and densities between the particles and the liquid. Moreover, in this instance the sedimentation depends also on the speed of rotation, and then Stokes' law must be modified as follows:[7]

$$t = \frac{1}{K} \frac{\eta \ln x_2/x_1}{\omega^2 \, r^2 \, (d_p - d_m)},$$

where $x_2 - x_1$ is the distance through which a particle sedimented in time t when the angular speed of rotation is ω rad/sec (see Fig. 2). A centrifuge can

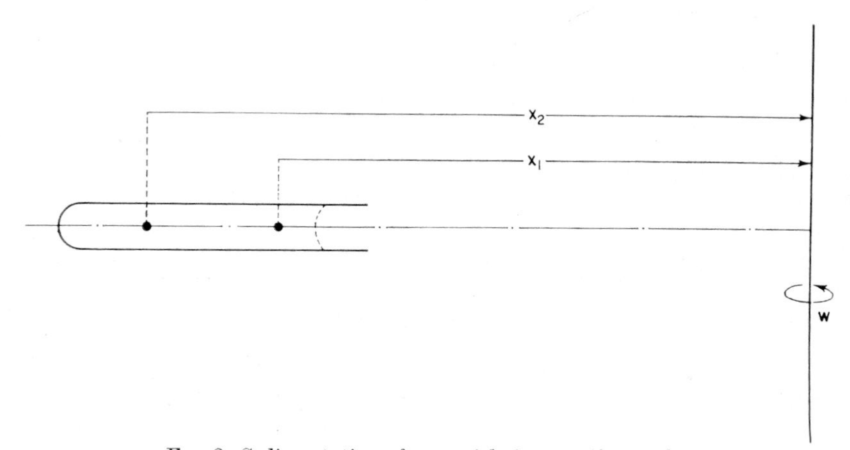

FIG. 2. Sedimentation of a particle in centrifuge tube

be used either for a simple separation, i.e. throwing down or floating just one component or it can be used for fractionation. In the latter instance one uses the term fractional or differential centrifugation. The various components

[7] T. SVEDBERG and J. B. NICHOLS, *J. Amer. chem. Soc.* **45**, 2910 (1923); see also ref. 6.

of a system are separated by centrifuging at various speeds. The coarse ingredients, such as cells or cell fragments, are thrown down first, i.e. by a relatively low-speed centrifuging at 3000 or 4000 rev/min. (The speed 3000 rev/min = 50 rev/sec; the angular velocity then is $\omega = 2\pi \cdot 50 = 314$ rad/sec.) None of the dissolved macromolecules are displaced at such speed. A preparative separation of macromolecular substances from a solution can be achieved only by means of an ultracentrifuge in which the macromolecules are exposed to gravitational forces exceeding gravity one hundred thousand times, and more.[8] The very large components, such as most of the viruses, and large glycogens, can be thrown down by centrifuging at 10,000–15,000 rev/min. The medium size macromolecules are slowly sedimented at higher speeds of 30,000–40,000 rev/min. Special precautions must be observed in working with such speeds, e.g. in accurately filling and sealing the tubes, and reducing the air pressure in order to avoid heating. The technical problems have been solved in such popular instruments as the Spinco preparative ultracentrifuge. It must, however, be emphasized that there are certain limitations in the possibility of separation by this method. A relatively clean separation is possible only when the components differ considerably in their particle sizes or molecular weights or densities. Complex mixtures composed of many components, such as blood serum, are not separable this way to a great extent. The same is true for the polydisperse mixtures of starch or glycogen; the heavier fractions will be thrown down first, but they will not be homogeneous. Especially difficult is the preparative separation of the linear macromolecules, since the sedimenting entities become entangled, the sedimenting material becomes like a gel, and carries within it also the lightest components to be separated.

Filtration, ultrafiltration, dialysis, and similar methods.[9] These methods are illustrated by screening grains through sieves. The interstices in a filter paper, however, are much smaller and less uniform than the holes in a sieve. The ordinary materials used for filtration, such as a cotton fabric, filter paper, or glass wool, are composed of an irregular fibrous meshwork, and such filter aides are characterized by estimating an average pore size. Very convenient are the sintered glass filters which are now offered in various sizes and various average pore diameters. For the purpose of clarification, the porous diatomaceous silica preparations (e.g. the Celite from Johns-Manville Corp.) are convenient. A layer of such material most conveniently is obtained by filtering a suspension through a sintered glass filter under slight pressure. Dispersions

[8] T. Svedberg and K. O. Pedersen, *The Ultracentrifuge* Clarendon Press, Oxford, 1940; J. B. Nichols and E. D. Bailey, in Weissebrger's *Physical Methods in Organic Chemistry* 2nd ed., Part. I, p. 621ff., Interscience, New York, 1949.

[9] A. B. Cummins in Weissberger's *Technique of Organic Chemistry*, Vol. III, p. 485ff., Interscience, New York, 1950. See also B. Jirgensons and M. Straumanis, *A Short Textbook of Colloid Chemistry*, Pergamon Press, London, 2nd ed., 1961.

of carbon or paper pulp can be used for the same purposes. The average pore diameters for the various coarse filter aides range somewhere between 0·01–0·05 mm, while the fine filters retain smaller particles of approximately 0·001 mm or 1 μ. Colloidal particles and macromolecules are not retained by such ordinary filters, but certain fractionation through filtration can be achieved by means of ultrafilters. An ultrafilter is a gel possessing extremely fine channels or capillaries which are permeable only to small molecules. Cellophane and nitrocellulose (collodion) are the most common materials for ultrafiltration. The average pore size of these ultrafilters can be varied in the range of 0·01–1 μ. The "hard" ultrafilters with a pore size of 0·01–0·02 μ retain all of the very large and medium size macromolecules, whereas the "soft" ultrafilters of an average pore diameter of 0·05–0·1 μ will retain only the largest components. It must, however, be emphasized that ultrafiltration is nothing like a mechanical screening, since the filtered substances often are interacting with the macromolecules of the filter. Adsorption of the macromolecules in the meshwork of the ultrafilter often occurs causing a decrease of the filtration rate with time, and sometimes a complete clogging. It has been found that the diameter of particles, e.g. viruses, which had passed through an ultrafilter, is considerably smaller than the average pore diameter of the ultrafilters used.[10]

Dialysis is a very important procedure in the isolation and purification of macromolecules. The commercially available Cellophane tubes are convenient for this purpose. If a solution of a high polymer is poured in to such a tube, and the tube immersed in a container with water, an exchange of the micromolecular components takes place through the membrane. The micromolecular impurities which are present in the solution diffuse through the Cellophane into the water, while some water moves into the tube. All of the large and medium size macromolecules remain inside the tube, since they are too large to pass the Cellophane membrane. Only the smallest of the macromolecules, such as those of lysozyme, diffuse very slowly through a normal Cellophane membrane.[10a] Dialysis is used chiefly for the liberation of macromolecular solutions from electrolytes, e.g. sodium, sulfate, ammonium, chloride, and other ions, and of micromolecular nonelectrolytes, such as sugar, urea, alcohol, etc. The dialysis rate can be speeded up by stirring, and by continuous change of the outer water. Heating also facilitates dialysis, though this is

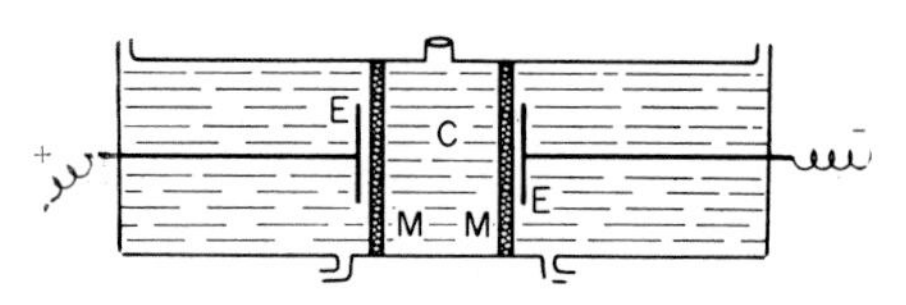

FIG. 3. Electrodialyser. *E*, electrodes; *M*, membranes; *C*, middle compartment containing the solution

[10] W. F. ELFORD, *Proc. Roy. Soc. London* B. **112**, 384 (1933); J. D. FERRY, *Chem. Rev.* **18**, 373 (1936); K. SOLLNER, *J. Phys. Colloid. Chem.* **49**, 47, 171 (1945).

[10a] L. C. CRAIG, W. KONIGSBERG, A. STRACHER and T. P. KING, in *Symposium on Protein Structure* p. 104 (A. NEUBERGER, ed.), Methuen, London, 1958.

usually avoided because of the instability of the large molecules, i.e. their possible denaturation by heating. The removal of small ions can be facilitated by electrodialysis. Direct current is applied through the solution separated from water by semipermeable membranes (see Fig. 3).

Fractional precipitation and extraction. These methods are used for the isolation and purification of all natural high polymers. Extraction can be used for two major purposes: removal of undesired impurities or for obtaining some macromolecular compound from a solid starting material. Fats and other micromolecular lipids are the most common impurities which are removed by extraction with water-immiscible solvents. After this procedure, some of the macromolecular ingredients of the material can be brought into solution by extraction with salt solutions. Many seed globulins are extracted this way. However, such extracts are never pure, and further purification by centrifugation, filtration, and precipitation etc. must be done. Only coarse impurities, such as fragments of cells, can be removed by centrifugation and filtration, while the micromolecular contaminants are eliminated by dialysis. What then remains is usually a mixture of macromolecules which can be fractionated more or less completely by fractional precipitation. Numerous precipitants are used in the fractionation of natural polymers: salts, acids, alkalies, alcohols, acetone, etc. Ammonium sulfate is one of the most common salts used for these purposes, especially for the proteins.[11] This is due to its high solubility and to its ability to precipitate many proteins. Methyl-, ethyl-, and propyl alcohols, and acetone are common precipitants for both proteins and polysaccharides. Very often the organic nonsolvents for a particular high polymer are used together with certain buffer solutions of a definite pH and ionic strength. Such precipitation usually is accomplished at low temperatures of −5 to 0 °C, in order to avoid denaturation.

There are certain simple rules governing the phenomena of dissolution and precipitation. First: "like dissolves like". Macromolecular hydrocarbons, such as rubber, are soluble in hydrocarbons (benzene, hexane), whereas the highly polar polysaccharides, nucleic acids, and proteins are insoluble in hydrocarbons but they are soluble in certain polar solvents. The liquids which are nonsolvents for the particular polymer, and which are miscible with the respective solvent, then can be used as precipitants. For example, alcohol can be used as a precipitant for rubber which is dissolved in benzene. These simple polarity considerations, however, are insufficient for a full prediction of solubility, since, for example, not all polysaccharides and proteins are soluble in water. It appears that the solubility depends on several other factors, such as the amount and distribution of the polar groups, as well as on the molecular size and shape. The relationships are complicated, and important special cases will be discussed in several following chapters. However, there

[11] J. F. Taylor in *The Proteins* p. 1ff., Vol. I, (H. Neurath and K. Bailey, ed.), Academic Press, New York, 1953.

are certain general rules with respect to molecular size and shape, namely — *the solubility decreases with increasing molecular weight and molecular asymmetry.* When a precipitant is added to a polymer-homologous mixture of glycogens, the larger components are precipitated first, and the smaller follow after reaching a higher concentration of the precipitant in the mixture.[12] This is qualitatively true even for substances differing slightly in their chemical composition, e.g. the smaller albumins need more ammonium sulfate for precipitation than the larger serum globulins; a partially degraded gelatin requires more acetone for precipitation than undegraded gelatin. The shape factor is conspicuous in such instances as the highly soluble glycogens, the less soluble starches, and the very insoluble cellulose. The globular glycogens, even those possessing molecular weights of several millions, are readily soluble, while the fibrous starches and cellulose derivatives are soluble only with difficulty or practically insoluble. Similar rules hold for the nucleic acids, when the solubility of the very large and asymmetric native preparations is compared with the solubility of degraded products: the latter are much more soluble than the former. In this instance increase in solubility is facilitated by the decrease in both molecular size and asymmetry.

If a macromolecular mixture contains ionogenic functional groups, the solubility and precipitability is influenced also by the dissociation of these groups. This must be considered in the fractional precipitation of such organic macromolecules as proteins and nucleic acids. The solubility of macromolecular acids increases with degree of ionization, hence they will be precipitated in acid solution, when the dissociation of their acidic groups will be suppressed. Alkaline components, such as the histones, on the contrary, are precipitated in alkaline solutions. Ampholytic macromolecules, such as the proteins, are most readily precipitated at the *isoelectric point,* i.e. at a pH at which the number of positive charges equals the number of negative charges on the ampholytic macromolecules.[13]

For a successful fractional precipitation of macromolecules the same rules apply as for any simple separation procedure in quantitative analysis: the precipitant must be added slowly, under stirring, to a dilute solution. In spite of these precautions, a clear-cut separation of macromolecules is more difficult than that of small molecules, especially if the macromolecules are fibrous. Even with the extreme care in precipitation, the lumps of the fibrous precipitate encompass the other components present in the solution. This happens to a lesser extent with the globular serum proteins. Yet, even the most carefully precipitated albumin contains several per cent of the globulins. Redissolving and reprecipitation helps in obtaining purer preparations.

[12] E. HUSEMANN, *J. prakt. Chem.* **158**, 163 (1941); G. V. SCHULZ and B. JIRGENSONS *Z. physik. Chem.* B **46**, 105 (1940); L. H. CRAGG and H. HAMMERSCHLAG, *Chem. Rev.* **39**, 261 (1946); E. L. SKAU and assoc., *J. physic. Chem.* **49**, 281 (1945).

[13] J. T. EDSALL and J. WYMAN, *Biophysical Chemistry* Vol. I, Academic Press, New York, 1958.

The fractional precipitation of polymer-homologous mixtures, such as those of the glycogens, has been studied to a great extent (see ref. 12). If v_0 is the original volume in milliliters of the solution which precipitates after adding v ml of the precipitant,

$$\gamma = v/(v + v_0)$$

is defined as the *precipitability* of the high polymer. According to Schulz and assoc.,[12] the more concentrated the solution the less of a precipitant is needed to produce the formation of a solid phase. This is expressed with the equation:

$$\ln c = a - b\gamma,$$

where c is the concentration of the macromolecular substance, and a and b are constants. The dependence between the degree of polymerization P and precipitability also is very simple, namely:

$$\gamma = A + B/P^m,$$

where A, B, and m are constants.[12] For linear macromolecules the exponent $m = 1$, for spherical macromolecules, like glycogen, $m = 2/3$. In a fractionation of such polydisperse polymer substances the precipitant is added slowly under stirring, and the first fraction is removed after a certain time; more of the precipitant then is added to the remaining solution until a second fraction appears, and so forth. It must, however, be borne in mind that none of these fractions are homogeneous; it can readily be ascertained that the *mean* molecular weight or degree of polymerization of the first fraction is higher than that of the following fractions.

Chromatographic methods. Chromatography is the most recent addition to the methods of isolation and purification of natural polymers, and a brilliant future is predicted by many experts for this new approach. The importance of these endeavors is illustrated by the enormous literature which has been published about chromatography during the last years.[14] There are several types of chromatographic work, and, considering the underlying phenomena, they can be classified into three major groups: (1) partition, (2) adsorption–desorption, and (3) ion exchange. In *partition* chromatography the substances are distributed between two immiscible liquid phases due to their solubility in them. When repeated distribution occurs between liquids without a solid supporting phase, this method is called *countercurrent distribution.*[15] One of the liquid phases, however, may be supported by a porous solid which usually is placed in a vertical tube, and another liquid may be percolated down the column. Partition chromatography has been very successful in separation of

(14) R. C. Brimley and F. C. Barrett, *Practical Chromatography*, Reinhold, New York, 1953; E. Lederer and M. Lederer, *Chromatography* 2nd ed., Elsevier, Amsterdam, 1957. C. Calmon and T. Kressmann, *Ion Exchangers in Organic and Biochemistry* Interscience, New York, 1957.

(15) L. C. Craig and D. Craig in Weissberger's *Technique of Organic Chemistry*, p. 171ff. Vol., III, Interscience, New York, 1950.

many micromolecular substances, while its applications for large molecules are somewhat limited. Several proteins, however, have been successfully separated by this method, especially when denaturation could be prevented at the interphase.(16)

Adsorption chromatography is the original type of chromatography, devised as early as 1906 by Tswett. The strange name "chromatography", meaning

FIG. 4. Fraction collector

"color writing", also originates from these early experiments, since Tswett managed to separate on a column the pigments from extracts from green leaves. They appeared as colored zones in a column of chalk, when solvent was percolated through the column. It may be interesting to note that Tswett

(16) P. VON TAVEL and R. SIGNER, *Adv. Protein Chem.* **11**, 237 (1956).

was a Russian, and that his name in that language means color. The method was rediscovered by R. Kuhn, and in the early thirties it was applied successfully for the separation of numerous micromolecular compounds.[17] Later it was used also for the separation of proteins and other natural macromolecules.

Adsorption chromatography is based on the fact that a certain adsorbent, e.g. finely divided porous solid, has different affinities for different substances. Adsorption or sorption causes a weak binding of substances on the surfaces. For a certain adsorbent and a certain substance to be adsorbed (adsorptive), the amount adsorbed depends on the surface area, concentration, and temperature, as outlined in detail in texts on surface chemistry.[18] Since the surface area depends on subdivision, the finer a powder the greater its adsorption capacity. Moreover, adsorption is facilitated by a decrease of temperature, and it is more complete in the case of dilute solutions than in concentrated solutions. When two or more substances are present in the solution, they will compete for the free surfaces, and the substance with the highest affinity for the adsorbent will be adsorbed first. If the mixture is applied to the top of a column containing the adsorbent, the first component will remain in the first zone on the top. Next will be adsorbed the component with lesser affinity for the surface of the adsorbent, and some components may even pass through the column without being adsorbed at all. The adsorbed components can be separated by pushing the column out of the tube, dividing it into the zones, and eluting the adsorbed substances with proper solvents. Direct elution, without pushing the column out of the tube, appears to be possible in many cases, since a solvent applied to the top will wash out first the least strongly adsorbed component. The effluent is collected in a series of tubes by means of a fraction collector (Fig. 4). If the substance to be separated is colorless, it is tested for by taking small aliquots from each tube, and determined by some analytical method (e.g. spectrophotometry); only the contents of the tubes containing it are pooled, and the substance is recovered. When many components appear in the effluent, they will be found in different groups of tubes. Adsorption–desorption methods can be applied, of course, also without the use of a column, and without such gradual elution. Thus finely divided carbon is very well known as a means for liberating solutions of various organic substances from colored impurities. Aluminium hydroxide, kieselgur, calcium carbonate are some of the common inorganic adsorbents used batchwise or in columns. Paper pulp, starch, and activated carbon are examples of organic materials used as adsorbents. The plasma protein prothrombin, for example, is specifically adsorbed on alkaline earth salts; tricalcium phosphate has been used for the purification of catalase and other enzymes.[19]

[17] R. Kuhn and E. Lederer, *Ber. dtsch. chem. Ges.* **64**, 1349 (1931).

[18] J. J. Bikerman, *Surface Chemistry, Theory and Applications* 2nd ed., Academic Press, New York, 1958; H. G. Cassidy, *Adsorption and Chromatography* Interscience, 1951; H. G. Cassidy, *Fundamentals of Chromatography,* Interscience, New York, 1957.

[19] S. Moore and W. H. Stein, *Adv. Protein Chem.* **11**, 191 (1956).

Ion exchange chromatography. Separation on the surfaces of ionized solids is now the most important method for the isolation and purification of macromolecular substances. Also it appears now that adsorption very often is associated with ion exchange. The ion exchange techniques became popular after the introduction of the synthetic polystyrene resins (Dowex, Nalcite Amberlite). These ion exchangers are space polymers, i.e. the long macromolecular chains of the polystyrene are cross-linked to an insoluble meshwork or lattice containing such dissociable groups as $-SO_3H$, $-COOH$, or $-NH_2$. These resins are classified, first, into the more or less strongly acid *cation exchange* resins, and the basic *anion exchangers*. The materials are offered by various companies in the form of fine beads of a variety of dimensions, either as free acids or bases or their salts. Since the beads are impenetrable for large molecules, the efficiency of the more finely screened resin will be greater than that of coarse grains. Very important for the ion exchange is also the number of the ionogenic groups per unit weight, since the ions on the surface of the particles are the active sites. Finally, since adsorption at the surfaces also is involved in many cases, the chemical properties of the lattice are important in some instances. One of the most important cation exchangers is Dowex 50; it is a sulfonated polystyrene cross-linked by divinylbenzene. Amberlite CR-50 is a less acidic carboxylic cation exchange resin. Dowex 2 is an example of anion exchange resin in which the active group is dimethylethanolammonium ion. The following exchange reactions may occur at the active sites:

Cation exchange: $R \cdot SO_3H + Cat.^+ = R \cdot SO_3Cat + H^+$

$$R \cdot COOH + Cat.^+ = R \cdot COOCat + H^+$$

Anion exchange: $R \cdot NH_3OH + An.^- = R \cdot NH_3An + OH^-$

$$R \cdot N(CH_3)_2(CH_2CH_2OH)OH + An^- = R \cdot N(CH_3)_2(CH_2CH_2OH)An + OH^-.$$

The original acid or alkaline resin can be first neutralized and then used for exchange, for example:

$$R \cdot COONa + Cat.^+ = R \cdot COOCat. + Na^+, \text{ or}$$
$$R \cdot NH_3Cl + An.^- = R \cdot NH_3An + Cl.^-$$

Since most of the natural organic macromolecules are large multivalent anions containing such active groups as carboxyls, phosphates, or sulfates, the anion exchange reactions are more important for the separation of natural high polymers than the cation exchange reactions. In the case of amphoteric macromolecules, such as the proteins, the latter will be bound to a cation exchange resin at a pH which is lower than the isoelectric point, i.e. in a more or less strongly acid solution. It is obvious then that both the binding of a particular component in an ion exchange column and its elution must depend on the *acidity* of the solutions used for the treatment. Also the *ionic strength* of the buffer used for the elution is of importance, since the dissociation of the resin–polymer compound is facilitated by high ionic strength. All these phenomena have been more or less thoroughly treated in several monographs and papers.[20]

Important semi-synthetic anion exchange resins have been developed recently by Sober and associates.[21] The diethylaminoethyl (DEAE) cellulose has already attested itself as a very potent means for the separation and purification of many proteins [22] and other macromolecules. Both ion exchange and adsorption seem to be involved. All negatively charged macromolecules are bound in the DEAE–cellulose column due to electrostatic attraction between the cationic sites of the DEAE-cellulose and anions of the polymer, and probably also because of adsorption. The elution is accomplished by buffers of certain definite pH and ionic strength. The less negative components will be eluted first, and they will be collected in the first tubes on the fraction collector. The macroions possessing a high anionic density are bound in the column very tenaciously, and their release may be facilitated by increasing the acidity and ionic strength of the buffer used for the elution (see ref. 19, 21, and 22).

Ion exchange chromatography is now applied successfully not only for the separation of macromolecular mixtures, but also for deionization of such solutions. This is accomplished according to the same principle as desalting of water. A mixed bed anion and cation exchange resin is placed in a tube, and the solution applied to the top. All anions are bound at the anionic sites of the anion exchanger, and all cations at the cation exchanger, the equivalent amount of OH^- and H^+ ions being released into the solutions and combining to water. Non-ionic macromolecules will percolate freely without being bound in the column. Multilayer mixed bed ion exchange columns have been developed which can be used also for the deionization of proteins. Serum albumin thus can be liberated from the last trace of electrolytes much more conveniently than it was possible by electrodialysis.[23]

There are several precautions which must be observed in the chromatographic isolation and purification of macromolecules. First, denaturation at the interfaces can occur. This can be avoided by working at sufficiently low temperatures, e.g. using jacketed columns and cold water circulation. In order to ascertain reliable results in partition and adsorption chromatography, the temperature, moreover, must be kept constant. While the ion exchange is not sensitive to small variations in temperature, the partition between two liquid phases certainly is very sensitive to temperature change. There are several general technical precautions, such as a homogeneous (channel-free)

[20] C. Calmon and T. R. E. Kressmann, *Ion Exchange in Organic and Biochemistry* Interscience, New York, 1957; H. Deuel and K. Hutschneker, *Chimia* **9**, 49 (1955); N. K. Boardman and S. M. Partridge, *Biochem. J.* **59**, 543 (1955).

[21] E. A. Peterson and H. A. Sober, *J. Amer. chem. Soc.* **78**, 751 (1956); H. A. Sober, F. J. Gurter, M. M. Wyckoff and E. A. Peterson, *ibid.* **78**, 756 (1956).

[22] See for example: B. Jirgensons, T. Ikenaka and V. Gorguraki, *Makromol. Chem.* **28**, 96 (1958).

packing of the columns, proper washing of the resins, adjustment of the flow rate on elution, etc.[20, 21, 23] Improperly purified and incompletely washed DEAE–cellulose, for instance, releases some soluble semi-colloidal hemicellulose which can contaminate the high polymer preparation to be separated in the column.

Separation by means of electrophoresis. Electrically charged macromolecules, such as those of proteins, nucleic acids, pectins, and several other polysaccharides, migrate under the influence of direct current. The electrophoretic velocity v is directly proportional to the potential gradient E/l, expressed in volts per centimeter, to the electrokinetic potential of the particle ζ (the zeta potential), and to the dielectric constant D of the solvent. It is inversely proportional to the viscosity η of the solvent. For spherical particles[24]

$$v = \frac{(E/l)\,\zeta\,D}{6\,\pi\,\eta}.$$

Electrophorate mobility u is defined as $v\,l/E$ or velocity at unit potential gradient. The electrokinetic potential or zeta potential depends on the number of charge units carried by the particle, e.g. a protein molecule. The proteins which contain a large number of free carboxyl groups will travel to the positive pole faster than those containing less of these groups.

Preparative electrophoresis methods can be classified into two large groups: *free boundary* and *zone* electrophoresis. The application of free boundary electrophoresis was impressively demonstrated by Theorell[25] who isolated with the aid of this method the flavine enzyme from yeast. The electrophoresis was performed in a U-shaped tube composed of several flattened cylinders with ground ends. The contents of these cylinders could be separated by properly adjusted thin discs. After a certain time of electrophoresis, the contents of the cylinders were analyzed, and a high concentration of the enzyme was found in one of the sections of the tube. The *electrophoresis convection* method also belongs to this type.[26] The solution to be fractionated is introduced into a narrow vertical channel which is separated from the electrode compartment by two membranes. The components with the highest mobility will reach the membrane toward the oppositely charged electrode first, and they will sink to the bottom compartment of the channel, due to the high density of this more concentrated part of the solution. Thus after a certain time the bottom reservoir will be enriched with the fast moving component, and the top reser-

[23] H. M. Dintzis, Thesis, Harvard University, 1952.

[24] H. A. Abramson, L. S. Moyer and M. H. Gorin, *Electrophoresis of Protein* Reinhold, New York, 1942; J. T. Overbeek, *Adv. Colloid Sci.* **3**, 97 (1950); M. Bier (ed.), *Electrophoresis* Academic Press, New York, 1959.

[25] H. Thoerell, *Biochem. Z.* **275**, 1 (1934); H. Svensson, *Adv. Proteins Chem.* **4**, 251 (1948).

[26] J. R. Cann, J. G. Kirkwood, R. A. Brown and O. J. Plescia, *J. Amer. chem. Soc.* **71**, 1603 (1949); J. G. Kirkwood, J. R. Cann and R. A. Brown, *Biochim. Biophys. Acta* **5**, 301 (1950); J. R. Cann, *J. Amer. chem. Soc.* **75**, 4213 (1953).

voir with the slow migrating fraction. This method has been successfully applied for the subfractionation of the serum γ-globulins. The method was

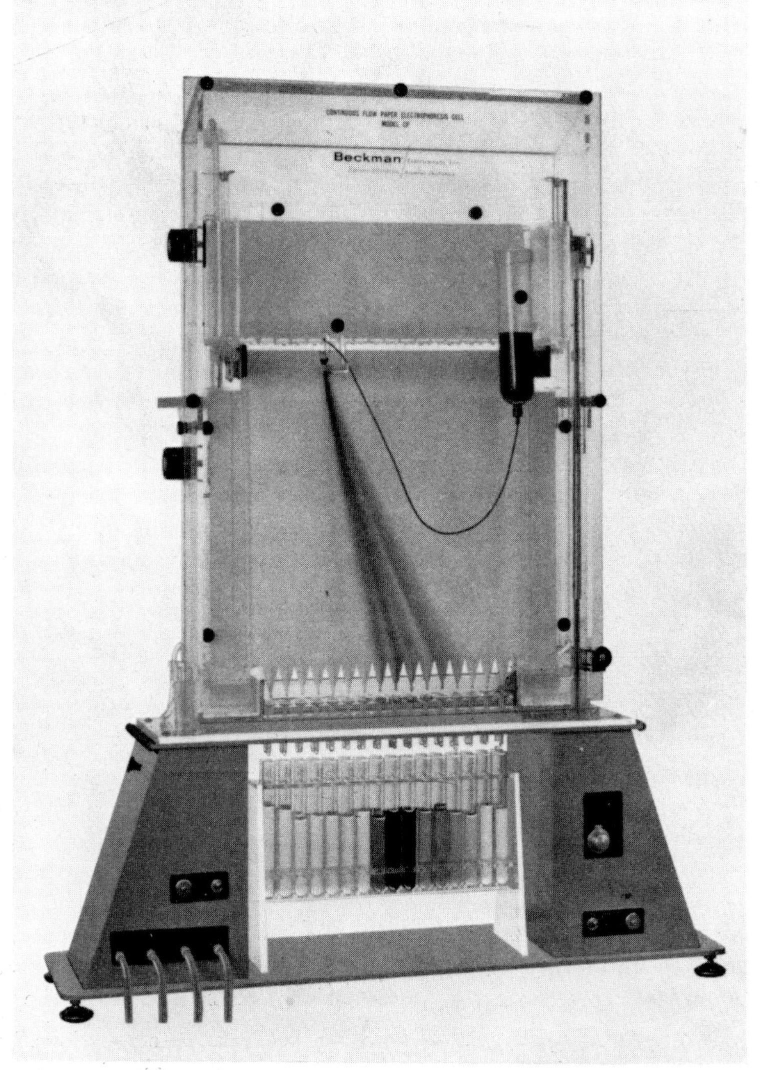

FIG. 5. Preparative continuous flow electrophoresis

recently modified by using several oblique channels, and passing the supernatant of the first channel into the bottom of the next, etc.[27] This device was applied successfully, for instance, for the isolation of poliomyelitis viruses from mouse brain extracts.[27]

[27] A. POLSON, *Biochim. Biophys. Acta* **11**, 315 (1953).

In *zone electrophoresis* the solution is supported by a porous solid, such as filter paper or powdered glass. Preparative electrophoresis can be accomplished by applying the sample and the conducting solvent at the top of a vertically fastened sheet of paper connected with the electrodes at each side (Fig. 5). The electrically neutral macromolecules will descend vertically down the sheet, whereas the charged components will be pulled sidewise. The fractions are collected in tubes at the bottom of the sheet.[28] Instruments for this purpose are now commercially available (from Spinco Division of Beckman Corp., Palo Alto, California). Recent studies on zone electrophoresis have been conducted in Tiselius laboratory in Uppsala [28a] by using columns instead of paper sheets, and it was shown that zone electrophoresis in columns is better controllable than on paper. Large columns are used for preparative separations, and very small columns were found useful for handling quantities as small as those used on paper strips.

One of the greatest precautions to be observed in preparative electrophoresis is heating up of the system due to the current, hence proper cooling is essential.

Finally, it should be mentioned that even such electrically neutral macromolecules as those of glycogen or starch can be subjected to electrophoresis. This is possible by means of boric acid which forms relatively strongly ionized complex compounds with the alcoholic OH groups of these substances, as follows [29]:

$$H_2BO_3^- + \begin{matrix} HO \\ HO \end{matrix}\!\!>\!R\cdots \rightleftarrows \left[\begin{matrix} HO \\ HO \end{matrix}\!\!>\!B\!<\!\begin{matrix} O \\ O \end{matrix}\!\!>\!R\cdots\right]^- + H_2O.$$

Criteria of Purity and Nativity

The question of the purity of a natural organic high polymer is closely associated with the problem of its nativity. As indicated in the beginning of this chapter, a very thorough purification of a macromolecular ingredient of a tissue can lead to its denaturation. The truly native state of a macromolecule is that condition at which it exists in a living cell or bodily fluid. The extreme lability of natural organic macromolecular systems is strikingly demonstrated by the phenomenon of blood clotting: a chain of far reaching macromolecular changes occurs on mere drainage of the blood from the vessel.

Purity and homogeneity. It is relatively easy to detect various foreign micromolecular impurities, such as fats, sugars, salts. Traces of these impurities can be detected readily by various analytical micromethods, e.g. the

(28) A. Tiselius and P. Flodin, *Adv. Protein Chem.* 8, 461 (1953); W. Grassmann and K. Hannig, *Naturwiss.* **37**, 397 (1950).

(28a) A. Tiselius, in *Symposium on Protein Structure* p. 93 (A. Neuberger, ed.), Methuen, London, Wiley, New York, 1958.

(29) A. B. Foster, *Adv. Carbohydr. Chem.* **12**, 81 (1957); A. B. Foster, P. A. Newton-Hearn and M. Stacey, *J. chem. Soc. London* 30 (1956).

sodium by flame photometry, or the nucleotides by absorption spectrophotometry. It is usually not difficult to liberate the macromolecular substance from these impurities by some of the methods described in previous sections.

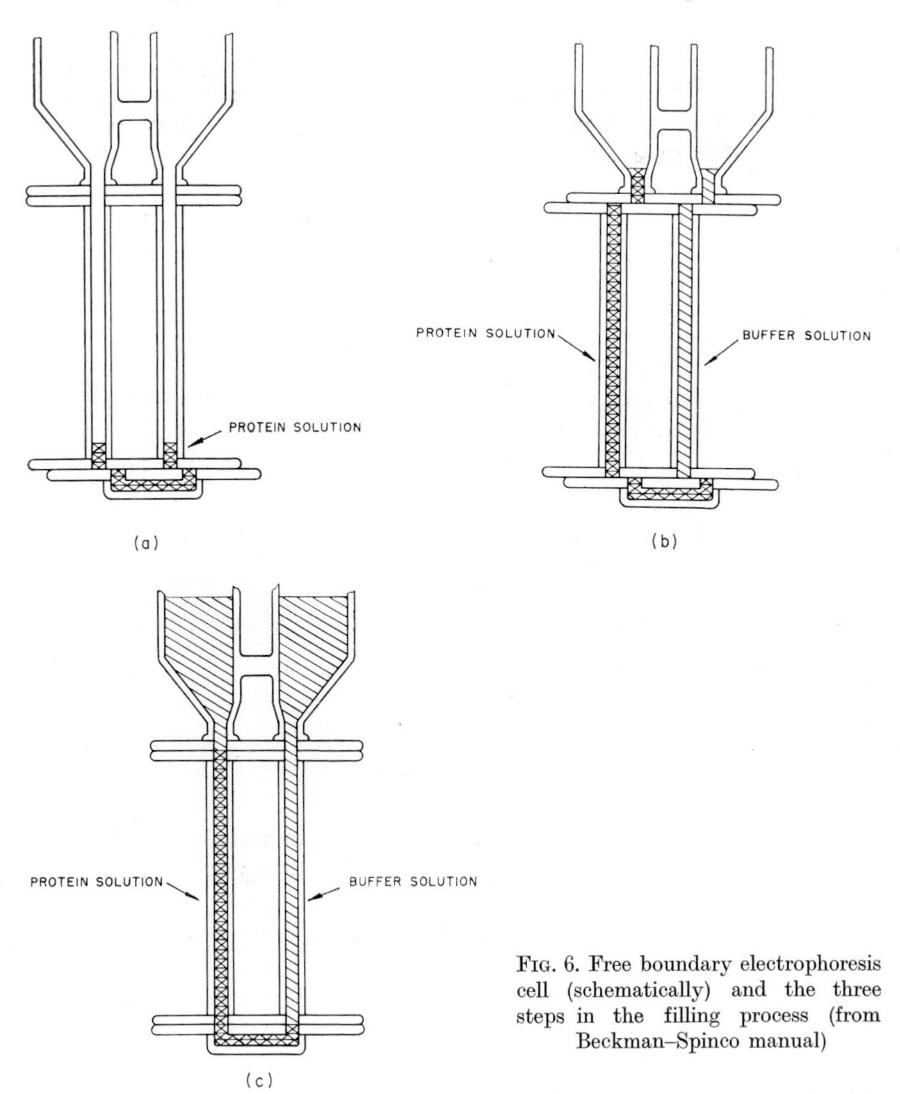

FIG. 6. Free boundary electrophoresis cell (schematically) and the three steps in the filling process (from Beckman–Spinco manual)

More difficult are the problems concerning the presence of macromolecular contaminants. If the macromolecular impurity differs chemically from the main component, its detection usually is not much of a problem; for example it is easy to detect traces of protein in a glycogen preparation, e.g. by a sensitive colorimetric reaction for protein. However, it is much more difficult to determine whether the particular glycogen contains some other polysaccharide closely resembling glycogen.

One encounters at this point the difficult problem to distinguish a foreign component from a polymer-homologue. All natural polysaccharides such as the starches, cellulose preparations, and glycogens are polydisperse, i.e. the preparations contain macromolecules of various sizes. If all macromolecules in such a preparation possess identical composition and structure, the substance will be *pure*, although it will be inhomogeneous in respect to molecular size. The difficulties involved are obvious, since it is practically impossible

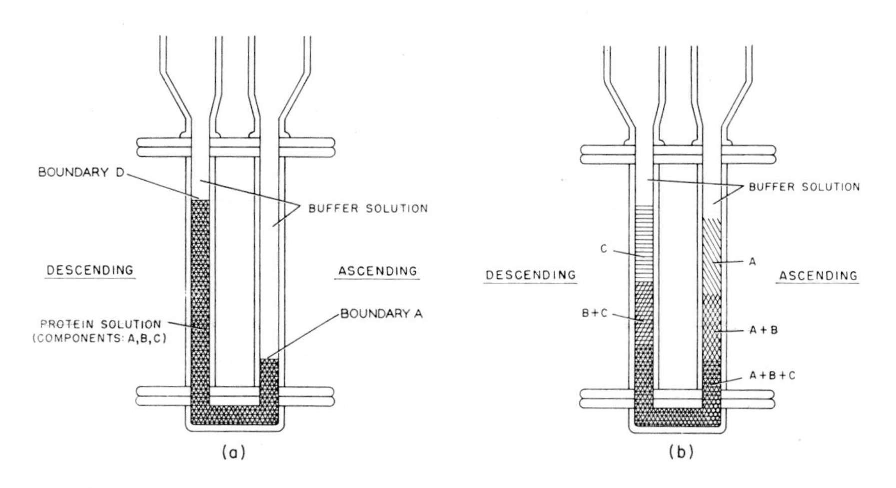

Before electrophoretic separation **After electrophoretic separation**

FIG. 7. Separation of electrically charged components in free boundary electrophoresis (from Beckman–Spinco manual)

to detect and study slight structural differences with such large and complicated molecules. Moreover, the macromolecules in a supposed homogeneous preparation may be in dynamic equilibrium with some of their isomeric modifications. Only a few of the smallest proteins, such as insulin are known to be completely homogeneous and pure, by the highest presently available analytical standards. The best preparations of all ordinary proteins appear to be mixtures of closely related components which can be distinguished by various criteria.[30] Although most of the globular proteins, such as serum albumin or hemoglobin, are practically homogeneous with respect to their molecular size, slight compositional and other inhomogeneities have been ascertained. For example, human serum albumin contains a component possessing free reactive sulfhydryl group (—SH), another component without this group, and probably a small amount of a sugar-containing fraction.

[30] J. R. COLVIN, D. B. SMITH and W. H. COOK, *Chem. Rev.* **54**, 687 (1954).

Testing by means of sedimentation and electrophoresis. These are the most common methods for testing purity and homogeneity. The sedimentation properties are investigated by means of the analytical ultracentrifuge which will be described in the next chapter. Although the method reveals the presence of several components, its capacities are often overestimated. First, the method is not very sensitive in disclosing the presence of components differing slightly in molecular weight from the major component. Second, the method reveals only substantial weight differences but it is unable to show any slight differences in chemical composition and structure of the macromolecules.

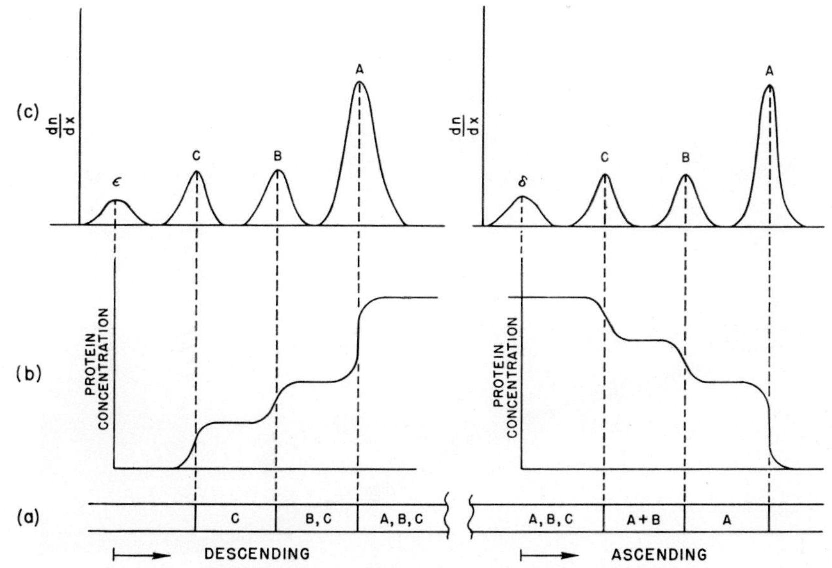

FIG. 8. Schlieren patterns and concentration gradients in electrophoretic separation. dn/dx is the refractive index gradient which corresponds to the concentration gradient (from Beckman–Spinco manual)

Indeed, many instances are known when preparations which appeared homogeneous in the analytical ultracentrifuge proved to be inhomogeneous by other criteria. Furthermore, the sedimentation rate is greatly influenced by molecular shape; heavy asymmetric particles may sediment with the same velocity as much lighter spherical molecules, thus implying homogeneity while actually the preparation is inhomogeneous.

Analytical electrophoresis is one of the most important methods, and in most cases it is more revealing than the sedimentation method. Again, it is applied either as free boundary electrophoresis or zone electrophoresis. The free boundary method was developed by Svedberg, Tiselius, Longsworth, and others.[31] The electrophoresis cell in the free boundary instruments is rectan-

[31] A. TISELIUS, *Trans Faraday Soc.* **33**, 524 (1937); L. G. LONGSWORTH, *Chem. Rev.* **30**, 323 (1942); see also ref. 24.

gular in cross section, and it is composed usually of three sections which can be made to slide one over the other. The three steps of filling the cell are illustrated in Fig. 6. The cell then is connected with the electrode compartments which are large tubes containing concentrated chloride solution in which are immersed reversible silver–silver chloride electrodes. The cell and the electrodes are immersed in a constant temperature bath which is operated at a temperature

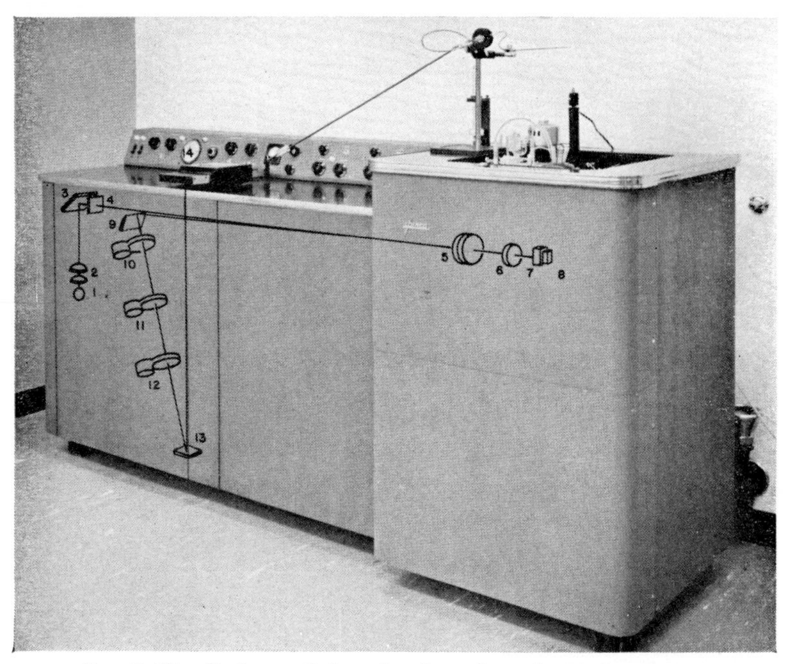

FIG. 9. The Beckman–Spinco free boundary electrophoresis and diffusion instrument

mean 0 °C in order to minimize the disturbing effects of convection resulting from the heating effect of the current. Under the influence of the current, the components having different electrophoretic mobilities begin to separate in both limbs of the cell, as shown schematically in Fig. 7. The boundary shift is observed, and it can be photographed, at certain time intervals, most commonly with the aid of the Philpot–Svensson cylindrical lens optical system. The components appear as peaks due to the fact that this optical system reveals the refractive index gradients which represent the concentration gradients of the various components (see Fig. 8). The Beckman–Spinco free boundary electrophoresis instrument is illustrated in Fig. 9.

Free boundary electrophoresis is quite a laborious procedure, and, aside from several pitfalls, it has the disadvantage of requiring relatively large amounts of material. These are the reasons that electrophoresis in supporting media (zone electrophoresis) is competing strongly with the free boundary method. *Filter paper electrophoresis* is becoming an universal tool, first, because of its convenience, simplicity and speed. Moreover, it is a *micromethod* giving

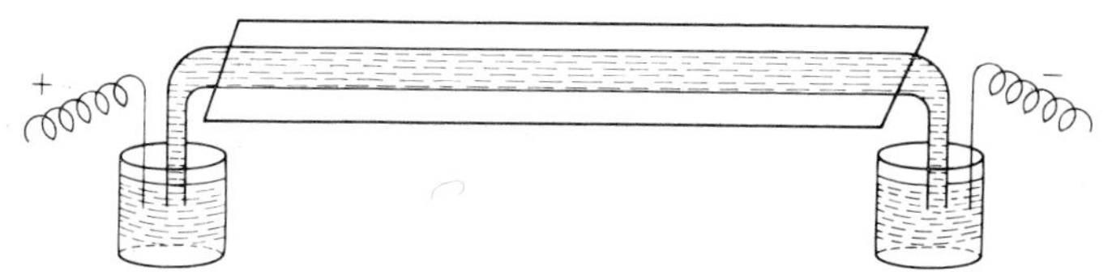

FIG. 10. Electrophoresis on paper strip

reliable results with milligram quantities and less of the substance to be tested. Only some 10–30 λ (1 λ = 0·001 ml) of a 1% solution of a protein or other charged high polymer is needed. The drop is placed on a filter paper strip wetted with a buffer solution and placed on a glass plate. The ends of the strip

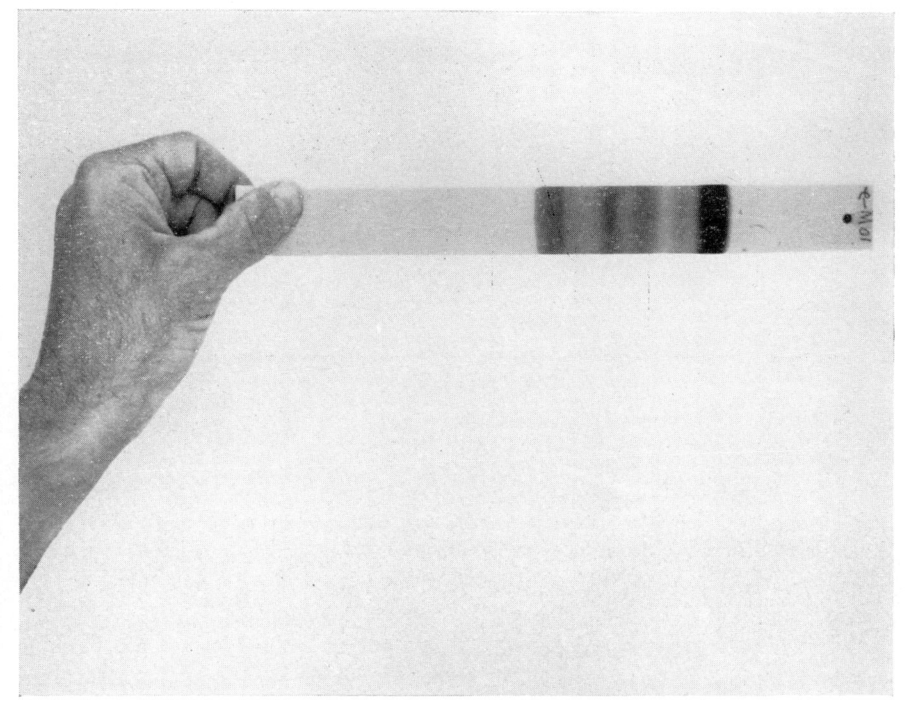

FIG. 11. Components separated by electrophoresis on paper

are immersed into the conducting buffer solution which is connected with platinum electrode chambers (Fig. 10). When the macromolecular substance is colored, its migration can be observed directly without further treatment of the paper strip. Colorless macromolecules are revealed by developing the strip after a certain time of electrophoresis, usually after 16–24 hr. For example, the polysaccharide–borate complexes are developed by staining with iodine, [29] while proteins can be stained with bromophenol blue containing mercury

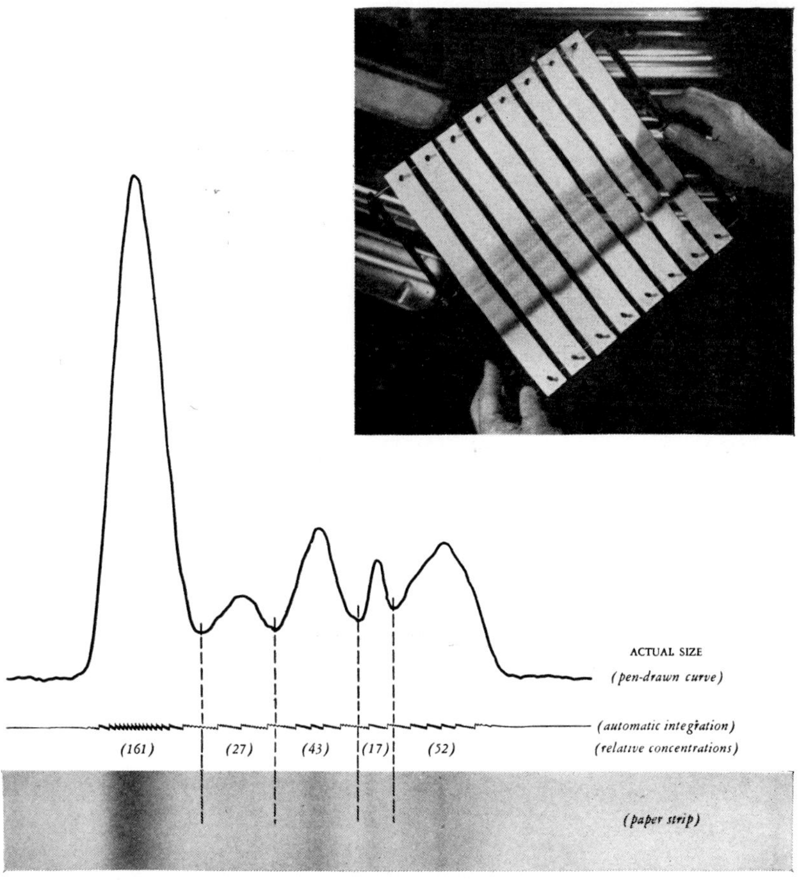

FIG. 12. An example of a diagram showing the distribution of components separated in paper electrophoresis. The diagram shows the result of densitometric scanning of a stained strip of paper

salts.[32] The various components in a protein then appear as blue spots or bands, depending on the method of application of the drop (Fig. 11). The

[32] M. LEDERER, *Introduction to Paper Electrophoresis* 2nd ed., Elsevier, Amsterdam, Van Nostrand, Princeton, 1957; L. P. RIBEIRO, E. MITIDIERI and O. R. AFFONSO, *Eletroforese em papel* Servico Grafico do I.B.G.E., Rio de Janeiro, 1958 (this book contains a bibliography with 2547 references); CH. WUNDERLY, *Die Papierelektrophorese* Sauerlaender, Aarau and Frankfurt am Main, 1954; R. J. BLOCK, E. L. DURRUM, G. ZWEIG, *A Manual of Paper Chromatography and Paper Electrophoresis* Academic Press, New York, 1955; H. KUNKEL and A. TISELIUS, *J. Gen. Physiol.* **35**, 89 (1951).

amount of the various components also can be determined, even by several methods. The developed paper strips can be cut into pieces, the color eluted, and its amount determined colorimetrically; or, more conveniently, the strips can be scanned with a densitometer, and the color intensity plotted as a function of the distance on the strip. Curves with peaks resembling those obtained by means of the cylindrical lens method in free boundary electrophoresis are produced by such plots (Fig. 12).

Even more revealing but somewhat more laborious than paper electrophoresis is *electrophoresis in soft gels* as supporting media.[(33)] Starch or agar gels of high water content have been successfully used for testing homogeneity

FIG. 13. High resolution of protein components by electrophoresis in starch gel (after O. Smithies)

of various proteins. Because of the very small pore size of the gel, it acts not only as a supporting medium, thus stabilizing the moving boundary but also as a sieve, thus facilitating a more complete separation than is possible in paper. Many more components have been revealed by this method, for example, in the β-globulin fraction of blood serum, than by free boundary or paper electrophoresis (Fig. 13).

None of the zone electrophoresis methods are ideal. The most important difficulties of the paper electrophoresis are: (1) adsorption of the migrating substances on the whole path of migration which, of course, results in an incomplete separation: (2) differences in the staining properties of the various components (e.g. the globulins bind somewhat less bromophenol blue than the albumins), and (3) the effects of the electro-osmotic flow. All these effects may cause considerable errors in quantitative evaluation of the amounts of the components and their mobilities, although they do not affect much the ability to detect them.

The solubility method has been used for testing the homogeneity of crystallized proteins. Although only a relatively pure and native material can be crystallized, crystallinity has long been known as an unreliable criterion for the homogeneity and purity of macromolecular substances. The homogeneity of protein crystals is tested by dissolving increasing amounts of the crystals in a solvent. Various amounts of protein are equilibrated at a constant temperature with equal volumes of a salt solution, and the amount dissolved is then determined quantitatively. The solubility is plotted against the amount of protein used, and the homogeneity is evaluated from these curves. Homo-

(33) O. SMITHIES, *Biochem. J.* **61**, 629 (1955); S. A. KARJALA, *Makromol. Chem.* **28**, 103 (1958). P. BERNFELD and J. S. NISSELBAUM, *J. biol. Chem.* **220**, 851 (1956).

geneous substances show a sharp break in the curve, i.e. the solubility increases with increasing amount of the solid up to a certain point and then becomes constant, irrespective of the amount placed in the solvent. Inhomogeneous specimens on the contrary exhibit smooth curves (see Fig. 14 and ref. 11).

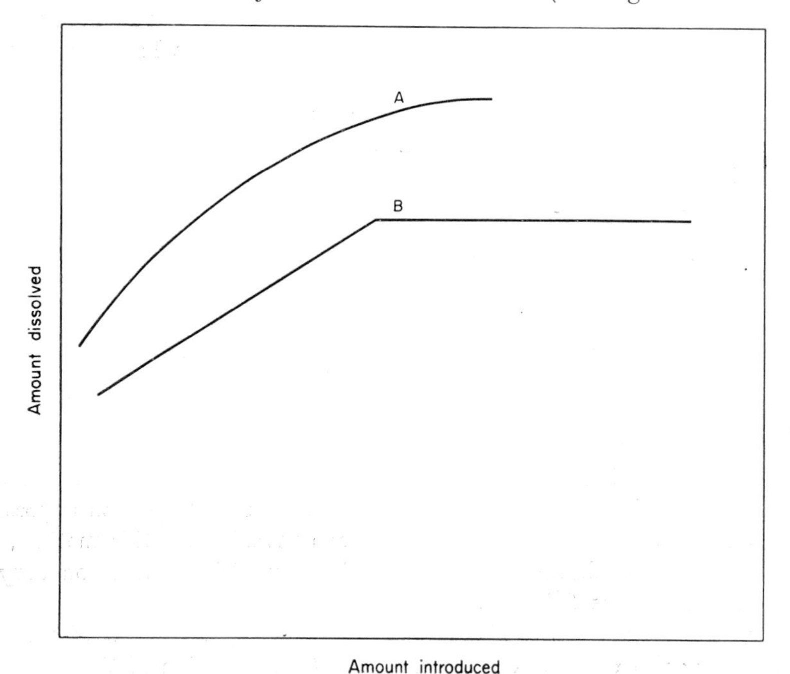

FIG. 14. Solubility curves of inhomogeneous (curve *A*) and homogeneous (curve *B*) preparations of macromolecular substances

Several enzymes which appeared homogeneous in the solubility test were resolved into two or three components by electrophoresis or chromatography.

Analytical chromatography of macromolecular substances on the DEAE–cellulose, calcium phosphate, and other adsorbents and ion exchangers has proven to be one of the most efficient methods in determining extranous macromolecular material in high polymers. Several components have been revealed this way in serum γ-globulin, serum albumin,[21] and in crystallized rennin.[22] Only some 10–50 mg of the substance are dissolved and applied to small columns; the effluent is collected in a series of tubes, an equal volume of, say, 2·0 ml in each, and the concentration of the polymer is determined by some sensitive analytical method, the proteins, for example, by the method of Lowry *et al.*[34] The color readings, which correspond to the concentration of the macromolecules in each tube, are then plotted versus number of tubes

[34] O. H. LOWRY, N. J. ROSEBROUGH, A. L. FARR and R. J. RANDALL, *J. biol. Chem.* **193**, 265 (1951).

in the consecutive elution series, and graphs like that presented in Fig. 15 may be obtained. Many examples of analytical protein chromatography are presented in recent reviews and books.[35]

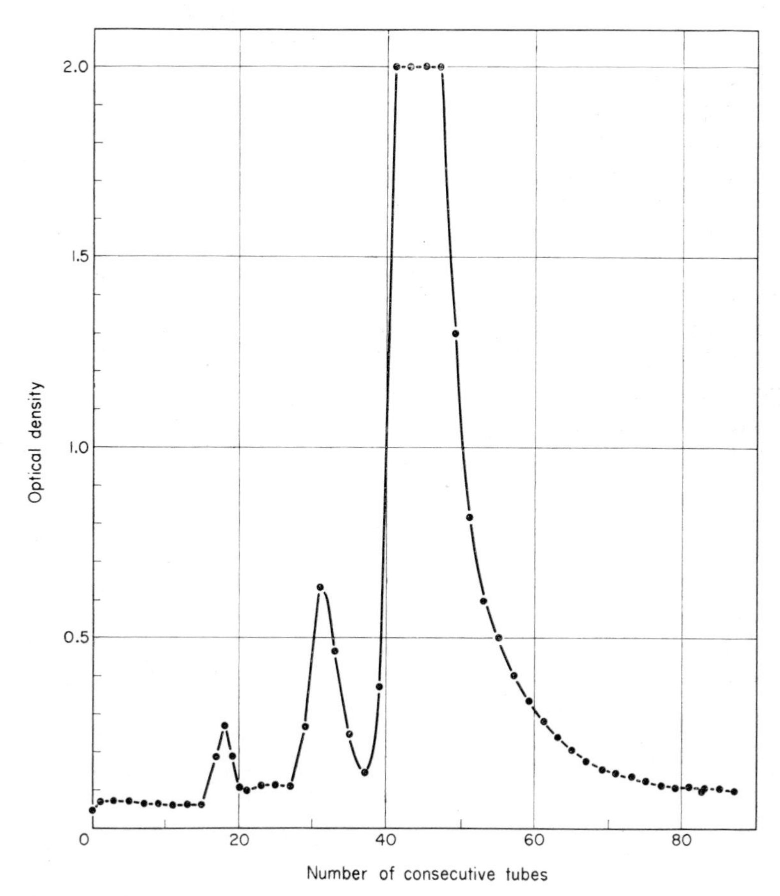

Fig. 15. Chromatographic resolution of a serum albumin fraction into three components. This resolution was accomplished by gradual elution of the proteins from a DEAE–cellulose column with phosphate buffers. Concentration of the components in the consecutive tubes of the fraction collector are expressed as optical density

Analytical chromatography seems to have a great future not only for the determination of protein homogeneity but also for the characterization of polysaccharides and nucleic acids. The analytical runs using buffers of various

[35] C. Calmon and T. R. E. Kressman, *Ion Exchange in Organic and Biochemistry* Interscience, New York, 1957; S. Moore and W. H. Stein, *Adv. Protein Chem.* **11**, 191 (1956).

pH and ionic strength, are used to find the most favorable conditions for preparative separation. A more homogeneous material is obtained this way. Various difficulties may be encountered, and conclusions about homogeneity should be made only after careful reinvestigation. If, for example, a substance is very weakly bound in the column, it may be too easily washed out and appear in the first tubes thus seeming to be homogeneous, while actually being composed of several components. Rechromatography with a smaller flow rate and lower ionic strength may resolve the specimen into two or more subfractions. Such observations have been made in the Biochemistry Laboratory of The University of Texas M. D. Anderson Hospital and Tumor Institute with several preparations of Bence–Jones proteins. The homogeneity was tested by chromatography on DEAE cellulose columns using phosphate buffers for gradient elution, the pH being changed between 7·0 and 8·0. Only one peak appeared in the elution curve when a high phosphate concentration between 0·05–0·2 *M* was used for the elution. Resolution into two components could be achieved by washing with lower phosphate concentrations, starting with 0·005 *M* and finishing the elution with 0·10 *M* phosphate buffer (of the same pH and with the same flow rate). Since the protein still appeared in the first tubes, it was suspected that an even better resolution could be achieved by working with even lower salt concentration and flow rate. Indeed, a clear-cut resolution into three components was accomplished, when the concentration of the second buffer was reduced to 0·05 *M* (unpublished results).

The possibility of artifact formation is another point to be considered in chromatography tests. Sensitive macromolecules may be denatured, especially when they are tenaciously bound at the surfaces, and when drastically acting elution agents must be used for getting the polymer off the column. Two major factors determine the binding of macromolecules in the ion exchange columns: (1) the *charge density*, and (2) the *molecular shape*. The DEAE–cellulose is positively charged, and it binds all sorts of negatively charged macromolecules; the latter are the more difficult to elute the more negatively charged groups they contain per unit of their surface area. Thus the proteins containing many carboxyl groups in their side chains are relatively strongly bound on the surfaces of anion exchange resins. Another factor here is the acidity, i.e. pH of the solution, since the charge depends also on the degree of dissociation. Macromolecular acids will interact with a positively charged anion exchanger better the higher the pH. (Since the amine residues in the exchanger are strongly basic their dissociation is influenced by the pH increase less than that of the carboxyl.) The elution, on the contrary, is facilitated by a decrease of pH. The shape factor is also of importance, due to adsorption effects, even in ion exchange chromatography. The simple fact to be considered at this point is that an uncoiled thread has a larger surface area than a tighly coiled thread: Fibrous macromolecules are generally more strongly adsorbed than globular entities.

Homogeneity considerations from chemical data may lead to decisive conclusion if the molecular weight of the macromolecular substance is known. Suppose one isolated an apparently homogeneous polymer of $M = 10,000$, and the chemical analysis shows that this substance contains $^1/_2\%$ of a constituent (that might be an amino acid residue in a protein) of $M = 100$. This result indicates that the macromolecular preparation is inhomogeneous, since *one* is the smallest possible number of a constituent molecule, and, if its relative weight is 100, it should be 1·0% in a macromolecule possessing the molecular weight of 10,000. If the analysis and the M value is correct, the conclusion from such results could be that only one half of the macromolecules contain the particular residue, and that another component devoid of it is present in the preparation.

Criteria for the native state of isolated macromolecules. *Biological behavior* is the most decisive criterion for the native state. Most impressive are the examples of crystallized enzymes and hormones, as well as the highly purified and crystallized viruses. The important fact that the native state of these large and complex units is not altered during the isolation is demonstrated by activity tests in the various stages of separation. If proper care is observed in the isolation of an enzyme or virus, the activity increases with the degree of concentration. It is true that a macromolecule of an enzyme in a crystal is not exactly in the same state as in a living cell, but the slight differences seem to be fully reversible when the crystal is introduced into the appropriate biological medium. In a crude analogy with living beings, it can be said that a macromolecule of an enzyme in a crystal is in a kind of passive or "dormant" state. As indicated before: the globular macromolecules are much more easy to isolate preserving their native state than the fibrous macromolecules. This is especially true for such complicated fibrous entities as the macromolecules of the nucleic acids and nucleoproteins. The native state of these preparations is very difficult to ascertain.

Solubility and the ability to crystallize. These are other important though crude criteria of the native state. Many proteins, such as egg albumin, γ-globulin of serum, etc. become insoluble when the native state is damaged in some way. Distortion of the unique native configuration usually is followed by aggregation and by a decrease in solubility. Such damaged macromolecules lose their ability to crystallize.

Various physical criteria of the native state. The gross configuration of macromolecules can be studied by a variety of physical–chemical methods, such as sedimentation in the analytical ultracentrifuge, viscosity measurement, the study of light scattering, etc. All these methods will be discussed in the following chapter. The viscosity of the solutions of globular proteins, for instance increases when the macromolecules are distorted and unfolded. X-ray spectra, the infrared spectra, and especially the optical rotation of organic macromolecules render information about the structure and configuration. Attempts have been made to study the macromolecular structures in living cells and tissues by various optical methods in order to compare the configuration of the isolated preparations with the native configuration.[34]

Some striking achievements have been recorded recently, especially in the field of plant viruses. The tobacco mosaic virus has been isolated in pure state, and, moreover, it was split into two components — the protein and ribonucleic acid —, and the components were recombined and reactivated.[35] The reconstituted virus particles appeared in the electron microscope as rods of similar dimensions as the original native virus, and the artificially reactivated virus was able to cause lesions and to grow on tobacco leaves.

The greatest goal in these endeavors is the synthesis of natural macromolecules by the methods of synthetic organic chemistry. This would not only elucidate completely the structural details, but, if the synthetic substances were biologically active, remove also last doubts about slight configurational differences, i.e. its native state. Science is still very far from this goal. Oxytocin is one of the largest biologically active molecules thus far synthesized by the methods of synthetic chemistry; its molecular weight is only 1007.[36] The synthesis of insulin is still a distant goal. The synthetic peptide hormones are biologically active, hence they can be considered as being similar if not identical with the molecules produced by cells. This supports the hope that biologically active macromolecules will be synthesized.

[34] G. Oster and A. W. Pollister (ed.), *Physical Techniques in Biological Research* Vol. III, Academic Press, New York, 1956.

[35] H. Fraenkel-Conrat and R. C. Williams, *Proc. nat. Acad. Sci.* **41**, 690 (1955).

[36] V. du Vigneaud, Ch. Ressler, J. M. Swan, C. W. Roberts and P. G. Katsoyannis, *J. Amer. chem. Soc.* **76**, 3115 (1954). The synthesis of lysine-vasopressin, another pituitary hormone, also was accomplished by a group of chemists in the same laboratory: M. F. Bartlett, A. Jöhl, R. Roeske, R. J. Stedman, F. H. C. Stewart, D. N. Ward and V. du Vigneaud, *J. Amer. chem. Soc.* **78**, 2905 (1956).

CHAPTER 3

THE SIZE, SHAPE, AND HYDRATION OF MACROMOLECULES

> Das Molekulargewicht einer Verbindung ist die Summe der Gewichte der Atome, die im kleinsten Teilchen durch Hauptvalenzen gebunden sind.
>
> H. STAUDINGER (*Organische Kolloidchemie*, p. 41, 1950)

Chemical and Physical Molecular Weights

Staudinger's definition, as given above, is the common definition of the chemical molecular weight. It is applicable only to those substances that are homogeneous and whose chemical composition and structure are known in full detail. This is the great goal for the macromolecular chemist, and he is approaching it slowly. The "macromolecule" of insulin is the largest one to which it is possible now to apply this definition of the true chemical molecular weight as *sum* of atomic weights: it is 5733. There is still quite a way to the conventional limit of 10,000, i.e. the approximate lower range of the domain of large molecules, but the protein chemists are close to a full understanding of the structure of several macromolecules in the molecular weight range higher than 10,000. Although the structure of insulin is not yet supported by synthesis, it is very likely that the presently accepted formula is correct.[1] Direct physical–chemical methods, however, are only able to give less accurate values, ranging somewhere between 6000 and 6500.[2] Unfortunately the macromolecular chemist must be content with these less accurate physical molecular weights, since most of his preparations are inhomogeneous, and since the structure and composition of some of the apparently homogeneous high polymers is not completely elucidated. The physical molecular weights obtained with such polydisperse mixtures as rubber, nitrocellulose, or gelatin, are average values which can vary within wide limits depending on the preparation, as well as on the method of determination. However, even for practically homogeneous proteins, such as serum albumin, the best, i. e. presently available most accurate physical–chemical methods, have rendered values

[1] A. P. RYLE, F. SANGER, L. F. SMITH and R. KITAI, *Biochem. J.* **60**, 541 (1955); F. SANGER, in *Currents in Biochemical Research* p. 434 (D. E. GREEN, ed.), Interscience 1956.

[2] E. J. HARFENIST and L. C. CRAIG, *J. Amer. chem. Soc.* **74**, 3087 (1952); E. FREDERICO, *Nature* **171**, 570 (1953); D. W. KUPKE and K. LINDERSTROM-LANG, *Biochim. Biophys. Acta* **13**, 153 (1954).

between 65,000 and 73,000. These variations may be due partially to the differences in the various albumin preparations, although considerable differences are found even with the same preparation. In spite of this, the physical method is essential, even if the exact formula is known, in order to determine the possible association in solutions.

In addition to the straightforward addition of atomic weights, the chemical methods are helpful in estimating the minimum molecular weight. This is possible when the large molecules in a homogeneous preparation contain a small amount of certain active groups or elements differing from the bulk of the macromolecule. If A is the relative weight of this group and a its analytically determined percentage, the minimum molecular weight M then can be calculated from

$$M = 100\, A/a.$$

For example, 0·338% iron is found in pure mammalian hemoglobin. Since the atomic weight of iron is 55·85, the molecular weight of 16,500 is obtained, when these values for a and A are introduced in the equation. The physical molecular weights are found to be larger, namely 66,000–68,000; hence one has to assume that these larger molecules, as measured in solutions, are composed of four subunits of $M = 16{,}500$. It is not established yet whether

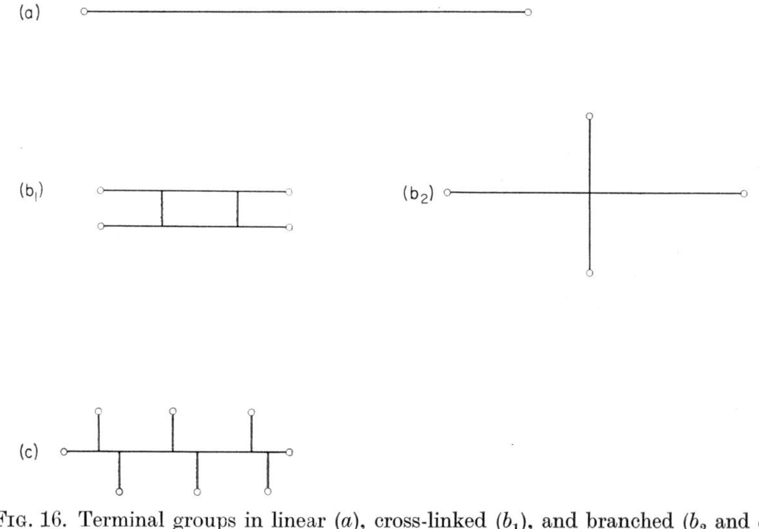

FIG. 16. Terminal groups in linear (a), cross-linked (b_1), and branched (b_2 and c) macromolecules

these subunits are mutually linked by primary or secondary bonds, and the question on the true chemical molecular weight of hemoglobin will be answered only after complete elucidation of its structure.

The chemical methods have another application: when the macromolecules are linear, the molecular weight can be determined by analyzing the terminal groups. Unfortunately the preparations of linear polymers are usually polymolecular, hence only average values can be obtained. The method has value for well fractionated specimens of linear polymers of relatively low or moderate molecular size. Determination of terminal groups, in conjunction with other methods, is able to render information about possible branching of these linear molecules: in the case of branching the chemical method will give smaller values for M than other methods. This method is insensitive for very large linear molecules, since the end groups then comprise a vanishingly small portion of the material. These relationships are illustrated in Fig. 16. The possibilities of branching and ring formation by variations with a linear chain are unlimited, and in the illustration are chosen a few simple cases. In all four instances the molecular weight, illustrated by the length of the lines, is the same. In a completely linear case (a) only two active terminal groups are found (illustrated as circles); in b_1 and b_2 the number of terminal groups is four, and the structure of b_1 differs from the structure of b_2. In the instance c the branching is more extensive than in b_1 or b_2. These examples show both the limitations and usefulness of this method. Structures like a are known in the amylose of starch, the chains like c are found in the amylopectin of starch, and structural types of bridged chains (b_1) are found in proteins, whereby each end of a chain in this case has a different terminal group.

Molecular Weight Averages

It has already been indicated that the molecular weight of polymolecular substances depends on the *method* of determination. These differences in the molecular weights obtained by various methods are not due to experimental errors but *to inherent effects of molecular size distribution on the values of mean molecular weights.* The molecular weight as found by chemical analysis or osmotic pressure measurement is the *number average molecular weight* M_n. It is the ratio of the total mass m to the total number of moles n, that is m/n. The number average molecular weight M_n is obtained by methods which measure the effects caused by the *number* of molecules; for example the osmotic effect of one large molecule is the same as the effect caused by a small molecule.[3] In a mixture of polymer-homologs, such as ordinary gelatin or glycogen, are present $n_1, n_2, n_3, \ldots$ moles of the macromolecules with the molecular weights $M_1, M_2, M_3, \ldots$ respectively. The number average molecular weight is defined by:

$$M_n = \frac{n_1 M_1 + n_2 M_2 + n_3 M_3 + \ldots}{n_1 + n_2 + n_3 + \ldots} = \frac{\Sigma\, n_i M_i}{\Sigma\, n_i}.$$

The M_n value is the integral result as obtained experimentally, while neither any of the $n_1, n_2, \ldots$ nor $M_1, M_2, \ldots$ values can be determined separately.

[3] R. U. Bonnar, M. Dimbat and F. H. Stross, *Number-Average Molecular Weights* Interscience, New York, 1958.

Thus the equation merely explains the meaning of this molecular weight average. Now, it is important to realize that whenever the molecular weight of the same specimen is determined by sedimentation velocity or light scattering effects, the molecular weight values obtained are larger than by the methods which measure the number effects. This is due to the fact that in the sedimentation or light scattering the larger molecules produce larger effects than the smaller ones. The *weight average* molecular weight M_w obtained by these methods is defined as:

$$M_w = \frac{m_1 M_1 + m_2 M_2 + m_3 M_3 + \ldots}{m_1 + m_2 + m_3} = \frac{\Sigma n_i M_i^2}{\Sigma n_i M_i}.$$

Here $m_1, m_2, m_3, \ldots$ are the masses of each species, and each m value is obtained by multiplying the respective n by the corresponding M. Thus the molecular weight appears in the sum of the denominator and as its square in the numerator. This squaring of M is the reason that M_w is larger than M_n, because $\Sigma M_i^2/\Sigma M_i$ is larger than M. Hence, the average molecular weight of a

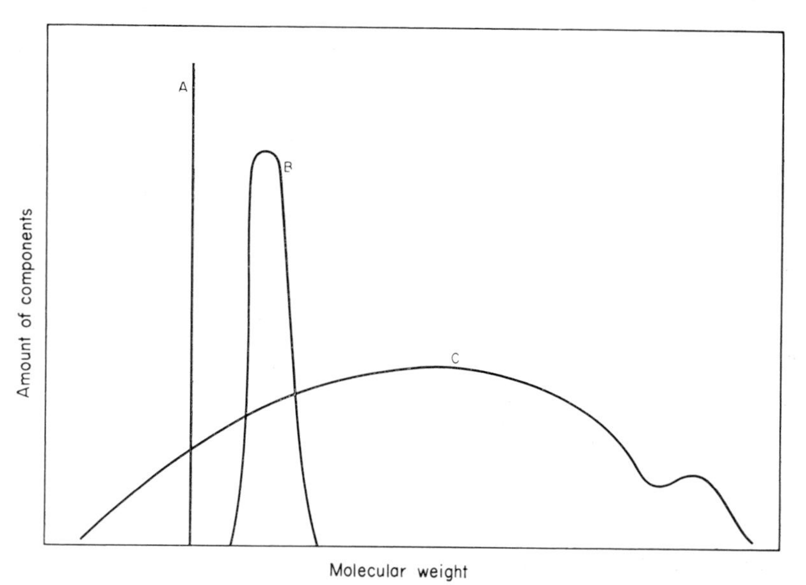

FIG. 17. Molecular size distribution for homogeneous (A) and inhomogeneous (B and C) substances

polymolecular substance when measured by means of light scattering or sedimentation velocity *must* be larger than that obtained by osmotic pressure data.

The greater the difference between M_w and M_n the less homogeneous the sample. Since the homogeneity can be determined by several other independent methods (see chap. 2), it is possible to compare the inhomogeneity data on a broad basis. The inhomogeneity usually is expressed graphically by plotting the amount of each component versus its molecular weight, as shown in Fig. 17. An absolutely homogeneous substance in such graph would give a vertical line at a certain M value, and in such case $M_w = M_n$. Well fractionated samples of glycogens or amylose will give steep distribution curves showing that 90% or more of the material differs little in the M values of the components, while strongly inhomogeneous mixtures exhibit flat curves. Several maxima are not unusual in the mixtures of polymer homologs.

Examples showing actual values for number and weight average molecular weights for dextrans are presented in Table 1. The dextrans are microbial polysaccharides of the same composition as starch or glycogen, i.e. $(C_6H_{10}O_5)_n$ (see chap. 10). The molecular size is characterized by either the molecular weight or degree of polymerization (n, most commonly denoted by P); since the radical weight for $C_6H_{10}O_5$ is 162, $M = 162\,P$.

TABLE 1
THE NUMBER AND WEIGHT AVERAGE MOLECULAR WEIGHTS FOR DEXTRAN FRACTIONS [4]

Designation of the fraction	M_n	M_w	M_w/M_n
A	41,000	47,000	1·14
B	38,000	50,000	1·31
C	64,000	76,000	1·18
D	95,000	170,000	1·79
E	240,000	540,000	2·25

The ratio M_w/M_n expresses the inhomogeneity which for the fraction E is the highest, and for A the lowest.

Molecular Weight Determination by Osmotic Pressure Measurement

Osmotic pressure is a colligative property which depends on the *number* of acting entities. The other colligative effects, such as elevation of the boiling point, depression of freezing point or vapor pressure, are usually not applicable for large molecules, because the effects are very small; moreover, the effects are liable to distortion by several uncontrollable side effects. If a solution is separated from the solvent by a semipermeable membrane, there will be a tendency to equalize the concentration in the whole system, i.e. the solute will tend to pass through the membrane and distribute itself homogeneously in the solvent. When the solute molecules are small enough in order to pass through the membrane, they just do so, and an equivalent amount of solvent takes their place traveling the opposite way. If, however, the solute molecules are too large to go through the pores, the solvent will enter the solution and dilute it. The volume of the cell containing the solution thereby increases

[4] M. WALES, P. A. MARSHALL and S. G. WEISSBERG, *J. Polymer Sci.* **10**, 229 (1953).

exerting a pressure which can be measured, for example, by the rise of the meniscus in a tube attached to the cell (Fig. 18).

The molecular weight calculation is based on Van't Hoff's law, according to which the osmotic pressure p depends on the molar concentration of the solute c/M, and on temperature:

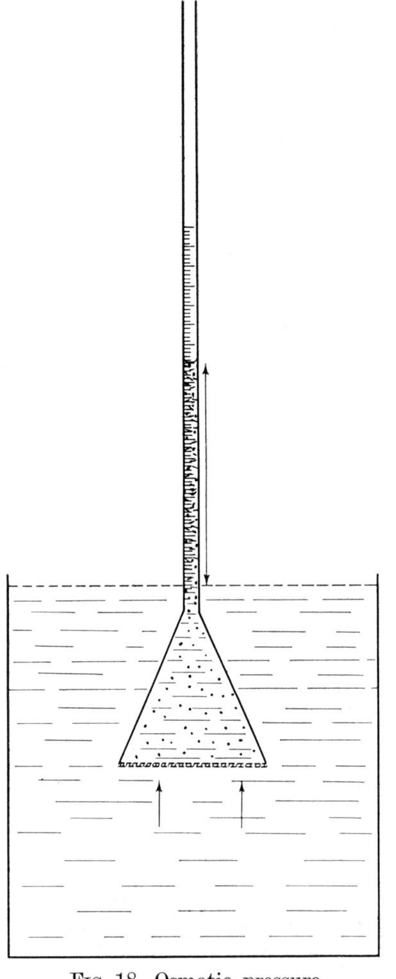

Fig. 18. Osmotic pressure

$$p = R\,T \cdot c/M$$

(R is gas constant, and c the weight of the substance in grams per liter). This is a limiting law which is valid only for the so called ideal solutions, i.e. for solutions in which the molecules do not interact. A rigorous theoretical treatment leads to a general expression that is applicable to macromolecular systems for a wide concentration range:[5]

$$p/c = R\,T/M + B\,c + C\,c^2 + D\,c^3 + \cdots$$

In this equation B, C, and D are constants determined by the molecular interaction. While C and D usually can be neglected, the interaction constant B must be considered even for dilute solutions of high polymers. The relations usually are expressed graphically by plotting the reduced osmotic pressure p/c against concentration c, as shown in Fig. 19. In the case of non-interacting, more or less ideal systems, the p/c values do not change appreciably with concentration, and the relationship can be expressed by a straight line parallel to the abscissa. Such instances actually have been encountered with such globular macromolecules as glycogen or serum albumin. The reduced osmotic pressure of the solutions containing linear macromolecules, however, increases with raising concentration. In the very low concentration range the relationship may be linear, cor-

[5] P. J. Flory, *Principles of Polymer Chemistry* p. 269ff., Cornell University Press, Ithaca, 1953; G. V. Schulz, in *Das Makromolekül in Lösungen* p. 374ff , Springer, Berlin/Göttingen/Heidelberg, 1953; J. Stauff, *Kolloidchemie*, Springer, Berlin/Göttingen/Heidelberg, 1960.

responding to the equation $p/c = RT/M + Bc$, where B is the slope, and RT/M the intercept on the ordinate from which the M value then is computed. This is rendered more difficult when there is a strong curvature in the whole concentration range.

Since the osmotic pressure ideally is proportional to c/M, i.e. inversely proportional to the molecular size, it is very sensitive to micromolecular

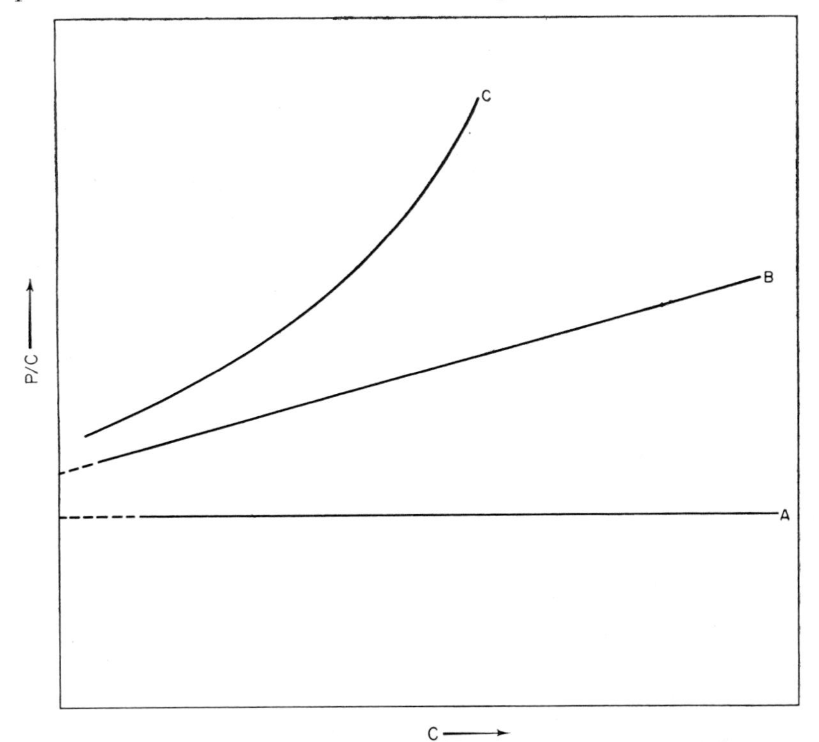

Fig. 19. Dependence of reduced osmotic pressure (p/c) on concentration (c) for non-interacting (A), weakly interacting (B), and strongly interacting (C) macromolecules

impurities. The solution of a high polymer may be liberated from these impurities by dialysis. However, if the macromolecules themselves contain ionogenic groups, such as COOH in proteins, it is impossible to liberate the solution from the micromolecular counter ions because of the tendency to maintain electrostatic equilibrium in the system. If a macromolecular electrolyte $R \cdot COONa = R \cdot COO^+ + Na^-$ is separated from water by a semipermeable membrane, part of the sodium ions indeed will leave the solution but they will be replaced by an equivalent amount of hydrogen ions from water. Since the macro-ions usually are polyvalent, there will be many H^+ and Na^+ ions around each $R \cdot COO^-$ or, more correctly, $R \cdot (COO^-)_n$. As the osmotic pressure depends on the number of particles, the macro-ions will have relatively little effect, since their, activity will be overshadowed by activity of the hydrogen and sodium ions. For this reason, the osmotic pressure of macromolecular electrolytes is measured not in pure aqueous solutions but in buffer solutions. It can be shown that these effects (Donnan effects) which are caused by the presence of restrained macro-ions, and which result in anomalous osmotic pressure values, as well as acidity variation, can be best suppressed by using a low concentration of the macromolecular electrolyte and a high buffer concentration.[6]

The osmotic pressure can be measured with different types of instruments. The old method was to introduce the solution into a thimble composed of suitable membrane material into which was inserted a glass tube; the latter was tightly bound to the thimble, and the device inserted into a container with water. The osmotic pressure was determined by measuring the rise of the liquid in the tube. Various refinements were gradually introduced, e.g. it was found in certain cases that higher precision can be achieved by using flat membranes fastened between perforated discs, by using narrow capillary tubes, and by immersing the osmometer into a constant temperature bath. The methods now can be divided in several groups: (1) the classical approach by measuring the rise of the liquid in a capillary tube, (2) by applying counter-pressure and determining the flow of the solvent, or (3) by weighing, i.e. determining the amount of liquid entering the cell by weighing the cell. The methods are described in detail in handbooks.[7] One of the most important factors in osmometry is the proper *membrane*. It must be freely permeable for the solvent and impermeable for the macromolecules. Regenerated cellulose (Cellophane and similar materials) or nitrocellulose are the most common materials now used. Furthermore, the surface tension properties of the solution and solvent must be considered, and the rise due to capillarity must be subtraced in order to get the correct pressure. The temperature must be carefully checked, since the osmotic pressure increases with increasing temperature. Various improvements have been introduced recently in the technique of osmometry,[8] such as a more rigid supporting of the membrane by fastening between two perforated discs, by a very careful selection of the membrane material, or by using electronic devices for checking pressure changes.[9]

[6] F. G. DONNAN, *Chem. Rev.* **1**, 73 (1924); G. SCATCHARD, *J. Amer. chem. Soc.* **68**, 2315 (1946); G. SCATCHARD, A. C. BATCHELDER and A. BROWN, *ibid.* **68**, 2320 (1946).

[7] R. H. WAGNER in WEISSBERGER'S *Physical Methods in Organic Chemistry* 2nd. ed., Vol. I, part I, p. 487, 2nd printing, Interscience Publ., New York, 1952.

[8] J. V. STABIN and E. H. IMMERGUT, *J. Polymer Sci.* **14**, 209 (1954). The Stabin osmometers are available commercially (from J. V. STABIN, 601 E. 19 St., Brooklyn 26, N. Y.); H. HELLFRITZ and H. KRAMER, *Kunststoffe* **46**, 3 (1956); the Hellfritz osmometers can be purchased from Hellma GmbH., Glastechnische Werkstätten, Müllheim, Germany.

[9] D. S. ROWE and M. E. ABRAMS, *Biochem. J.* **67**, 431 (1957). The Rowe electronic osmometers are available from Nash and Thompson, Ltd, Oakcroft Road, Chessington, Surrey, England.

The time of measurement has been reduced with the newest equipment to 1–2 hr (or less) instead of days required formerly. A modern instrument is sketched in Fig. 20.

The osmotic pressure method is applicable for the molecular weight determination in the range 20,000–800,000. At the lower limit of $M = 10{,}000$–$15{,}000$ the measurements may involve errors which are due to imperfections

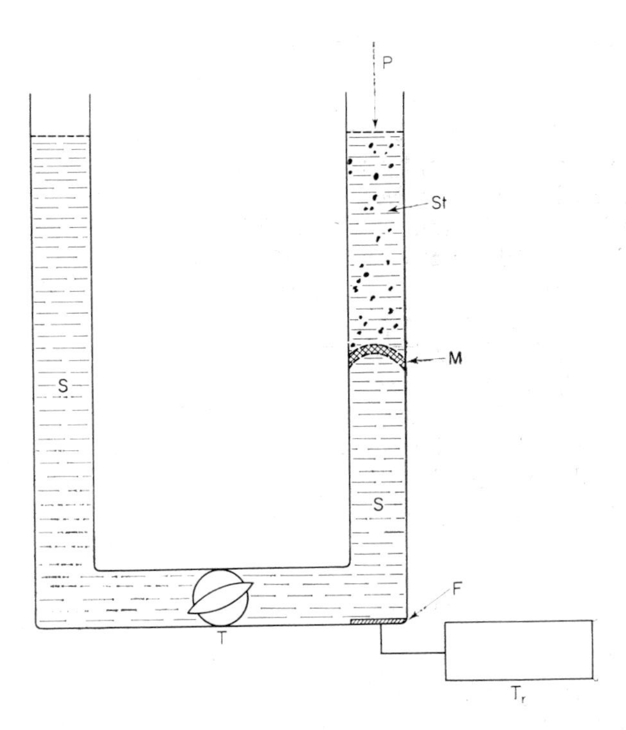

FIG. 20. A diagram of the Rowe electronic osmometer. *S* — solvent; *St* — solution; *M* — membrane; *T* — tap; *F* — platinum foil diaphragm; *Tr* — electronic transducer. When the tap is closed transfer of solvent through the semipermeable membrane deflects the center of the platinum foil and this movement is converted into a galvanometer deflection by a mechano-electronic transducer which forms part of a balanced bridge circuit. A variable hydrostatic pressure is applied to the solution by means of a vernier manometer so as to oppose the osmotic pressure and the point of pressure balance (solvent transfer) is determined from the galvanometer readings and counter pressures (p)

of the membrane, i.e. that a small fraction of the macromolecules may escape through the wider pores into the solution. At the upper limit the pressures are very small, hence the error proportionally increases. The osmotic pressure method does not render any information on the homogeneity of the high polymer.

The Size, Shape, and Homogeneity of Macromolecules from Sedimentation and Diffusion Data

Sedimentation and diffusion measurements are more laborious and require more expensive equipment than osmotic pressure work. These efforts are compensated by additional information on homogeneity and shape of the macromolecules to be studied.

Diffusion causes spreading of the macromolecules from an undisturbed solution–solvent boundary into the pure solvent. This spreading is due to the chaotic molecular motion, i.e. it is directly proportional to temperature, and is statistically determined; the spreading boundary is not absolutely sharp, but some of the macromolecules, by mere chance, are pushed farther than others. Hoewever, the larger the molecules the more slowly they spread. Diffusion is characterized quantitatively by determining the diffusion constant, called also diffusion coefficient: the number of grams of a substance transported per second across an area of one square centimeter perpendicular to which there is a gradient of one gram per cubic centimeter per centimeter. Diffusion is now determined mostly in the Tiselius-type rectangular electrophoresis cells (see Fig. 6, p. 29) at a constant temperature by using the cylindrical lens optics. The conditions at the solution–solvent boundary are shown by this type of refraction optics as a peak thus expressing the *rate of change of concentration* dc/dx (see Fig. 8). Photographs of these peaks are taken at definite time intervals, and analysis of the peaks permits the calculation of the diffusion constant.[10] This calculation is based on Fick's law

$$\partial c/\partial t = \partial(D\, \partial c/\partial x)/\partial x,$$

where c is concentration, t time, and x distance in the direction of diffusion. This differential equation was integrated by Boltzmann under the assumption that c is a function only of $y = x \cdot t^{\frac{1}{2}}$ thus obtaining:

$$D = -\frac{1}{2}\, dy/dc \int_0^c y\, dc.$$

The values of D then are computed for example by graphical integration.

Direct correlation of the calculated diffusion constant with the molecular weight is possible only for some special cases. According to the Stokes–Einstein relation

$$D = R\,T/6\,\pi\,\eta\,N\,r,$$

[10] H. P. LUNDGREN and W. H. WARD, in *Amino Acids and Proteins* p. 312ff. (D. M. GREENBERG, ed.), Thomas, Springfield, Illinois, 1951. A. L. GEDDES in WEISSBERGER's *Physical Methods of Organic Chemistry* Vol. I, part. I, Interscience, New York, 2nd printing, 1952. L. J. GOSTING, *Adv. Protein Chem.* **11**, 430 (1956).

where R is the gas constant, T absolute temperature, η absolute viscosity, N Avogadro's number, and r radius of the spreading molecule. This relation, however, is valid only for an ideal solution in which the macromolecules are unhydrated spheres. Since $M = 4\pi N \varrho r^3/3$, the molecular weight

$$M = \frac{R^3 T^3 \varrho}{16 \pi^2 \eta^3 N^2 D^3},$$

where ϱ is the density of the material.

A simpler procedure for the determination of diffusion constants was introduced by Northrop and Anson.[11] The solution is separated from the solvent by a porous diaphragm (Fig. 21), and the diffusion is studied by analyzing aliquots taken from both the upper and lower compartments after certain time intervals. The diffusion constant is calculated from an approximated solution of Fick's law, as follows:

$$D = -\frac{q}{Kt} \cdot \frac{1}{c_1 - c_2},$$

where q is the amount of substance passing through the diaphragm in time t, K is a cell constant, and c_1 and c_2 are the concentrations in the upper and lower compartments, respectively. The method is a relative one, and the cell must be calibrated with substances of known D values in order to estimate the constant K. This method has the same advantages and disadvantages with respect to free boundary diffusion as zone electrophoresis to free boundary electrophoresis. In the Northrop–Anson method the boundary is stabilized, and the transfer can be determined very easily; however, bulk streaming through excessively large pores, as well as adsorption of the material in the diaphragm must be avoided. Generally the method has justified the expectations.[11]

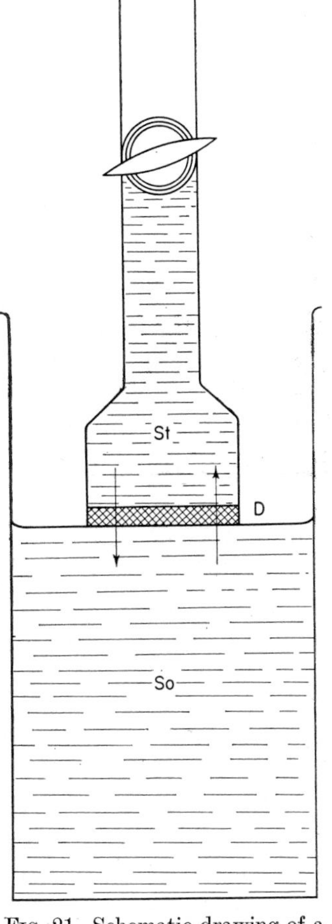

FIG. 21. Schematic drawing of a device of diffusion measurement by the porous diaphragm method. *St* — solution; *So* — solvent; *D* — porous diaphragm of sintered glass

[11] J. H. NORTHROP and M. L. ANSON, *J. Gen. Physiol* **12**, 543 (1929); G. S. HARTLEY and D. F. RUNNICLES, *Proc. Roy. Soc. London* A **168**, 401 (1938); J. C. GAGE, *Trans. Faraday Soc.* **44**, 253 (1948).

Sedimentation studies in the analytical ultracentrifuge are able to furnish important information about molecular size, shape and homogeneity.[12] The centrifugal force acting on a mole of macromolecules at a distance x from the axis of rotation is computed as the difference between the centrifugal weight $M\,x\,\omega^2$ and the buoyancy exerted by the displaced liquid $M\,x\,V\,\varrho\,\omega^2$:

$$M\,x\,\omega^2 - M\,x\,V\,\varrho\,\omega^2 = M(1-\varrho\,V)\,x\,\omega^2,$$

where ϱ is the density of the solution, ω the angular velocity of rotation, and V the partial specific volume of the solute. (The partial specific volume is a density function, and it is inversely proportional to the density). This centrifugal force is equated to a resisting force $f \cdot \mathrm{d}x/\mathrm{d}t$, where f is the frictional force per mole, hence,

$$M(1-\varrho\,V)\,x\,\omega^2 = f \cdot \mathrm{d}x/\mathrm{d}t \cdots \tag{1}$$

Svedberg suggested the term *sedimentation constant*, s, defined as

$$s = \frac{\mathrm{d}x/\mathrm{d}t}{x\,\omega^2},$$

instead of the sedimentation velocity $\mathrm{d}x/\mathrm{d}t$. The sedimentation constant is a very important characteristic for a macromolecular substance, although it is by no means always in a simple quantitative relation to the molecular weight. The latter can be calculated from equation (1) as follows. First, the integrated expression for s

$$s = \frac{\ln x_2/x_1}{(t_2-t_1)\,\omega^2}$$

is used for the calculation of s, where x_2 and x_1 are the distances the macromolecules have migrated in times t_2 and t_1 respectively. Then, the frictional force $f = R\,T/D$, where R is the gas constant, T absolute temperature, and D diffusion constant is calculated. Introducing these expressions in (1), M can be calculated:

$$M = \frac{R\,T\,s}{D(1-\varrho\,V)} = \frac{R\,T \ln x_2/x_1}{D(1-\varrho\,V)(t_2-t_1)\,\omega^2} \cdots \tag{2}$$

Since the sedimentation depends on many factors, the s-values are corrected to conditions at 20 °C in pure water. Moreover, since the sedimentation constant depends on concentration, the sedimentation runs are made at various concentrations c of the high polymer, the s-values are plotted against c, and extrapolated to zero concentration. This finally corrected constant is denoted by $s^0_{20,w}$. Its absolute unit is second, and the magnitudes of the constant range somewhere between 10^{-13} and $180 \cdot 10^{-13}$ sec. The constants are now commonly expressed in the 10^{-13} units, called svedbergs, and denoted by S.

[12] T. Svedberg and K. O. Pedersen, *The Ultracentrifuge* Clarendon Press, Oxford, 1940; H. K. Schachman, *Ultracentrifugation in Biochemistry* Academic Press, New York, 1959; H. K. Schachman in *Methods in Enzymology* (S. P. Colowick and N. O. Kaplan, ed.), Vol. IV, p. 32, Academic Press, New York, 1957; H. P. Lundgren and W. H. Ward in *Amino Acids and Proteins* p. 312ff. (D. M. Greenberg, ed.), Thomas, Springfield, Illinois, 1951.

The molecular weight can also be determined by the *sedimentation equilibrium method.*[12] The solution is spun at a relatively low speed of 10,000 to 25,000 rev/min until equilibrium between sedimentation and diffusion is reached, and the equilibrium concentrations are determined by optical means at several levels of the cell. The molecular weight is calculated from

$$M = \frac{2\,R\,T \ln c_2/c_1}{(1 - \varrho\,V)\,(x_2^2 - x_1^2)\,\omega^2}, \tag{3}$$

where c_1 and c_2 are the concentrations at x_1 and x_2 respectively. This method has the advantage that the molecular weight can be computed without knowing the diffusion constant, and that relatively low speeds are needed. However, a very long time is required to attain the equilibrium state, and relatively large errors are involved in the determination of the c values. In the instance of a polymolecular solution this method usually gives the so-called z-average which is defined by

$$M_z = \frac{\Sigma\, n_i\, M_i^3}{\Sigma\, n_i\, M_i^2};$$

the M_z values are always larger than the M_w values obtained by the sedimentation method. $M_z = M_w = M_n$ only in homogeneous (monodispersed) systems, such as some proteins.

Both sedimentation and diffusion rate depend not only on the molecular size but also on the molecular shape, density, and hydration. Linear macromolecules diffuse and sediment more slowly than compact spherical macromolecules of comparable density and hydration. This resistance to displacement is characterized by the frictional force f in equation (1), as well as in the relation

$$f = R\,T/D.$$

The frictional force, on the other hand, can be calculated from Stokes' law by assuming that the macromolecules are unhydrated spheres. This frictional force f_0 is expressed by

$$f_0 = 6\,\pi\,\eta\,N^3\,(3\,M\,V/4\,\pi\,N)^{\frac{1}{3}},$$

where η is viscosity and N Avogadro's number, and M the molecular weight obtained from (3) or some independent method. The ratio f/f_0, the *molar frictional ratio* for the solutions of high polymers is larger than 1, and its magnitude indicates the degree of asymmetry and hydration. The frictional ratio of most globular proteins is 1·1–1·5, and that of the highly asymmetric tobacco mosaic virus is 3·1. Since the particles of this virus are definitely known to be *long* rods, the f/f_0 certainly does not reflect the degree of asymmetry. It must be emphasized that the calculation for both f and f_0 is subject to a series of experimental errors. Moreover, a relatively high f may be caused not only by regular asymmetry but by specific shaping, e.g. spherical but loosely built sponge-like macromolecules diffuse more slowly than compact spheres. Finally, the affinity of similarly shaped macromolecules for water may be different (hydration). In the efforts to resolve the effects of hydration and shape certain assumptions must be made about the shape; for example, it can be assumed that the macromolecules are prolate ellipsoids of revolution.[13] Generally, it must be admitted that the information about shape and hydration these methods are able to provide is very limited and indirect (see the next chapter).

The first experiments on analytical ultracentrifugation were started in the early twenties in University of Wisconsin and in Uppsala, Sweden, under

FIG. 22. The Spinco analytical ultracentrifuge

the leadership of T. Svedberg.[12] The instruments were improved later to a high perfection, and fields up to 500,000 g were reached at about 1935. The equipment, however, was so expensive that only a few ultracentrifuges were built. The horizontally placed heavy stainless steel rotors were driven by means of oil turbines, and the rotation occurred in a streaming low pressure hydrogen atmosphere for cooling. Many rotor explosions occurred due to imperfections in the material and slight imbalance. Meantime, Henriot and Huguenard showed in 1925 that very high speeds could be achieved without

(13) J. L. ONCLEY, *Ann. N. Y. Acad. Sci.* **41**, 121 (1941); F. PERRIN, *J. Physique Radium* **7**, 1 (1936); see also: H. SCHERAGA and L. MANDELKERN, *J. Amer. chem. Soc.* **75**, 179 (1953).

mechanical bearings. They whirled a small cone-shaped rotor by *jets of compressed air*. Since the rotation was relatively uniform, it was tried to follow the sedimentation in cells built in such "spinning top" rotors. Even better results were achieved when another rotor containing the cell with solution was hung from the "spinning top". These new type instruments, developed

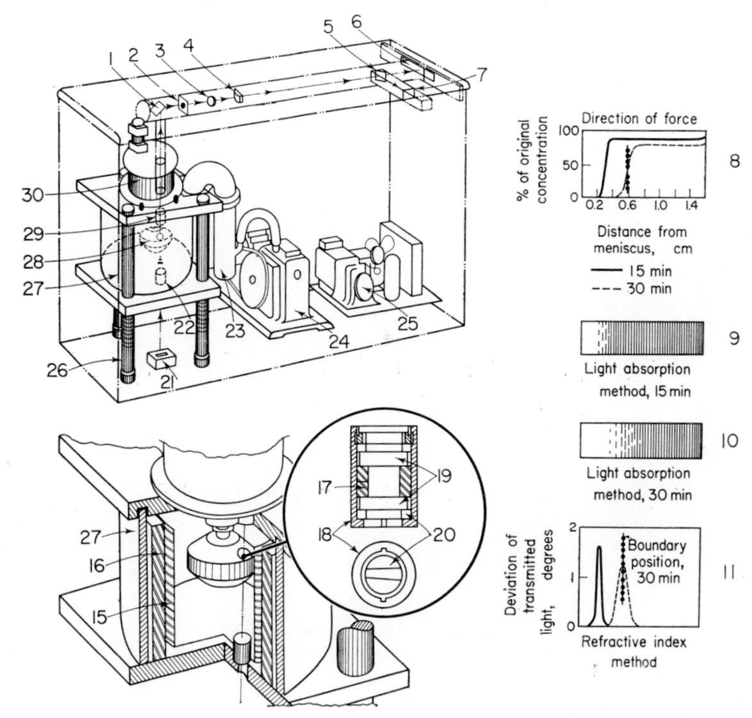

FIG. 23. Schematic diagram of the Spinco Model *E* analytical ultracentrifuge. 1–6 — optical system; 30 — drive; 27 — vacuum chamber; 21 — light source; 17–20 — parts of cell and housing; 23 — diffusion pump; 24 — mechanical pump; 25 — refrigeration

in 1932–1936 by Beams, Pickels, and others, were much more convenient and cheaper than the oil turbine machines. Moreover, it appeared that a hanging rotor may become self-balancing thus eliminating a series of difficulties. These developments in perfecting and simplifying the equipment were successfully continued by Pickels [14] and others resulting in the now commonly used electrically driven Spinco ultracentrifuge. The instrument is illustrated in Fig. 22–23. One of the essential parts is the rotor built of duraluminum (Fig. 24). This has holes for the cell and the counterbalance. The solution is poured into the middle section between two thick quartz windows. The rota-

[14] E. G. PICKELS in *Biophysical Research Methods* p. 67ff. (F. UBER, ed.), Interscience, New York, 1950.

tion takes place in a vacuum chamber, and the sedimentation is observed by means of a light beam entering the cell from underneath, then above the cell being reflected horizontally where it passes a series of lenses. The boundary then can be observed directly and photographed automatically at convenient time intervals. The most commonly used cylindrical lens optical

FIG. 24. Analytical Spinco rotor, counterbalance, cell housing, and parts of the cell (in front)

system gives boundaries similar to those in Tiselius free boundary electrophoresis. In simple cases one symmetrical peak indicates that the substance studied is homogeneous with respect to sedimentation, while several peaks and shoulders on peaks indicate inhomogeneity of the masses of the components (Fig. 25). The sedimentation constants are calculated from the positions of the peaks at certain time intervals, knowing the speed of rotation, enlargement factors of the optics etc.

Various improvements in the cell construction, temperatuie measurement during the run, as well as in the evaluation of the results, have been introduced recently by various investigators.[15] An extremely simple instrument for

[15] S. M. KLAINER and G. KEGELES, *J. physic. Chem.* **59**, 952 (1955); H. K. SCHACHMAN and W. F. HARRINGTON, *J. Polymer Sci.* **12**, 379 (1954); R. HERSH and H. K. SCHACHMAN, *J. Amer. chem. Soc.* **77**, 5228 (1955); A. GINSBURG, P. APPEL and H. K. SCHACHMAN, *Arch. Biochem. Biophys.* **65**, 545 (1956).

semiquantitative studies has been elaborated by Ford.[16] This is essentially a spinning top air driven rotor with radial holes containing capillaries with

a

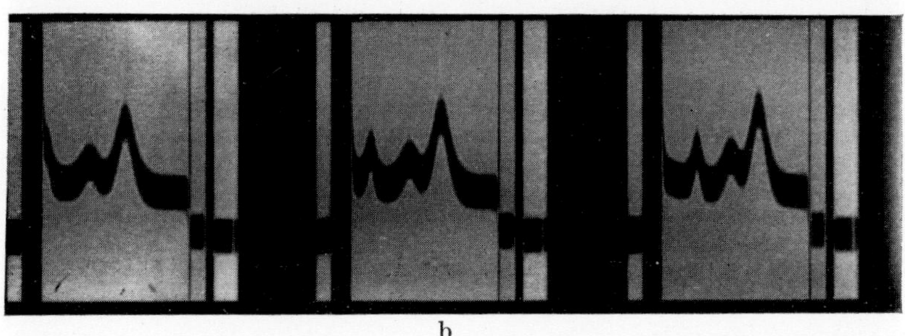

b

FIG. 25. Sedimentation diagrams of a homogeneous (a) and inhomogeneous (b) macromolecular substance in the Spinco ultracentrifuge at 56,100 rev/min. The sedimentation proceeds from right to left. The homogeneous a sediments more slowly than either of the 3 components of the inhomogeneous mixture (b). Each of the 3 photographs was taken in 8 min. intervals. The size of the peaks depends on the concentration of the components

the solution to be studied. The sedimentation can not be observed during the run, but the centrifuge is stopped at given time intervals, the capillaries then being examined.

Molecular Size and Shape Determination by the Method of Light Scattering

When a beam of light strikes a molecule, the electrons of the constituting atoms are made to vibrate, and the molecule becomes a source of scattered light. These scattering phenomena were studied theoretically some 80 years ago by Lord Rayleigh who came to the following conclusions: The intensity of the scattered light is proportional to the intensity of the incident beam, to the second power of the volume of the molecules v^2, to the number of the

[16] T. F. FORD, G. A. RAMSDELL and L. W. KLIPP, *J. physic. Chem.* **59**, 922 (1955).

molecules, and to the square of the difference between the refractive index of the molecules and the medium; the intensity of the scattered light is inversely proportional to the fourth power of the wave length, λ^4. The wave length dependence explains such common phenomenon as the *opalescence* in the solutions of many high polymers, e.g. of a starch solution: it appears yellowish when viewed against light, and bluish in reflected light. This is due to the fact that the short-wave light (blue and violet) is scattered much more than the longwave yellow and red light.

The first extensive studies on the molecular weight determination by the method of light scattering were conducted by Putzeys and Brosteaux [(17)] on proteins. They calculated the molecular weights on the basis of the classical assumptions that the macromolecules are noninteracting spherical scatterers being much smaller than the wave length of the light employed. Shortly afterwards, Debye elaborated a more generally applicable theory [(18)] which was successfully applied in the following years for the study of many macromolecular substances. In this theory the effect of the dissolved macromolecules on the scattering is considered in terms of local fluctuations of concentration. The treatment is similar to that of the osmotic pressure, taking in account the interaction of the components. In Debye's theory the scattering effects are expressed by the turbidity τ defined as the natural logarithm of the fractional decrease in the transmitted intensity of the beam per unit length, or

$$I/I_0 = e^{-\tau l},$$

where I_0 denotes the intensity of the incident beam, I the intensity of the light after it has passed through the length l of the solution, and e the base of the natural logarithms. The fundamental equation developed for the scattering by small particles and macromolecules in dilute and moderately concentrated solutions reads:

$$H\,c/\tau = 1/M + 2\,B\,c, \qquad (1)$$

where τ is the turbidity, c concentration, M molecular weight, and H a complex expression

$$H = \frac{32\,\pi^3\,n_0^2\,[(n - n_0)/c]^2}{3\,N\,\lambda^4};$$

here n_0 is the refractive index of the solvent, n the refractive index of the solution, N the Avogadro number, and λ the wave length. Since the value of $(n - n_0)/c$, the specific refractive increment, can be considered as constant for a definite system, and if the wave length is not changed, the magnitude of H can be taken as a constant, and equation (1) is an expression of straight line. When $H\,c/\tau$ is plotted against c, the molecular weight is obtained from the intercept $1/M$ on the ordinate, and the interaction constant B from the slope of the straight line. Some illustrative examples are presented in Fig. 26. [(19)]

(17) P. Putzeys and J. Brosteaux, *Trans. Faraday Soc.* **31**, 1314 (1935).
(18) P. Debye, *J. Phys. Colloid Chem.* **51**, 18 (1947).
(19) M. Halwer, G. C. Nutting and B. A. Brice, *J. Amer. chem. Soc.* **73**, 2786 (1951).

More detailed information on the subject is available from monographs and review articles.[20]

It must be pointed out that Debye's equation (1) is applicable only to particles or macromolecules whose dimensions are not larger than about 1/20 of the wave length. Now, when, for example, the green lines of mercury

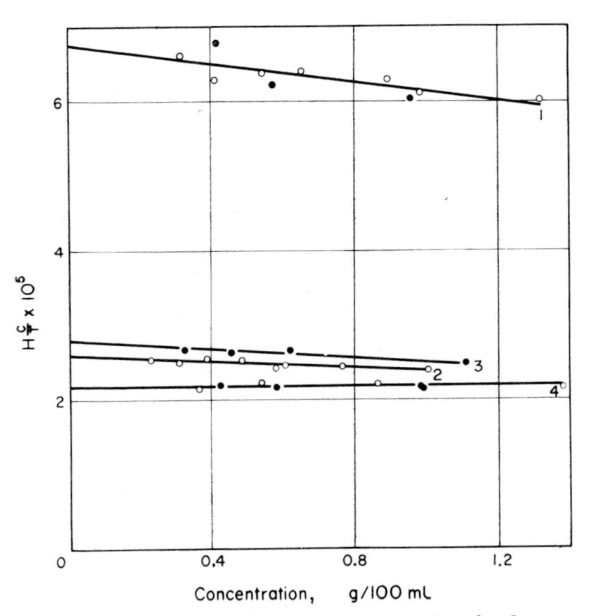

FIG. 26. Dependence of light-scattering on concentration for lysozyme (curve 1), lactoglobulin (curves 2 and 3), and ovalbumin (curve 4) according to Halwer, Nutting and Brice

spectrum are used, this maximum length would be 546/20 = 27·3 mμ or 273 Å. This well covers the range of the smaller and medium size macromolecules, but not such very large entities as the larger proteins, viruses, nucleic acids, or undegraded cell particles. While the molecular shape is unimportant for the very small macromolecules in this treatment, the situation is different when the scattering units approach the size of the waves to be scattered. This is due to internal interference effects of the relatively large scatterers; some of the waves become weakened, especially in the backward direction, and the "scattering envelope" becomes asymmetric. The intensity of the light scattered from a solution containing very large molecules is different a different angles. This dissymmetry of scattering is a very important

(20) K. STACEY, *Light Scattering in Physical Chemistry* Academic Press, New York, 1956; H. C. VAN DE HULST, *Light Scattering by Small Particles* Wiley, New York, 1957; P. DOTY and J. T. EDSALL, *Adv. Protein Chem.* **6**, 37 (1951); G. OSTER, *Chem. Rev.* **43**, 319 (1948); M. BIER in *Methods of Enzymology* p. 147 (S. P. COLOWICK and N. O. KAPLAN, ed.), Vol. IV, Academic Press, New York, 1957.

property, as it allows us not only to draw conclusions about the *size* but also about the *shape* of the very large molecules. While the scattering of the smaller macromolecules, which obey equation (1), is not much affected by their shape, and, hence no conclusion about shape can be made, the situation is different

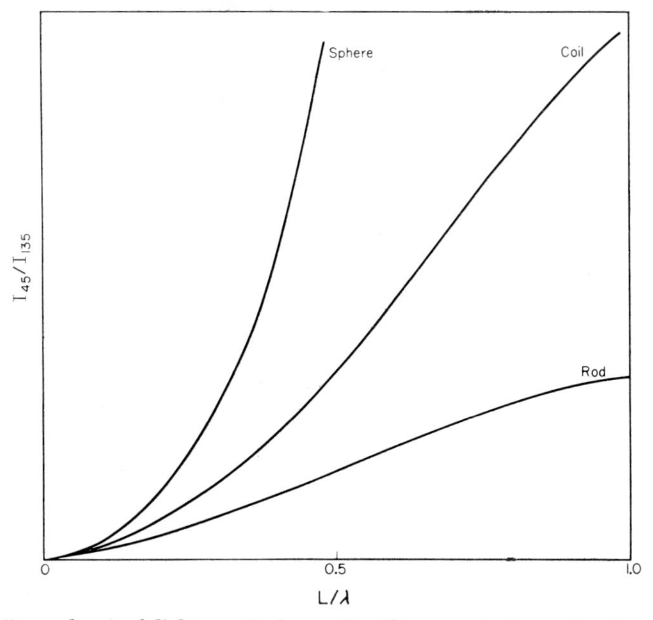

FIG. 27. Dependence of light scattering ratio (dissymmetry) on the dimensions of macromolecules (for spheres, coils, and rods)

with the large particles. Mie elaborated a theory of scattering by relatively large spheres as early as 1908, and the interest in this field was strongly reactivated in the forties when Debye, Doty, Zimm, and others became interested in its application to the study of large molecules. Several methods are now available for the solution of these problems. One is based on the theoretically derived dissymmetry function which can be correlated with the molecular shape.

Special attention was paid to the three most commonly encountered shapes, such as compact spheres, stiff rods, and randomly coiled fibers. In Fig. 27 are presented these theoretically derived dependencies, whereby the dissymmetry, defined as the ratio of the scattering at 45° and 135° angles (I_{45}/I_{135}), is plotted versus L/λ, where L is the diameter of the sphere, or length of the rod, or the mean square end-to-end distance of a coil. The theory was tested on such relatively well investigated systems as the rod-shaped tobacco mosaic viruses [21], and excellent aggreement was found between the length (L) as derived from light scattering dissymmetry, electron microscopy, and visco-

(21) G. OSTER, P. M. DOTY and B. H. ZIMM, *J. Amer. chem. Soc.* **69**, 1193 (1947).

sity data. The light scattering was measured at different angles as a function of concentration of the virus, and the dissymmetry was plotted versus concentration; the intrinsic dissymmetry then was obtained by extrapolating to zero concentration. From this value, using the theoretical dissymmetry curve for rods, the length L was calculated. This classical result gave a strong impetus to further developments in this field, and the method now is one of the best for the study of macromolecules.

Unfortunately the results are not always as clear cut, and it is difficult to decide what the actual shape of the macromolecules in a particular case is. In reality, there are unlimited possibilities of intermediate cases, for example between solid spheres and coils. It appears that linear macromolecules may be very slightly folded or tightly coiled depending on the solvent. Similar intermediate cases can be thought between coils and rods: the shorter linear macromolecules often are almost completely extended, while the longer ones coil up. For this reason another method in applying dissymmetry measurements is found to be extremely useful. In this method, which was proposed by Zimm,[22] the scattering is measured at various angles, and extrapolated to zero angle. Similar measurements are made with the same solution at different concentrations, and the values are extrapolated to zero concentration. When drawn on the same chart, the curves form a grid, an example being presented in Fig. 28.[23] The four curves, representing the limiting values, all cross the ordinate at the same point, from which the molecular weight M can be calculated. These results on the nucleic acid and its sodium salt indicate that the molecular weight did not change when pH was varied from 6·5 to 2·6. Moreover, the change in slope indicates that the molecular volume, and possibly shape, were changed considerably during these pH changes. The macromolecules seem to become more compact on acidification. Also it must be pointed out that the expression $K\, c/R_{\Theta}$ often used in these plots is essentially equivalent to $H\, c/\tau$.

Zimm has shown [22] that this extrapolation to zero angle and zero concentration permits not only the evaluation of the molecular weight but also a calculation of the average dimension of the macromolecules. The root-mean-square radius from the center of mass of the macromolecule, denoted also as radius of gyration, is obtained from the slope and intercept of the angular scattering, curve viz.:

$$\text{Initial slope/Intercept} = 16\,\pi^2\, r^2/3\,\lambda^2,$$

where r is the radius of gyration. This evaluation is independent of any assumptions of structure and configuration, i.e. it seems to be equally valid for unbranched and branched linear macromolecules (provided the molecular weight is not too high).

[22] B. H. Zimm, *J. chem. Physics* **16**, 1099 (1948).
[23] M. E. Reichmann, B. H. Bunce and P. Doty, *J. Polymer Sci.* **10**, 109 (1953).

Finally, it must be admitted that we have considered the scattering effects at the same time disregarding certain important factors, such as degree of

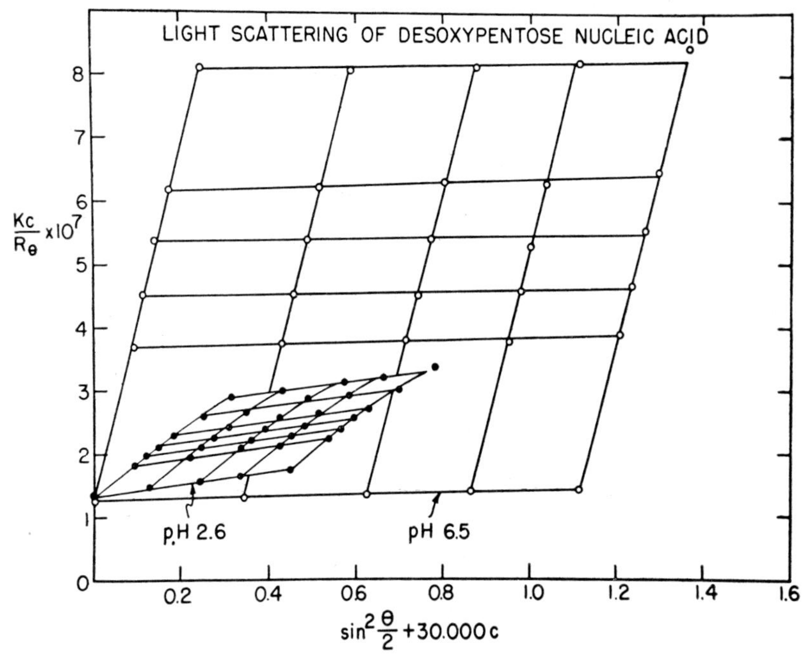

FIG. 28. Zimm plot of light scattering data for nucleic acid and its salt, according to Reichmann, Bunce and Doty

polarization of the light under certain conditions, absorption of the light, temperature, and the effects of electrical charges. The absorption and fluorescence effects have been studied e.g. by Brice *et al.* (24)

The experimental procedure involves photometry, and highly sensitive photocells and galvanometers are used for the measurement. Moreover, the refractive indexes must be determined with the highest possible accuracy. Light scattering photometers are now commercially available, for example from Phoenix Precision Instrument Company, Philadelphia, and in Fig. 29 is presented a diagrammatic sketch of such photometer, and in Fig. 30 its photo. Determination of the τ values involves careful calibration and adjustment of the beam by means of filters and slits. One of the greatest difficulties in light scattering work is the liberation of the solutions from dust, air bubbles, and similar coarse impurities which can distort the results. Filtration through ultrafine filters and spinning in a preparative ultracentrifuge are helpful.

(24) B. A. BRICE, G. C. NUTTING and M. HALWER, *J. Amer. chem. Soc.* **75**, 824 (1953).

The molecular weights obtained by means of the light scattering method in general agree with those obtained by other methods, such as sedimentation

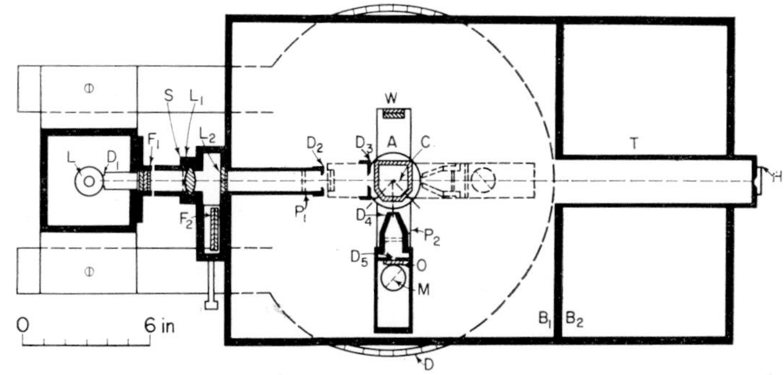

FIG. 29. A diagram of the light scattering photometer of Brice. L — light source; F_1 — monochromatic filters; C — cell with solution; M — photomultiplier tube

and diffusion, and for the homogeneous proteins also with the values computed from the osmotic pressure data. However, the precision of the values is still relatively low. Thus, several authors have obtained for bovine serum albumin values ranging between 70,000 and 99,000.(19) The very high values may be

FIG. 30. Light scattering photometer according to Brice

caused by aggregation, but even with the most homogeneous albumin preparations the result varies somewhere between 70,000 and 77,000. The best recent sedimentation-diffusion data give for this protein the M of 65,000–73,000. For β-lactoglobulin, the light scattering method gave a value of 35,700 for the molecular weight [19] while the sedimentation methods produced values between 35,400–41,500. The molecular weight of lysozyme was found to be 14,800[19], whereas sedimentation and diffusion, as well as the osmotic pressure measurements gave 14,700–17,000. For the polymolecular (polydisperse) substances, such as starch, glycogen, gelatin, etc. the variations are much larger, since they depend then on the method of isolation and fractionation. Moreover, in such cases the weight average molecular weight M_w obtained by means of light scattering or sedimentation is always larger than the M_n value obtained from osmotic pressure data.

Double Refraction of Flow and Molecular Shape

This method is based of the fact that a solution containing asymmetric macromolecules becomes birefringent when subjected to a strong velocity gradient. The refractive index of a resting solution is independent of the direction of observation, while a streaming solution exhibits in the direction of streaming different refractive properties from those associated with other direction. This double refraction or *streaming birefringence* is usually due to *orientation of the asymmetric macromolecules* along the stream lines. The orientation is more complete the longer the macromolecules and the greater the orienting force (velocity gradient), and the orientation is opposed by the thermal motion.[24a]

Double refraction of flow is studied chiefly by means of the Maxwell device consisting of two concentric cylinders, one of them being static and the other to be rotated. The solution is poured into the outer cylinder, and upon motion of it the asymmetric macromolecules, if such are present, tend to orientate along the stream lines in the gap between the walls of the cylinders. The change of the refractive properties is observed by appropriate optical methods, for example, by using Nicol prisms or birefringent plates. When Nicol prisms are used, the birefringence is characterized by an angle X, the so-called extinction angle, explained in Fig. 31.

Theoretical studies have shown that the extinction angle X, can be correlated with the *rotary diffusion constant* F which depends on the asymmetry of the oriented particle. The rotary diffusion constant characterizes the rotary motion of rod-shaped particle about its short axis, and the theory shows that this rotation must depend on the length of the rod:

$$F = 3\,k\,T/16\,\pi\,\eta\,L^3.$$

[24a] A. E. Alexander and P. Johnson, *Colloid Science*, chapt. XIV, Clarendon Press, Oxford, 1949.

In this equation k is the Boltzmann constant, T absolute temperature, η absolute viscosity of the solution, and L the length of the particle. The theory also shows that:

$$\tan 2X = 6F/G,$$

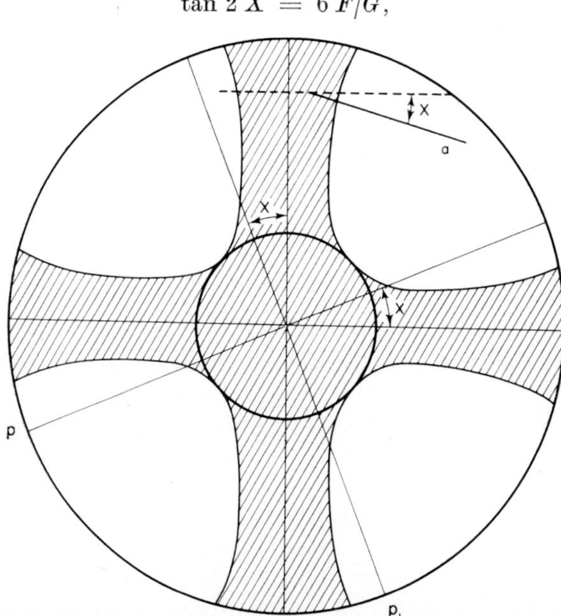

FIG. 31. The cross-shaped shadow in birefringent medium in the gap between concentric cylinders. The angle X is equal to the angle formed between an oriented rod-shaped particle (a) and the stream lines. The angle X varies between 0 and 45°; it is zero in the instance of full orientation

TABLE 2

PARTICLE LENGTH FROM STREAMING BIREFRINGENCE AND SEDIMENTATION–DIFFUSION DATA [25]

	Length L from flow birefringence ($m\mu$)	Length L from sedimentation and diffusion* ($m\mu$)
Tobacco mosaic virus	720	300
Helix hemocyanin, $M = 8{\cdot}9 \cdot 10^6$	89	113
$M = 4{\cdot}3 \cdot 10^6$	89	82
Fibrinogen, human	70	70–75
Nitrocellulose, $M = 613{,}000$	36	43
$M = 199{,}000$	20	22

* This L value is calculated from the frictional ratio f/f_0 assuming a certain shape (ellipsoid of revolution) and hydration.

[25] The data on the proteins are taken from S. W. FOX and J. F. FOSTER, *Introduction to Protein Chemistry* p. 224, Wiley, New York, 1957; the nitrocellulose data are from H. MOSIMANN, *Helv. chim. Acta* **26**, 61 (1943).

where G is the flow gradient determined by the speed of the rotating cylinder. From these equations, by introducing the experimentally determined values of T, η, X, and G, the length L can be computed.

When the macromolecules are but slightly asymmetric, the birefringence is weak, and the experimental errors large. The flexible linear macromolecules are more or less stretched out in the flow gradient, and the dimension calculated from the flow birefringence data may differ from the actual dimension of the coil in a resting solution.[26] Some examples are presented in Table 2.

Since experimental errors are involved in both methods, and since the theoretical foundation also is far from being perfect, the agreement is quite noteworthy.

Direct Observation of Macromolecules in the Electron Microscope

Even the largest of the macromolecules, such as those of glycogen or nucleic acid (M = 5–10 million), are invisible in the most potent light microscopes, because the molecules are *smaller* than the light waves. Electron microscopy is based on the fact that electron beams exhibit the properties of very short waves which would distinguish small objects some 1–5 Å apart. The electrons are shot in a high potential gradient in vacuum, and they are directed by means of electrostatic or electromagnetic coils acting as lenses. A specimen of a macromolecular substance is spread in a thin layer, and placed in the way of the beam. The contrasts of the image are produced due to mass and density differences of the preparation. A magnification of 20,000–60,000 is usually employed, and photographic enlargements up to 300,000 give quite good pictures. Hence, a macromolecule with a diameter of 10 Å may be enlarged to a 0·3 mm large spot.

The first electron microscopes were built in Germany in the early thirties, and they were developed independently in the U. S. A., England, Belgium, and other countries. During the forties electron microscopy became a standard method for the study of inorganic substances, viruses, cells, and organic macromolecules, and a voluminous literature is available on that subject.[27] The instruments have been steadily improved, and a variety of them is offered by several companies. An electron microscope of the Radio Corporation of America is shown in Fig. 32. Examples of electron microscopic photographs of large molecules are presented in Fig. 33 and 34.

In spite of the high potentialities of the electron microscopy, only some of the largest macromolecules have been photographed and measured. The large and massive iodobenzoyl glycogen was the first macromolecule which

[26] R. Cerf and H. A. Scheraga, *Chem. Rev.* **51**. 185 (1952); V. N. Tsvetkov and E. Frisman, *Acta Physiochim. U.S.S.R.* **20**, 61 (1945); V. N. Tsvetkov, *J. Polymer Sci.* **23**, 151 (1957); R. Signer in Weissberger's *Physical Methods of Organic Chemistry* 2nd ed., part. III, Vol. I, p. 2255, Interscience, 1954.

[27] R. W. G. Wyckoff, *Electron Microscopy*, Interscience, New York, 1949; C. E. Hall, *Introduction to Electron Microscopy*, McGraw-Hill, New York, 1953.

could be made visible.[28] Many others followed, e.g. Hall obtained good electron micrographs of single macromolecules of edestin ($M = 300{,}000$)

FIG. 32. An electron microscope of the Radio Corporation of America. (This particular instrument is used in the Virus Laboratory of the University of Texas M. D. Anderson Hospital and Tumor institute by Dr. L. Dmochowski who is seen at the instrument)

and catalase ($M = 250{,}000$). Although the exact details regarding the shape are still questionable, the shape and dimensions appeared in good agreement with the indirectly obtained sizes and shapes.[29] A small drop of a solution containing the macromolecules to be studied is placed on a very thin film of collodion, and the liquid is allowed to evaporate. Sharpening of

[28] E. HUSEMANN and H. RUSKA, *J. prakt. Chem.* **156**, 1 (1940).
[29] C. E. HALL, *J. biol. Chem.* **185**, 45, 749 (1950).

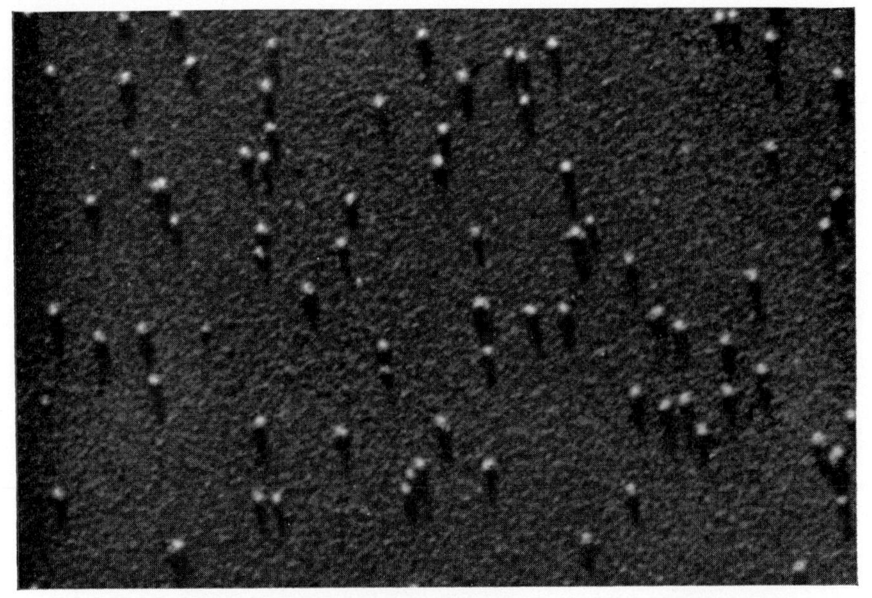

FIG. 33. The macromolecules of alkaline phosphatase (magnification about 90,000×) in electron microscope (magnification 160,000×) (by *Courtesy* of Dr. C. E. Hall, Massachusetts Institute of Technology)

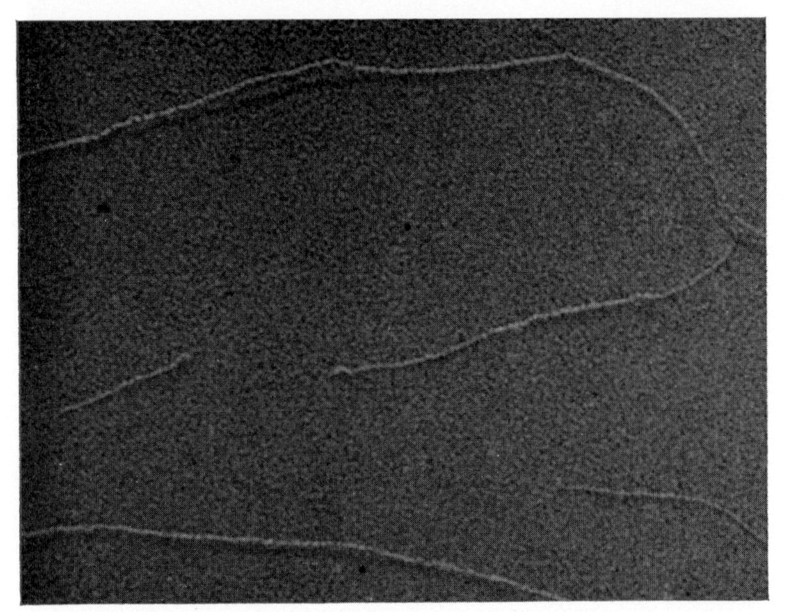

FIG. 34. The macromolecules of deoxyribonucleic acid (DNA) as revealed in the electron microscope (magnification 115,000×). *Courtesy* Dr. C. E. Hall (see also: C. E. Hall and M. Litt, *J. Biophys. Biochem. Cytol.* **4**, 1, 1958)

the images is achieved by shadowing the surface with metal vapor, and by other methods. Important in the technique is the fact that the supporting collodion film itself acts as a "transparent" medium, because the macromolecules of the collodion (nitrocellulose) are extremely thin, and the gel is completely amorphous. Single linear macromolecules are invisible in the electron microscope; the fibrous strands of fibrin, or cellulose, as shown in electron micrographs, are bundles of many linear macromolecules.

Since the preparation of specimens for electron microscopy involves evaporation, and other rather drastic procedures, denaturation may be involved in some cases, if extreme precautions are not observed in handling the specimens. Biological specimens, such as viruses or cell preparations, are now usually embedded in the amorphous methacrylates (e.g. butyl methacrylate). The methacrylate gel does not affect the electron beam appreciably but it prevents the distortion of the delicate specimen in the high vacuum. Moreover, such embedding permits the preparation of very thin slices as needed for the electron microscopy. The original preparation may be first dehydrated, then impregnated with the monomer, which then is polymerized, and thus the preparation becomes fixed in a consistent medium. Distortions still are not quite excluded. "We are now coming to realize more and more clearly how serious and universal is the resulting cellular damage".[30] Most of the large molecules, however, can be treated without serious damage.

Molecular Weight Determination by X-rays

X-rays can be applied to the study of macromolecules in several ways. First, they can be used for the study of the structure. This is done by means of structural analysis of the X-ray diffraction spectra, and it will be discussed briefly in chap. 5. Second, a more limited crystallographic study can be made on crystals composed of large molecules; this analysis allows us to calculate the molecular weight and hydration. Third, the molecular size and shape of large molecules in solution can be studied by means of low angle X-ray scattering. The latter method is principally identical with the previously discussed method of light scattering, with the difference that the scattering, due to the very small wave length of the X-rays, must be measured extremely close to the primary beam. The position of the bands is determined by photography followed by accurate measurement of the film. Several proteins have been studied by this method, and the results are in a fair agreements with those of other methods.[30a]

[30] R. W. G. Wyckoff in *The Cell* Vol. I p. 1 (quoted from p. 15), (J. Brachet and A. Mirsky, ed.), Academic Press, New York, 1959.

[30a] D. P. Riley and D. Herbert, *Biochim. Biophys. Acta* **4**, 374 (1950); D. C. Dervichian, G. Fournet and A. Guinier, *Bull. Soc. Chim. biol.* **31**, 101 (1949); J. W. Anderegg, W. W. Beeman, S. Shulman and P. Kaesberg, *J. Amer. chem. Soc.* **77**, 2927 (1955); O. Kratky, *Makromol. Chem.* **35 A,** 12 (1960).

The molecular weight of crystallized high polymers can be determined by wide angle X-ray diffraction, if the approximate molecular weight is known from other measurements. The X-ray spectroscopy data permits the calculation of the volume of the molecule, and this volume, in combination with the density and water content of the crystal, yields the value for the anhydrous molecule.[31]

In Table 3 are compiled a few data on pure crystallized proteins, as obtained by these and other methods.

TABLE 3
MOLECULAR WEIGHTS OF SEVERAL CRYSTALLIZED PROTEINS

Protein	X-ray method	Light scattering	Sedimentation and diffusion	Osmotic pressure
Lysozyme	13,900* 15,680	14,800	14,700	16,600
β-Lactoglobulin	35,500	35,700	35,400	35,000–38,000
Egg albumin	37,500	45,700	49,000	41,500–46,000

* The lower value is calculated for water and chloride free protein, the higher for the hydrated lysozyme hydrochloride crystals [(K. J. PALMER, M. BALLENTYNE and J. A. GALVIN, *J. Amer. chem. Soc.* **70**, 906 (1948)].

Hydration of Macromolecules

Hydration is binding of water to the macromolecules. Since most of the natural organic macromolecules contain various polar groups, such as —COOH, $-NH_2$, —OH, it is natural that water must be bound to them by either hydrogen bonds or dipole attraction. Precise determination of the amount of hydration, however, is a difficult problem. Molecular weight determination on protein crystals shows that a certain portion of water is tightly bound inside the macromolecules, and another portion forms layers around them. Swelling and shrinkage of methemoglobin crystals occurs in steps, the crystal changing from one lattice type to another without any intermediate states being observable.[32] The closest layer comprises about 0·3 g per g protein, and the layers have a thickness of about 4 Å, i.e. of the same order as that of water molecules in ice. However, since the surface of protein macromolecules is not uniform and contains many non-polar groups, the "hydration shell" probably is not uniform. It is plausible that more water will be bound at the polar groups than elsewhere on the surface of the large protein molecule, while a uniform distribution is likely in such cases as the polysaccharides.

The most straightforward approach to the study of hydration would be to determine the adsorption or binding directly, i.e. by placing dry substances

[31] F. R. SENTI and R. C. WARNER, *J. Amer. chem. Soc.* **70**, 3318 (1948).

[32] M. F. PERUTZ, *Research* **2**, 52 (1949); W. L. BRAGG, E. R. HOWELLS and M. F. PERUTZ. *Acta Cryst.* **5**, 136 (1952).

in moist air, and weighing. Such experiments have been performed by several authors, the results usually being expressed by plotting the amount of bound water against relative vapor pressure (Fig. 35). The lower part of the curve refers to "chemically" bound water, while the upper part indicates binding by cohesion and occlusion. It is, however, very difficult to draw a borderline between these ways of binding. The 95% or more water as found in a water melon or cucumber certainly is not "water of hydration" but it is mechanically immobilized (occluded) water. Only a small portion of this water is bound by hydrogen bonds to the macromolecules of the cells, while the larger portion is immobilized in the reticular meshwork of the fibrous macromolecules and their associations.

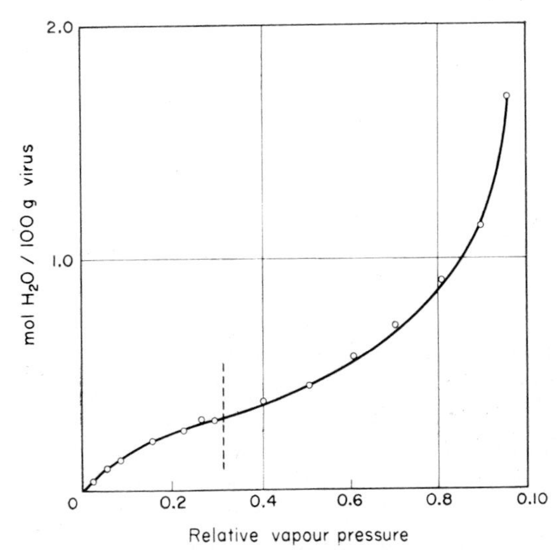

FIG. 35. Water vapor adsorption isotherm for tobacco mosaic virus at 25°, according to Katchman, Cutler and McLaren

Attempts have been made to correlate the amount of bound water with the number of polar groups.(33) It was found that in starch, regenerated cellulose, gelatin, albumin, and several other proteins the number of polar groups is larger than the number of tightly bound water molecules. The first portion of water is bound at a polar high polymer in a weakly exothermic reaction by liberating 3–6 kcal per mole water, while the additional portions are adsorbed without any measurable energy release. According to the vapor sorption experiments 1 g of proteins generally binds ("chemically", by H-bonds) 0·05–0·2 g of water. In addition to the ambiguity of distinguishing this amount from the loosely adsorbed amount, one cannot be sure that the "dry" protein used does not contain some chemically bound water not removable by the usual drying procedures.

Determination of hydration of macromolecules in solution has not been satisfactorily solved. It is obvious that the amount of water bound by the large molecules should be determinable from the hydrodynamic behavior of the solution. The more water they bind the more sluggish they must be in diffusion, sedimentation, and similar phenomena. However, these hydrodynamic

(33) A. D. McLAREN and J. W. ROWEN, *J. Polymer Sci.* **7**, 289 (1950).

properties depend not only on hydration but also on molecular shape, and the hydration and shape effects are virtually inseparable. This is why both the shapes and hydration values as estimated from the frictional ratio f/f_0 are subject to criticism. For the cases where the actual shapes are approximately known, the amount of hydration is estimated between 0·1 and 0·5 g water per 1 g of the hydrophilic high polymer.

Many other methods have been proposed for the study of hydration in solution, and most of them have been subjected to strong criticism and discarded. It seems that physical methods deserve special attention, as they seem to be somewhat more reliable than other methods. The first is the dielectric dispersion method.[34,35,36] The high dielectric constant of water itself, 80, is due to the high polarity and association of water molecules. When polar macromolecules are introduced into the water, the dielectric constant is raised even more. The measurements are carried out by determining the capacitance of a condenser containing the solution. The electrical field applied leads to orientation of the polar molecules, and the capacitance increases. Important is the fact that this change of capacitance and orientation depend on the frequency of the alternating field. This dependence of the dielectric constant on the frequency is called *dielectric dispersion,* and it can be correlated with the size, shape and hydration of the polar macromolecules. Buchanan *et al.*[35] could find by this method that proteins bind in solution 0·3–0·4 g water per 1 g protein; one third or less of this amount is bound very tightly, so that the water molecules are unable to rotate, while the rest is attached more loosely. The solutions of the nucleic acids and polar electrically charged carbohydrates have been studied by this method by Allgen *et al.*[36].

The other method is the *compressibility* measurement by means of *sound wave velocity* determination.[37] Pasynskii showed[37] that the hydration h, expressed in grams of water per gram of dissolved material, is correlated with the compressibility coefficient β by

$$h = \frac{(1 - \beta/\beta_0)\,(100 - g)}{g},$$

where β_0 is the compressibility coefficient of the solvent, and g the concentration of the solute in grams per 100 g solution. The β-values are determined by measuring the sound velocity v from $\beta = 1/v^2 d$, where d is the density of the solution. The method was tested first by determining the hydration of simple inorganic ions, since these values were known from reliable transference data, and the method was found satisfactory. The method then was

[34] J. L. Oncley, *Chem. Rev.* **30**, 433 (1942).

[35] T. J. Buchanan, G. H. Haggis, J. B. Hasted and B. C. Robinson, *Proc. Roy. Soc.* A **213**, 379 (1952).

[36] L.-G. Allgén, *Biochim. Biophys. Acta* **13**, 446 (1954); L.-G. Allgén and S. Roswall, *J. Polymer Sci.* **12**, 229 (1954); **23**, 635 (1957).

[37] A. Pasynskii, *Koll. Zhurn.* (*Russ.*) **8**, 53 (1946); *Acta Physicochim. U.S.S.R.* **22,** 137 (1947); *J. Polymer Sci.* **29**, 61 (1958).

applied to macromolecules in aqueous solutions and also to many other non-aqueous systems. It was found that 1 g gelatin binds 0·27 g water, while 1 g nitrocellulose in acetone solution can hold 0·58 g acetone. This amounts to a little more than one molecule of acetone per one $-ONO_2$ group of the nitrocellulose. A more general term — *solvation* — is used for such binding of solvent in various systems.

Although all the data show that the amount of tightly bound solvent is very small, so that it is not quite enough even to form a dense solvent envelope around each macromolecule, the hydration (and generally — solvation) problem is not completely solved. Several authors have advanced the idea that water as such is already highly organized, and that the macromolecules increase the degree of order even more. Attempts then have been made to explain some properties of the solutions as changes of an icelike hydration sheath which envelops each macromolecule.[38] Although this sheath is much more weakly attached than the water bound at the polar groups, it may have, according to this view an effect on various properties of the solution, and even on the configuration of the macromolecules themselves.

Thermodynamics of Solution and Solvation Effects

Dissolution of polar hydrophilic macromolecules can be interpreted as reaction with water: the water molecules, due to the thermal motion, penetrate into the interstices of the macromolecular solid, combine with it, thus loosening the aggregate, and finally disintegrating it fully. The hydrated macromolecules then spread into the water and become distributed evenly, due to the molecular Brownian motion and stirring of the system. These molecular–kinetic interpretations hold well for such polar systems as proteins–water, or nitrocellulose–acetone, but they are not applicable for non-polar mixtures, such as rubber–hexane. An alternative treatment of these phenomena is offered by thermodynamics.[39]

The changes in a system are spontaneous when the free energy F of the system decreases, i.e. when ΔF is negative. This possibility, according to the principles of thermodynamics, is determined by three factors: (1) the change of the heat content ΔH, (2) the temperature T, and (3) the entropy change ΔS, or:

$$\Delta F = \Delta H - T\,\Delta S.$$

At a constant temperature, the free energy change is determined only by the change in heat content and by the entropy change. Direct experimental measurements of the heat of mixing have shown that the change of the heat content upon dissolution of rubber or dilution of its solutions is very small. Consequently, the entropy change ΔS is the decisive factor which ensures a

(38) I. M. Klotz, *Science* **128**, 815 (1958).

(39) G. Gee, *Adv. Colloid Sci.* **2**, 145 (1946); *J. chem. Soc.* 280 (1957); P. J. Flory, *Principles of Polymer Chemistry* chapt. 12–14, Cornell Univ. Press, Ithaca, N. Y., 1953.

negative ΔF and spontaneous dissolution. In other words: the spontaneous solution of rubber in benzene is due to a large increase in entropy. This can be visualized as an increase in disorder of the molecular configurations upon solution. It has been shown [39] that the entropy change in these systems is so large that a negative free energy is ensured even in the event of a small positive change of the heat content. Now, it is interesting to note that no significant solvation could be detected by the compressibility method [37] in the solutions of nonpolar macromolecules in nonpolar solvents; hence, the phenomena in these systems cannot be explained in the same molecular–kinetic fashion as it was done with the polar systems. One may, however, wonder whether the thermodynamic approach could not be as useful also for polar systems, i.e. that the entropy changes may be important also for them. The dissolation in polar systems is an exothermic process, due to interaction effects, and it may seem that in these instances a negative free energy and spontaneous solution should be always ensured. However, the situation in polar systems is much more complicated than in nonpolar ones. The entropy change in polar systems is smaller than in nonpolar systems, since the solvent molecules which react with the solute become more ordered (decrease in entropy) when attached to the polar groups. Moreover, the degree of disorder of the polar macromolecules in a polar solvent is less than the disorder of the nonpolar units in nonpolar solvents. In other words: the solvated polar macromolecules are less flexible than are the nonpolar chains. Various intermediate degrees of flexibility, solvation, and entropy change are possible, depending on the solvent etc., as it will be shown in the next chapter.

CHAPTER 4

VISCOSITY OF SOLUTIONS OF MACROMOLECULAR SUBSTANCES

> In any attempt to interpret the machinery of a living cell, it is essential to know something about the mechanical properties of the protoplasm in the cell that is being investigated.
>
> L. V. HEILBRUNN (*The Dynamics of Living Protoplasm*, p. 10, Academic Press, New York, 1956)

THE STUDY of the mechanical properties of macromolecular systems has proved to be rewarding not only in biology but even more so in the high polymer technology and in the fundamental chemistry of large molecules. The terms *consistency* and *viscosity* are those mostly used for the description of the mechanical behavior, and the importance of this approach is manifested in the fact that even a special discipline, called *rheology*, has developed in the last decades. Since the phenomena in such systems as protoplasm or rubber latex are very complex, we shall be concerned in this chapter chiefly with the solutions of pure isolated high polymers. A whole chapter is devoted to the subject because of its exceptional importance in obtaining information on the size, shape, and configuration of macromolecules by very simple experimental procedures.

General Terms

The viscosity coefficient η is a proportionality constant characterizing the resistance to deformation of a system. It determines the magnitude of the frictional force f acting between two layers of liquid of the area A in a velocity gradient $\mathrm{d}v/\mathrm{d}x$, or

$$f = \eta A \, \mathrm{d}v/\mathrm{d}x,$$

in direction x perpendicular to the lines of flow. Thus η expresses the magnitude of the frictional force at $A = 1$ and $\mathrm{d}v/\mathrm{d}x = 1$. The unit of the *absolute viscosity* is one *poise* (after Poiseuille), and its dimensions are dyne cm^{-2} sec, or g cm^{-1} sec^{-1}. The absolute viscosity thus is the force acting on unit area (1 cm^2), forcing adjacent layers to glide past each other at a relative speed of 1 cm/sec. The absolute viscosity of liquids and solutions is strongly dependent on temperature. The absolute viscosity of water at 20·5 °C is 0·0100 poise (P) or 1·00 centipoise (CP). The reciprocal of the absolute viscosity $1/\eta$ is called *fluidity*. Ether has a high fluidity, i.e. a low viscosity; glycerin is of low fluidity (high viscosity). The *kinematic viscosity* is the ratio of the absolute viscosity to the density of the liquid.

The *relative viscosity* (η_{rel}) is obtained by comparing a property proportional to the absolute viscosity; for example, comparing the flow time of a solution through a capillary with the flow time of pure solvent. The relative viscosity is the ratio of the solution viscosity to the solvent viscosity, or:

$$\eta_{rel} = \eta_{solution}/\eta_{solvent}.$$

Since the macromolecules always increase the internal friction of a liquid, the numerical values of the relative viscosity are always larger than 1.

The *specific viscosity* η_{sp} measures the increase of the internal resistance as produced by the macromolecules, and it is defined as

$$\eta_{sp} = \frac{(\eta_{solution}) - (\eta_{solvent})}{\eta_{solvent}} = \eta_{rel} - 1.$$

Both relative and specific viscosity are pure numbers without dimensions.

The *reduced specific viscosity* or *reduced viscosity* is obtained by dividing the specific viscosity by the concentration of the solution, i.e. η_{sp}/c. The numerical values of the reduced viscosity depend on the definition of concentration, c usually being given in grams per 100 ml. Since viscosity of solutions is strongly dependent on concentration, the reduced viscosity expresses the property better than relative or specific viscosity. The reduced viscosity has the same preference to relative or specific viscosity as the reduced osmotic pressure has to an unspecified pressure value. The reduced viscosity of a certain macromolecular solution usually is determined at a series of c; the results are expressed graphically as $\eta_{sp}/c = f(c)$, and the curve extrapolated to $c = 0$, thus obtaining the *intrinsic viscosity* $|\eta|$ or $[\eta]$:

$$\text{Intrinsic viscosity, } |\eta| = \lim \eta_{sp}/c, \quad c \to 0.$$

The most common unit used for these quantities of reduced and intrinsic viscosity is dl/g. Various other proposals have been made for the handling and expression of viscosity data.[1]

Viscosity Measurement

The capillary viscometer. The determination of viscosity by measuring the flow time through capillaries is based on Poiseuille's law which was discovered more than a hundred years ago. Poiseuille found that the volume V of a liquid which flows through a capillary is directly proportional to the flow time t, the pressure p under which the liquid flows, and to the fourth power of the capillary radius r^4; the volume is inversely proportional to the length l of the capillary, and to the viscosity η:

$$V = \pi\, t\, r^4\, p/8\, l\, \eta, \tag{1}$$

[1] L. H. CRAGG, *J. Colloid Sci.* **1**, 261 (1946); W. HELLER, *ibid.* **9**, 547 (1954); R. SIGNER, *Makromol. Chem.* **17**, 39 (1955); H. STAUDINGER, *Organische Kolloidchemie* 3rd ed., Vieweg, Braunschweig, 1950.

from which the absolute viscosity can be calculated, if the other quantities are known. Since the reduced and intrinsic viscosity are more important for the study of macromolecules than the absolute viscosity, the exact values of V, r, p, and l need not to be determined. When a solution and solvent is measured in the same capillary viscometer, the values of V, r, and l are constant; together with $\pi/8$ they can be joined in a constant K_v, and equation (1) is changed to

$$\eta = K_v \, p \, t.$$

The pressure p changes with the level of the liquid in the tube, and it depends also on the density of the liquid. If the starting level is kept the same, the pressure will depend only on the density. (For very diluted solutions the density difference between the solution and solvent can be neglected without involving a serious error). If the flow time of the solution is t_1, and its density ϱ_1, and the flow time and density of the solvent t_0 and ϱ_0, respectively, the relative viscosity will be

$$\eta_{\text{rel}} = t_1 \, \varrho_1 / t_0 \, \varrho_0 ,$$

from which the specific and reduced viscosity is computed easily. When the density ratio is neglected, the reduced kinematic viscosity is obtained.

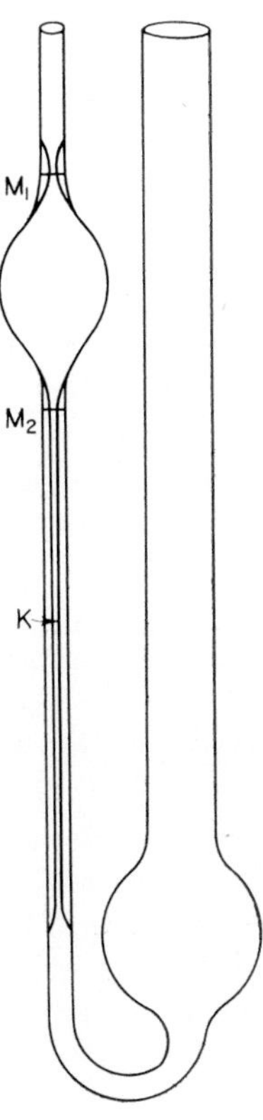

FIG. 36. Capillary viscometer of Wilhelm Ostwald. M_1 —upper mark; M_2— lower mark; K — capillary

The first conveniently applicable capillary viscometers were built by Wilhelm Ostwald in the eighties of last century in Riga (Latvia), and this design still remains dominant, and of unexcelled utility wherever viscosity is measured. It is essentially a U-shaped tube, one limb containing a capillary (Fig. 36). The liquid is drawn by suction into the upper bulb, and the time required for the flow is determined with the greatest possible precision with a timer. The starting moment is that at which the level passes the upper mark, the end when it passes the lower mark. The measurement must be made at a constant temperature (at least $\pm$ 0·10 °C but better at $\pm$ 0·01 °C) and with a timing precision of at least $\pm$ 0·1 sec.

Various modifications of the Ostwald viscometer have been proposed. The Cannon–Ubbelohde capillary viscometer contains an additional tube which eliminates the pressure differences if the volume of the liquid is changed. In the ordinary Ostwald viscometer the flow time depends on the volume, in the Cannon–Ubbelohde viscometer it does not. Thus this instrument is convenient for the determination of the intrinsic viscosity requiring measurements at various dilutions.[2] Another useful modification is that of Fenske permitting variation of the pressure. It has been found that the viscosity of many solutions of high polymers depends on the flow gradient dv/dx effectuated by the pressure. An increase of the pressure produces a faster flow which can be expressed in terms of volume per unit time, or V/t. It is obvious that a variation of these V/t values will be produced also by measuring the same solution in different viscometers with different size capillaries. Since the volume V is proportional to the fourth power of the capillary radius r^4 [equation (1)], the gradient will be higher the wider the capillary. Very fast flow must be avoided because of the following reasons: (1) a larger error in the time measurement, and (2) the possibility of causing turbulent flow. It has been shown that no corrections are needed, if the V/t values are in the limits 0·01–0·002; for example, if the volume of the upper bulb is 1·0 ml the flow time must be not less than 100 sec.[3] Of course, it is self evident that the capillary must be clean, and the solution must not contain coarse particles that could possibly clog the capillary. Since the flow time t is proportional to the length of the capillary l [equation (1)], the flow gradient can be diminished by using a helical capillary. The length increase by taking a longer vertical capillary, however, would not help, since this would change the height and pressure.

The rotating cylinder viscometer. This type of viscometer, first proposed by Couette, resembles the Maxwell device described in the previous chapter. However, for viscosity measurement both concentric cylinders are mobile. The motion of the outer cylinder that contains the liquid to be studied produces a flow gradient. This shear stress sets the concenteric inner cylinder in motion which is proportional the viscosity. Since the flow gradient or shear stress in this instrument can be varied conveniently by changing the speed of rotation of the container, such instruments are of utility for the study of the dependence of viscosity and consistency on shear stress. Sensitive and convenient viscometers of this type are now commercially available.[4] For example, Fig. 37 illustrates the principle of a coaxial cylinder assembly as suggested by Eisenberg and Frei.[4] The inner cylinder is made so that, when immersed in the liquid under test, it has a bouyancy of nearly zero; the bearing system consists of a conical jewel resting in a sharp pivot point, and it is virtually frictionless. The torque is measured by equilibrating it with electrostatic torque produced in capacitor stator plates. The viscous torque thus is precisely measured by the voltage applied to the capacitor, and can be

[2] M. R. Cannon, *Ind. Engng. Chem. Analyt. Ed.* **16**, 708 (1944); The Cannon-Ubbelohde viscometers are available from Cannon Instrument Co., Box 812, State College, Pennsylvania.

[3] G. V. Schulz, *Z. Elektrochem.* **43**, 479 (1937); W. Philippoff, *Viskosität der Kolloide*, Steinkopff, Dresden, 1942; H. B. Bull, *J. biol. Chem.* **133**, 39 (1940); Ch. Tanford and J. G. Buzzell, *J. physic. Chem.* **60**, 225 (1956).

[4] H. Eisenberg and E. H. Frei, *J. Polymer Sci.* **14**, 417 (1954). Viscometers available from the Polarad Electronic Corporation, Long Island, N. Y.

read from charts correlating this voltage with the viscosity. The relative and specific viscosities are obtained by simply comparing the compensation voltages for the solution and solvent. The photo of the instrument is in Fig. 38.

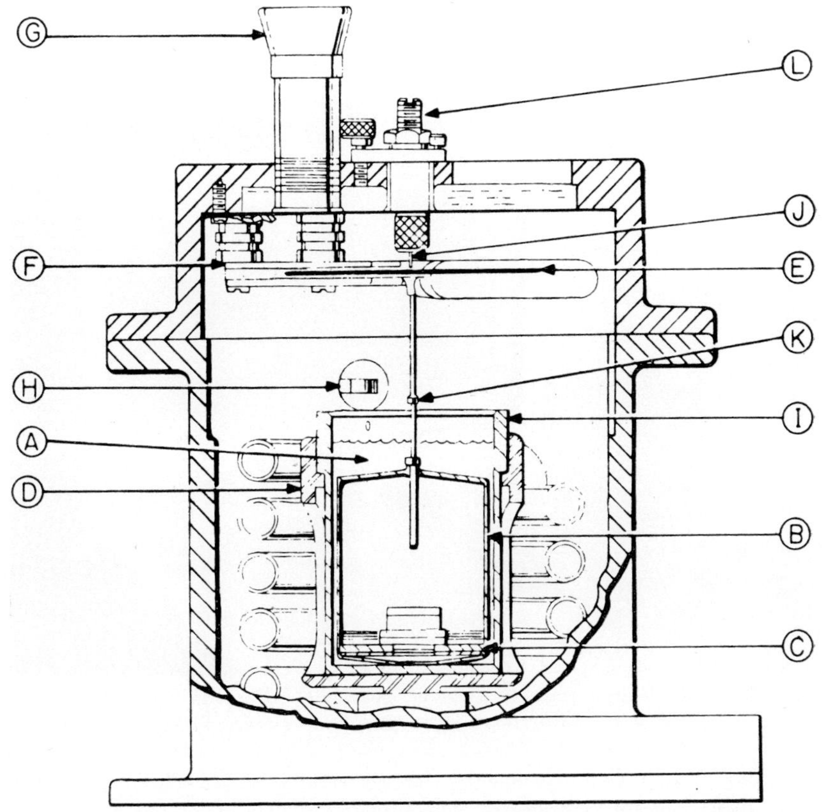

FIG. 37. Cross section of the test chamber of the Polarad rotating cylinder viscometer. *A* — test solution; *B* — float-vane assembly; *D* — outer cylinder; *E* — moving vanes; *F* — stationary plates; *J* — pivot; *L* — pivot holder

Viscosity measurement by applying Stokes' law. According to Sir George Stokes (1850), viscosity determines the rate of settling of particles: the more viscous the liquid the slower the sedimentation rate. For small beads of radius r and density ϱ the sinking rate v can be expressed by

$$v = 2\,g\,r^2(\varrho - \varrho_0)/9\,\eta,$$

where ϱ_0 is the density of the liquid, and g the acceleration constant of gravity. From this equation, the viscosity can be calculated when the other quantities are known. An instrument that employs the Stokes' law has been constructed by Hoeppler; the viscosity with this device is determined by measuring the time required for a ball to reach the bottom of a slanting cylinder filled with the liquid to be studied. The Stokes law has been applied also for viscosity

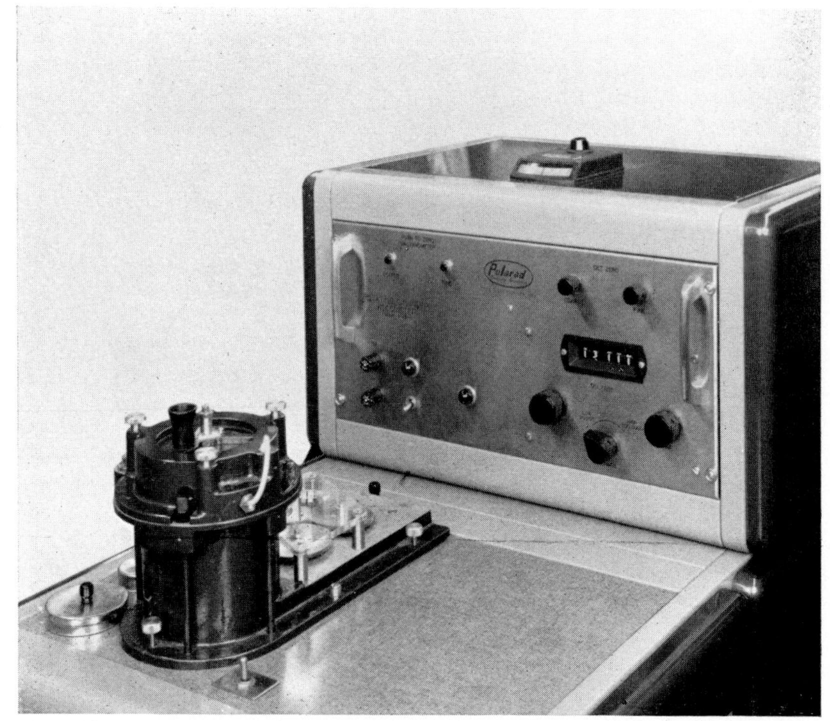

FIG. 38. The Polarad rotating cylinder electronic viscometer (*by Courtesy of Polarad Electronics Corporation, Long Island, N. Y.*)

studies on a microscale, especially for the study of the flow and internal friction properties of protoplasm. The movement of a small body is observed and measured in these objects under a microscope.[5]

The Viscosity Effects of Globular and Linear Macromolecules

There is a striking difference between the viscosity effects produced by globular and linear macromolecules. Globular macromolecules, such as glycogen or albumin, have an insignificant effect on viscosity of water, whereas the fibrous nucleic acid salts increase the viscosity in a quite spectacular fashion. Hence a few viscosity measurements give reliable information about the *molecular shape*. The intrinsic viscosity of solutions of globular macromolecules is low, i.e. about 0·03–0·06 dl/g whereas solutions of linear high polymers possess intrinsic viscosity values somewhere between 0·5–25, and higher. The reduced

[5] L. V. HEILBRUNN, in *Biophysical Research Methods* chapt. 4 (F. M. UBER, ed.), Interscience, New York, 1950.

specific viscosity of the solutions of globular high polymers changes very little with concentration, whereas it increases rapidly with concentration in the case of linear macromolecules. In a polymer-homologous series of globular polymer the viscosity of the solutions is independent of molecular weight, while in linear polymers it increases with increasing M or degree of polymerization, P. Finally, the highly consistent solutions of the linear polymers exhibit a pronounced dependence of the viscosity on the shear stress or flow gradient, G. These contrasts are summarized in Table 4.

TABLE 4

VISCOSITY BEHAVIOR OF SOLUTIONS CONTAINING GLOBULAR OR LINEAR MACROMOLECULES

	Globular	Linear (fibrous)
Reduced viscosity, common limits	0·03–0·08 dl/g	0·5–30 dl/g
$\eta_{sp}/c = f(c)$	slight dependence	increases with c
$\eta_{sp}/c = f(M)$	independent of M	increases with M
$\eta_{sp}/c = f(G)$	independent of stress	depends on stress

The dependence of the viscosity on concentration. It has been shown by A. Einstein (in 1906) that the viscosity of a system containing relatively large spherical particles increases with concentration according to the equation

$$\eta_{rel} = 1 + 2{\cdot}5\Phi,$$

where Φ represents the volume concentration of the particles. This expression was modified into a more convenient form by Staudinger and Husemann [(6)], as follows:

$$\eta_{sp} \cdot \varrho/c = K_e = 0{\cdot}025,$$

where c is given in grams per deciliter. The validity of this relation has often confirmed, for example, by Eirich *et al.* [(6a)] on suspensions of tiny glass beads or yeast cells. Extensive studies on various macromolecular preparations showed that the magnitude of the constant K_e equals 0·025 only in the instances when the dispersed particles are nonhydrated spheres. For *hydrated spherical* macromolecules, such as those of glycogen, the constant is larger, although it is *independent of the molecular weight*, as shown in Table 5.[(7)]

According to Einstein's equation, the reduced viscosity η_{sp}/c should be independent of concentration. This holds for compact unhydrated spheres while glycogen, and the various globular proteins possessing not quite spherical and somewhat flexible hydrated macromolecules, exhibit a slight increase of the reduced specific viscosity with concentration, especially at high c. In Table 6 is shown an illustrative example of a slightly asymmetric and

(6) H. STAUDINGER and E. HUSEMANN, *Ber. dtsch. chem. Ges.* **68**, 1691 (1935).
(6a) F. EIRICH, M. BUNZL and H. MARGARETHA, *Kolloid-Z.* **74**, 276 (1936).
(7) E. HUSEMANN, *J. prakt. Chem.* **158**, 167 (1941).

somewhat flexible globular protein, namely bovine serum albumin in 0·15 *M* sodium chloride solution of pH 5·2 (unpublished results of the author).

TABLE 5
THE REDUCED VISCOSITY AND K_e-VALUES OF GLYCOGENS OF DIFFERENT MOLECULAR WEIGHT

Molecular weight	Reduced viscosity	K_e
20,300	0·081	0·12
52,000	0·086	0·13
110,000	0·081	0·12
200,000	0·083	0·12
450,000	0·085	0·13
930,000	0·081	0·12
1,530,000	0·078	0·12

If the reduced viscosity values are plotted against concentration, a straight line with a slightly positive slope results (Fig. 39), and this can be expressed by

$$\eta_{sp}/c = |\eta| + k\,c,$$

where k is the slope constant. For the solutions of globular macromolecules the magnitude of this constant is somewhere about 0·005–0·02.[8] A similar linear equation has been derived theoretically by Huggins[9]:

$$\eta_{sp}/c = |\eta| + k_1\,|\eta|^2\,c.$$

The Huggins equation is applied for highly diluted solutions of fibrous macromolecules, such as the nucleic acids, the starch amylose, nitrocellulose etc. The viscosity of 0·05%–0·2% solutions of the salts of nucleic acids is so high that the solutions tend to set, and precise measurements can be made only with very dilute solutions, usually between 0·005–0·03 g/100 ml. Although the concentration dependence for such linear polymers at these very low concentrations is linear, the reduced viscosity values are so high that it is difficult to make simultaneous plots of fibrous and globular substances on the same

TABLE 6
THE REDUCED SPECIFIC VISCOSITY OF SERUM ALBUMIN AT VARIOUS CONCENTRATIONS

Concentration, *c* (g/100 ml)	Reduced viscosity
1·35	0·041
1·81	0·044
2·41	0·045
3·22	0·045
4·30	0·048
5·74	0·050
7·66	0·055
8·86	0·059

[8] B. JIRGENSONS and E. C. ADAMS, *Makromol. Chem.* **24**, 159 (1957).

[9] M. L. HUGGINS, *J. Amer. chem. Soc.* **64**, 2716 (1942); see also e.g. C. E. H. BAWN, *Trans. Faraday Soc.* **47**, 97 (1951); M. L. HUGGINS, *Physical Chemistry of High Polymers*, Wiley, New York, 1958.

graph (Fig. 39). The numerical values of the Huggins constant k_1 range mostly between 0·60 and 5·0.

An equally striking difference is found between the globular and fibrous macromolecules in respect to the reduced viscosity dependence on molecular

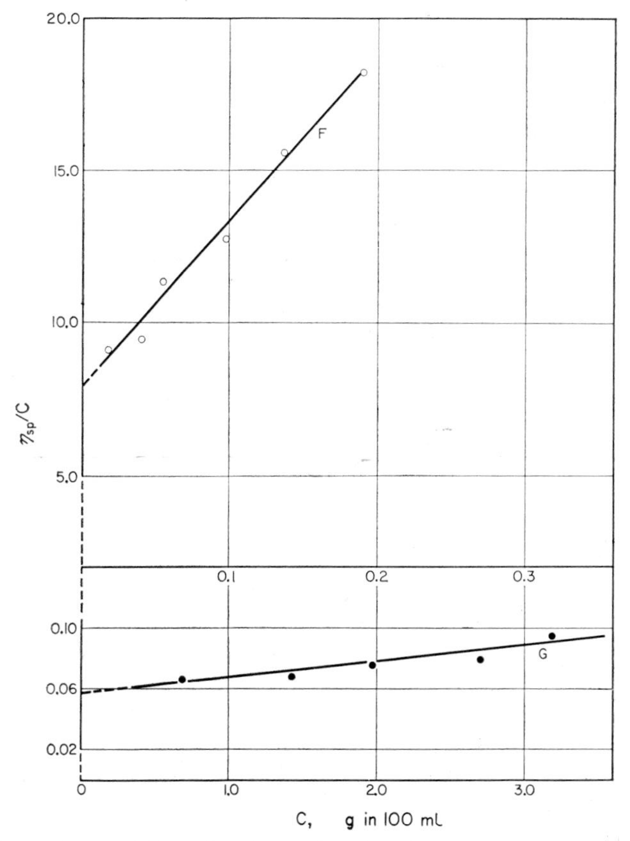

FIG. 39. Dependence of the reduced specific viscosity on concentration for fibrous (curve F) and globular (curve G) macromolecules. F represents sodium salt of a deoxyribonucleic acid, and G a γ-globulin (measurements of the author)

weight. While the viscosity of the globular glycogens is independent of their molecular weight (Table 5), the reduced or intrinsic viscosity of the solutions of linear polymers increases with increasing molecular weight. This important relationship will be discussed in the following section.

Relationship Between the Intrinsic Viscosity and Molecular Weight of Linear High Polymers

About 30 years ago H. Staudinger made the important discovery that the reduced viscosity of the solutions of linear high polymers is proportional to the degree of polymerization P or to the molecular weight of the polymer, viz.:

$$\eta_{sp}/c = K_m \cdot P.$$

This enabled the application of the simple viscosimetric method for the molecular weight determination of many linear high polymers. In the following decades, many hundreds of papers dealing with the molecular weight determination of linear high polymers by viscometry have been published. The molecular weights obtained by means of viscometry were compared with those obtained by other methods, and it was established (by Flory, Houwink, Kuhn, Mark, and others) that the empirical law, as formulated by Staudinger, must be slightly modified, namely that

$$\eta_{sp}/c = |\eta| = K \cdot M^a, \quad c \to 0, \tag{2}$$

where a is another constant. For most linear high polymers the value of a varies between 0·6 and 0·8. The smaller the numerical value of a the more tightly coiled are the linear macromolecules, the smallest value of a being 0·50. In the instance of $a = 1{\cdot}0$ the modified equation becomes identical with the original Staudinger's equation. Both the constants K and a have been determined for all of the most important synthetic and natural linear high polymers, whereby the light scattering method now is the most widely used reference method. Since most of the natural linear high polymers are polymolecular, the viscosimetrically obtained M-values represent molecular weight averages, and are denoted by $\overline{M}_v$. The viscosity molecular weight average is essentially a weight average, since the longer macromolecules influence viscosity more than the shorter ones. This is particularly so in good solvents, when the macromolecules are well stretched out. In poor solvents, where the fibrous units are tightly coiled, the M_v average is close to the M_n. For the samples which are practically homogeneous with respect to the molecular weight $M_v = M_w = M_n$.

The contants K and a are determined using the logarithmic form of equation (2), viz.

$$\log |\eta| = \log K + a \log M,$$

which is an equation of a straight line. The intrinsic viscosity of several specimens of known molecular weight is determined, and $\log |\eta|$ is plotted against $\log M$. The constant K then is computed from the intercept on the ordinate, and the constant a is represented by the slope. It must be borne in mind that the constants depend not only on the chemical composition and structure of the particular high polymer but also on the *solvent*, and to a lesser extent also on the temperature. The solvent, as already mentioned, has a decisive effect on the *degree of coiling* of the fibrous macromolecules: in a good solvent they are solvated and only slightly coiled, whereas in a poor solvent the intramolecular attraction between the segments is greater than the affinity to the solvent, and the macromolecule coils up tightly (Fig. 40). *The more extended the macromolecules the higher the viscosity of the solution.* These considerations apply chiefly to *polar* linear macromolecules in polar solvents, such as the polysaccharides or nucleic acids in water, or to mixtures of water

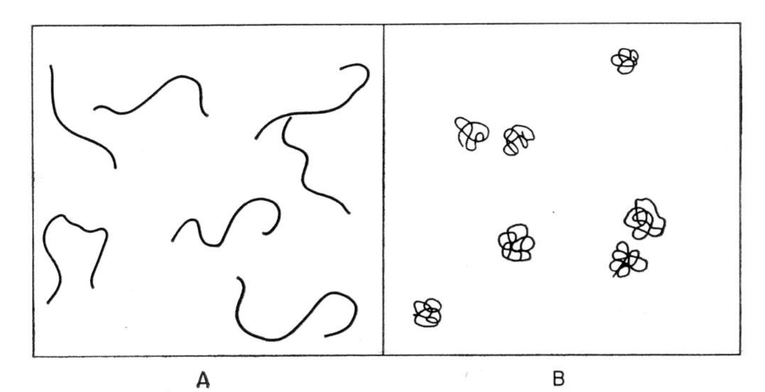

FIG. 40. Linear macromolecules in a good (A) and in a poor (B) solvent

with other polar substances. In nonpolar systems (rubber in liquid hydrocarbons) the solvation is insignificant, and the configuration of the linear macromolecules depends solely on the *flexibility* of the chain. The latter is determined by the chemical composition and structure. Moreover, the important fact must be considered that the *configuration* of linear macromolecules in solution is *continually changing.* Not only the whole molecule but also its segments, due to the thermal motion, change their relative positions in space in a quite chaotic fashion. Hence it is impossible to ascribe any definite values to the length of the units or to the diameter of the coils. The flexible more or less coiled macromolecules are characterized by the mean diameter, or by the root mean square distance between the ends of the chain.[(10)] These quantities characterize the macromolecular *volume.* Due to the thermal motion, the effective volume of a highly extended chain is always larger than the effective volume of a tightly coiled chain of the same moleculear weight.

Molecular weight calculation from the intrinsic viscosity and sedimentation constant. According to Mandelkern *et al.* [(11)], the molecular weight of linear polymers can be computed from the intrinsic viscosity and sedimentation constant, as follows:

$$M = \left[\frac{s\,|\eta|^{1/3}\,N\,\eta_0}{2.5\cdot 10^6\,(1-V\varrho)}\right]^{3/2},$$

where s is the sedimentation constant, $|\eta|$ the intrinsic viscosity of the solution, η_0 the viscosity of the solvent, N Avogadro's number, V the specific

(10) P. J. FLORY, *Principles of Polymer Chemistry* chapters 7, 10 and 14, Cornell University Press, Ithaca, N. Y., 1953.

(11) L. MANDELKERN, W. R. KRIGBAUM, H. A. SCHERAGA and P. J. FLORY, *J. chem. Physics* **20**, 1392 (1952).

volume of the substance, and ϱ density of the solution. Application of this relation to a preparation of nucleic acid gave the value of 5,800,000 in good agreement with the molecular weight obtained by the method of light scattering.[12]

The above equation is applicable to globular macromolecules as well[12a] if instead of the value $2.5 \cdot 10^6$ (the constant denoted generally by β) is taken a smaller value of $2.1-2.2$ $(.10^6)$. According to Schachman,[12b] for globular proteins and similar molecules in dilute aqueous salt solutions the molecular weight M can be determined from

$$M = \frac{4690 \cdot S^{3/2} \cdot |\eta|^{1/2}}{(1 - V\varrho)^{3/2}}$$

where S is the corrected sedimentation constant in Svedberg units, and $|\eta|$ the intrinsic viscosity in dl/g. The number 4690 includes the other factors which are constant. Trial calculations have shown that this equation yields correct values for the molecular weights of such proteins as serum albumin, lysozyme, or pepsin.

Viscosity and axial ratio of rigid macromolecules. The fact that the viscosity of solutions containing asymmetric rigid particles is higher than the viscosity of solutions with spherical particles has been recognized long ago. Eisenschitz showed in a theoretical study on the hydrodynamics of systems containing long rod-shaped particles that the *viscosity must increase with increasing asymmetry.*[13] A few years later this conclusion was confirmed by experimental measurements on models, for example on dispersions of glass fibers of various asymmetry.[14] Very impressive were also the data obtained with the rod-shaped tobacco mosaic virus particles[15] whose shape was confirmed by means of the electron microscopy. A quantitative correlation of the viscosity with the axial ratio L/D, where L is the length, and D the diameter, also has been attempted, and Simha's equation[16] has been confirmed as being in close agreement with the facts. The theoretically derived expression reads as follows:

$$\eta_{sp}/\Phi = \frac{(L/D)^2}{15\,(\ln 2\,L/D - 3/2)} + \frac{(L/D)^2}{5\,(\ln 2\,L/D - 1/2)} + 14/15,$$

where Φ is the volume concentration of the particles or macromolecules.

[12] M. E. Reichmann, S. A. Rice, C. A. Thomas and P. Doty, *J. Amer. chem. Soc.* **76**, 3047 (1954).
[12a] H. A. Scheraga and L. Mandelkern, *J. Amer. chem. Soc.* **75**, 179 (1953).
[12b] H. Schachman in *Methods in Enzymology* (S. Colowick and N. Kaplan, eds.), vol. IV, Academic Press, New York, 1957, p. 103.
[13] R. Eisenschitz, *Z. physik. Chem.* **163**, 133 (1933).
[14] F. Eirich, H. Margaretha and M. Bunzl, *Kolloid-Z.* **75**, 20 (1936).
[15] M. A. Lauffer, *J. Amer. chem. Soc.* **66**, 1188 (1944).
[16] R. Simha, *J. physic. Chem.* **44**, 25 (1940).

The intrinsic viscosity of solutions in which the macromolecules are rigid rods varies with molecular weight differently from when they are random coils: for rods the approximate dependence is

$$|\eta| = K M^2.$$

No instances are known where the intrinsic viscosity increases with the square of molecular weight. Exponents larger than unity, however, are not uncommon; for instance, for the rod-shaped macromolecules of collagen the dependence was found to be [16a]:

$$|\eta| = 1{\cdot}23 \cdot 10^{-9} M^{1.80},$$

and for the helical gently bent macromolecules of the deoxyribonucleic acid the dependence reads [16b]:

$$|\eta| = 1{\cdot}45 \cdot 10^{-6} M_w^{1.12}$$

The Viscosity of Ionized High Polymers

Electrical charges on *linear* macromolecules affect the viscosity much more than in the instance of *rigid* particles. The macromolecules of the globular proteins can be considered as relatively rigid, and any change in the degree of dissociation of the ionogenic groups has a relatively slight effect on the viscosity. Recent studies have shown that the so called *electroviscous effect* has been often overestimated.[17] In the instance of slightly flexible macromolecules, such as the globular proteins, the effect of the ionization on the viscosity is in fact very complex. It ought to be separated into two separate phenomena: the charge as such and the deformation effect caused by mutual repulsion of the macromolecular segments. A pure electroviscous effect could be studied only with strictly rigid particles. It is questionable whether any of the globular protein macromolecules are quite rigid. Detailed studies of the effects of pH and ionic strength variation on the intrinsic viscosity of several globular proteins have been published recently.[18] The intrinsic viscosity of serum albumin, as found in this study, varies only between 0·036 and 0·041 when the pH is varied between 4·3 and 10·5, and the ionic strength between zero and 0·50 (see Table 7). The deformation effects caused by the variation in ionization of the COOH groups and NH_2 groups in proteins have been studied by Pasynskii,[19] taking into account also the possible changes in hydration. He comes to the conclusion that the deformation caused by variation in the ionization of globular proteins is negligible. Even in the case of the rather extended and flexible gelatin the deformation caused by the elec-

[16a] T. Nishihara and P. Doty, *Proc. Natl. Acad. Sci.* **44**, 411 (1958).
[16b] P. Doty, B. Bunce McGill and S. A. Rice, *ibid.* **44**, 432 (1958).
[17] F. Booth, *Proc. Roy. Soc.* A **203**, 533 (1950).
[18] Ch. Tanford and J. G. Buzzell, *J. physic. Chem.* **60**, 225 (1956).
[19] A. G. Pasynskii, *J. Polymer Sci.* **29**, 61 (1958); R. S. Czerniak and A. G. Pasynskii, *Kolloidny Zhurnal* **10**, 245 (1948).

trical charges was found to be small. This is explained as being due to the relatively small number of ionogenic groups present in the proteins (see also Table 7).

TABLE 7

INTRINSIC VISCOSITY AND NUMBER OF FREE CHARGE UNITS OF BOVINE SERUM ALBUMIN ACCORDING TO TANFORD AND BUZZELL [18]

pH	Ionic strength	Number of free charges per molecule	Intrinsic viscosity	Slope
4·3	0·01	+ 7	0·0393	0·0035
	0·15	+ 8	0·0374	0·0033
4·8	0·01	+ 1	0·0377	0·0033
	0·15	− 2	0·0376	0·0027
5·0–5·6	0	0	0·0406	0·0054
	0·01	− 4	0·0361	0·0035
	0·15	− 10	0·0371	0·0027
	0·50		0·0376	0·0025
7.3	0·01	− 11	0·0412	0·0049
	0·10	− 18	0·0365	0·0028
8·5	0·02	− 20	0·0406	0·0064
	0·15	− 27	0·0417	0·0023
9·3	0·02	− 23	0·038	0·0098
	0·15	− 31	0·040	0·0029
10·5	0·05	− 39	0·041	0·0063
	0·50		0·041	0·0030

The third column of Table 7 shows the number of free charges, as calculated from titration data, per molecule of albumin. Since the molecular weight of serum albumin is approximately 70,000, the charge density is very small.

In contrast to the proteins, the viscosity of the ionized *linear* polysaccharides and other charged *polyelectrolytes* is strongly affected by ionization. This difference is due to two reasons: (1) the very high charge density, and (2) to the flexibility of the fibrous macromolecules. In the event of maximum ionization, these linear macromolecules stretch out, due to the mutual repulsion of the charged segments, and the viscosity increases enormously. This stretching, however, is strongly affected by the presence of the small counter ions and electrolytes introduced into the solution. This is illustrated in Fig. 41 where the reduced viscosity of the linear polysaccharide, chondroitin sulfuric acid is plotted versus concentration.[20] In the presence of high and medium concentrations of a salt, the polyelectrolyte shows a normal dependence of the reduced viscosity on concentration, while at very low ionic strength strange curvatures are observed. The abnormal decrease of the reduced vis-

[20] M. B. MATHEWS, *Arch. Biochem. Biophys.* **43**, 181 (1953).

cosity with increasing concentration, that is observed in the absence of foreign ions, is explained as a result of coiling due to the interfering effects of the counter ions. The more diluted the solution the less these counter ions (H^+

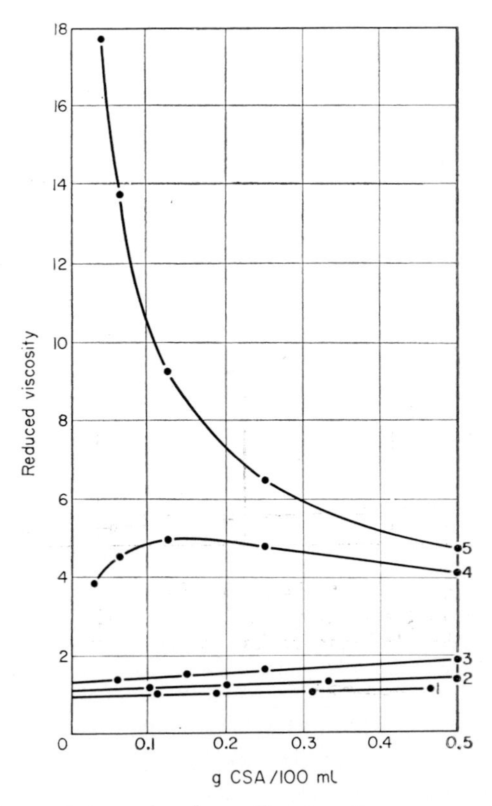

FIG. 41. Dependence of the reduced specific viscosity on concentration of chondroitin sulfate in the absence and presence of salts. Curve 1, chondroitin sulfate in 0·15 M sodium phosphate buffer of pH 7·0 with 0·2 M NaCl; curve 3, 0·022 M sodium phosphate buffer of pH 7·0; curve 4, 0·001 M phosphate of pH 7·0; curve 5, distilled water (data of M. B. Mathews)

or Na^+ or other cations) interfere with the repulsive effect of the negatively charged segments of the chain, and the macromolecule can stretch out strongly. It should also be pointed out that these effects are displayed and can be checked only in diluted solutions of 0·01–0·5 g per 100 ml; at still higher concentrations of 1–4 g/dl the reduced viscosity rises again, now because of the formation of internal structures (gelation).

Various interesting cases of less flexible but highly charged polyelectrolytes have been studied. Especially interesting and important are the nucleic acids which will be described in detail in chap. 19.

Systems Exhibiting Anomalous Flow Properties

Dependence of the viscosity on shear stress. According to the concept outlined in the beginning of this chapter, the viscosity coefficient of a liquid or solution is a constant which is independent of the flow gradient dv/dx (shear stress). These ideas were first developed by Newton, and, accordingly,

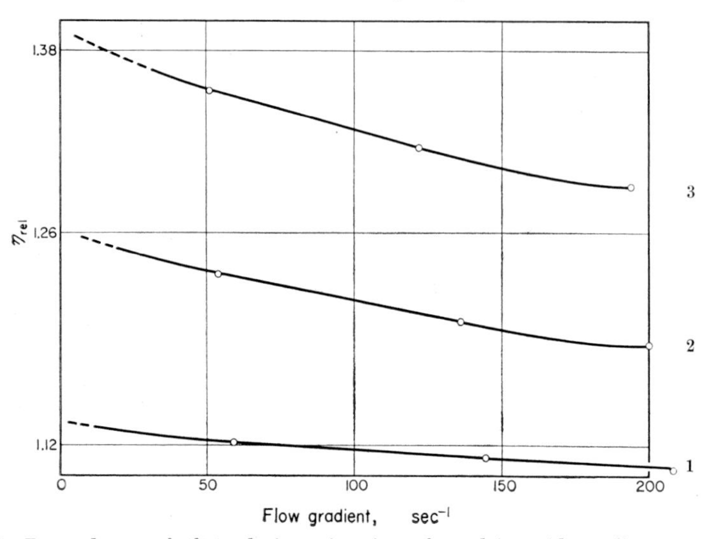

Fig. 42. Dependence of the relative viscosity of nucleic acid on flow gradient. Concentration of the fibrous macromolecules was 75 mg/l (curve 1), 50 mg/l (curve 2) and 25 mg/l (curve 3) (data of Reichmann *et al.*, l.c. 12)

all systems for which this concept holds are called Newtonian systems. The solutions of globular macromolecules are Newtonian solutions. In the case of a *linear* high polymer, however, the systems are Newtonian only under certain specific conditions, viz. at extreme dilutions, or at high temperatures of 40–60°, or higher. The longer the macromolecular chains the lower the concentrations at which the solution becomes *non-Newtonian*. For example, the undegraded nucleic acids (and their salts) exhibit the anomalous flow properties at concentrations as low as 0·05–0·1 g/dl (at room temperatures of 20–25 °C). In a non-Newtonian solution the viscosity depends on the shear stress, i.e. the *resistance to deformation decreases with increasing stress*, as illustrated in Fig. 42. It would be meaningless to determine the intrinsic viscosity of such solutions at just one gradient, since the intrinsic viscosity value will depend on this gradient. Consequently, in order to obtain comparable results, the intrinsic viscosity must be determined at various stresses, and extrapolated to zero. The most convenient equipment for such studies is the rotating coaxial cylinder device.

The decrease of the viscosity by increasing stress can be explained as follows. In very dilute solutions, the shearing force causes a partial orientation of the fibrous macromolecules along the stream lines, whereby the internal friction decreases. In the case of more concentrated systems which already have begun to set, the high viscosity is due to the formation of an internal meshwork; when the shearing force has disrupted these structures, the viscosity decreases.

Thixotropy. The term *consistency,* instead of viscosity, is used for the systems of linear high polymers which tend to gel, and are definitely non-Newtonian. It is often observed that the consistency of such systems changes *reversibly.* For example, certain protein gels are liquefied upon shaking or shearing in the gap between coaxial cylinders, but the liquid sets again when the shearing force is removed. This phenomenon was named *thixotropy,* and it is explained by assuming the formation of weak secondary linkages between the macromolecules (and the solvent). These links are so weak that they can be disrupted by a relatively small stress; when this is removed, they reform again. All these phenomena of the consistency changes in non-Newtonian systems are of considerable interest for a number of technological as well as biological problems.

CHAPTER 5

THE CHEMICAL STRUCTURE OF MACROMOLECULES

The optical rotatory power of a substance is known to be extremely sensitive to changes in molecular conformation.

W. KAUZMANN [1]

GREAT advances have been made in the understanding of the structure of large molecules. Although the physical methods, such as X-ray diffraction or optical rotation, have contributed considerably to the solution of these problems, the *chemical* methods have been even more revealing. First of all, the very existence of large molecules was ascertained by chemical methods. This was done by performing chemical reactions, under very mild conditions, and by proving that the macromolecular carbon skeleton in these reactions did not change.

Chemical Modification of Large Molecules

Some thirty years ago, only a few scientists believed in the existence of large molecules. The concept then dominant was that the molecules of rubber or cellulose were very small (M about 500–1000), and that the entities in the solutions of these substances were aggregates of the small molecules. Staudinger and his associates were the first who advocated the macromolecular concept as early as the early twenties, and who also furnished experimental evidence supporting this concept (see chapt. 1). The hydrogenation of rubber was one of the first reactions of this kind. Even more convincing were the results on starch, glycogen, and cellulose. Well fractionated specimens of starch amylopectin were used, and their molecular weight, i.e. degree of polymerization, was determined by osmotic pressure measurement of starch in formamide. The same starch fractions were acetylated, and the molecular weight of the triacetates of starch was determined in acetone and chloroform solutions. Finally, the triacetates were carefully saponified (avoiding oxygen), and the molecular weight of the recovered amylopectin was determined again from the osmotic pressure of their formamide solutions. The results are presented in Table 8.[2]

[1] W. KAUZMANN, *Ann. Revs. Phys. Chem.* **8**, 426 (1957).

[2] H. STAUDINGER and E. HUSEMANN, *Ann.* **527**, 195 (1937); H. STAUDINGER, *Chem. Ztg.* **77**, 3 (1953).

The average molecular weights of the triacetates, of course, are found to be larger than those of the unacetylated starches, because of the added acetyl

TABLE 8

MOLECULAR WEIGHT AND DEGREE OF POLYMERIZATION OF AMYLOPECTIN OF STARCH, ITS TRIACETATE, AND OF THE AMYLOPECTIN RECOVERED FROM TRIACETATE

Starch fractions in formamide solution		Triacetate in acetone		Triacetate in chloroform		Recovered amylopectin in formamide	
$\overline{M}$	$\overline{P}$	$\overline{M}$	$\overline{P}$	$\overline{M}$	$\overline{P}$	$\overline{M}$	$\overline{P}$
30,000	185	54,000	190	53,000	190	30,000	185
62,000	380	112,000	390	110,000	390		
91,000	560	155,000	540	155,000	540	93,000	570
153,000	940	275,000	960	275,000	960	140,000	870

groups; the degree of polymerization, however, *remains the same.* (A slight degradation has occurred only on the saponification of the larger macromolecules of the average molecular weight of 153,000.) Thus it was proven that in the conversions

$$\text{Amylopectin} \rightarrow \text{Triacetate} \rightarrow \text{Amylopectin}$$

the *macroradicals remain the same.* If the particles in solution were aggregates (micelles) composed of many small molecules, their triacetates should form different aggregates in different solvents, and it would be inconceivable how the saponification would result in the same original aggregates. Moreover, the recovery of the original amylopectin was ascertained also by viscosity and optical rotation data, as shown in Table 9.[(2)]

TABLE 9

OPTICAL ROTATION AND VISCOSITY OF AMYLOPECTIN IN FORMAMIDE

Original starch fractions			Starches recovered from triacetates saponification		
$\overline{P}$	Specif. rotation	η_{sp}/c	$\overline{P}$	Specif. rotation	η_{sp}/c
185	196°	0·12	185	196°	0·12
560	206	0·33	570	207	0·33
940	216	0·56	870	215	0·47

Since both optical rotation and viscosity are sensitive to changes in molecular configuration, the origin of the recovered product is unquestionable. Similar polymer-analogous conversions have been recently accomplished with even much larger amylopectins ($M = 14,000,000$), as will be shown in chapter 8.[(3)] Numerous other polymer-analogous reactions, i.e. conversions of macromolecules preserving their gross structure, have been accomplished

(3) L. P. WITNAUER, F. R. SENTI and M. D. STERN, *J. Polymer Sci.* **16**, 1 (1955).

recently not only with polysaccharides but also with proteins. For example, polyamino acid chains can be "grafted" on such delicate proteins as serum albumin or chymotrypsin without damaging or changing in any way the structure of the macromolecules.[4]

There is no more doubt that the atoms constituting the large molecules of rubber or the polysaccharides are joined by primary valency bonds. The same holds for the various synthetic high polymers which are formed from simple monomers (styrene, butadiene, acrylic acid etc.) in exothermic reactions.[5] The mechanisms of the various types of polymerization have been elucidated quite thoroughly, and it is established that the mers are linked by covalent bonds. Many high polymers resembling closely some of the natural products also have been synthesized. There are some unsolved fundamental problems in the realm of proteins and nucleic acids, especially with some of the larger proteins. Although the general structural pattern is clearly established, some important details are still obscure. Thus, for example, the true chemical molecular weight of proteins like myosin or fibrinogen is unknown; some of the larger proteins probably are composed of subunits linked by secondary bonds (see chap. 12–18).

General Chemical Methods for the Solution of Structural Problems

In this section will be given a very brief account on the general chemical approaches that are used in structural studies of large molecules. A more detailed discussion in each special case will be presented in the respective chapters in the Second Part.

As already mentioned in chapt. 3, important information on the molecular size can be obtained by precise *analytical data on the composition* of the high polymeric substance. Extremely important are data on atomic groups that are located *at the ends of the chain*. When the molecular weight is established, the amount of terminal groups reflects the degree of *branching*. When the absence of branching is ascertained, the quantity of the analytically determined end groups is inversely proportional to the molecular weight. It is noteworthy that wrong conclusions about the chemical structure of macromolecules have been made by incorrect interpretation of analytical data. For example, since no definite terminal groups could be detected in undegraded specimens of rubber or cellulose, it was inferred that the molecules of these substances are cyclic. Later, when it was found that the linear macromolecules are extremely long, this impossibility of detecting the terminal groups was

[4] R. R. Becker and M. A. Stahmann, *J. biol. Chem.* **204**, 745 (1953).

[5] A. Schmidt and C. Marlies, *Principles of High-Polymer Theory and Practice* McGraw–Hill, New York, 1948; P. J. Flory, *Principles of Polymer Chemistry* Cornell University Press, Ithaca, N. Y., 1953; G. M. Burnett, *Mechanism of Polymer Reactions* Interscience, New York, 1954; N. G. Gaylord and H. Mark, *Linear and Stereospecific Addition Polymers; Polymerization with Controlled Propagation* Interscience, New York, 1958.

explained as being due just to this extreme length; the terminal group then comprises a too small portion of the total and escapes detection. The series of polysaccharides cellulose–amylopectin–glycogen represent a fine example where the degree of branching has been established by chemical analysis (see chapt. 7 and 8). The method of terminal group determination is very important also for the study of the chemical structure of proteins (see chapt. 12–16).

Analysis of the terminal groups, of course, is not the only method of structural study, since all natural organic macromolecules contain other chemically reactive groups along the chains. There are the double bonds in rubber, the hydroxy groups in the polysaccharides and nucleic acids, and the reactive groups in the side chains of proteins. Many polysaccharides and proteins, as well as all nucleic acids are acids, i.e. contain acidic groups. The acidic polysaccharides, such as chondroitin sulfuric acid or hyaluronic acid, are true polyacids, and the same can be said about the nucleic acids, while the proteins are polyampholytes. Moreover, the proteins contain such reactive groups as the sulfhydryl groups —SH, and the hydroxy groups. It may be useful to classify all this multitude into two major groups: (1) the relatively simple macromolecules containing only *one* type of reactive groups at the chains, and (2) macromolecules with *many* kinds of reactive groups. This may be schematically illustrated as follows:

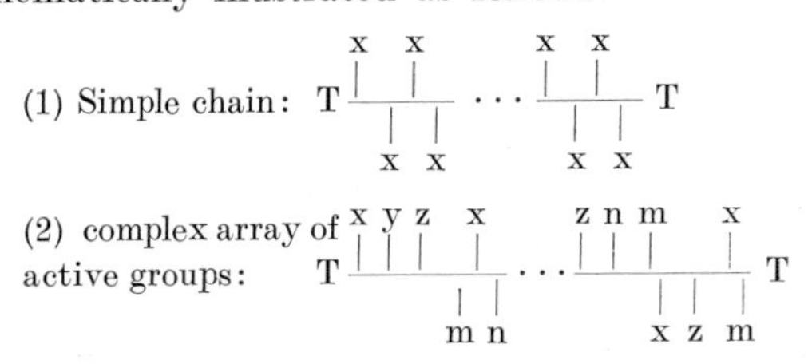

Examples of the first group possess the active groups in a regular sequence, while the macromolecules of the second group are of an irregular, very complex structure. The proteins and nucleic acids represent the second type, while rubber and cellulose belong to the first group. The matter in certain proteins is complicated even more by the fact that some of the reactive groups, such as the SH groups in proteins may form an *interchain link* with another chain thus forming an even larger and more complex entity. It is relatively easy to detect these various active groups and to determine their amount quantitatively; it is, however, much more difficult to find the position of these groups in the chain.[6,7]

There is one particularly important aspect in these structural studies: the *homogeneity* of the specimen. When we apply the homogeneity criterion

(6) F. Sanger, *Adv. Protein Chem.* **7**, 1 (1952).

(7) C. B. Anfinsen and R. R. Redfield, *Adv. Protein Chem.* **11**, 1 (1956); see also *Sulfur in Proteins* (Falmouth Symp., May, 1958), Academic Press, New York and London, 1959.

to the structural types 1 and 2, the following four possibilities emerge: (1) a homogeneous high polymer of homogeneous structure (type 1), (2) a polymolecular specimen of homogeneous structure (type 1), (3) a homogeneous substance of complex structure (type 2), and (4) a polymolecular substance of complex structure. Homogeneous high polymers of homogeneous structure are unknown. The second possibility is represented quite abundantly: rubber, cellulose, the starch amylose all are examples of polymolecular substances of uniform structure. The third possibility is realized in certain homogeneous proteins, such as insulin. It is obvious that it makes sense to study the sequence of the amino acids only on such homogeneous proteins. Since the mers (amino acids in this instance) appear in an irregular sequence, a fragment of the macromolecule is a different substance, as it is evident from the scheme showing the array of active groups. When such molecule is split into halves, two different molecules are obtained, while splitting of a uniform chain renders chemically identical (or very similar) molecules. Finally, the fourth possibility is the most common one. Most proteins and also the nucleic acids are not only polymolecular but they are mixtures of more or less similar components. The first step in any chemical study of such substances is to try to separate these components (see chapt. 2).

Structural Analysis from X-ray Diffraction Patterns

Analysis of the *X*-ray diffraction pattern (spectrum) is the most important method for structural studies of solid substances, including the organic macromolecules. In 1912, M. von Laue envisaged the possibility of studying the electromagnetic wave nature of X-rays by using a crystal as a diffraction grating. Since there were already indications that this radiation must be of a very short wave length, only such atomic diffraction grating could be expected to produce the effect. The experiment was carried out by Friedrich and Knipping by directing a beam of "white" (polychromatic, i.e. with a variety of wave lengths) *X*-rays on a stationary zinc blende crystal. The effect was positive, and it had a tremendous impact on various future developments, such as the study of the *X*-rays themselves, as well as the structure of crystals, and even the atoms. The most important fundamental work on the structure of crystalline solids, that is our topic, was done by W. H. Bragg (father) and W. L. Bragg (son) in England. A series of fine monographs is available for those interested in the details of the method and its applications.[8]

[8] A. Guinier, *X-Ray Crystallographic Technology*, Hilger and Watts, London, 1952; H. P. Klug and L. E. Alexander, *X-Ray Diffraction Procedure* Wiley, New York, 1954; J. M. Robertson, *Organic Crystals and Molecules* Cornell Univ. Press. Ithaca, N. Y., 1953; H. S. Peiser, H. P. Rooksby and A. J. C. Wilson, *X-Ray Diffraction by Polycrystalline Materials* Institute of Physics, London, 1955; Sir Lawrence Bragg, *The Crystalline State*, Bell, London, 1949.

A crystalline solid is built of a multitude of repeating units: atoms, ions, or molecules. In simple, perfect crystals, such as sodium chloride, there is a perfect order in the arrangement of these units, while in macromolecular substances there may be various degrees of order. A complete order is to be found only in a few macromolecular materials, such as single crystals of some pure proteins. Much more common in high polymers is an imperfect or partial crystallinity that is realized in a multitute of ways and degrees. For example, a linear polymer may contain crystalline and amorphous portions, or the material may be incompletely oriented in all parts of the specimen. Furthermore, a specimen may be composed of a multitude of very small, microscopic or submicroscopic (colloidal) crystalline particles. Depending on this, the *X*-ray diffraction methods can be classified into three groups:

(1) diffraction by single crystals,

(2) diffraction by crystalline powders, and

(3) diffraction by unstretched or stretched fibers.

The purpose of a complete structural analysis is to determine the location of the various atoms of a macromolecule located in the crystal, and this is possible only in the case of single crystals provided their structure is not extremely complex. The largest molecule whose structure has been established by means of *X*-ray structural analysis of crystals is that of vitamin B-12, a molecule many times smaller than that of insulin or lysozyme. A considerable progress in elucidation of the complete spatial arrangement of atomic groups in some of the smaller proteins has been achieved recently, as will be shown on the next pages.

The experimental methods used depend on the properties of the specimen and purpose in mind. For the study of single crystals, two principal approaches can be considered: (1) the Laue method of irradiating a stationary crystal with "white" *X*-rays, or (2) the rotating crystal method by using monochromatic *X*-rays. The first method is used only for preliminary experiments with the purpose of learning something about the basic crystallographic properties of the substance. The second method is the one applied for a detailed study of the diffraction patterns as related to the structure. A schematic illustration of the equipment is presented in Fig. 43. The *X*-rays are produced by irradiating a metal target (anticathode) with electrons accelerated in vacuum in a high voltage gradient. These high speed electrons impinge on the electrons of the metal making them oscillate and emit energy in the form of high frequency (i.e. short wave length) radiation. The wave length of the emitted *X*-rays depends chiefly on the anticathode metal, copper being the most commonly applied material emitting waves with the length of 1·3–1·5 Å. The beam is made monochromatic by passing it through thin foils of nickel or by special crystal monochromators, and it is then directed toward the crystal to be studied. The diffraction effects produced by the crystal are effectuated by the interaction of the waves with the electron shells of the atoms, and the diffracted beams are detected by means of photographic film placed around the crystal in a cylindrical camera. A similar equipment is used also for the study of fibers or powders. Omitting here the description of the optical phenomena, let us state briefly that the spots, arcs, and rings

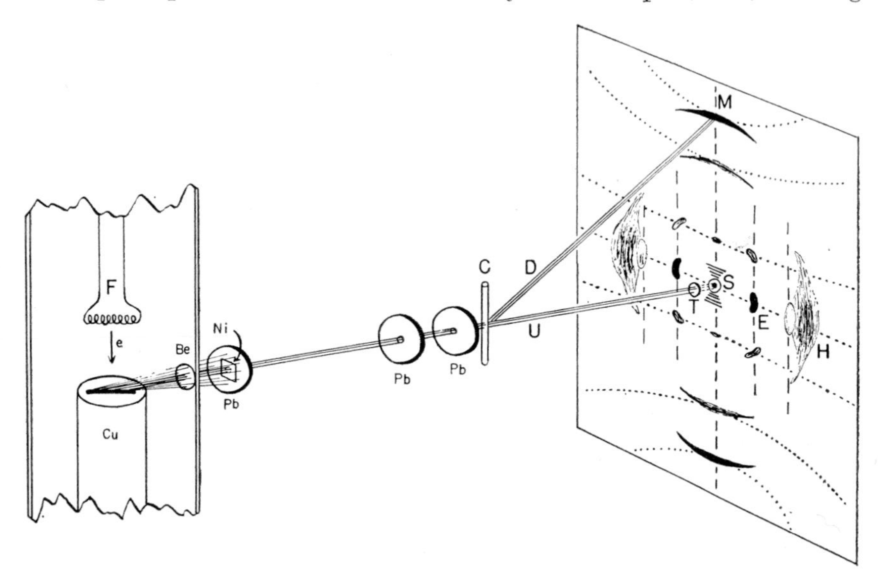

FIG. 43. Schematic illustration of the X-ray diffraction equipment. F — incandescent filament; Cu — anticathode; Be and Ni — beryllium and nickel foils; Pb — collimating system (pinholes in lead); C — a fiber preparation; U — undiffracted beam; D — diffracted beam (from R. S. Bear, *Advanc. Protein Chem.* **7**, 74, 1952)

on the photographic film are the results of the interplay of the impinging X-ray with the electron shells of the atoms, and that three types of X-ray diffraction patterns can be distinguished, depending on the preparation:

(1) the single crystal spot diagram,

(2) the fiber diagram, and

(3) the powder diagram.

An example of a single crystal diffraction diagram is presented in Fig. 44, a typical fiber diagram is shown in Fig. 45, and a powder diagram in Fig. 46. It is obvious that the fiber diagram is something intermediate between the spot and powder diagram. A fiber can be considered as a collection of small crystallites which are more or less completely oriented along the length of the fiber axis, while in a powder the crystallites are disordered. It is important to know that analysis of the powder and fiber diagrams is able to convey limited information on the structure. It is possible to deduce from such diagrams the main spacings, and to determine the dimensions of the *unit cell*, i.e. the smallest portion of the crystal possessing the optical properties characteristic for the whole crystal. The unit cell, however, is not necessarily a single molecule. In certain instances, such as some of the small proteins, the unit cell is composed of several molecules. In contrast, the unit cell in cellulose

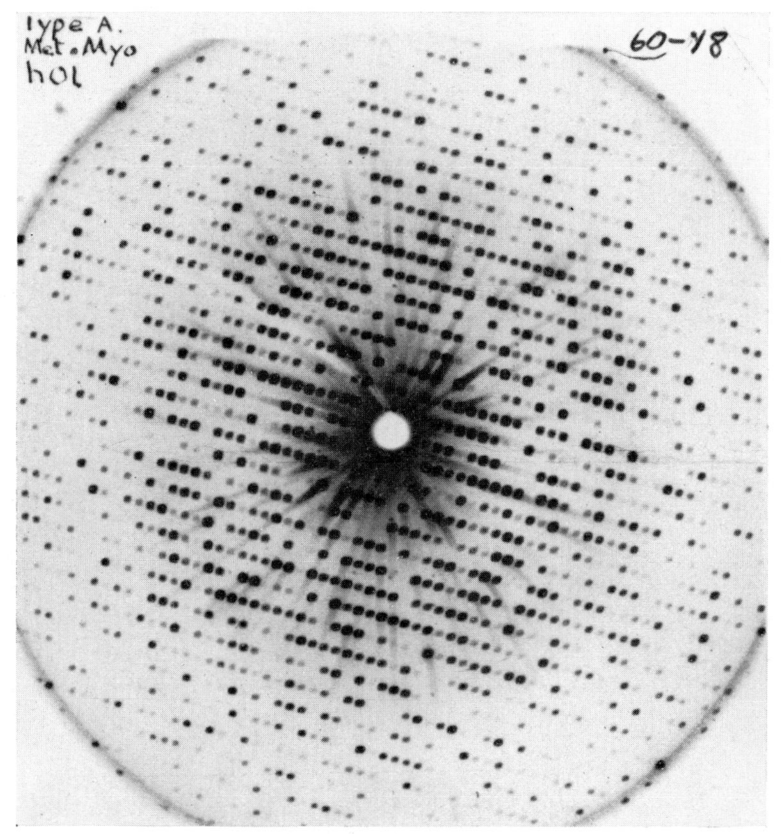

FIG. 44. *X*-ray diffraction pattern of a single crystal of myoglobin (by *Courtesy* of J. C. Kendrew)

is composed of four glucose residues of only a small section of the long chains *running through many unit cells.* The macromolecule of cellulose in a fiber is many hundred times longer than the dimension of the unit cell along the fiber aixs. The same applies to such macromolecules as silk, collagen, chitin, the nucleic acids, etc. It also should be borne in mind that the *X*-ray diagrams of substances like nucleic acids, collagen, or myosin do not reveal all structural details. For example, the *X*-ray diagram does not show the location of certain amino acid residues in the collagen fibers. The same applies to the impressive *X*-ray diffraction patterns of single protein crystals, such as shown in Fig. 44. Analysis of the electron density distribution in the various directions of the

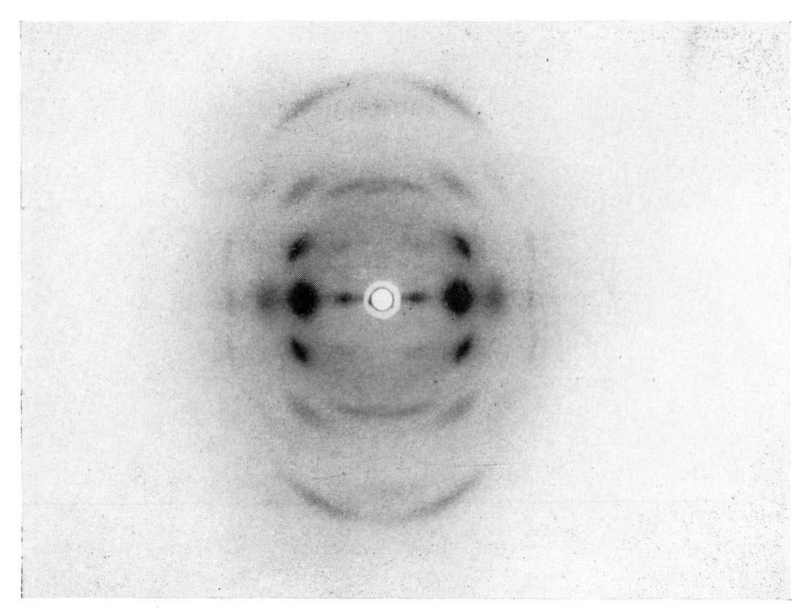

FIG. 45. *X*-ray fiber diffraction pattern. *Bombyx mori* silk fiber (by *Courtesy* of C. H. Bamford)

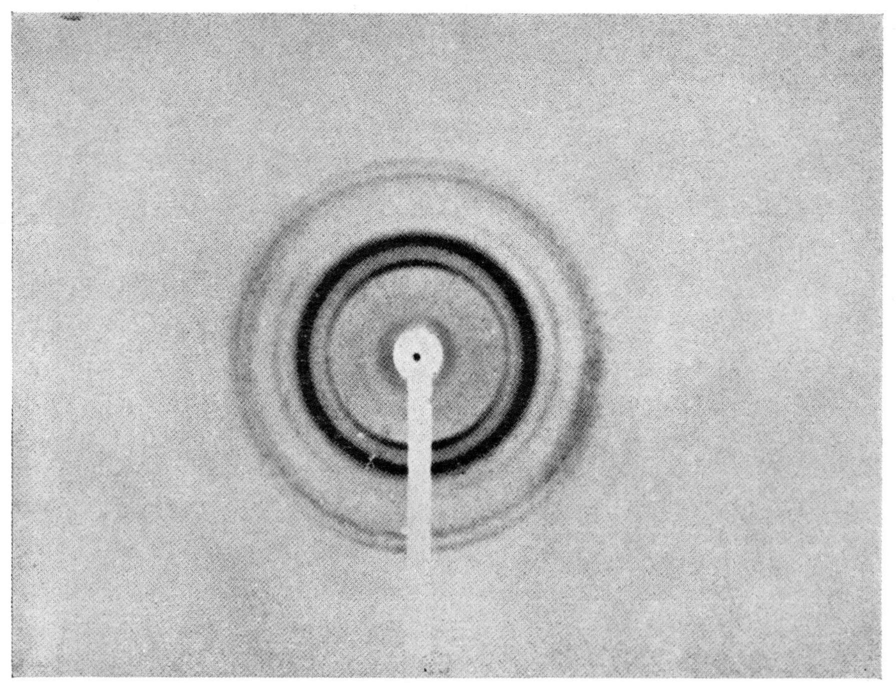

FIG. 46. *X*-ray powder diagram. A longitudinal section of bone of rat femur

crystal has so far given some information about the *general layout*, but *not about the exact location of atomic groups*, such as the side chains of the amino acid residues.

In order to show the difficulties involved in the structural analysis, we shall elaborate a little on this subject. First, it ought to be pointed out that the general layout of the spots, such as in Fig. 44, does not convey information on the spatial distribution of the atomic groups in a solid high polymer. It is, however, the *intensity*, i.e. blackening of the spots that is to be considered. The pattern of these intensities is directly related to the *electron density* within the structure, and this relationship is not simple. First, the measured intensity is related to the square of the scattering power of the atom, thus involving the uncertainty in the sign (both negative and positive quantities become positive upon squaring). Second, the *phase* relationships between the atoms are not given by the X-ray data. In some simpler cases where the correct structure can be assumed from chemical and other data, such as cellulose, the correct answer may be obtained by *trial analysis*. Since the atomic scattering values are known, the intensities can be computed theoretically for any simple assumed atomic configuration.[9] Thus the configuration whose theoretically calculated scattering intensity will be the closest to the measured intensity will be the true configuration in the crystal. For such complicated crystals as myoglobin or insulin this method, however, is valueless. Another method involves the application of the Fourier series.[8, 9] The electron density along a lattice line in a crystal is a periodic function, and the measured intensities of reflection can be correlated to the structural parameters appearing in that function. The electron density is usually calculated for different values of two variable co-ordinates for each projection employing the measured intensities, and the results are presented in the form of "contour maps" in which the positions of equal electron density are indicated by a series of contour lines (Fig. 47). The central peaks in these maps have the co-ordinates of the atomic nuclei, whereby the density is higher around the nuclei of the heavier atoms. The method requires a large number of intensity measurements and a considerable work of calculation that is now usually performed by means of electronic computers. The method has been successfully applied for the structural analysis of various organic compounds of moderate complexity. Certain modifications of this approach have been proposed by Patterson[10] and Harker.[11]

In spite of the various experimental and theoretical refinements, very little progress could be recorded in the elucidation of the structure of protein crystals. However, in 1953 Perutz made the important discovery that more

[9] See for example, S. Glasstone, *Textbook of Physical Chemistry* p. 355ff., Van Nostrand, New York, 1951 (also ref. 8).

[10] A. L. Patterson, *Phys. Rev.* **46**, 372 (1934); *Z. Kristallogr.* **70**, 517 (1935).

[11] D. Harker, *J. chem. Physics* **4**, 381 (1936).

structural details can be revealed by studying *isomorphous pairs* of crystals [12]. The X-ray diagram of hemoglobin was compared with the diagram of isomorphous hemoglobin containing a heavy atom (mercury) in each protein molecule. The greatest success with this new approach has been achieved recently by Kendrew [13] with myoglobin, a molecule considerably simpler than hemo-

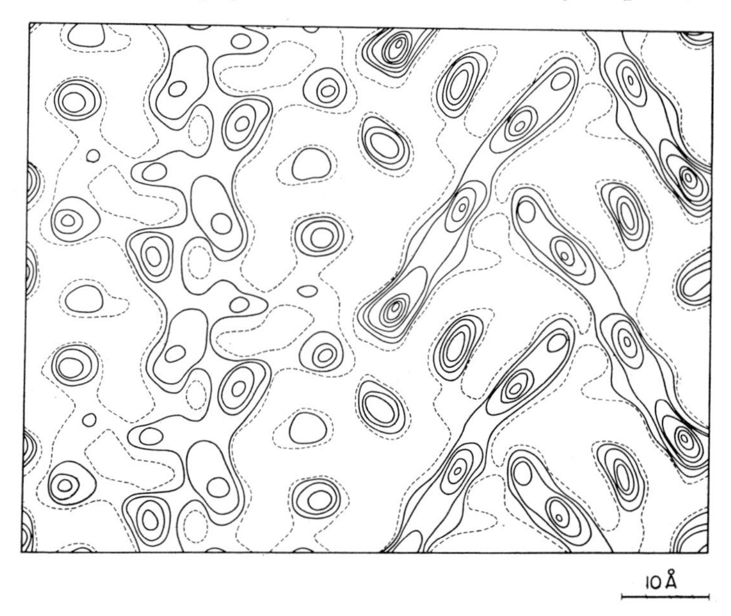

FIG. 47. Electron density contour lines

globin. Kendrew was able to attach different heavy atoms to different places of the myoglobin molecule, and many hundreds of reflections of five isomorphous myoglobins were measured. The electron densities were computed for all terms of spacings greater than 4 Å, and the results were projected in the form of a three-dimensional electron density model (Fig. 48). The model indicates the electron densities in parallel sections through two adjacent myoglobin molecules, and this projection enabled the construction of a model of the macromolecule represented in Fig. 49. "All in all, the model poses more questions than it answers. It gives us a first glimpse of the configuration of a protein molecule, but it is a tantalizing glimpse because the picture is so blurred that one cannot recognize side-chains, nor be certain

(12) D. W. GREEN, V. M. INGRAM and M. F. PERUTZ, *Proc. Roy. Soc.* A **225**, 287 (1954); M. F. PERUTZ, *Endeavour* **17**, 190 (1958).

(13) J. C. KENDREW, G. BODO, H. M. DINTZIS, R. G. PARRISH and H. WYCKOFF, *Nature* **181**, 662 (1958); J. C. KENDREW, *ibid.* **182**, 164 (1958); F. H. C. CRICK and J. C. KENDREW, *Adv. Protein Chem.* **12**, 133 (1957); M. M. BLUHM, G. BODO, H. M. DINTZIS and J. C. KENDREW, *Proc. Roy. Soc.* A **246**, 369 (1958).

how the backbone is folded–even whether it is a helix at all — nor know how the hem group is attached to the rest of the molecule. Many of the questions

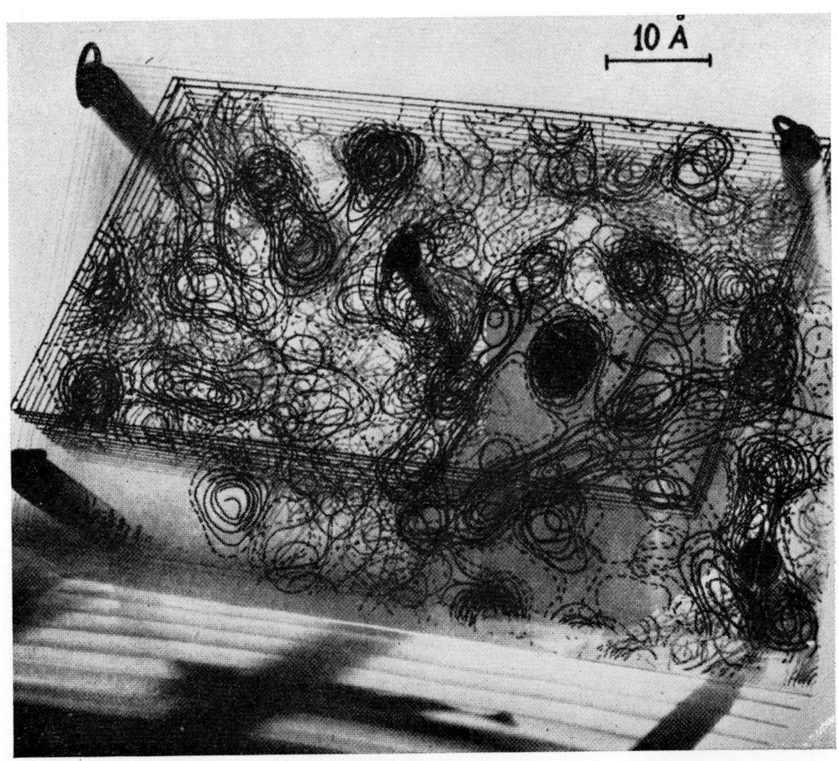

Fig. 48. Three-dimensional map showing the distribution of electron density along a series of parallel sections through two adjacent myoglobin molecules (after J. C. Kendrew)

could be cleared up if an electron density map could be drawn at higher resolution, even if that resolution stopped short of separating individual atoms. There seems no reason in principle why the resolution should not be improved, although an extension to atomic resolution is at the moment beyond our reach. At present, data are being collected for the 10,000 reflections out to 2 Å, and we hope that the electron density map prepared from these will in due course show us some of the finer details of the structure".[14] There is no doubt that the described *isomorphous replacement method* of Perutz and Kendrew has great potentialities for revealing structural details. The method is being applied in several laboratories to the study of smaller proteins, and important results can be expected in the coming years. More recently,[14a]

(14) J. C. Kendrew, *Nature* **182**, 764, 767 (1958).

(14a) J. C. Kendrew, R. E. Dickerson, B. E. Strandberg, R. G. Hart, D. R. Davies, D. C. Phillips, and V. C. Shore, Nature **185**, 422 (1960).

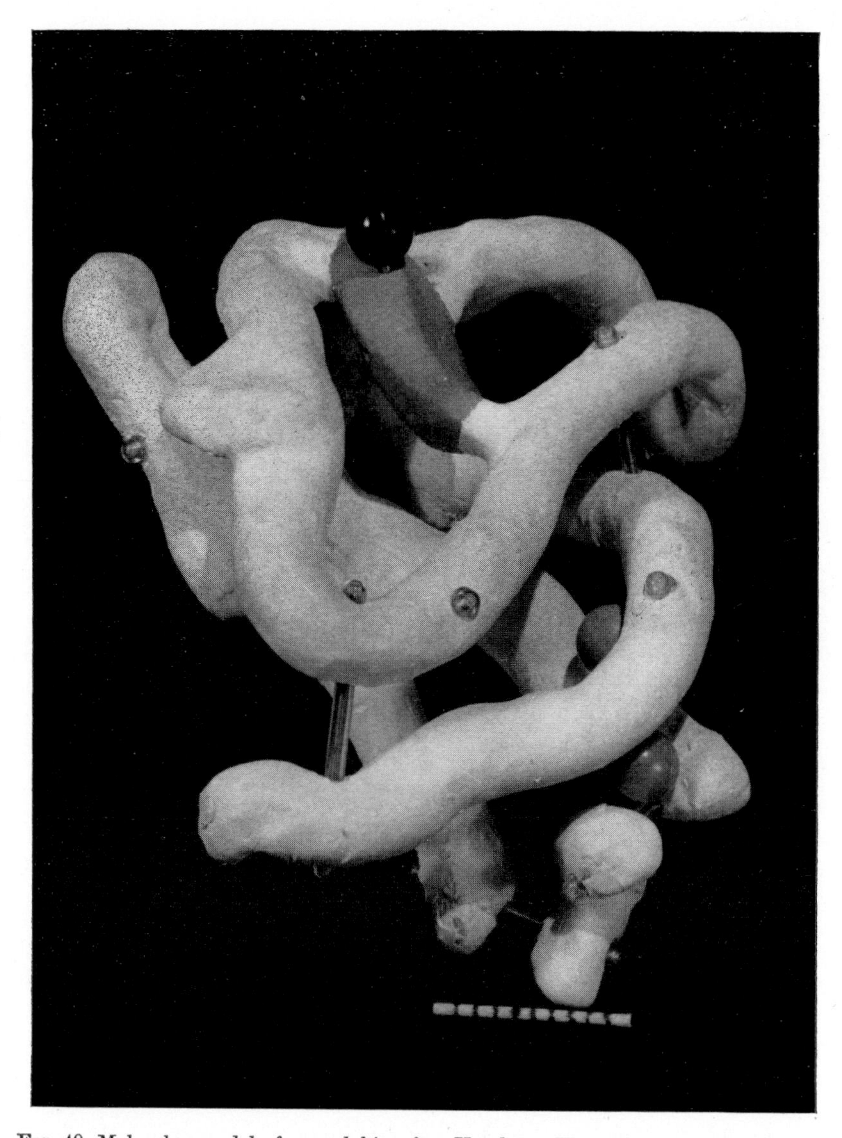

FIG. 49. Molecular model of myoglobin after Kendrew. The light sausage represents the polypeptide chain; the grey disk is the hem group; the balls represent heavy atoms attached to the myoglobin for the purpose of structural study (by *Courtesy* of J. C. Kendrew)

Kendrew *et al.* could demonstrate the presence of α-helical conformation (or configuration) in the crystals of myoglobin (see Part II).

Structural Studies by Spectroscopic Methods

While emission of *X*-rays is caused by the electrons residing in the deeper shells in the atom, visible and ultraviolet light is emitted by the outer electrons. In the instance of emission, they jump over to a lower energy level; in absorption the reverse takes place. The wave length of the ultraviolet light that is useful for the characterization of large organic molecules lies in the range of about 2500–3600 Å. The proteins absorb somewhere between 2500–3000 Å, and this absorption is due to the presence of aromatic residues in the peptide side chains. The nucleic acids exhibit a much stronger absorption at 2600 Å, and this is known to be caused by the large number of purine and pyrimidine residues. If the macromolecules absorb visible light (4000–7000 Å) the substance appears colored. Only a very limited information about the structure of large molecules can be obtained from the analysis of the ultraviolet and visible spectra, although they are of importance for the characterization and analytical determination of the substances.

Important information on the structure of large molecules is furnished by the *infrared spectroscopy*. The absorption bands of these spectra are related to the vibrations of atomic groups within the macromolecule. The wave length of the most frequently employed infrared rays ranges between 0·75 microns (μ) = 7500 Å and 20 μ, but the absorption commonly is expressed in frequencies, i.e. the reciprocal wave length. The equipment needed for these studies in commercially available, and the method is described in detail in several monographs and review articles.[15] The rays are produced by an incandescent filament of a rare earth oxide (or other material), reflected by mirrors, and dispersed into a spectrum by prisms of sodium chloride, lithium fluoride etc. The rays are detected by a sensitive thermocouple, the current being modified and amplified in order to increase the sensitivity, and modern instruments permit recording of the absorption in a rather broad section of spectrum. Examples of such spectra are presented in Fig. 50. In proteins, most interesting are the absorption peaks which could be assigned to the vibration of the —NH— and =CO groups of the peptide chains.[16] These data rendered a substantial support to the currently established concept that hydrogen bonded —NH— and =CO groups are present in peptides and proteins, not the enolized peptide bonds —C(OH)=N—, as was assumed earlier by some authors. However, an unequivocal interpretation of infrared

(15) L. J. Bellamy, *Infrared Spectra of Complex Molecules*, Methuen, London, 1954; C. Clark in *Physical Techniques in Biological Research* p. 205ff. (G. Oster and A. W. Pollister, ed.), Academic Press, New York, 1955; R. D. B. Fraser, *Progress in Biophys. and Biophys. Chem.* **3**, 47 (1953); D. L. Wood, in *Methods in Enzymology* Vol. IV, p. 104 (S. P. Colowick and N. O. Kaplan, ed.), Academic Press, New York, 1957.

(16) I. M. Klotz, P. Griswold and D. M. Gruen, *J. Amer. chem. Soc.* **71**, 1615 (1949); E. J. Ambrose, A. Elliott and R. B. Temple, *Nature* **163**, 859 (1959); see also C. H. Bamford, A. Elliott and W. E. Hanby, *Synthetic Polypeptides* chapt. 5 and 6, Academic Press, 1956; E. R. Blout, *Ann. New York Acad. Sci.* **69**, 84 (1957).

spectra is not always possible, since the vibrational effects of several groups often fall in the same peak. Another great disadvantage of the method is that the infrared absorption spectrum of a macromolecular (or any substance) is strongly affected by the solvent, e.g. water. Hence solid specimens usually are investigated.

A more subtle refinement of this method involves the use of polarized infrared light. It appears that the absorption of polarized light depends on

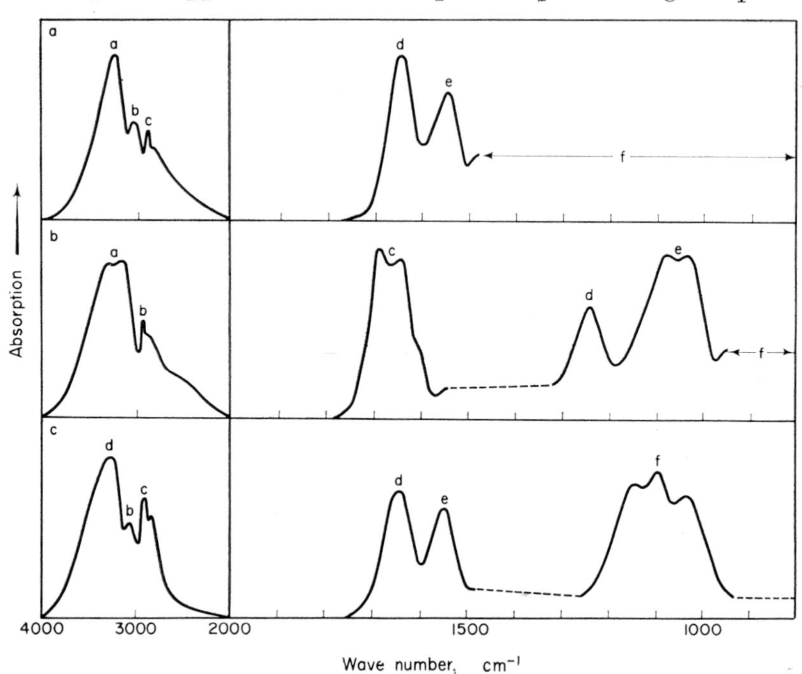

FIG. 50. Chief infrared absorption bands in: *a* — proteins; *b* — nucleic acids; *c* — polysaccharides, according to Fraser. In proteins, the peaks *a* and *b* are attributed to N—H hydrogen bond stretching, *c* to C—H stretching, *d* to C=O stretching, and e to covalent N—H bonding (R. D. B. Fraser, *Progress in Biophys.* **3**, 47, 1953)

the orientation of the absorbing groups with respect to the plane of polarization of the incident beam. If the specimens are well oriented, the absorption can be determined in two directions, i.e. parallel and perpendicular to the direction of orientation. These effects of the so called *infrared dichroism* have been studied with a considerable success for example on oriented samples of nucleic acids, in order to determine the orientation of the purine and pyrimidine rings.

The Optical Rotation of Natural Organic Macromolecules

The optical rotation method, in contrast to the *X*-ray diffraction or infrared spectroscopy, has received very little attention in the current monographs and reviews on macromolecules. The underlying optics and classical experimental techniques have been thoroughly reviewed in an article by Heller.[17] This article, however, does not provide any information about the results with natural macromolecules. A few such results on optically active polypeptides and proteins are presented in the review article by Doty and Geiduschek.[18] A wealth of important information on the optical rotation of polyamino acids and proteins in relation to structure and configuration has been published, however, in the journals during the last decade. Earlier optical rotation studies have already provided important information in the study of polysaccharides, while the nucleic acids thus far are still quite neglected in this respect.

"The utility of optical rotation lies in its unparalleled sensitivity to spatial configuration, to which *other physical methods* are generally insensitive".[19] Moreover, by means of this method one can study the macromolecules *in solution*, i.e. in a more natural state than the solid crystals.

The technique of optical rotation measurement is very simple: a beam of light is polarized in a polarizing prism, the polarized light then passes through the solution and the effect produced by the solute is determined by rotating an analyzing prism. The optics in a visual polarimeter usually is arranged in such a way that the field of vision appears as a divided disc. The rotation angle is determined by rotating the analyzer prism until both halves of the disc are exactly of the same brightness. The traditional light source in polarimetry is sodium light (wave length about 589 mμ); it was obtained formerly by melting and evaporating sodium chloride in a gas flame, and more recently by means of electrical sodium lamps. Only in the last decade has more use been made of other more effective light sources, such as mercury burners or xenon lamps. These light sources provide not only the green and blue lines of the visible spectrum but also the extremely effective ultraviolet light. A modern commercially available ultraviolet range spectropolarimeter is illustrated in Fig. 51 and 52.[20] The beam first passes a monochromator that cuts out a narrow band of the spectrum; the monochromatic light then is reflected into the polarizing prism, passes through the solution to be examined, and the effect is measured by rotating the analyzing prism. The brightness is determined by a photocell, and the sensitivity is increased by proper amplification of the current. It has also been established that the highest precision

(17) W. Heller in Weissberger's *Physical Methods of Organic Chemistry* 2nd ed., Vol. 1, part. 2, p. 1491ff., Interscience, 1949; 3rd. ed., p. 2147ff., 1961.

(18) P. Doty and E. P. Geiduschek in *The Proteins* Vol. I, part A, p. 393ff. (N. Neurath and K. Bailey, ed.), Academic Press, New York, 1953. See also C. Djerassi, *Optical Rotatory Dispersion*, Mc Graw-Hill, New York, 1960.

(19) J. A. Schellman, *Compt. rend. trav. lab. Carlsberg*, **30**, 364 (1958).

(20) H. Rudolph, *J. Opt. Soc. Am.* **45**, 50 (1955); The high precision photoelectric spectropolarimeters are available from O. C. Rudolph and Sons, Caldwell, New Jersey. Recording spectropolarimeters are available from Rudolph Instruments Engineering Co., Little Falls, New Jersey.

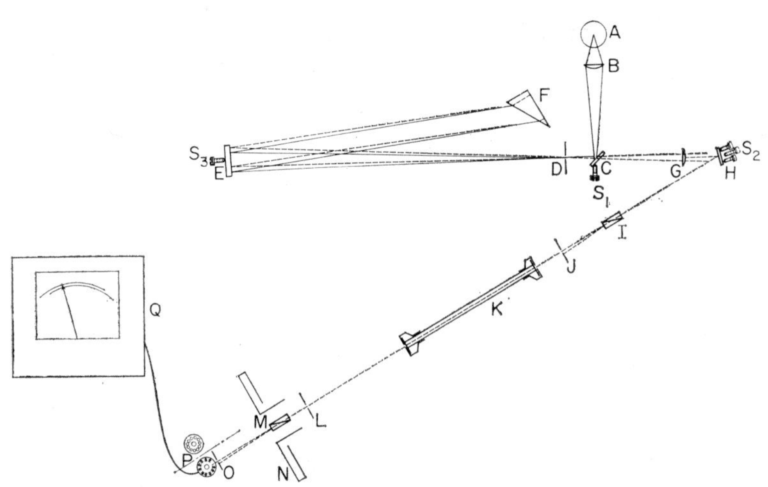

FIG. 51. Schematic drawing of the O. C. Rudolph photoelectric spectropolarimeter. *A* — light source; *F* — quartz dispersion prism; *D* — slit; *I* — quartz polarizer prism; *J* — diaphragm; *K* — sample tube; *M* quartz analyzer prism; *P* — photomultiplier tubes; *Q* — photometer and galvanometer unit

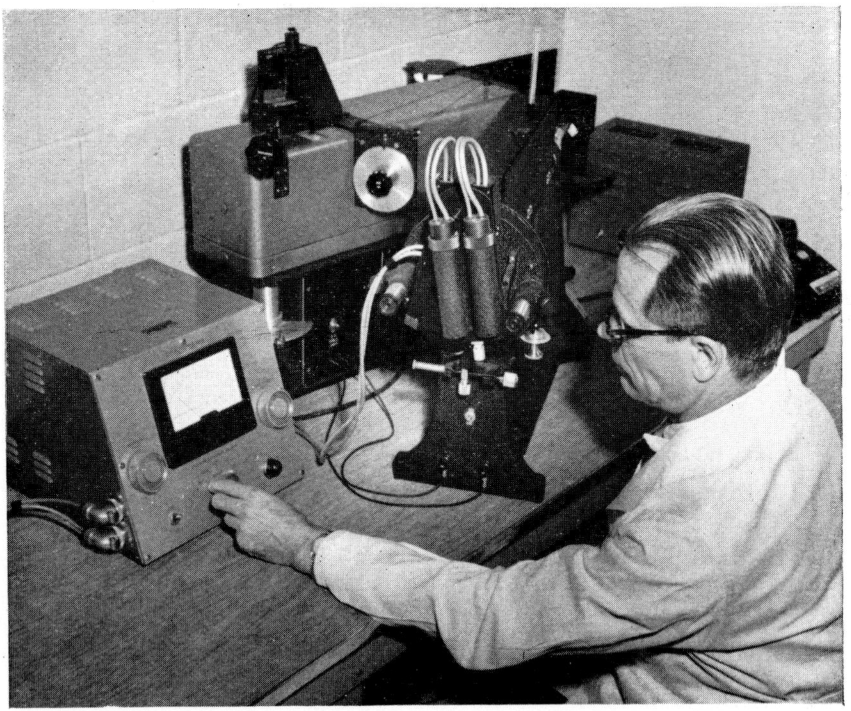

FIG. 52. Photoelectric spectropolarimeter (O. C. Rudolph & Sons, Model 80) in the Biochemistry Department of University of Texas M. D. Anderson Hospital and Tumor Institute

is obtained not by direct estimation of the extinction point but by measuring the *relative* intensity on both (+ and —) sides of the extinction point, and by determining the latter by extrapolation. This approach partially eliminates also the errors caused by a possible slight variation of the intensity of the incident beam. Comparative measurements have shown [20] that the degree of precision of the photoelectric polarimetry in the visible spectrum is about the same as that of visual polarimetry, while the latter is helpless in the most interesting part of spectrum — the ultraviolet range.

The magnitude of optical activity of a substance is expressed by the *specific rotation* $[\alpha]$:

$$[\alpha] = \frac{\alpha \cdot 100}{c \cdot l},$$

where α is the observed rotation angle, c concentration in grams per 100 ml, and l length of the tube (thickness of the solution) in decimeters. The specific rotation is only slightly influenced by the temperature, but it is strongly dependent on the *wave length* of the polarized light: *the numerical value of the specific rotation increases with decreasing wave length* (Table 10). Hence

TABLE 10

THE SPECIFIC ROTATION OF SEVERAL HIGH POLYMERS AT VARIOUS WAVE LENGTHS (author's data)

Substance	Wave length in mμ	Specific rotation, $[\alpha]_\lambda$
Serum albumin, human, pH 5·0, $c = 2{\cdot}12\%$, $T = 25\,°C$	546·1	− 82·2°
	435·8	− 155·5
	404·7	− 197·0
	390·6	− 221·9
	365·5	− 284·0
	334·1	− 408·0
	313·0	− 533
Chymotrypsinogen, pH 4·3, $c = 4{\cdot}32\%$, $T = 25\,°C$	578	− 78·0°
	546·1	− 89·7
	435·8	− 163·1
	404·7	− 200·2
	390·6	− 222·2
	365·5	− 274·5
	334·1	− 375·9
γ-Globulin, human, pH 6·2, $c = 1{\cdot}95\%$, $T = 25\,°C$	578	− 52·0°
	546·1	− 59·5
	435·8	− 104·4
	404·7	− 127·6
	365·5	− 171·1
	334·1	− 226·2
Deoxyribonucleic acid (Na salt), pH = 7·8, $c = 0{\cdot}032\%$, $T = 25\,°C$	546·1	+ 208°
	435·8	+ 392
	404·7	+ 467
	366·3	+ 632
	365·0	+ 633
	334·1	+ 923

the rotation angles when employing ultraviolet light are much larger than with the visible light. The specific rotation value of a substance must be specified by indexing the wave length; usually the temperature also is indicated, for example $[\alpha]_D^{25}$ means that the optical activity was measured at 25 °C by means of sodium light ($\lambda = 589$ mμ).

The optically active organic macromolecules contain asymmetric carbon atoms, i.e. the grouping

$$\begin{matrix} R_1 & & R_3 \\ & C & \\ R_2 & & R_4 \end{matrix}$$

However, it is now known that this "short range" asymmetry is not the only cause for the optical activity of large molecules. If it were the only cause the specific rotation would not change for example, upon unfolding of the globular proteins. In fact, the specific rotation increases about two-fold upon the expansion of these macromolecules. This indicates that the optical activity is determined not only by the asymmetric carbon atoms, i.e. the asymmetrically arranged groups around them, but also by the *gross configuration* of the whole chain.[1] It has been found that optical activity is exhibited even by such macroscopic models as copper spirals if appropriate long waves (microwaves) are used for the study of the polarization effects.[21] The experiments on the synthetic polyamino acids, especially the poly-γ-benzyl-L-glutamate, have rendered very impressive results on the dependence of optical rotation on the gross configuration of macromolecules.[22] It could be shown, by the method of light scattering and viscosity, that in some solvents these macromolecules assume the configuration of stiff helical rods, while in certain other solvents they appear as random coils. The optical rotatory properties of these configurations differed profoundly, especially in respect to the dependence of the specific rotation on the wave length.

A theoretical study on this dependence, the so called *rotatory dispersion*, was made more than fifty years ago by Drude who arrived at the well known equation

$$[\alpha] = \Sigma K_i/(\lambda^2 - \lambda_i^2),$$

where λ is the wave length, and K_i and λ_i are constants. It has been found that all proteins in the ordinary aqueous solutions (even if in a denatured state or mixed with various reagents) exhibit a simple *linear dependence* of their specific rotation on wave length.[23] Hence, the rotatory dispersion of

[21] I. Tinoco and M. P. Freeman, *J. physic. Chem.* **61**, 1196 (1957).

[22] P. Doty, J. H. Bradbury and A. M. Holtzer, *J. Amer. chem. Soc.* **78**, 947 (1956); P. Doty and R. D. Lundberg, *Proc. Nat. Acad. Sci.* **43**, 213 (1957); P. Doty and J. T. Yang, *J. Amer. chem. Soc.* **78**, 498 (1956).

[23] B. Jirgensons, *Arch. Biochem. Biophys.* **74**, 57, 74 (1958); **78**, 235 (1958); see also ref. 19. More recent studies have shown that this simple relationship holds ony for the visible and near-ultraviolet spectral range.

these systems can be expressed by an one-term Drude equation, viz.:

$$[\alpha] = K/(\lambda^2 - \lambda_0^2), \text{ or } [\alpha] \cdot \lambda^2 = \lambda_0^2 \cdot [\alpha] + K,$$

the latter form of the equation being suggested by Yang and Doty [24] who studied the rotatory dispersion in relation to configuration. It appears from these and other studies [25] that the constant λ_0 (or λ_c, as preferred by some authors) is directly related to the configuration, and it can be obtained most conveniently by plotting $[\alpha] \cdot \lambda^2$ against $[\alpha]$, and computing it from the

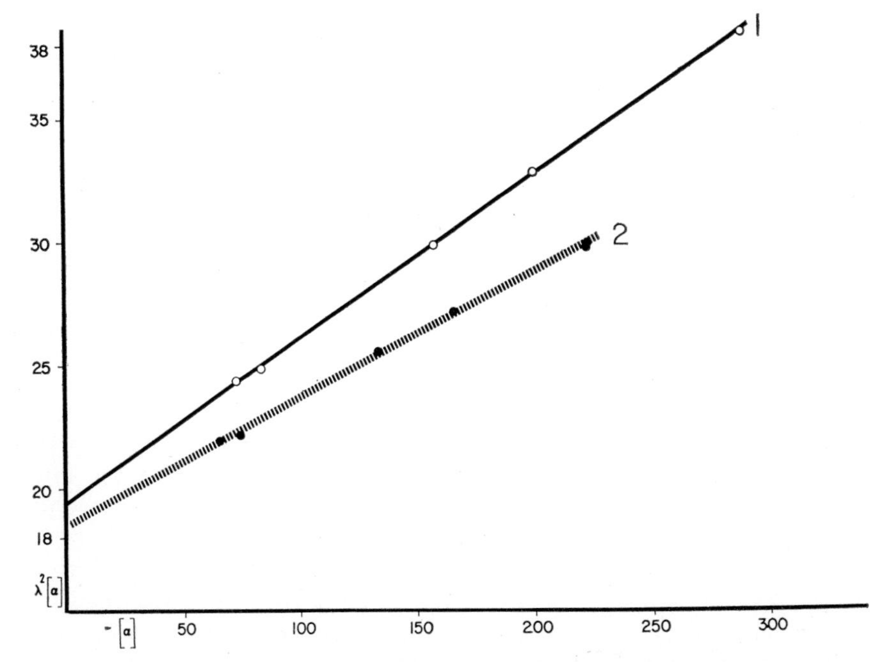

FIG. 53. The Yang-Doty plot of optical rotatory dispersion data. The dispersion constants are calculated from the slopes of the straight lines. Line 1 represents the rotatory dispersion of serum albumin, and line 2 the dispersion of a derivative of it (data of the author)

slope (Fig. 53). Interestingly enough, the poly-γ-benzyl-L-glutamate obeyed the one term Drude law only in the solvents in which it possessed the random coil configuration, while the helical rod configurations showed more complex dispersion.[22] This posed the important question on the actual configuration of the globular proteins. If the analogy with respect to the polyglutamates is assumed as being valid for the proteins, as it was suggested by Yang and Doty,[24] the globular proteins are more flexible than was previously thought and have little helical configuration. We shall return to these problems in chapt. 12.

(24) J. T. YANG and P. DOTY, *J. Amer. chem. Soc.* **79**, 761 (1957).

(25) CH. SCHELLMAN and J. A. SCHELLMAN, *Compt. rend. trav. lab. Carlsberg* **30**, 463 (1958).

Optical rotation studies have been helpful also in structural studies on polysaccharides,[26] but the method thus far has been neglected in the study of the nucleic acids. It has been reported that the linear one-term Drude equation holds for the deoxyribonucleic acid, and that the magnitude of the dispersion constant (λ_0) is about the same as that for proteins.[27] The interesting fact that the specific rotation of ribonucleic acid decreases upon degradation has been reported by Gierer.[28] This finding supports the earlier mentioned contention that optical activity is strongly dependent on the *gross* configuration, since the asymmetric carbons are not directly affected by the degradation. The specific rotation of the undegraded ribonucleic acid, as measured with the green light of 546 mμ, was found to be $+ 210°$, while the mixture of the polynucleotides and nucleotides produced in enzymic degradation possessed a specific rotation of only $+ 20°$. The contrary is true in the instance of cellulose in which case the optical activity of the macromolecule differs but slightly from that of the degradation products.[26] The optical rotation data on methylated glucose, cellobiose, -triose, -tetrose, and undegraded methylcellulose actually provided proof that the bonds throughout the whole macromolecule are equal.

In conclusion; the efforts of correlating the optical rotation with the structure and configuration have been only partially successful, and more work is required in both theory and experimental study. Kauzmann has shown [1,29] that in proteins not only the contribution of the asymmetry centers and that of the chain backbone configuration must be considered but also the interactions between the groups of the asymmetry centers, as well as the interactions between these groups and the backbone. "Clearly, then the large changes in rotation that occur when helices are transformed into random coils must not be considered to be the result of a change in the polypeptide backbone alone. The change is just as much determined by the interactions between the backbone and the side chains, and by the interactions between the side chains".[30] This has been largely neglected in some of the recent theortical studies on this problem.[31]

(26) K. Freudenberg, *J. Polymer Sci.* **23**, 791 (1957). In this article is summarized earlier work.

(27) T. W. James and B. H. Levedahl, *Biochim. Biophys. Acta* **17**, 453 (1955).

(28) A. Gierer, *Z. Naturforsch.* **13b**, 477 (1958).

(29) W. Kauzmann, *Quantum Chemistry* chapt. 15 and 16, Academic Press, New York, 1957.

(30) W. Kauzmann, *Ann. Revs. Phys. Chem.* 8, 433 (1957).

(31) D. Fitts and J. Kirkwood, *Proc. Nat. Acad. Sci.* **42**, 33 (1956); *J. Amer. chem. Soc.* **78**, 2650 (1956); W. Moffitt, *J. chem. Physics* **25**, 467 (1956); *Proc. Nat. Acad. Sci.* **42**, 736 (1956).

PART II

CHAPTER 6

RUBBER AND SIMILAR POLYISOPRENES

> The unique structural feature common to all rubber-like substances is the presence of long polymer chains... In the unstrained state the chains normally occur in randomly coiled arrangements, but they are able to rearrange to other configurations, and in particular to more highly extended ones.
>
> PAUL J. FLORY [1]

AS POINTED out by Flory,[1] Mark,[2] and others, the presence of long randomly coiled chains is only one of the requirements that guarantee the remarkable property of rubber-like elasticity. There are two other requirements: (1) the macromolecular network must have a certain stability, and (2) the system must possess certain internal mobility. Since condition (1) in fact opposes (2), it can be predicted that rubber-like elasticity will be displayed only under certain limited conditions. When there is too little interaction between the chains, they will slip along each other upon deformation, and instead of elastic recovery there will be a permanent flow. If, on the contrary, the internal mobility is too much suppressed by many strong interchain links, the system will become hard and brittle. In the absence of covalent interchain crosslinks, the internal mobility of the nonpolar chains will depend chiefly on the *temperature*. The higher the temperature the more mobile the chains and their segments. At the very low temperature of liquid air, on the other hand, rubber crystallizes and becomes brittle. The elastic properties can be modified also by *crosslinking* the fibrous macromolecules: a moderate amount of crosslinks reduces permanent flow on deformation and ascertains the return to the original status, while excessive crosslinking produces a hard solid. It is also obvious that, in the absence of crosslinks, the elasticity is favored by greater *length of the chains*, and the recovery is ascertained in part by the entanglement of these flexible fibers. The problem of rubber-like elasticity, due to its practical importance, has been extensively treated by many authors.[1,2,3] Attention has been paid to the interesting fact that

(1) P. J. FLORY, *Principles of Polymer Chemistry* p. 432, Cornell University Press, Ithaca, New York, 1953.

(2) H. MARK and A. V. TOBOLSKY, *Physical Chemistry of High Polymeric Systems* Interscience, New York, 1950.

(3) K. H. MEYER, *Natural and Synthetic High Polymers* p. 185ff., Interscience, New York, 1950; K. H. MEYER, G. VON SUSICH and E. VALKÓ, *Kolloid-Z.* **59**, 208 (1932).

rubber becomes warm on stretching, and that the system at the same time becomes more ordered (decrease of entropy). "Since there is only one stretched form, but many twisted forms, the chains tend to return to one or another of the statistically more probable twisted forms, such as they assume in unstretched rubber. The elastic force of rubber and other elastomers is thus based on a phenomenon similar to the pressure of a gas".[(4)] Rubber and similar so-called "elastomers" or "elastics" can be considered thus as something between solid and liquid bodies.

Meyer also pointed out the fact that several of the animal tissues, such as the elastic fibers and muscle fibrils display certain elasticity.[(3)] However, the conditions in these protein fibers are much more complex than in rubber, viz. these protein fibers are polar systems in which the interactions are governed also by hydrogen bonding and electrostatic attraction and repulsion.

Rubber in Plant Tissues [(5)]

According to Bonner,[(5)] there are over 2000 species of plants that produce rubber and other polyisoprenes. The vast majority of these species, however, contain these unsaturated hydrocarbons only in very small amounts usually mixed with terpenes and waxes. Thus the distribution of the polyisoprenes in nature is much wider than ordinary assumed. The number of species which contain a significant amount of rubber ranges in a few hundred, most of them being tropical plants, including the commercially most important rubber producer *Hevea brasiliensis*. The Hevea rubber tree is cultivated mostly in Southeast Asia in huge plantations. Gutta-percha or simply gutta also is produced by tropical trees, such as *Palaquium gutta*, *Mimusops balata*, and *Achras sapota*. The latter is the main source of chicle, the base for chewing gum. Chicle is a mixture of Gutta and triterpenols. The "balata" obtained from *Mimusops balata* appears to be structurally identical with the gutta which is a polyisoprene closely related to rubber. It is noteworthy that there are certain plants which contain much more rubber than the *Hevea* rubber tree, if the rubber content is calculated on the basis of dry weight of the ingredients. The guayule (*Parthenium argentatum*) and koksaghyz (*Taraxacum kok saghyz*) contain over 20% of rubber. There are old tales that the Aztecs made rubber footballs from the guayule, while the koksaghyz was extensively cultivated in the U. S. S. R. for somewhat different purposes. Especially arround 1940 there was a nation-wide campaign in the Soviet Union to increase the production of this rubber plant in the collective farms, since the government wanted to be independent of imports, and the synthetic rubber production was insufficient.

(4) K. H. Meyer, ref. (3), p. 228.

(5) J. Bonner, *Plant Biochemistry* chapt. 27, Academic Press, New York, 1950. See also: A. A. Prokofiev, *Bull. Acad. Sci. USSR* 909 (1939); G. Krotkov, *Botan. Rev.* **11**, 417 (1945); J. Bonner and A. W. Galston, *ibid.* **13**, 543 (1947).

Since rubber is insoluble in water, it appears in the plant tissue in the form of microscopic or colloidal dispersion. The milky sap of rubber plants is called latex. The particles in the *Hevea* latex are mostly egg- or pearshaped, and their size varies usually between 0·1–2 μ, while in the koksaghyz latex the particles are all round and smaller (0·01–0·5 μ). The formation of such dispersion is a quite interesting problem which has not been satisfactory solved. It is only known that the particles are stabilized, i.e. prevented from coalescence, by a layer of protein (and lipid) that is electrically charged. The proteins and phosphatides present in rubber have been studied by Tristram.[(6)] Six or seven electrophoretically different proteins have been found in the latex,[(7)] and some of them are enzymes.

The synthesis of rubber in the plant tissue has been elucidated to a certain extent, especially by means of isotopically labeled precursors, such as ^{14}C of the acetate added to a synthetic culture medium.[(8)] According to Bonner and Arreguin, the acetate is first converted to β-methylcrotonic acid[(8)] which is the common precursor for rubber and for the terpenes as well. The biosynthesis then could be envisaged as follows:

$$\underset{\text{Acetate}}{2CH_3COOH} \rightarrow \underset{\text{Acetoacetate}}{CH_3COCH_2COOH} \rightarrow \underset{\text{Acetone}}{CH_3COCH_3} \xrightarrow[+CH_3COOH]{}$$

$$\rightarrow \underset{\beta\text{-methylcrotonic acid}}{(H_3C)_2C{=}CHCOOH} \rightarrow \text{Rubber}$$

$$\downarrow$$

$$\text{Terpenes}$$

Rubber will be formed from the precursor by linear condensation of the reduced and activated β-methylcrotonic acid, while the terpenes will be synthesized by cyclic condensation. Most of the experiments have been done with excised stems of the guayule plant in tissue cultures on suitable synthetic nutrient. It was found that no rubber was produced by the stem unless an extract from the leaves of the guayule was added to the nutrient, and this extract could be replaced either by acetate or the β-methylcrotonic acid. The activity of the labeled acetate went to the macromolecules of the biosynthetized rubber.[(8)] The purpose of this biosynthesis for the plant itself is obscure. Since there are no enzymes in the plants which could facilitate the breaking down of rubber, it cannot be mobilized as a reserve food; nor does it serve as any kind of protection of the plant body. According to Bonner, rubber is a nonfunctional byproduct of cellular metabolism.

(6) G. R. Tristram, *Biochem. J.* **34**, 301 (1940); **35**, 413 (1941); **36**, 400 (1942).

(7) C. P. Roe and R. H. Ewart, *J. Amer. chem. Soc.* **64**, 2628 (1942).

(8) J. Bonner and B. Arreguin, *Arch. Biochem.* **21**, 109 (1949); Arreguin and Bonner, *ibid.* **26**, 178 (1950); B. Arreguin, J. Bonner and B. J. Wood, *Arch. Biochem. Biophys.* **31**, 234 (1951).

Isolation and Properties of Rubber and Gutta

The *Hevea* latex contains 20–60% of rubber, and small amounts of proteins, carbohydrates, phospholipids, and salts. The rubber is isolated chiefly by precipitation with acids which denature the stabilizing protein, and cause agglomeration of the rubber particles. The precipitate is washed with water and dried by squeezing out the water between corrugated rolls. The product thus obtained is an almost colorless, elastic sheet; it contains not only a certain amount of moisture but also about 0·5% of protein and smaller quantities of phospholipids, waxes, etc. In order to get rid of the moisture, the material may be dried in a current of hot air, while the other impurities are not so easy to remove. For the purpose of further purification and fractionation, rubber is dissolved in benzene, hexane, or similar hydrocarbons, and precipitated by adding slowly, under stirring, acetone or alcohol. A certain purification and fractionation is already achieved at dissolution, since a portion of the rubber usually only swells but does not dissolve in the hydrocarbon or similar solvent. This insoluble fraction is then removed and analyzed, and it appears that this fraction contains almost all of the protein impurity. The soluble rubber is subfractionated by adding a nonsolvent, whereby the larger macromolecules precipitate first, since they are less soluble in the solvent mixture than the smaller components, as has been ascertained by comparing the properties of the fractions.[9]

Analysis of the well washed, reprecipitated, and dried fractions indicates that they all are of the same composition, viz. C_5H_8. The only difference between the fractions could be found in their *average molecular weight* and some physical chemical properties depending on it. All preparations of rubber, even the most mildly and carefully handled ones, are polymolecular mixtures of polymer-homologues with a rather broad molecular weight distribution. This can be narrowed down by fractionation to a certain extent, although even the many times refractionated components are never of a quite uniform molecular size.

Rubber is a highly elastic amorphous substance that softens on warming, and crystallizes at very low temperatures. The *X*-ray diffraction pattern of unstretched rubber at room temperatures is very similar to that of the liquids, i.e. it exhibits a broad diffuse zone without any inhomogeneity. Upon stretching, however, the pattern changes into a fiber diagram which permits us to learn something about the configuration and lattice properties of the substance.[10] It was found, by comparative *X*-ray studies on stretched

(9) E. L. Skau and assoc., *J. physic. Chem.* **49**, 281 (1945).

(10) A. J. A. van der Wyk and L. Misch, *J. chem. Physics* 8, 127 (1940); C. W. Bunn in *Fibres from Synthetic Polymers* chapt. 11, R. Hill, ed., Elsevier, Amsterdam, New York, 1953; C. W. Bunn, *Adv. Colloid Sci.* Vol. 2, p. 95ff. (H. Mark and G. S. Whitby, ed)., 1946.

rubber and gutta, that rubber is a *cis*-polyisoprene while gutta is a *trans*-isomer, viz.:

$$\cdots -H_2C\diagdown C{=}HC\diagup CH_2{-}H_2C\diagup C{=}HC\diagdown CH_2{-}H_2C\diagdown C{=}HC\diagup CH_2{-}\cdots$$

(each C bearing a CH_3 group)

Rubber (cis-)

$$\cdots -CH_2\diagdown CH_2\diagup C(CH_3){=}CH\diagdown CH_2\diagup CH_2\diagdown C(CH_3){=}CH\diagup CH_2{-}\cdots$$

Gutta (trans-)

The cis-isomerism of the rubber, i.e. the bending of the chain on the same side with respect to the double bond, has the consequence that the chains cannot align and crystallize as easily as in the trans-configuration of gutta. The latter, although of the same chemical composition as rubber, is a hard and only slightly elastic substance; it softens and becomes more elastic on heating to 50 °C. Isoprene, C_5H_8, is formed upon heating of both rubber and gutta to higher temperatures that lead to depolymerization. Especially important for the elucidation of the structure was the early work of Harries (1904) who showed that laevulinic aldehyde is formed upon ozonization and hydrolysis, viz.:

$$\cdots -CH_2{-}C(CH_3){=}CH{-}CH_2{-}CH_2{-}C(CH_3){=}CH{-}CH_2{-}\cdots + O_3 \rightarrow$$

$$\cdots -CH_2{-}\underset{CH_3}{C}(O{-}O)(O)CH{-}CH_2{-}HC_2{-}\underset{CH_3}{C}(O{-}O)(O)CH{-}CH_2{-}\cdots + H_2O \rightarrow$$

Rubber ozonide

$$\cdots -CH_2{-}\underset{CH_3}{C}{=}O + OHC{-}CH_2{-}CH_2{-}\underset{CH_3}{C}{=}O + OHC{-}CH_2{-}\cdots$$

Laevulinic aldehyde

This reaction together with the fact that isoprene is formed on distillation of rubber provided the basis for the concept that it is a polyisoprene. The degree of unsaturation makes the polyisoprenes more reactive than the other (saturated) polymeric hydrocarbons, such as polyethylene. The macromolecules of rubber are attacked slowly by the oxygen of air; rubber can be hydrogenated, it combines also with sulfur, the halogens, and hydrogen chloride. The sulfur compound of rubber is the most important derivative, and it will be described in the last section of this chapter. Of a considerable commercial importance is also the chlorinated rubber and rubber hydrochloride which is a chemically resistant saturated compound of the structure

$$\cdots -CH_2{-}\overset{Cl}{\underset{CH_3}{C}}{-}CH_2{-}CH_2{-}CH_2{-}\overset{Cl}{\underset{CH_3}{C}}{-}CH_2{-}CH_2{-}CH_2{-}\overset{Cl}{\underset{CH_3}{C}}{-}\cdots$$

The *synthesis of rubber* has a long and interesting history.[11] It is no exaggeration to compare the struggle for synthetic rubber with the ardent efforts of the alchemists for artificial gold. This is due to the importance of rubber in the modern technology, especially in the military branch (tires, waterproof garments and footwear, tubing, etc.), and the geographic limitations in the availability of natural rubber. The first large-scale effort to synthesize rubber was undertaken during the First World War in Germany, since it was cut off from the overseas rubber supplies by the blockade. Polymerization of isoprene was attempted, but the resulting polyisoprene had only a slight similarity to natural rubber, and its mechanical properties, even after various treatments, were much inferior to those of vulcanized natural rubber. The Russian chemist Lebedev (1910) was probably the first who succeeded in preparing a synthetic rubber of relatively good quality; however, he used butadiene $CH_2{=}CH{-}CH{=}CH_2$ as starting material. Later, all the chief efforts pivoted about this monomer, chiefly in Germany and the U. S. S. R., later also in the U. S. A. Large scale syntheses of rubber, using butadiene, styrene, and several less important monomers, began in the forties (e.g. over 108,000 tons in 1943 in Germany alone). A variety of types of synthetic rubber were produced, and some of these types even exceeded natural rubber in the resistance to wear or to heat, aging, or chemicals. However, all these artificial products (Buna's, GR-S, etc.) were high polymers which differed from natural rubber in structure, composition, and properties. It appears that the greatest difficulty in synthesizing natural rubber was to order the isoprene mers exactly in the all-cis configuration. This was finally accomplished only in 1955 in the U. S. A., almost simultaneously in two industrial research laboratories, by means of the *stereospecific* catalysts.[12] In the presence of these catalysts a variety of other macromolecules of definite configuration have been synthesized recently. These highly stereospecific polymerizations may be of interest also for the understanding of the biosynthesis of the naturally occurring macromolecules, such as the formation of keratin in a growing hair. "A molecule growing from the catalytic complex on the surface of a crystal is like a hair growing from its root: that is, the monomers are added at the root . . . No one will be misled into supposing that these complexes bear any basic resemblance to a living organism. Nevertheless the analogies between the way they build giant molecules and the way an organism does are striking, and very hopeful for the future of polymer chemistry. A living creature builds its high polymers, precisely tailored according to a set design, by means of catalysts (enzymes). We are now in a

[11] Harry L. Fisher, *Chemistry of Natural and Synthetic Rubbers* 2nd. ed., Reinhold, New York, 1957; J. Le Bras and I. E. Berck, *Rubber* Chemical Publ., 1957.

[12] See for example: S. E. Horne, Jr., J. P. Kiel, J. J. Shipman, V. L. Folt, C. F. Gibbs, E. A. Willson, E. B. Newton and M. A. Reinhart, *Ind. Engng. Chem.* 48, 784 (1956).

position to hope that, with man-made catalysts, we shall be able to produce predesigned giant molecules in the same controlled and orderly way".[13]

The Macromolecules of Rubber in Solution

The pioneering work on the properties of rubber solutions has been done by Staudinger in 1920–30 in Zurich, Switzerland, and Freiburg, Germany.[14] First, Staudinger introduced his viscosimetric method (see chapt. 4), and applied it to a large number of native and partially degraded rubber specimens. The viscosimetric method was standardized by osmometry, and since all rubber preparations are polymolecular and the osmotic number average molecular weight differs from the viscosity average, these early measurements could give only approximate values. At any rate, it was ascertained by Staudinger *et al.* that the rubber molecules are *very large*. Moreover, since the viscosity of the diluted solutions was very high, Staudinger made the correct assumption that the macromolecules are *fibrous*. The average molecular weight (M_n) of the least soluble fractions is about 400,000, while the more soluble fractions have lower M_n values of 50,000–200,000, depending on the method of fractionation and degree of degradation.[15] Since the macromolecules of rubber in solution are very flexible, they uninterruptedly change their configuration, and they are randomly coiled. Consequently the viscosity of the solutions does not increase with molecular weight (chain length) according to the simple relation $|\eta| = K\,M$, as was formerly assumed, but according to $|\eta| = K\,M^a$, where a is a fraction (see chapt. 4). For the solutions of natural rubber in toluene, $K = 5 \cdot 10^4$ and $a = 0{\cdot}67$.[15] If the solvent is altered by adding 10–15% alcohol, the macromolecules assume more compactly coiled configurations, and a approaches 0·5. The more compactly the chains are coiled the less the viscosity increases with an increase in the molecular weight.

Important information about the behavior of the rubber in solution has been gained also by considering the energetics of the system.[16] The thermal effects on solution and dilution have been found to be very small. The effects are of about the same order as by mixing two nonpolar liquid hydrocarbons. And since the change in the heat content is so small, the spontaneous dissolution can be attributed only to a large increase in entropy (see p. 73). This means that the macromolecules of rubber upon solution attain an even more disorderly state than in the solid. Dissolution of rubber in solvents like benzene, toluene, or petroleum ether cannot be interpreted as a result of solvation of the rubber by the solvents but it is due to the tendency to attain a

[13] G. Natta, *Scient. American* **197**, No. 3 (1957), p. 104.

[14] H. Staudinger, *Die hochmolekulare organische Verbindungen, Kautschuk und Zellulose*. Springer, Berlin, 1932.

[15] See for example: W. C. Carter, R. L. Scott and M. Magat, *J. Amer. chem. Soc.* **68**, 1480 (1946).

[16] G. Gee in *Adv. Colloid Sci.* **2**, 145 (1946), especially p. 155.

state of greater disorder. In these processess a very small amount of heat (0·1–1·5 cal/g rubber) is absorbed,[16] while in the instance of chloroform as solvent the process is slightly exothermic (— 3 cal/g) indicating slight solvation. It is interesting that very low values for the solvation have been found also by the direct compressibility method of Pasynskii.[17] For example, it was found that the solvation of natural rubber in benzene amounted only to 0·5 g/g rubber, and in carbon disulfide to 0·65 g/g rubber. The solvation of several specimens of synthetic rubber was found to be practically zero.

A very important paper on the molecular size, shape, and thermodynamic properties of rubber solutions was published a few years ago by Schulz and his associates.[17a] First, a method was elaborated which ensures complete dissolution without any (or quite insignificant) degradation, and the molecular size and configuration was studied by means of light scattering. The molecular weight ($\bar{M}_w$) of undegraded natural rubber in cyclohexane was found to be 1,300,000. The average end-to-end distance of the chains in the statistical macromolecular coils was found to be 1750 Å. The heat of dilution was positive (endotherm), and low. The work substantiated the contention that the linear and flexible macromolecules are not branched.

Cross-linking of Rubber (Vulcanization) [18]

The macromolecules of the soluble component of rubber are not cross-linked, and they possess a remarkable degree of mobility exhibited in the ease of deformation. A slight amount of cross-links between the chains can be assumed for the insoluble portion which, though insoluble, swells to a great extent. From a practical point of view it is extremely important to improve the mechanical and chemical properties of the material. Raw rubber melts readily, it is attacked by light and oxygen, especially its allotropic form ozone, and deteriorates in time; for some other purposes, raw rubber, moreover, is not strong enough. Hence a considerable amount of effort has been (and still is) spent on the improvement of rubber. The methods used for this purpose are as different as the various products made of rubber, although all the labor pivots around the *cross-linking of the fibrous macromolecules.* This can be accomplished by various means, but treatment with sulfur and sulfur compounds is of special importance. However, the mixing of rubber with other solids is a problem itself. In the ordinary "mastication" rubber is milled between teeth-studded rolls, so that it becomes soft and flaky, and readily miscible with sulfur and various other substances. However, this milling procedure results in certain degradation, and hence it must be carefully controlled. A variety of substances are mixed into the starting material, depending on the final product to be made. Tire rubber, for instance, contains

[17] A. Pasynskii, *Koll. Zhurnal* 8, 53 (1946).
[17a] G. V. Schulz, K. Altgelt and H.-J. Cantow, *Makromol. Chem.* **21**, 13 (1956).
[18] E. H. Farmer, *Adv. Colloid Sci.* **2**, 299 (1946).

about 3% sulfur, 4% zinc oxide, and 40–50% of carbon black (filler); moreover, small amounts of stearic acid, tar, etc. are added in order to improve the miscibility, and, finally, a small amount of an antioxydant improves the stability of the rubber considerably. The cross-linking then is achieved by heating the properly shaped mix at a certain high temperature. For the highly elastic products, such as surgical gloves, no carbon is added.

The mechanism of vulcanization is not fully understood. There is, however, not much doubt that sulfur and zinc oxide react with the chains thereby forming *cross-links* of the type

$$\text{C—S—C, or C—S—S—C, or C—S—Zn—S—C.}$$

The formation of these interchain bonds, according to Farmer [18], occurs only in part at the expense of the double bonds, since the unsaturation is not completely eliminated on vulcanization. Only in a few special cases,

FIG. 54. Schematic illustration of rubber macromolecules cross-linked with sulfur. *A* — low degree of cross-linking; *B* — high degree of cross-linking

such as cold vulcanization by means of sulfur monochloride S_2Cl_2 the reaction can be formulated as follows

$$\begin{array}{c} \diagdown C{-}CH_3 \\ \| \\ \diagup C{-}H \end{array} + S_2Cl_2 + \begin{array}{c} \diagdown C{-}CH_3 \\ \| \\ \diagup C{-}H \end{array} \rightarrow \begin{array}{ccccc} & | & & | & \\ Cl{-} & C{-}CH_3 & & Cl{-} & C{-}CH_3 \\ & | & & & | \\ {-} & C & {-}S{-} & & C{-} \\ & | & & & | \\ & H & & & H \end{array} + S.$$

There are, moreover, certain other possibilities, viz. linking the sulfur at two double bonds of the same chain:

$$\begin{array}{c} \qquad\quad \overline{\qquad\qquad S \qquad\qquad} \\ \cdots{-}CH{-}\underset{\displaystyle CH_3}{\overset{|}{\underset{|}{C}}}{-}CH_2{-}CH_2{-}CH{-}\underset{\displaystyle CH_3}{\overset{|}{\underset{|}{C}}}{-}\cdots \\ \underline{\qquad\qquad S \qquad\qquad} \end{array}$$

or even of the formation of direct carbon to carbon interchain bonds upon the activation of the bonds. This is substantiated by the facts that the cross-linking can be increased by irradiation with high energy nuclear radiation from nuclear reactors.[19] The rubber mixes containing large proportions of solid fillers, such as carbon black, of course are harder than the compositions without these fillers. In their absence, the hardness increases with the quantity of sulfur used for vulcanization, whereby the elasticity decreases. This is due to the fact that upon excessive cross-linking the internal mobility of the chains is restricted (Fig. 54). The mechanical properties of a hard rubber (ebonite) vulcanized with 20–30% sulfur differ very strongly from those of tire rubber vulcanized with a small amount of sulfur but containing 40% of carbon black. In the first instance the elasticity is lost because of chemical cross-linking; in the second instance the mechanical strength and resistance to wear is increased without losing much of the elastic properties. The carbon particles are not chemically linked with the network, they are able to glide in the interstices of the slightly cross-linked fibers, and thus do not interfere with the elasticity to any great extent.[20]

(19) A. Charlesby, *Research* 8, 288 (1955); *J. Polymer Sci.* **14**, 547 (1954); F. A. Bovey, *The Effects of Ionizing Radiation on Natural and Synthetic High Polymers* Interscience, New York, 1958.

(20) R. Houwink, *Makromol. Chem.* (*Staudinger-Festband*), **18/19**, 119 (1956).

CHAPTER 7

POLYSACCHARIDES. CELLULOSE AND ITS DERIVATIVES

...These observations, taken all together, establish strictly the uniformity of the chain. Cellulose, as its structure is now known, is a substance of high precision.

K. FREUDENBERG [1]

Cellulose in Nature

Cellulose is the most abundant organic compound in nature. Contrary to rubber, the function of cellulose in plants is well established: cellulose is the major structural material of plant bodies. "Through untold past eons, the dictatorial process of natural selection brought about the adoption and development of this polysaccharide so that it now serves generally as the principal cell wall component".[2] What was the basis for this selection? Why was not rubber or any other hydrocarbon chosen for this purpose? — It seems to be, in the first place, the *polarity* that accounts for the exceptional role of the polysaccharides in plants. Polarity conditions, first, the affinity to water, to ions, and to the many polar organic substances used in plant life; even a relatively passive constituent of cell walls, in order to secure permeability, must be polar. There are more reasons for polarity: it guarantees attraction between two and more linear macromolecules. The structural framework of cells is not built of isolated, irregularly meshed macromolecules but of strong, uniform strings or bundles of tightly aligned macromolecules. Intermolecular attraction due to cohesion and hydrogen bond formation between the polar groups secures the formation of very strong microfibrils that comprise the structural framework. But polarity alone would not be a sufficient condition if it were not supported by other features, namely: *length*, *uniformity*, and *restricted flexibility* of the chains. It is known that only long macromolecules are able to form fibers, although the length alone is an insufficient quality for the formation of strong fibrils; the linear units must be *uniform* in order to be able to align into sheaves, in order to crystallize. Besides cellulose, there are many more polar and long chain polysaccharides, yet they cannot compete with cellulose as structural materials, because

(1) K. FREUDENBERG, *J. Polymer Sci.* **23**, 791 (1957), p. 795.

(2) R. L. WHISTLER and CH. L. SMART, *Polysaccharide Chemistry* p. 66, Academic Press, New York, 1953.

their macromolecules are less uniform than those of cellulose. And finally, the peculiar structure of the polysaccharide chain molecules imposes certain restrictions on their flexibility that in solutions is partially due to solvation. In solutions, the macromolecules of cellulose and its derivatives are much more extended than those of rubber.

The *biosynthesis* of cellulose is little investigated. Some light has been thrown on this important phenomenon but recently by means of labeled precursors. Thus Greathouse reported in 1953 that administration of D-glucose-1-^{14}C (i.e. glucose labelled with carbon-14 in the position 1) to cotton bolls during the period of most rapid cellulose synthesis resulted in accumulation of the ^{14}C in the C-1 position of the synthesized cellulose.[3] These results indicate that the glucose monomers are added to the cellulose chain without being first degraded. Brown and Neish [4] performed similar experiments with wheat plants by injecting glucose-1-^{14}C, or sorbitol-1-^{14}C, or labeled succinic acid. The radioactivity of the sorbitol and succinic acid was found to be evenly distributed between the various carbons of the cellulose of the wheat plant, while the glucose-1-^{14}C activity went chiefly to the C-1 position in the cellulose. These results indicate that the C skeleton of the sorbitol and succinic acid must be split and rearranged, while glucose can be attached to the cellulose without degradation. The enzyme systems involved in these conversions in these higher plants thus must be quite complex, and nothing is known about the mechanism of their action. Somewhat more promising, however, are the prospects with the synthesis of bacterial cellulose, especially in the instance of the vinegar microbes (*Acetobacter xylinum*). It has been mentioned already in 1949 by Mühlethaler,[5] chiefly on the basis of electron-microscopic observations, that the microfibrils of the cellulose do not seem to grow from the body of the microbe but outside it, in the medium. This indicates that the enzymes catalyzing the conversions are outside the cells, a fact that is encouraging for their isolation. In 1957, Greathouse, reported the isolation of this cell-free enzyme system that promoted the conversion of labeled glucose and other precursors into bacterial cellulose. [6] Greathouse concludes (ref .6, p. 4507): "Thus, the mechanism of cellulose polymerization is complex. At least two major mechanisms appear from these studies, (1) direct polymerization, possibly involving phosphorylation and (2) cleavage of the hexose and resynthesis of hexose phosphates from trioses such as glycerol. Hexose phosphates have been isolated and identified as intermediates in the biosynthesis of cellulose from D-glucose, thus the reason for suggesting these products as possible energy sources in the major mechanism of polymerization".

[3] G. A. Greathouse, *Science* **117**, 553 (1953).

[4] S. A. Brown and A. C. Neish, *Canad. J. Biochem. Physiol.* **32**, 170 (1954).

[5] K. Mühlethaler, *Biochim. Biophys. Acta* **3**, 527 (1949).

[6] G. A. Greathouse, *J. Amer. chem. Soc.* **79**, 4503, 4505 (1957).

Usmanov [7] studied the formation of cellulose in cotton tissue and found that the synthesis at first is very slow, showing an acceleration by the fifteenth day after bloom with a subsequent slow-down again and complete cessation at about the fortieth day after bloom (*S*-shaped growth curve).

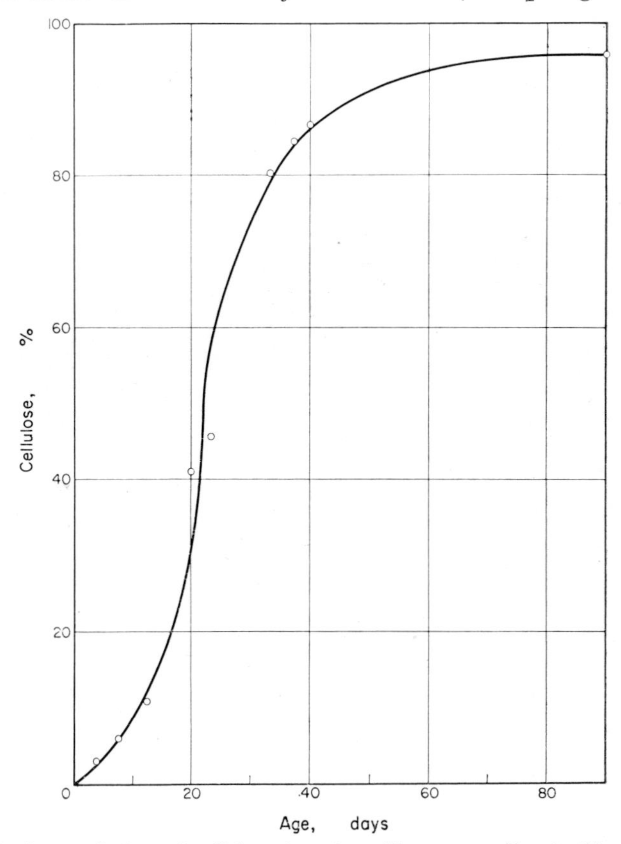

FIG. 55. Accumulation of cellulose in cotton fibers, according to Usmanov[7]

Viscosity measurements on cellulose specimens isolated at various stages of growth showed that the early cellulose is of a low degree of polymerization which later shows an abrupt increase and then remains constant. The early cellulose is also more porous and has a higher sorption capacity and heat of solution than the fully ripened cellulose, i.e. the formation of the dense microfibrils through intermolecular hydrogen bonding increases with the chain length in the period of its growth. Moreover, the quantity of monoses in the tissue decreases as the amount of cellulose increases (see Fig. 55). An electron micrograph of cellulose is presented in Fig. 56.

[7] H. U. USMANOV, *J. Polymer Sci.* **23**, 831 (1957); H. U. USMANOV and V. A. KARGIN, *Chemistry and Physical Chemistry of High Molecular Compounds* p. 189, Akademizdat (Russ.), 1952.

We shall not discuss here the detailed histological aspects of the submicroscopic structures in various plant tissues.[8] It has already been indicated, with respect to distribution, that cellulose is found not only in trees and grasses but also in microbes; it may be added that this structural poly-

FIG. 56. Electron micrograph of cellulose obtained from *Bacterium xylinum* (magnification 22,000×) (by *Courtesy* of K. Mühlethaler)

saccharide is found also in a variety of marine plants. While the cellulose of the seed hairs of cotton or in the bast fibers of ramie is 95–98% pure, its content in dried straw or wood amounts to only 40–60%. The cellulose content of leaves and grasses is even lower, usually 15–30%, with the exception of such leaf fibers as Manila hemp, banana, and sisal hemp that contain 50–70% cellulose (on dry basis). The other major ingredients that accompany cellulose in wood, stalks, leaves, and hulls are various other polysachharides and lignin. Moreover, the plant tissues, aside of the usual water and mineral content, contain waxes, lipids, proteins, terpenes, tannic acid, and a great variety of other organic substances. If we disregard some special cases, such as some of the rubber plants, the most important quantitatively are the *pentosans* and *lignin*. The lignin content of the various woody tissues amounts to 20–40%, while in straws, stalks, and hulls it is 15–25%. The pentosans and other similar polysaccharides are more abundant in stalks and hulls (20–30%) than in woods (7–22%, see ref. 2).

[8] R. D. PRESTON, *The Molecular Architecture of Plant Cell Walls*, Wiley, New York, 1952; A. FREY-WYSSLING, *Submicroscopie Morphology of Protoplasm* 2nd English ed., Elsevier, Amsterdam 1953.

Molecular Structure, Size, and Configuration of Cellulose [9]

Although the cellulose content of several plant materials is very high, the isolation of pure cellulose is a difficult problem. This is due to the high degree of crystallinity of the long and uniform macromolecules. The various impurities not only are tightly adsorbed on the surface of the microfibrils of cellulose but they may be even trapped within them. Dispersion of the microfibril into separate macromolecules, however, is a difficult task, since the intermolecular cohesion and hydrogen bonding within the fibrils is extremely strong. A mild treatment simply will not dissolve the material, while a drastic treatment may lead to degradation. Cotton linters is the best starting material for the highest purity cellulose, and wood is the most important source for industrial cellulose products. Cotton fiber is first extracted with alcohol and ether in order to liberate the fibers from the lipids and waxes. The fibers then are treated with diluted (about 1%) solution of sodium hydroxide which facilitates the removal of the traces of lignin, acidic polysaccharides, and proteins. The fibers finally are washed with dilute acetic acid and water. It has been found that degradation can be practically eliminated if all these operations of purification are performed under an inert gas, such as nitrogen. In chemical industry, the manufacture of cellulose involves treatment of chopped wood, stalks, etc. with a hot solution of calcium hydrosulfite $Ca(HSO_3)_2$; this chemical, apart from some bleaching effect, dissolves lignin and most other impurities, and disperses cellulose in the form of a filterable suspension.

The chemical composition of cellulose corresponds to the formula $(C_6H_{10}O_5)_n$. Hydrolytic decomposition of cellulose can be accomplished by either enzymic action or by strong acids, and the final hydrolysis product is D-glucose. Detailed chemical studies by Freudenberg, Haworth, Willstaetter, Zechmeister, and others have established that cellulose is a linear polymer of β-D-glucopyranose, viz.:

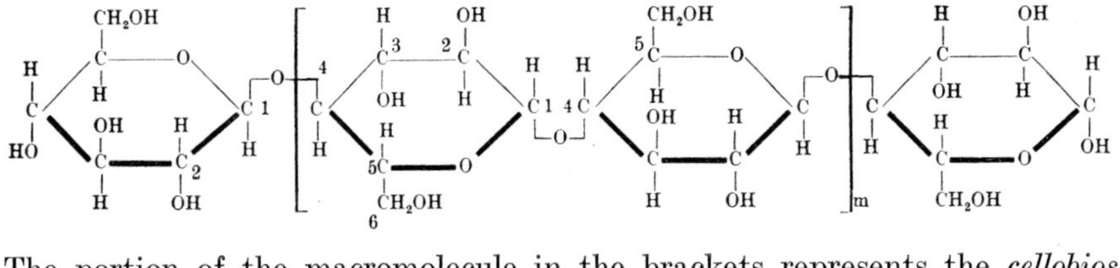

The portion of the macromolecule in the brackets represents the *cellobiose* residue which, however, is not a discrete structural element, since *all bonds between the glucopyranose rings are identical.* Cellobiose, as well as cellotriose, cellotetraose, and cellohexaose all have been isolated from partial hydrolytic decomposition products, and they all are small pieces of the long macromole-

[9] E. Ott, H. M. Spurlin and M. W. Grafflin (ed.), *Cellulose and Cellulose Derivatives* 2nd ed., Vol. I and II, 1954, Vol. III, 1955, Interscience, New York; K. Ward (ed.), *Chemistry and Chemical Technology of Cotton* Interscience, New York, 1955.

cules formed on random scission. It must be borne in mind that all residues in the long chains are chemically identical, except the two *terminal* groups which differ from the others by possessing four hydroxils instead of three. Attempts to determine these terminal groups, however, have failed, a fact that is explained by the extreme length of the chain, so that the terminal groups comprise a vanishingly small portion of it, and thus escape analytical determination. Methylation of cellulose, and hydrolysis of the methylcellulose yields only trimethylglucose.

The linear macromolecules in the natural materials are joined in long macroscopic fibers; for example, the cotton fibers have a diameter of 0·01–0·04 mm. The electron microscope shows that these fibers are composed of much thinner microfibrillae with a diameter of only 0·02 μ or 200 Å. These filaments are composed of many linear macromolecules, since each macromolecule has a cross section of only 6–7 Å. The arrangement of the units must be parallel to the long axis, i.e. as in sheaves, including some twisting, as discerned by means of the electron micrograms (Fig. 56). Such arrangement, of course, leads to a high degree of order, i.e. crystallinity, as confirmed by the X-ray diffraction studies. According to Polanyi, Sponsler, Dore, Meyer, Misch, and others,[10] the unit cell is very small, and probably belonging to the monoclynic type. The identity period along the fiber axis is 10·3 Å that would be the approximate length of the cellobiose unit. One central chain in the unit cell is surrounded by four other chains at the corners of the imaginary structural unit. The density of 1·60 has been obtained from the X-ray data which is close to the actual density of 1·57. This agreement indicates that the chains are packed throughout the whole fiber as tightly as in the crystalline sections, since truly amorphous regions would result in a lower density. The successive links of the β-glucose residues are rotated through 180°, hence the chains have a diagonal screw axis as a symmetry element. The bond energies also have been estimated for the structural models. The glucosidic carbon–oxygen bonds along the chain amount to 50,000 cal/mole, while the secondary hydrogen bonds between the atoms of the adjacent chains possess a bond energy of 6000–12,000 cal/mole. The involvement of the hydrogen bonds in the internal stabilization of the bundles is ascertained also by infrared spectroscopy.[11] Slight structural differences in the spatial arrangement of the groups and hydrogen bonding have been found in native cellulose preparations from various sources. Mechanical strength and elasticity depend on the secondary structure; a high degree of crystallinity favors greater tensile strength, while a somewhat irregular interweaving of the chains produces a greater elasticity and flexibility.[12] The best estimates

(10) See for example K. H. Meyer, *Natural and Synthetic High Polymers* p. 298ff., Interscience, New York, 1950.

(11) J. W. Ellis and J. Bath, *J. Amer. chem. Soc.* **62**, 2859 (1940); J. Mann and H. J. Marrinan, *J. Polymer Sci* **32**, 357 (1958); D. W. Jones, *ibid.* **32**, 371 (1958).

(12) H. G. Ingersoll, *J. Applied Phys.* **17**, 924 (1946).

of the amount of the fully crystalline and partially oriented portions in the various fibers are obtained by the measurement of heavy water uptake.[13] These results indicate that only 21% of cotton fiber is amorphous (or incompletely crystalline).

The *molecular weight* of cellulose cannot be determined from the X-ray diffraction data, since the chains run through many unit cells. In order to determine the molecular weight, cellulose must be dissolved. Only a few solvents can be found that dissolve cellulose without considerable degradation, notably the cuprammonium hydroxide $[Cu(NH_3)_4](OH)_2$. The numerical values found for various cellulose preparations by various authors range between 10^4 and 10^7. The highest values have been found by Golova and Ivanov,[14] while Gralen and Svedberg found for various native cellulose values between $4{\cdot}6 \cdot 10^5$ and $1{\cdot}7 \cdot 10^6$.[15] Viscometry and osmometry gave 259,000 for bleached cotton linters, while raw linters gave a higher value of 437,000 that corresponds to a degree of polymerization P of 2700.[16] The problem was recently carefully reconsidered by Schulz and Marx[17] who showed that the solutions in cuprammonium hydroxide are extremely polydisperse, and that they probably contain some not fully dissolved fragments of the microfibrills. Instead of determining the molecular weight directly in cuprammonium hydroxide, they converted the cellulose specimens to the polymer-analogous nitrates, and determined their molecular weight by sedimentation–diffusion and viscometry.[17] The possibility of degradation was considered in each step of the procedure, and evidence was presented that no degradation occurred in the course of purification and conversion into nitrates. The molecular weight distribution in the various specimens also was determined, and it was found to be reproducible and characteristic for each cellulose type. The results are summarized in Table 11. It was also found that cotton and flax cellulose is more homogeneous with respect to molecular size than the smaller and less dense specimens of leaf and grass celluloses.

It is noteworthy that the cotton "Mainz I" was grown and harvested in a greenhouse in Mainz (Germany), and it was harvested from unopened capsules, while "Mainz II" was collected from opened capsules. The slight degradation is thought to be due to the exposure to light, but other causes are by no means excluded. The cellulose from "pine wood I" was extracted avoiding any possible degradation, whereas in the instance II it was isolated under more drastic conditions. It may be added that the degree of polymeri-

(13) V. J. Frilette, J. Hanle and H. Mark, *J. Amer. chem. Soc.* **70**, 1107 (1948); R. F. Nickerson, *Adv. Carbohydr. Chem.* **5**, 103 (1950).

(14) O. P. Golova and V. I. Ivanov, *Bull. Acad. Sci. U.S.S.R. Chem. series* 279 (1945).

(15) N. Gralen and T. Svedberg, *Nature* **152**, 625 (1943).

(16) H. Staudinger and R. Mohr, *Ber. dtsch. chem. Ges.* **70**, 2296 (1937).

(17) G. V. Schulz and M. Marx, *Makromol. Chem.* **14**, 52 (1954); M. Marx, *J. Polymer Sci.* **30**, 119 (1958), with a discussion by Schulz, Golova and others.

zation of the celluloses of paper pulp, as well as the regenerated celluloses as manufactured in industry are of lower molecular weight.

TABLE 11

AVERAGE DEGREES OF POLYMERIZATION $\overline{P}_w$ OF CELLULOSES AND THE INTRINSIC VISCOSITY OF THEIR NITRATES AFTER SCHULZ AND MARX [17]

Starting material	Cellulose content (%)	Viscosity dl/g (in acetone)	$\overline{P}_w$
Cotton, Mainz, I	83·6	44·5	7800
Cotton, Mainz, II	83·6	39·2	6600
Cotton, American	86·5	39·5	6700
Cotton, Egyptian	87·5	36·8	6200
Cotton linters	71.8	38·6	6500
Ramie fiber	59·8	38·6	6500
Flax fiber	54·8	45·5	8000
Coleoptiles of corn	4·0	11·0	1450
Roots of corn	9·4	18·4	2600
Bacterial cellulose (xylinum)	34·1	19.3	2700
Pine wood, I	77·9	23·0	3300
Pine wood, II	79·3	10·7	1400

The macromolecular nature of cellulose has been experimentally proven and established by the various polymer-analogous conversions of Staudinger and his associates,[18] and some of these reactions will be discussed in the following section.

Cellulose Derivatives

The oldest chemical treatment of cellulose involves bleaching and dyeing. Linen fabrics were bleached in sunlight. The early "chemist" also found out that a pretreatment of the linen or cotton fabric with alkaline and acid solutions facilitated bleaching and dyeing procedures. About one hundred years ago, John Mercer elaborated further on the alkali treatment of cotton, and introduced the procedure now known as mercerization. It appears that cellulose swells in concentrated solutions of alkalies, and becomes more receptive for dyes; moreover, the washed and dried fabric acquires a silky luster and certain beneficial mechanical properties.

Treatment of cellulose with alkali is now an important part in the manufacturing of viscose rayon and Cellophane. It appears that some of the hydroxyl groups of cellulose are more acidic than others, and that the hydrogen of these is exchanged for sodium thus forming some alcoxide groups R—O—Na. In the next step, carbon disulfide is added whereby the alcoxide groups are converted to xanthate groups, viz.:

$$R{-}O{-}Na + CS_2 = R{-}O{-}\overset{\overset{\displaystyle S}{\|}}{C}{-}S{-}Na.$$

[18] See for example, H. STAUDINGER, *Organische Kolloidchemie* 3rd. ed., Vieweg, Braunschweig, 1950, and the literature quoted therein.

This introduction of the xanthate groups converts cellulose into a polyelectrolyte, because the S–Na bond dissociates leaving the macromolecule negatively charged. In the ordinary xanthogenations every second or third glucose residue acquires one negative charge that leads to dissolution. Regeneration of the cellulose from these solutions is accomplished by a treatment with acid as follows:

$$R-O-\overset{\overset{\displaystyle S}{\|}}{C}-S-Na + H_2SO_4 = R-O-H + CS_2 + NaHSO_4.$$

In the rayon and Cellophane industry the regenerated cellulose is shaped by pressing the xanthate (the so-called viscose) through narrow clearances in an acid bath, and the regenerated cellulose is amorphous. The molecular weight of the regenerated cellulose is lower than that of cotton or other native fibers, if oxygen is not completely excluded. If, however, the oxidative degradation is avoided, the degree of polymerization does not change in these macromolecular conversions.[18] The excellent affinity of viscose rayon for various dyes is due to the amorphous texture of the material that contains interstices sufficiently large for the dye molecules. A partial orientation of the linear macromolecules of the meshwork occurs upon the stretching or compression of the material.

Cellulose ethers are found by treatment of alkali cellulose with alkyl halides, viz.:

$$R-ONa + CH_3X = R-O-CH_3 + NaX.$$

Methylation in aqueous solutions is always incomplete and associated with certain degradation. Since each of the glucose residues in cellulose chain contains three OH groups, trimethyl cellulose should be the final product. This, according to Freudenberg, is formed best by a treatment of cellulose with sodium and methyl iodide in liquid ammonia.[19] Various other alkyl and aryl residues can be introduced, and some of the ethers are of commercial importance. For example, hydroxyethyl cellulose containing the residues $R-O-CH_2CH_2-OH$ is prepared by the action of ethylene oxide on alkali cellulose. The less hydrophilic benzyl ether is produced by the interaction with benzyl chloride, viz.:

$$R-O-Na + ClCH_2C_6H_5 = R-O-CH_2C_6H_5 + NaCl.$$

Especially interesting are the recently developed derivatives containing acid or alkaline groups attached through ether bonds. The *carboxymethyl cellulose* is synthesized from alkali cellulose and chloroacetic acid:

$$R-O-Na + Cl-CH_2COOH = R-O-CH_2COOH + NaCl.$$

This acid cellulose derivative is soluble in water, it has high adsorptive capacity, and is widely used as an additive to washing powders for laundering.[20]

[19] K. Freudenberg and H. Boppel, *Ber. dtsch. chem. Ges.* **70**, 1542 (1937).

[20] J. V. Karabinos and M. Hindert, *Adv. Carbohydr. Chem.* **9**, 285 (1954); K. J. Nieuwenhuis, *J. Polymer Sci.* **12**, 237 (1954); H. Stüpel, *ibid.* **19**, 459 (1956).

For other purposes, the basic derivatives, such as the DEAE- and ECTEOLA-cellulose, are important.[21] The former is now widely used for the chromatographic separation and purification of proteins, while the latter finds application for the chromatography of the nucleic acids. The diethylaminoethyl (DEAE-) cellulose is prepared from cellulose, NaOH, and 2-chlorotriethylamine hydrochloride, as follows:

$$\underset{\text{cellulose}}{R{-}OH} + 2NaOH + Cl{-}CH_2CH_2{-}N(C_2H_5)_2 \cdot HCl = \underset{\text{DEAE-cellulose}}{R{-}O{-}CH_2CH_2{-}N(C_2H_5)_2} + 2NaCl + 2H_2O.$$

Many of the basic residues are introduced in each macromolecule, and probably only in those that are on the surface of the fibers, since the derivative is insoluble. Since the hydrated groups are ionized, the DEAE-cellulose acts as an anion exchanger ($-N(C_2H_5)_2 + H_2O = -N(C_2H_5)_2H^+ + OH^-$).

The possibilities of attachment of various atomic groups through ether bonds at different parts of the large polyfunctional molecule of cellulose, of course, are boundless. Thus far only a few practically important reactions have been explored. A series of new derivatives has been synthesized by Rogovin *et al.*,[22] and by Hess.[23]

Cellulose acetate (acetyl cellulose) and *nitrate* (nitrocellulose) are the most important members in the *ester* family. Cellulose acetate fibers and plastics are manufactured in large amounts, while the nitrates are now applied mostly in explosives. In the acetate rayon industry, the cellulose is pretreated with acetic acid and then acetylated by a mixture of concentrated acetic acid, acetic anhydride and sulfuric acid. Two to 2·6 acetyl groups are introduced this way in each glucose residue of the cellulose. The acetate is dissolved in acetone, and the rayon is spun by forcing the solution through fine orifices into warm air. Mixtures of the cellulose acetate and butyrate are used for molding various plastics. A complete acetylation of pure cellulose is accomplished by a mixture of acetic anhydride and pyridine, viz.:

$$[C_6H_7O_2(OH)_3]_n + m(CH_3CO)_2O \rightarrow [C_6H_7O_2(OCOCH_3)_3]_n,$$

$$\text{or } R{-}OH + (CH_3CO)_2O = R{-}O{-}\underset{\underset{O}{\|}}{C}{-}CH_3 + CH_3COOH \text{ for each hydroxyl group.}$$

Again, it has been shown by Staudinger *et al.* that cellulose can be acetylated without degradation, and that the original cellulose can be recovered upon saponification

$$[C_6H_7O_2(OCOCH_3)_3]_n + m\,NaOH \rightarrow [C_6H_7O_2(OH)_3]_n + m\,CH_3COONa,$$

without disrupting the anhydroglucose backbone. Due to the attachment of the acetyl groups, the macromolecule of the acetate, of course, is heavier

(21) E. A. PETERSON and H. A. SOBER, *J. Amer. chem. Soc.* **78**. 751 (1956).

(22) Z. A. ROGOVIN *et al.*, *Khim. Nauka i Prom.* (*Russ.*) **2**, 264 (1957); *J. Polymer Sci.* **30**, 537 (1958).

(23) K. HESS and H. GROTJAN, *Z. Elektrochem.* **56**, 58 (1952).

than the macromolecule of cellulose, yet the *degree of polymerization* (denoted by n in the above reaction schemes) remains the same. Some of these results, obtained on various specimens of fractionated acetates, are presented in Table 12.[24] The degree of polymerization was calculated from the intrinsic viscosity.

TABLE 12

AVERAGE DEGREE OF POLYMERIZATION $\overline{P}$ AND INTRINSIC VISCOSITY OF CELLULOSE ACETATE FRACTIONS AND THE CORRESPONDING RECOVERED CELLULOSE FRACTIONS AFTER STAUDINGER

Intrinsic viscosity of acetate in *m*-cresol (dl/g)	$\overline{P}$	Intrinsic viscosity of recovered cellulose in cuprammonium hydrox. (dl/g)	$\overline{P}$	Viscosity ratio
2·14	340	1·76	350	1·22
3·18	505	2·50	500	1·27
5·04	800	3·91	780	1·29
5·43	870	4·24	850	1·28
6·04	960	4·79	955	1·26
7·44	1180	5·83	1165	1·27
10·45	1660	8·40	1680	1·24

The intrinsic viscosity of the acetates in cresol differ from the viscosity of the corresponding regenerated cellulose fractions in cuprammonium hydroxide because of differences in the chain configuration and solvation. The viscosity ratio is remarkably constant, and the degree of polymerization has not decreased upon the saponification of the polymeric esters.

Cellulose nitrate or *nitrocellulose* is another important ester which is manufactured commercially by treating cellulose with a mixture of nitric and sulfuric acids. Two up to nearly all three hydroxyle in each of the anhydroglucose residues are nitrated, each according to

$$R{-}O{-}H + HNO_3 = R{-}O{-}NO_2 + H_2O.$$

Strangely enough, this treatment with such strong acids does not result in an excessive degradation which is explained by the fact that nitration occurs rapidly and the nitrate groups stabilize the macromolecule toward the acid.[25] It has been found that the degradation can be fully avoided by using a mixture of nitric and phosphoric acids. The various nitrocellulose specimens are characterized by their nitrogen content, solubility, and viscosity, as well as by stability on heating. Nitrocellulose is soluble in acetone and other ketones, as well as in esters, but it is insoluble in water or in hydrocarbons. The solutions, like those of other cellulose derivatives, are extremely viscous, and the average degree of polymerization (and molecular weight) can be deter-

[24] H. STAUDINGER, *Angew. Chem.* **64**, 149 (1952), also ref. 18, p. 132. See also H. STAUDINGER and T. EICHER, *Makromol. Chem.* **10**, 235 (1953).

[25] F. D. MILES, *Cellulose Nitrate* Interscience, New York, 1955.

mined from the intrinsic viscosity.[26] It was also shown by Staudinger and Mohr that the degree of polymerization practically does not change when the nitration is accomplished by a mixture of nitric and phosphoric acids under strictly controlled conditions.[26] A considerable amount of work has been done on correlating the viscosity and molecular weight data, as well as on the actual configuration of the macromolecules in solution.[27] These studies have resulted in the conclusion that the macromolecules of nitrocellulose in solution are less flexible and more extended than those of rubber and similar high polymers. In acetons solution, the macromolecules seem to be gently looped, not tightly coiled. More recently, comparative osmotic pressure, sedimentation-diffusion, and viscosity measurements on nitrocellulose have been done by Newman *et al.*,[28] and it was found that the original Staudinger equation correlating the viscosity with degree of polymerization is valid. It also was found that the viscosity was strongly shear-dependent, and this property was found to be the more pronounced the larger (longer) the macromolecules. Moreover, these authors confirmed the contention that nitrocellulose chains in good solvents are more extended than many other polymers are. Comparative viscosity, light scattering, and osmotic pressure studies on well fractionated nitrocellulose specimens have fully confirmed the validity of Staudinger's rule, as well as the general views on configuration.[29] In Table 13

TABLE 13
MOLECULAR WEIGHT, CHAIN END DISTANCE, AND INTRINSIC VISCOSITY OF NITROCELLULOSE FRACTIONS IN ACETONE
(after Holtzer, Benoit and Doty [29])

Sample	$\overline{M}_w$	Mean end-to-end distance (Å)	$\|\eta\|$, (dl/g)
Ca	89,000	540	1·45
C[b]	273,000	2250	3·54
Ba	400,000	1500	6·50
M 1[a]	640,000	2280	10·6
A 8	846,000	2165	14·9
Ab[b]	1,270,000	3180	24·5
A	1,550,000	3080	30·3
A 2[b]	2,510,000	4070	31·0
Aa[b]	2,640,000	5450	36·3

are compiled some of the data of this work. The molecular weight $\overline{M}_w$ and the mean square end-to-end chain distance were computed from light scattering data. The intrinsic viscosity was corrected for the shear gradient. Osmotic pressure measurements showed that the number average molecular weight $\overline{M}_n$ was approximately two times smaller than the weight average

(26) H. STAUDINGER and R. MOHR, *Ber. dtsch. chem. Ges.* **70**, 2296 (1937).
(27) H. MOSIMANN, *Helv. Chim. Acta* **26**, 61, 369 (1943).
(28) S. NEWMAN, L. LOEB and C. M. CONRAD, *J. Polymer Sci.* **10**, 463 (1953).
(29) A. M. HOLTZER, H. BENOIT and P. DOTY, *J. physic. Chem.* **58**, 624 (1954); see also E. IMMERGUT and H. MARK, *Ind. Eng. Chem.* **45**, 2483 (1953).

obtained from light scattering. This is due to the polymolecularity of the specimens that explains some of the earlier discrepancies, when the calibration was accomplished on the basis of osmotic data. It was found that the relation

$$|\eta| = 5{\cdot}0 \cdot 10^{-3}\, P_w$$

is valid for a wide range of P (the intrinsic viscosity is expressed in dl/g), and that the constant a in the modified Staudinger's equation $|\eta| = K\,M^a$ is 1·0, while for more flexible linear macromolecules a has a numerical value between 0·5 and 0·8, depending on solvent and the solute (see chapt. 4).

The intrinsic viscosity of cellulose nitrates and acetates in relation to configuration has been studied recently also by Flory *et al.* [30] It was found that the intrinsic viscosity of the solutions of these macromolecules depends markedly not only on the solvent but also on temperature. The observed decrease of the intrinsic viscosity with the increase in temperature was explained as being due to increased flexibility. The solvent interaction and thermodynamic parameters, such as entropy changes, also have been studied to a considerable extent.[31] Entropies of dilution of cellulose nitrate and acetate were found to be less than those obtained for comparable systems containing less polar and more flexible polymers. Thus the small entropy values are explained by the stiffness of the polysaccharide chain, and by the solvation effects that are absent in the case of such nonpolar systems as rubber in a hydrocarbon solvent. Although the nitrocellulose chains in a solution are more disordered than in a solid state, this disorder (entropy) is partially compensated by the ordering effect of solvation (orderly aligment of the formerly disordered solvent molecules at the linear chains). It is possible that this solvate layer also contributes to the stiffness of these chains.

Enzymic Degradation of Cellulose [32]

Many species of bacteria and fungi are able to decompose and metabolize cellulose in a variety of enzymic reactions. Certain animals, for example the snails, also produce cellulose-splitting enzymes, and are able to use this polysaccharide as food. Decay of plant remnants in the soil, and wood rotting are important examples of these processes that are thus far very little investigated. There are, for instance, two types of wood decay: the so-called brown and white rots. Both are caused by fungi, the former by a species which prefers cellulose and does not care for lignin, the latter by an organism which consumes lignin and leaves a modified white cellulose.[33] The reactions seem to be very

[30] P. J. Flory, O. K. Spurr, Jr. and D. K. Carpenter, *J. Polymer Sci.* **27**, 231 (1958).

[31] W. R. Moore, J. A. Epstein, A. M. Brown and B. M. Tidswell, *J. Polymer Sci.* **23**, 23 (1957); W. R. Moore and B. M. Tidswell, *ibid.* **29**, 37 (1958).

[32] R. G. H. Siu, *Microbial Decomposition of Cellulose* Reinhold, New York, 1951.

[33] F. F. Nord and J. C. Vitucci, *Adv. Enzymol.* 8, 253 (1948).

complex, and none of the enzymes have been isolated in pure state. It is obvious that it would be of great practical importance to understand the mechanism of these processes in order to control such decompositions. On the other hand, the fungi or their enzymes, if properly handled, might serve as a means to remove the undesired lignin from the cellulose-containing plant materials.

The Hemicelluloses [2,9]

Contrary to cellulose, which is a chemically well defined substance, the hemicellulose include a variety of polysaccharides. The prefix "hemi" in Greek means half, indicating smaller molecular size. The term hemicellulose actually covers an ill-defined class of polysaccharides that together with lignin accompany cellulose in plant tissues. The macromolecules of these hemicelluloses are much smaller than those of native cellulose, and the substances are soluble in alkali. One factor that facilitates the solubility is the presence of an acid component which forms a soluble salt with the alkali; another factor favoring the solubility is the relatively low molecular weight, usually between 10,000 and 40,000. A 4–16% sodium hydroxide solution is used for the extraction of the hemicelluloses from the plant material and the extract is fractionated by the addition of alcohol and partial neutralization of the alkali. The major components in the hemicellulose extracts are: the *xylans* and other pentosans, *uronic acids* (e.g. the polyglucuronic acid), the *mannans*, the *arabo-galactans*, and lignin. The latter, together with certain other organic substances is considered as an impurity, and is not included under the heading of "hemicellulose". None of the hemicelluloses are well characterized, and they are only partially investigated. The reasons for this are several: (1) it is very difficult to isolate a pure xylan or araban, (2) their composition depends on the source, and (3) some of the products can be considered as oxidative degradation products of cellulose. The latter remark applies to some of the acid components of the hemicellulose. It is known that a partial oxidation of cellulose may occur under the influence of oxygen of air, especially by irradiation with ultraviolet light, as well as upon bleaching with oxidizing agents, and that carboxyl groups may be formed on this oxidation. Genuine polyglucuronic acid also has been found in certain hemicelluloses, for example in straw. The chemical structure of polyglucuronic acid is very similar to that of cellulose, except that the carbon-6 is oxidized to carboxyl group in each anhydroglucose residue, viz.:

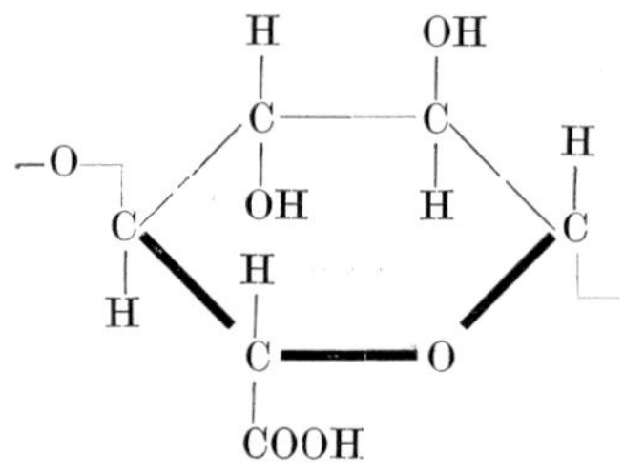

The xylans are more abundant than the polyglucuronic acids. The greatest portion of the xylane chain seems to be composed of D-xylopyranose units which are joined by 1,4-β linkages, as follows:

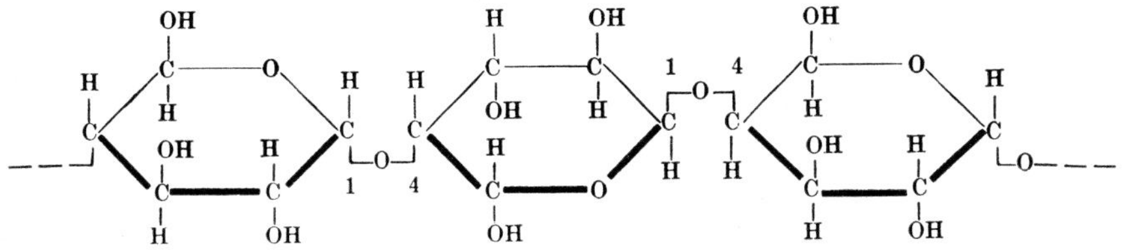

Corn cobs and oat hulls are the richest sources of xylan (28–34%), although beech wood also abounds with the pentosans. A small amount of glucuronic acid and some arabinose in addition to xylose have been found in the hydrolysis products of xylane. Xylan is levorotatory, and the specific rotation of various specimens in sodium hydroxide solutions has been found to be between $-78°$ and $-109°$ (sodium light). The specific rotation of the xylooligosaccharides was found to be $-72{\cdot}8°$ for xylohexaose, $-66°$ for the pentaose, $-60°$ for the tetraose, $-47°$ for the triose, and $-26°$ for the xylobiose.[34] Thus the specific rotation changes with the degree of polymerization in a similar manner as in the instance of cellulose,[1] an indication of the uniformity of the chain. It seems then possible that the other monosaccharides which are found with xylose upon the total hydrolysis of xylan do not originate from heterogeneous xylan chains but from the other hemicelluloses which have not properly separated in the course of isolation. The same can be said about the other hemicellulose components, such as the arabo-galactans and mannans. Pure mannan is a stereoisomer of cellulose, i.e. anhydromannopyranose groups are linked in chains instead of anhydroglucose. Moreover, the mannans are not fibrous but they are white powders, an indication of only a moderate degree of polymerization. According to Husemann[35] the degree of polymerization of a mannan from spruce wood is only 160.

In the manufacture of paper and cellulose, a part of the hemicelluloses, together with lignin, is dissolved and thus separated from cellulose; another portion of them, however, remains with the cellulose. The opinion prevails that a certain amount of hemicellulose is beneficial for the quality of paper pulp, namely that cellulose fibers felt more easily in the presence of hemicellulose. For the production of fibers and plastics, the hemicelluloses are not of much value, since the macromolecular chains are relatively short. In certain applications of purified cellulose and its derivatives, such as in case of the DEAE–cellulose ion exchangers, the presence of soluble cellulose (hemicellulose) is highly undesirable. According to our experience, a soluble

[34] R. L. Whistler and C. C. Tu, *J. Amer. chem. Soc.* **73**, 1389 (1951); also ref. 2, p. 143.

[35] E. Husemann, *J. prakt. Chem.* **155**, 15 (1940).

polysaccharide is leached out in the elution procedure even from relatively well washed DEAE-cellulose preparations. This soluble component does not pass Cellophane upon dialysis, and contaminates the protein or other substance to be fractionated. A very thorough treatment of the cellulose derivative with alkali and acid is required in order to remove the last trace of the soluble polysaccharides.

Lignin [36]

Lignin is not a polysaccharide but an aromatic polymer that accompanies polysaccharides in plant tissues. Chemical linkages between the lignin and polysaccharide have been suggested but not definitely verified. The quantity and quality of lignin differs in different species and tissues. Dry pine wood, for example, contains 28% lignin a part of which can be extracted from pulverized wood by hot alcohol or similar solvents. A more complete extraction requires more drastic treatment, for example with a mixture of sodium hydroxide and sodium sulfide at high temperatures. Lignin is yellow or brownish amorphous material of a high carbon content (62–65%), and its absorption spectrum in ultraviolet indicates the presence of aromatic groups. This is substantiated by chemical degradation that, depending on the method, yields such substances as eugenol, catechol, phenol, n-propylguaiacol, vanillin, etc. The chemical structure of lignin (or lignins) is not fully disclosed, although Freudenberg has presented evidence that lignin is a condensation product of coniferyl alcohol [37] and similar aromatic monomers. By introducing radioactive coniferin into spruce, the radioactivity was found to accumulate in lignin. Nord, however, has shown that there are several other precursors. [38] According to Russell,[39] lignin has a polyflavanone structure. The biosynthesis of lignin is uncertain, but there is definitely reason to believe that it originates in the cytoplasm from eugenol-like mers which are polymerized in the cell walls. Lignin in the plant tissue serves as a kind of ground substance or cementing material, and, like rubber, it is not further metabolized. Only some bacteria and fungi are able to attack lignin.

Very low molecular weights of 800–4000 have been reported for soluble lignin,[40] hence this polymer possibly is not a real high-polymer. However,

[36] F. E. Brauns, *The Chemistry of Lignin* Academic Press, New York, 1952; E. Hägglund, *Chemistry of Wood* 3rd. ed., Academic, Press, 1951; L. E. Wise and E. C. Jahn, *Wood Chemistry* 2nd ed., Vol. I and II, Reinhold, New York, 1952.

[37] K. Freudenberg, *Angew. Chem.* **68**, 84 (1956); K. Freudenberg in L. Zechmeister's *Fortschr. d. Chem. org. Naturstoffe* **11**, 43 (1954); K. Freudenberg, *J. Polymer Sci.* **16**, 155 (1955).

[38] F. F. Nord and G. de Stevens, *Naturwiss.* **39**, 479 (1952); W. J. Schubert and F. F. Nord, *Adv. Enzymol.* **18**, 349 (1957).

[39] A. Russell, *Science* **106**, 372 (1947).

[40] D. L. Loughborough and A. J. Stamm, *J. physic. Chem.* **40**, 1113 (1936).

it is quite possible that the molecules of the insoluble or not easily soluble lignins are larger than those of the soluble components. According to Nord, the mildest method for the isolation of lignin is the degradation of the cellulose and other polysaccharide components by fungi ("brown rot"). Thus isolated lignin appeared to be reasonably homogeneous in electrophoresis, and very similar to the soluble lignin extracted from the same material (Scots pine wood meal) with alcohol.[(38)] Further work along these lines may lead to a definite solution of the lignin problem.

CHAPTER 8

STARCH AND GLYCOGEN

Starch, its constituents amylose and amylopectin, as well as glycogen are the first natural high polymers for which the mode of biological synthesis is known. However, the formation of the particular submicroscopic structure of native starch granule is not yet explained.

P. BERNFELD [(1)]

Occurrence and Isolation of Starch and Glycogen

Starch and glycogen are important representatives of a quite large and diversified group of *branched chain polysaccharides*. Many other polysaccharides besides starch and glycogen possess branched macromolecules, and some of them will be mentioned in chapt. 9–11.

First of all, it must be pointed out that the terms "starch" and "glycogen" each cover a diversified class of polysaccharides, and that structurally one of the starch components is almost identical with the glycogens. While all glycogens are strongly branched macromolecules, starch is composed of two components — the branched *amylopectin* and the unbranched *amylose*. Strangely enough, amylopectin is more similar to glycogen than to amylose. It is impossible to draw a sharp borderline between amylopectin and glycogen, whereas the difference between amylose and amylopectin is quite explicit.

Both starch and glycogen are *reserve* substances, starch in plants, and glycogen in animals. However, lower animals and plants contain polysaccharides which can be classified either as amylopectins or glycogens. As an important reserve substance, starch is stored by the plants chiefly in the seeds, tubers, roots, and stem pith. Seeds contain usually 40–70% starch, while the other organs contain about 4–25%. In the commercially important starch industry, various starting materials are used, such as corn, wheat, rice, potato, tapioca, arrowroot, and sago palm pith. Since starch occurs in plant tissues in the form of discrete particles or granules (diameter 2–100 μ), the isolation procedure is based on extraction of the ground material with water. [(2)] After removal of the coarse tissue fragments by filtration, the starch remains as a dispersion which precipitates slowly. Sulfurous acid usually is added to the extract in order to facilitate swelling of the grains, prevent microbial growth and undesired enzymic reactions, and obtain a whiter product. The granules of various

(1) P. BERNFELD, *Adv. Enzymol.* **12**, 379 (1951), p. 424.

(2) R. L. WHISTLER and CH. L. SMART, *Polysaccharide Chemistry*, Academic Press New York, 1953; J. A. RADLEY, *Starch and its Derivatives*, Vol. I and II, 3rd ed., Wiley, New York, 1954.

plant species vary in size and structure, as well as in optical properties. The granules are optically anisotropic, partially crystalline, and the *X*-ray spectrum of the cereal starches differs from that of the tuber and root starches. At a higher temperature of 55–80 °C the granules become so strongly swollen that they disintegrate, thus forming a colloidal solution of starch. A complete dissolution, however, is practically impossible, since the macromolecules of the amylose component are aligned in sheaves or paracrystalline fibrils. As in cellulose, the linear macromolecules in the sheaves are linked to each other by secondary bonds. The details of the submicroscopic morphology of the starch grain are not fully elucidated, and one might wonder why nature has placed together these two macromolecular types — amylose and amylopectin — that are geometrically so different. The submicroscopic units in the concentric layers of the grain are arranged in a radial fashion, but the exact location and distribution of the amylose and amylopectin components is not known. The quantitative ratio of the components is always in the favor of amylopectin (see Table 14).

TABLE 14

GRAIN SIZE, GELATION TEMPERATURE, AND AMYLOSE CONTENT OF STARCHES

Source	Grain size (μ)	Gelation temp. (°C)	Amylose content (%)
Corn	4–26	64–71	26
Wheat	2–38	53–64	25
White potato	15–100	62–68	22
Sweet potato	15–55	82–83	20
Tapioca	5–36	69–70	17
Arrowroot	7–75	75–78	21

The highest amylose content has been found in lily bulb — 34% of the total amount of starch, while the so-called waxy corn starch may be devoid of amylose. These waxy or glutionous starches from waxy varieties of corn, barley and other plants are recessive mutants, and the production of amylose appears to be controlled by a single gene probably associated with one enzyme.[2,3]

Separation of amylose and amylopectin can be accomplished by various methods, for example by precipitating the amylose with butanol [4]. Finely ground starch is first extracted with methanol in order to remove lipids. The material then is suspended in water and dissolved by heating under pressure. After the removal of the coarse granular fragments, the amylose is precipitated by saturation with n-butanol while the solution is hot. The mixture is stirred, and then allowed to cool slowly thus causing a gradual

[3] J. BONNER, *Plant Biochemistry* chapt. 5, Academic Press, New York, 1950.
[4] T. J. SCHOCH, *Adv. Carbohydr. Chem.* **1**, 247 (1945).

precipitation of amylose. The amylopectin remains in the solution. Starch can be dissolved and fractionated also in liquid ammonia and formamide, and starch can be made water-soluble by a pretreatment with liquid ammonia.[5] No degradation of the macromolecules occurs on these treatments.

The aqueous solutions of starch which are obtained by boiling exhibit a kind of denaturation known as "*retrogradation*". The solutions gradually become more and more turbid, and they partially precipitate. Light scattering, viscosity, and other studies have shown that this retrogradation is a slow aggregation. The long linear macromolecules of the amylose thereby aggregate more readily and form more difficultly soluble crystallites than does amylopectin.[6] These processes are in practice very important in the starch pastes that are used as adhesives. Most adhesive are the molecularly dissolved starches, while the partially aggregated dispersions are inferior in this respect.

The simplest and most sensitive analytical test for amylose, amylopectin and glycogen is the reaction with iodine. Amylose gives an intense blue color, while the amylopectin–iodine complex is light blue–violet and that of glycogen is brown–red. Similar red–brown and yellow colors with iodine are obtained also with partial degradation products of starch, the so called *dextrins*. The structure of the starch–iodine complexes has been thoroughly investigated.[7]

Glycogen is found in animal tissues, the liver being one of the richest sources containing about 2–8% glycogen. The muscle of mammals, invertebrates, and the organs of lower animals, and even microbes also contain glycogen. In all instances it is a reserve carbohydrate which is metabolized for the purpose of releasing energy. Glycogen can be isolated from tissues by various methods. The old methods of extraction with hot alkali are more or less replaced with milder methods, such as extraction with water or with diluted, cold solution of trichloroacetic acid. It has been shown that the extraction with cold diluted trichloroacetic acid yields preparations with the highest molecular weights and greater homogeneity than application of the more drastic older methods.[8] Since proteins are precipitated with trichloroacetic acid, only glycogen and certain micromolecular compounds remain in the solution which is further purified in various ways. From this solution glycogen can be fractionally precipitated by alcohol, and purified by redissolving and reprecipitation.

There seem to be certain types of glycogens. The glycogens of lower animals seem to be more similar to amylopectin than the glycogens of higher

[5] J. E. Hodge, S. A. Karjala, and G. E. Hilbert, *J. Amer. chem. Soc.* **73**, 3312 (1951).

[6] J. F. Foster and M. D. Sterman, *J. Polymer Sci.* **21**, 91 (1956).

[7] R. E. Rundle and R. R. Baldwin, *J. Amer. chem. Soc.* **65**, 554 (1943); R. E. Rundle and D. French, *ibid.* **65**, 558 (1943).

[8] M. R. Stetten, H. M. Katzen, and DeWitt Stetten, Jr., *J. biol. Chem.* **232**, 475 (1958).

animals.[9] Moreover, a certain fraction of the glycogen present in a tissue cannot be extracted. This "residual glycogen" is metabolically more active than the extractable glycogen, and probably it is bound to proteins.[8]

Molecular Weight and Structure of Amylose, Amylopectin, and Glycogen [10]

The chemical composition of amylose, amylopectin, and glycogen can be expressed by the simple formula $(C_6H_{10}O_5)_n$, where n represents the degree of polymerization. A complete acid hydrolysis of all three polysaccharides yields D-glucose, whereas enzymic hydrolysis produces mostly maltose. Hence the chains in all three polysaccharides are built of α-D-anhydroglucose residues. Further structural details were disclosed by studying the degradation products of the methylated, acetylated, and otherwise chemically modified polysaccharides. Hydrolysis of completely methylated amylopectin yields about 4% tetramethyl glucose together with a large amount of trimethyl glucose. This indicates that either the chains are short or they are branched, since the tetramethyl glucose can arise only from the terminal glucose residues. Even more tetramethyl glucose is produced from the hydrolysis products of methylated glycogen, while a completely methylated amylose yields only a trace of the end-group glucose. This indicates that the macromolecules of glycogen are even more branched than those of amylopectin, whereas the chains of amylose are not branched at all.[11] A large volume of other chemical evidence supports the conclusion that in amylose the chains are composed of α-D-anhydroglycopyranose mers that are linked by 1,4 linkages, viz.:

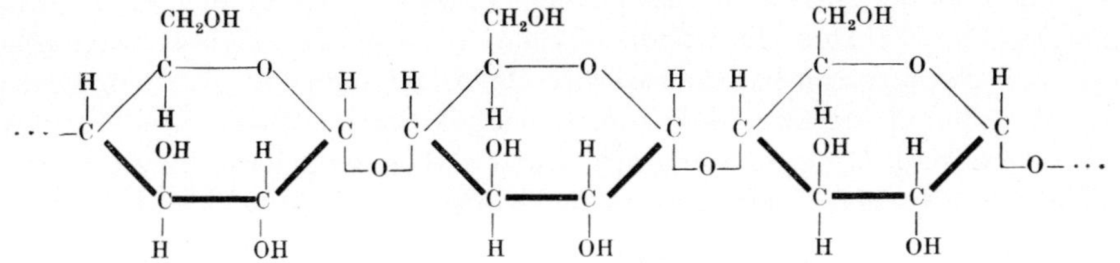

This is supported also by the more modern method of oxidation with periodate.[12] Formic acid is produced in this treatment from the nonreducing (one mole) and from the reducing end groups (two moles), while no formic acid is liberated from the intrachain anhydroglucose residues. These results confirm the earlier contention that the molecules of amylose are long un-

[9] E. CHARGAFF and D. H. MOORE, *J. biol. Chem.* **155**, 493 (1944); E. M. AFANASEVA and B. N. STEPANENKO, *Biokhimiya* **21**, 603 (1956).

[10] W. PIGMAN (ed.), *The Carbohydrates: Chemistry, Biochemistry, Physiology* Academic Press, New York, 1957; see also ref. 2.

[11] K. H. MEYER and P. BERNFELD, *Helv. chim. Acta* **23**, 875 (1940); K. H. MEYER, M. WERTHEIM and P. BERNFELD, *ibid.* **23**, 865 (1940), also ref. 2 and 10.

[12] T. G. HALSALL, E. L. HIRST and J. K. N. JONES, *J. chem. Soc.* 1427 (1947); A. L. POTTER and W. Z. HASSID, *J. Amer. chem. Soc.* **70**, 3488 (1948).

branched chains, whereas those of amylopectin are ramified. This ramification occurs through the 1,6-linkages, as follows:

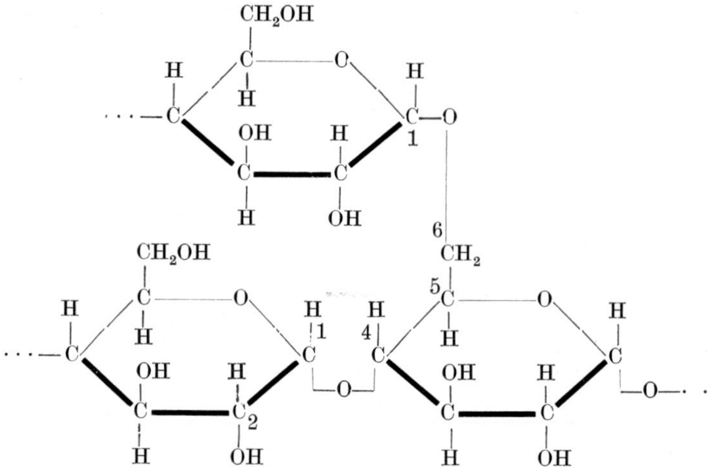

In amylopectin the average unbranched chain length ($\overline{\text{C.L.}}$) is 18–27 anhydroglucose units, while in glycogens it is only 8–16 units. Both amylopectin and glycogen preparations can be heterogeneous not only with respect to the molecular weight but also with respect to the degree of branching. Moreover, there is evidence that the core of the bush-like glycogen macromolecule is more branched than the exterior. It is estimated that in the interior there is one branch point for each 3–4 glucose residues, whereas the unbranched segments at the surface of the macromolecule may be as long as those in amylopectin [13]. Thus the macromolecular forms of the amylose, amylopectin, and glycogen can be schematically illustrated as in Fig. 57, whereby the ramification, of course, is three-dimensional. A few small molecules probably are held adsorbed or even chemically bound in these large bush-like structures. Since the macromolecules move to the positive pole in electrophoresis, they must contain negatively charged groups, such as adsorbed fatty acids or chemically bound phosphate (e.g. one function of the orthophosphoric acid esterified with one of the hydroxils and the others free). Traces of the sulfurous acid used in the isolation procedure also may be adsorbed in the macromolecules of starch. Water bound to the polar groups of the macromolecules by hydrogen bonds also can be regarded as a secondary constituent.

These structural considerations are fully supported by physicochemical data, such as *X*-ray diffraction, infrared spectra, optical rotation, streaming birefringence, viscosity, and sedimentation. For example, undegraded amylose exhibits streaming birefringence, amylopectin shows a weak effect of orientation, while the glycogens behave as if the macromolecules were spherical. The same is reflected in the viscosity of the solutions: for specimens of the

[13] D. J. MANNERS, *Adv. Carbohydr. Chem.* **12**, 261 (1957).

same average molecular weight, the viscosity drops in the order — amylose, amylopectin, glycogen.

With respect to *chain configuration*, it is important to remember that the amylose chain, even if completely extended, is not as linear as the macro-

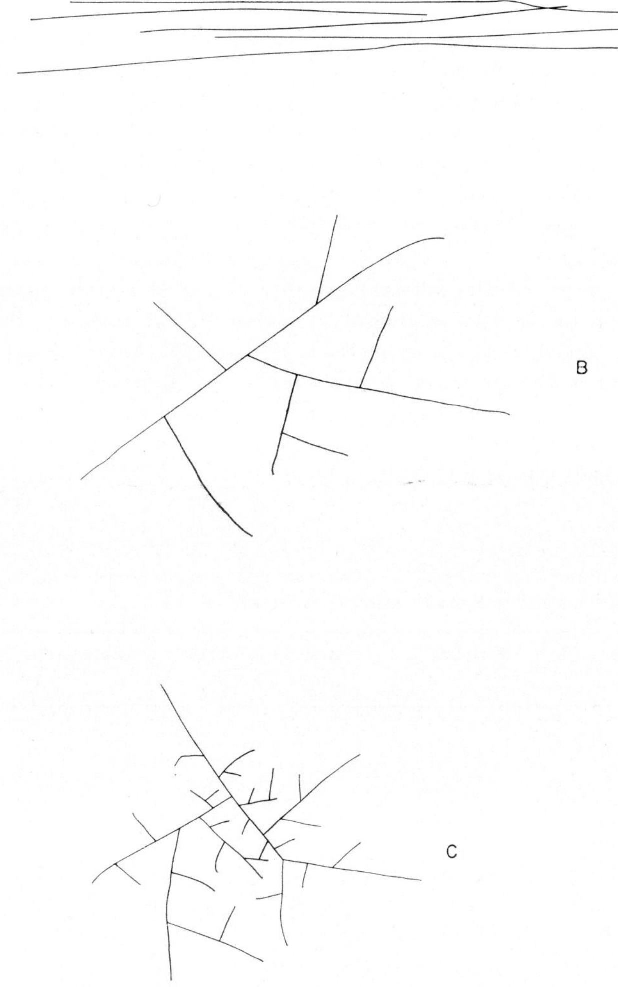

FIG. 57. Schematic illustration of molecular forms of amylose (*A*), amylopectin (*B*), and glycogen (*C*)

molecule of cellulose. This is due to the α-1,4-glucosidic linkages that impose steric limitations on the chain so that it becomes somewhat puckered. (A similar instance of affecting the chain configuration is that of natural rubber and gutta.) Because of this strain the chains tend to draw themselves in helical configurations, i.e. the actual shape of the macromolecule may resemble an extension spring, that has a rather high configurational stability. The inside of this "macromolecular spring" should be empty, and ready to accommodate various micromolecular substances, such as water, alcohol, or the heavy iodine atoms. [7] Similar configuration must have the linear branches of the ramified macromolecules of the amylopectin and glycogen.

The macromolecular nature of glycogen and starch was first envisaged by Staudinger and Husemann [14] about 1935–37, and the correct bush-like structure was first proposed by K. H. Meyer and Bernfeld. [11] The polymer-analogous conversions of starch and glycogen, accomplished by Staudinger and Husemann, rendered the most convincing proof that the units in solution are not some kind of micellar aggregates but large molecules (see p. 93, chapt. 5). All the preparations of these polysaccharides are polymolecular, and it is interesting to note that the average molecular weights were found to be higher in recent studies where carefully isolated undegraded specimens were used. While the molecular weight of starch and glycogen in the early determinations ranged somewhere between 10^5 and 10^6, much higher values between 10^6 and $5 \cdot 10^7$, and even higher, are found in recent studies. In a thorough investigation on the light scattering of potato amylopectin, the weight average molecular weights were found between 7 and 73 million, depending on the fraction, (Table 15). [15]

TABLE 15

MOLECULAR WEIGHT AND RADIUS OF GYRATION FOR AMYLOPECTIN FRACTIONS
(after Witnauer, Senti, and Stern, l.c. 15)

Fraction	Weight (%)	Molecular weight (millions)	Radius of gyration (Å)
1	5	73	2550
2	10	73	2550
3	16	47	1950
4	8	31	1660
5	13	23	1370
6	16	19	1250
7	8	14	1090
8	8	11	960
9	11	7	820

Polymer-analogous conversions into acetates, and deacetylation showed that even these very large macromolecules can be chemically modified without a substantial degradation. For example, the fraction with the average molecular weight 14 million was acetylated, and the molecular weight for the ace-

(14) H. STAUDINGER and E. HUSEMANN, *Ann.* **527**, 195 (1937); **530**, 1 (1937).

(15) L. P. WITNAUER, F. R. SENTI and M. D. STERN, *J. Polymer Sci.* **16**, 1 (1955); see also: S. R. ERLANDER and D. FRENCH, *ibid.* **32**, 291 (1958); C. T. GREENWOOD, *Adv. Carbohydr. Chem.* **11**, 335 (1956).

tate was determined; the amylopectin acetate then was deacetylated, and the molecular weight of the recovered amylopectin again was determined by means of light scattering. The average molecular weight for the recovered amylopectin was found to be 9·4 million; hence only an insignificant degradation of these giant molecules has occurred in these rather drastic conversions.[15]

It was believed for quite a time that the molecular weight of amylose is much smaller that that of amylopectin. Husemann, however, showed recently that the molecular weight of amylose is about 1,000,000. Actually, it could be shown that no reliable values of the molecular weight of unmodified amylose can be obtained, hence the amylose was acetylated under very mild conditions (at —15 °C), and the molecular weight of the corresponding polymer-analogous acetates was determined by the light scattering method.[16] The molecular weight of the amylose acetate was determined in acetone solutions, and it was found, 2,000,000 by light scattering, and 1,230,000 by osmotic pressure measurement. The difference between the weight and number average molecular weights indicates that the amylose was polymolecular.

Recent molecular weight determinations on glycogens which were isolated without any noticeable degradation also have given very high values.[15] In Table 16 are compiled data on various glycogens, including such important characteristics as optical rotation and average unbranched chain length ($\overline{C}.\overline{L}.$). The molecular weights are in millions, and the method of measurement is indicated in parentheses: (l) meaning light scattering, (s) sedimentation-diffusion, and (o) osmotic pressure. Even larger values than these have been found by Stetten *et al.*.[8] Hence it can be concluded that the macromolecules of glycogen are generally of the same size as those of amylopectin, namely about 10–50 million, or even higher, when in native state.

TABLE 16

MOLECULAR WEIGHT, BRANCHING, AND OPTICAL ACTIVITY OF GLYCOGENS FROM VARIOUS SOURCES[13]

Source	Molecular weight (in millions)	$\overline{C}.\overline{L}.$	$[\alpha]_{589}$
Cat liver	10·0 (l)	13	+ 193°
Fetal-sheep liver	14·8 (l)	13	+ 196
Dogfish	3·6	12	+ 195
Tetrachymena	9·8 (l)	13	+ 195
Anodonta	6·1 (o)		+ 192
Mytilus edulis	3·8 (s)	12	+ 196
Aerobacter aerogenes	9·2 (s)		+ 200
Yeast	2·4 (s)	13	+ 198

[16] E. HUSEMANN and H. BARTL, *Makromol. Chem.* **18/19** (Staudinger-Festband), 342 (1956).

Enzymic Breakdown and Synthesis of Amylose, Amylopectin, and Glycogen [1,2,10]

Barley malt is one of the most important sources of the starch-digesting enzymes, the so called *amylases*. It was soon found out that the enzymically active extract from malt, the so called diastase, contains several enzymes

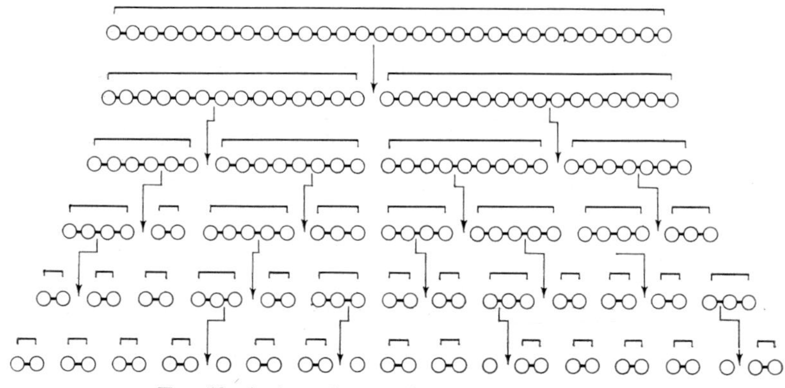

FIG. 58. Action of α-amylase on starch amylose

which are able to hydrolyze the starches into fermentable sugars, a practically very important procedure (brewing industries, etc.). Various animal tissues also contain the same enzymes that are responsible for the digestion of food containing the polysaccharides. Two types of amylases are known: the α- and β-amylases, and they both are present in diastase. The α-amylases produce the α-form of sugars whose optical rotation changes in the negative direction with time (downward mutorotation), while the β-amylases hydrolyze the starches to the β-form sugar exhibiting the optical rotation change in positive direction (upward mutorotation). The α-amylase digests amylose and amylopectin rapidly by facilitating the hydrolysis of the 1,4-glucosidic linkages; the macromolecules are first chopped to medium size dextrins which are then split further to maltose and smaller dextrins (Fig. 58 and 59). In the enzymic digestion of starch with α-amylase the viscosity as well as the coloring with iodine decreases rapidly in the course of degradation. The final digestion products in the instance of amylose are maltose and some glucose, while amylopectin produces maltose and micromolecular dextrins. This is due to the fact that the enzyme cannot attack the 1,6-links at the points of ramification. The β-amylase digests the macromolecules more gradually releasing one by one the maltose units from the branches (Fig. 60 and 61). The viscosity and turbidity decrease in this case slowly. While the iodine color disappears fully in the α-amylase treatment, it remains purple when amylopectin is digested with the β-amylase. This is due to the fact that this enzyme is able to clip off only the tips of the branches of the bush-like macromolecule. It appears that the β-amylase is able to digest only about one-half of each macromolecule of amylopectin, and thus this method can

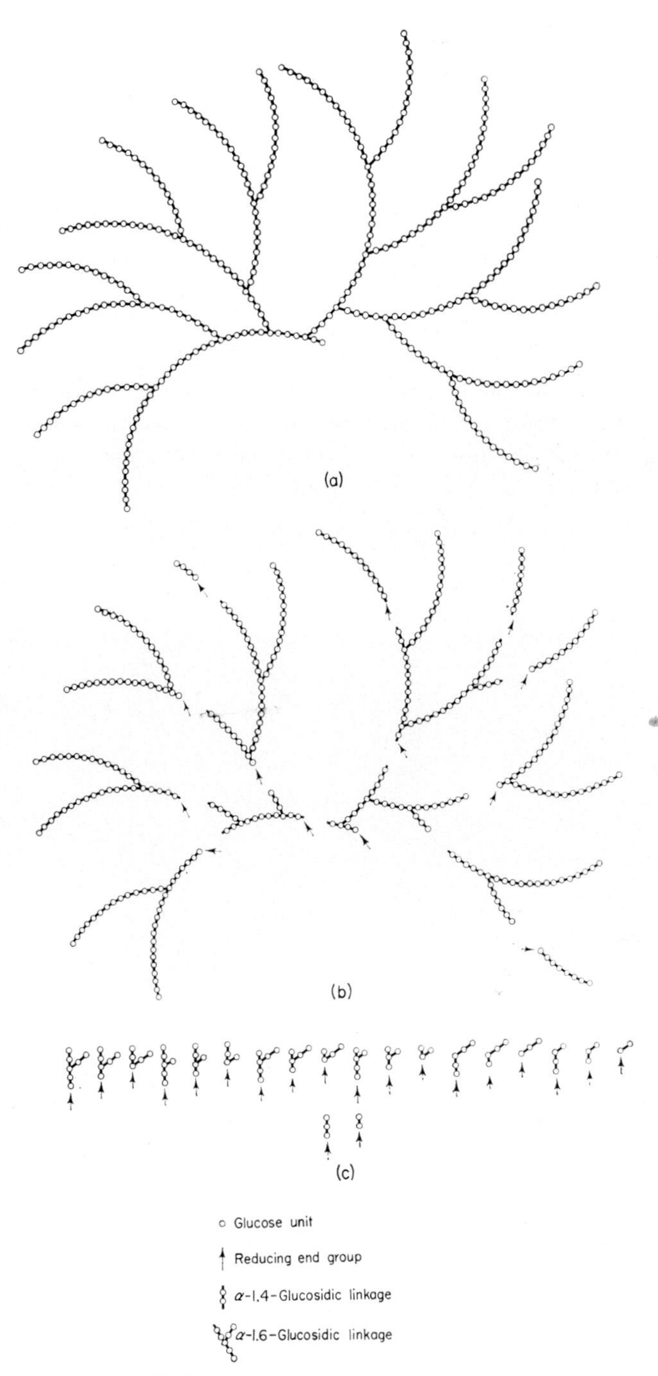

FIG. 59. Action of α-amylase on amylopectin

be used for structural studies on ramification. The remaining macromolecular core is the so-called *limit dextrin*. In the instance of amylopectin, where the outer branches are long, about 60% of the macromolecule is degraded to

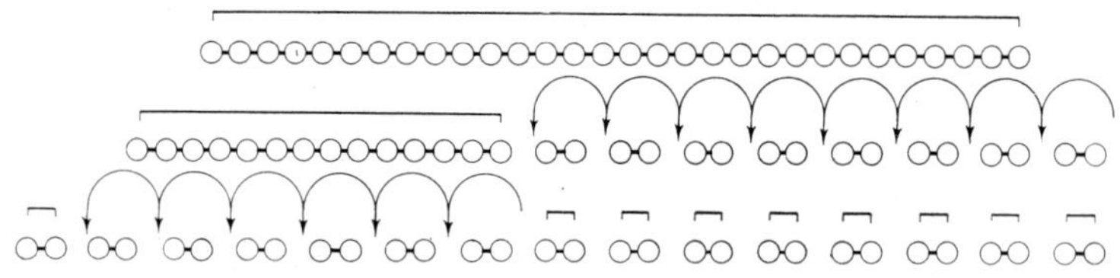

FIG. 60. Action of β-amylase on starch amylose

β-maltose, while the more highly branched glycogens release only 30–55% of their mass in the form of maltose. No undegraded dextrin core remains in the digestion of amylose, i.e. the linear macromolecule is completely converted to maltose.

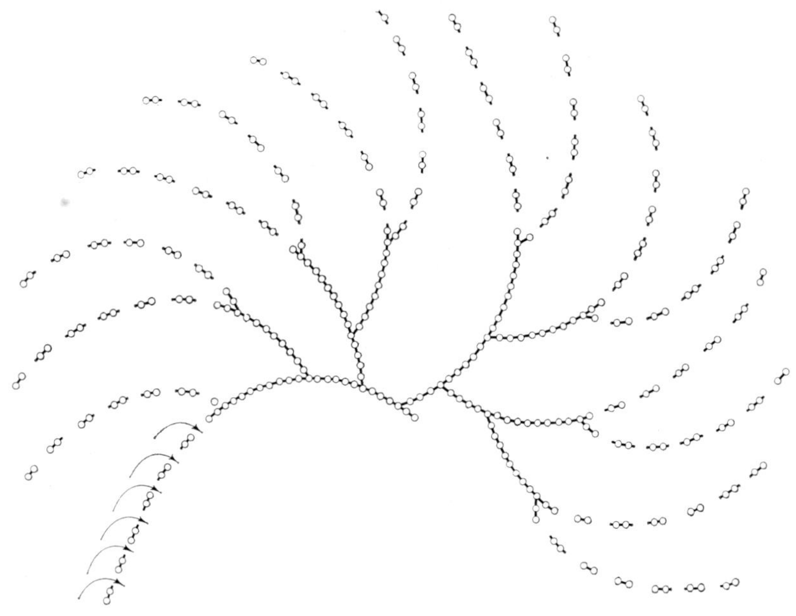

FIG. 61. Action of β-amylase on amylopectin of starch

The α- and β-amylases are not the only enzymes participating in the metabolism of starch and glycogen. Very important are the *phosphorylases* that catalyze not only the breakdown but also the synthesis of these polysaccharides. Phosphorylase has been found in muscle, where the reserve substance glycogen is degraded, also in other tissues, as well as in plants, and it was shown that the polysaccharide chains are degraded with the participation of inorganic phosphate.[17,18] Under the catalytic influence of the phosphorylase, the phosphate reacts with the C-1 carbon at the chain ends, and the glucose units are split off one by one in the form of α-D-glucose-1-phosphate, viz.:

$$(C_6H_{10}O_5)_n + \text{inorganic phosphate} \rightleftarrows (C_6H_{10}O_5)_{n-1} + \text{glucose-1-phosphate.}$$

This is a reversible reaction, and its course is determined solely by the concentrations of the components. If there is enough phosphate present, amylose is fully degraded. The enzymic effect of pure phosphorylase appears to be very similar to that of β-amylase, as phosphorylase attacks only the 1,4 glucosidic linkages. Hence in the instance of amylopectin or glycogen only a partial degradation up to the branch points is possible with pure phosphorylase. However, other enzymes that are capable of working on the 1,6 glucosidic linkages at the branch points of the chains also have been found in tissues.

According to the above equilibrium reaction, the degradation of the macromolecules will be facilitated by an excess of free phosphate. In the absence of it, and in the presence of an excess of glucose-1-phosphate, the opposite reaction, i.e. the *growths of the chains* can be predicted, and it was actually observed.[17,18] This synthetic action of phosphorylase consists in the lengthening of already existing chains, and no polymeric chains can be synthesized from pure glucose or maltose and glucose-1-phosphate. In other words: the biosynthesis of a polysaccharide requires a *primer*, a trace of pre-existing polysaccharide. In certain instances, e.g. when potato phosphorylase is used as the catalyst, this primer can be such a small molecule as maltotriose, while muscle phosphorylase requires the presence of larger primers.[19] The amylose prepared by enzymic synthesis is practically indistinguishable from natural amylose. Synthetic amylose is colored blue by iodine, it is hydrolyzed to maltose by β-amylase, and shows *X*-ray diagrams very similar to those of natural amylose. The molecular weight of the enzymically synthesized amylose seems to be somewhat lower than that of the native starch component.[20]

Amylopectin and glycogen cannot be enzymically synthesized by the phosphorylases alone. The building of the 1,6-glucosidic linkages at the branch points is facilitated by the so called *branching factor* or *Q-enzyme* that was first isolated from potato.[21] In the presence of this enzyme, the

(17) W. Z. Hassid, G. T. Cori and R. M. McCready, *J. biol. Chem.* **148**, 89 (1943); C. F. Cori and G. T. Cori, *ibid.* **135**, 733 (1940).

(18) G. Hanes, *Proc. Roy. Soc.* B **128**, 421 (1940); **129**, 174 (1940).

(19) M. A. Swanson and C. F. Cori, *J. biol. Chem.* **172**, 815 (1948).

(20) See for example: S. Peat, *Fortschritte d. Chemie org. Naturstoffe* **11**, 11 (1954); E. Husemann, *et. al.*, *Makromol. Chem.* **26**, 181, 199, 214 (1958).

(21) W. N. Haworth, S. Peat and E. J. Bourne, *Nature* **154**, 236 (1944); E. J. Bourne and S. Peat, *J. chem. Soc.* 877, 882 (1945); S. Nussenbaum and W. Z. Hassid, *J. biol. Chem.* **190**, 673 (1951); A. E. Bebbington, E. J. Bourne, M. Stacey and I. A. Wilkinson, *J. chem. Soc.* 240 (1952); M. Stacey, *Adv. Enzymol.* **15**, 301 (1954); M. Stacey in Symp. Soc. Exp. Biol. **12**, *The Biological Replication of Macromolecules* p. 185, Academic Press, New York, 1958.

linear amylose can be converted into the branched amylopectin in the absence of phosphate. Hence the Q-enzyme neither hydrolyzes nor synthesizes the chains but is able to open some of the 1,4 links and produce new 1,6-bonds between two activated chains. Such enzymes are called *transglucosidases.* The *amylose isomerase* that was isolated from rabbit muscle belongs to this type of enzymes. [22] It could be shown that this enzyme not only splits but also is able to form the α-1,6-glucosidic linkages of amylopectin and glycogen in the absence of phosphorylase or amylase. A glycogen-like polysaccharide could be synthesized in a combined action of muscle phosphorylase and amylose isomerase on glucose-1-phosphate. [22]

Enzymic syntheses of polysaccharides from maltose and sucrose also have been described. Some strains of microbes contain enzymes capable of reversible conversion of maltose into an amylose-like polysaccharide and glucose. [23] The coccus Neisseria *perflava* contains an enzyme system which facilitates the conversion of sucrose to glycogen-like polysaccharides and fructose. [24]

The variety of the enzymic reactions that may occur with polysaccharides is not confined to the examples thus far mentioned. Amylose, amylopectin and glycogen can undergo certain other changes, for example, amylose can be converted to interesting cyclic dextrins, the so called *Schardinger dextrins.* These are cyclic micromolecular carbohydrates composed of 6–8 residues of anhydroglucose linked through α-1,4 carbons, and they are produced by the aid of enzymes that are present in *Bacillus macerans.* [25] The Schardinger dextrins crystallize, and, according to their crystal form and size of the cyclic molecule they are classified in α, β, and γ dextrins containing 6, 7, and 8 anhydroglucose residues respectively. The optical rotation (using sodium light) of the α-dextrin is $+150°$, of the β-dextrin $+162°$, and of the γ—it is $+177°$. Being cyclic, the molecules are non-reducing and stable to enzymes and other digestive agents. Especially interesting is the fact that the 6-membered α-dextrin gives a crystalline blue iodine complex, whereas the iodine complexes with the β and γ dextrins are yellow-brown. This is brought in connection with the fact that amylose gives blue complex compounds with iodine by holding the iodine inside the helically wound chain. [7]

[22] A. N. PETROVA, *Biokhimiya* **13**, 244 (1948); **14**, 155 (1949); E. J. HEHRE, *Adv. Enzymol.* **11**, 297 (1951); A. N. PETROVA, *Biokhimiya* **17**, 129 (1952); M. STACEY, *Adv. Enzymol.* **15**, 301 (1954).

[23] A. M. TORRIANI and J. MONOD, *Compt. rend.* **228**, 718 (1949), also ref. 24.

[24] E. J. HEHRE, *Trans. N. Y. Acad. Aci.* **10**, 188 (1948); *Adv. Enzymol.* **11**, 297 (1951).

[25] K. FREUDENBERG and G. CRAMER, *Ber. dtsch. chem. Ges.* **83**, 296 (1950); D. FRENCH, *Adv. Carbohydr. Chem.* **12**, 189 (1957).

CHAPTER 9

THE PECTINS

> Thus "pectins" or "pectinic acids" designate those water-soluble polygalacturonic acids of varying methyl ester contents and degree of neutralization which show colloidal properties and are capable of forming, under certain conditions, gels with sugar and acid. [1]
>
> Z. I. Kertesz

Occurrence, Molecular Structure, and Size

The term "pectin" originates from the Greek "pectos" meaning set, congealed. The term covers a group of polysaccharides which have been further classified by different authors in different ways. Some authors include in this group not only the polygalacturonic acid derivatives but also some other polysaccharides which often accompany the polygalacturonic acid, notably the arabans and neutral galactans. [2] If we adopt the definition as formulated by Kertesz, [1] the soluble arabans and galactans should be disregarded. Moreover, the insoluble "protopectin" of the cell wall also would not be included in the discussion. Very little information of this insoluble component is available, and it is easy to see that this is due to the insolubility of this component, its fibrous structure, and reactivity. Together with other fibrous macromolecules, the protopectin constitutes the complex fabric of the tissue, and isolation of it by preserving its nativity is probably impossible.

The pectins are found in all higher plants, both in cell walls and intercellular layers, and they seem to have the function of a cementing substance which forms an integral part of the structures. While the straight cellulose fibrils constitute the major structural framework, like the steel skeleton of a building, the fibrous pectins serve as materials for the structural details. Moreover, the pectins probably have some functional significance. Since they are electrically charged, they are interacting with other electrically charged ingredients of the tissues. In the cell walls, for example, they probably affect the permeability of ions. It is also interesting that the pectins are present not only in roots and stems but also in fruits, and that the pectin content of fruits changes in the course of ripening. Hence pectins may have an active role in the metabolism of the reserve substances. One of the richest sources of pectin

(1) Z. I. Kertesz in *Methods in Enzymology* Vol. I, p. 158 (S. P. Colowick and N. O. Kaplan, ed.), Academic Press Publ., New York, 1955; see also Z. I. Kertesz, *The Pectic Substances* Interscience, New York, 1951.

(2) R. L. Whistler and Ch. L. Smart, *Polysaccharide Chemistry* chapt. 7, Academic Press, New York, 1953.

is lemon or orange rind which contains about 30% of this polysaccharide. Apples, turnips, beet pulp, and the inner bark of many trees are abundant with this substance. It also has been found that the very young cotton fibers contain as much as over 5% pectin, and that its amount decreases to 0·8% as the fiber matures.[2] A direct transformation of the pectin into cellulose, hemicellulose, or lignin, however, has not been proved.

Pectins are extracted commercially from citrus fruit peelings, apple pomace, or sugar beet pulp, and they are used in food product industry for making jellies. The extraction is accomplished with dilute acids or water, and the extracted pectins may be purified by reprecipitation with alcohol. The more drastic the extraction method the higher the yield and the more degraded are the macromolecules. Alkaline extraction yields the nonjellying salts of the polygalacturonic acids which are used as thickening agents.

Total hydrolysis of pectin yields D-galacturonic acid and methyl alcohol, indication that the polysaccharide is a methyl ester of polygalacturonic acid. Moreover, small amounts of galactose, arabinose, as well as acetic acid may be formed. The arabinose and galactose originate from the contaminating polysaccharides, while acetic acid originates from some OH groups which are acetylated. The degree of acetylation is usually very low, and it depends chiefly on the source of pectin; sugar beet pectin contains a few per cent acetyl, while the citrus and apple pectins are practically free of it. Since the pectins are strongly dextrorotatory (210–290° with sodium light), the anhydrogalacturonic acid residues are linked by the α-1,4 linkages. The carboxyl groups are either free or esterified with methyl groups. About 20–60% of the carboxyl groups of natural pectins are esterified, depending on the source and method of isolation. Saponification has been found to be associated with a considerable hydrolytic degradation,[3] while a more complete methylation, or esterification of the alcoholic hydroxyl groups, can be accomplished without a serious degradation of the chains.

A section of the partially methylated chain of the polygalacturonic acid of pectin can be illustrated as follows:

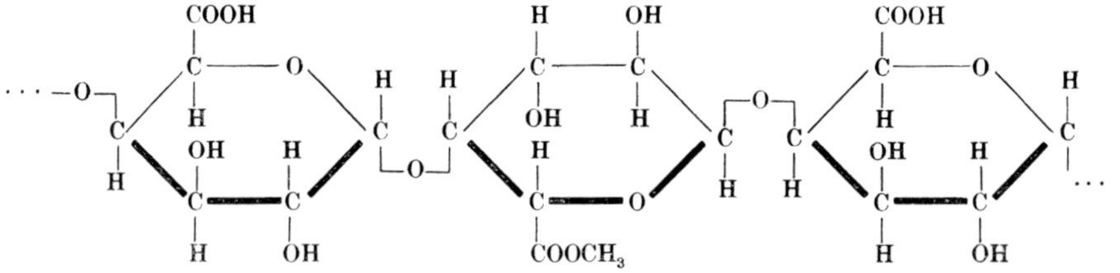

```
              COOH                          H       OH                          COOH
               |                            |        |                           |
               C ——— O                      C ——————— C                          C ——— O
 ···—O—┐      /|       \     H    H        /|        |  \      ┌—O—┐            /|       \        H
       C     / H        \    |    |       / OH       H   \     |    |          / H        \       |
       |   \   OH    H   /   C    C    \   H              /    C    C       \   OH    H    /      C
       H    \  |     |  /    └—O—┘      \  |             /     |    |        \  |     |   /       |  ···
             C ——— C                     C ——— O               H    H         C ——— C
             |     |                     |                                    |     |
             H     OH                  COOCH3                                 H     OH
```

In the pectins which are isolated by extracting with alkalies the carboxyl groups are neutralized, e.g. the hydrogen is replaced by sodium. The calcium salts of the polymeric acid are practically insoluble, and probably constitute some of the protopectin of the plant tissue.

[3] B. Vollmert, *Makromol. Chem.* **5**, 128 (1950).

Precipitated pectin is largely amorphous, but highly stretched films and fibers of pectin show a distinct fiber diagram. According to Palmer *et al.* the fiber identity period is about 13 Å, i.e. shorter than that of cellulose, and indicates a slight puckering of the chain. [4] The equatorial and meridional spacings change continuously upon moisture uptake, as the water molecules are bound to the polar groups and force them apart. [5]

The average molecular weights of the pectins have been found between 20,000 and 400,000. In this instance again the polymer chemist is confronted with the difficult problem of complete dissolution of the polymeric material without losing its nativity. It is possible that the molecular weight of the native protopectin in the plant tissue is much higher than the values obtained on the soluble products. The wide limits in which the molecular weights of the soluble specimens vary may be due either to degradation during isolation or to the method of study. Some illustrative data are presented in Table 15. [6] Since the macromolecules are linear, the sedimentation constants are relatively low, and the frictional ratios large. Due to the polymolecularity of the samples, the number average molecular weights determined by osmotic pressure measurements of the same samples are smaller than the weight average molecular weights. [7] The viscosimetric method was most conveniently applied to the nitrates obtained in a mild nitration of the original pectins. [3]

TABLE 15
MOLECULAR WEIGHT OF PECTINS [6]

Pectic material	Method	Molecular weight	Reference
Apple pectin	Viscosity	32,000–213,000	[8]
Apple pectin	Osmotic pressure	150,000	[9]
Apple pectin,	Sedimentation–diffusion	201,000	[10]
Apple pectin, commercial	Sedimentation–diffusion	67,000	[10]
Citrus pectin,	Sedimentation–diffusion	414,000	[10]
Citrus pectin, extracted	Sedimentation–diffusion	89,000	[10]
Red currant pectin	Sedimentation–diffusion	42,000	[10]
Flax pectin	Sedimentation–diffusion	64,000	[10]

The results obtained by Säverborn are especially instructive, since various pectins were compared by the same method of study. Moreover, the solvent in all instances was the same, 0·2 N sodium chloride. The frictional ratios

[4] K. J. PALMER and H. LOTZKAR, *J. Amer. chem. Soc.* **67**, 833 (1945); PALMER and M. B. HARTZOG, *ibid.* **67**, 1865, 2122 (1945).

[5] F. A. BETTELHEIM, C. STERLING and D. H. VOLMAN, *J. Polymer Sci.* **22**, 303 (1956).

[6] C. T. GREENWOOD, *Adv. Carbohydr. Chem.* **7**, 289 (1952).

[7] H. S. OWENS, H. LOTZKAR, T. H. SCHULTZ and W. D. MACLAY, *J. Amer. chem. Soc.* **68**, 1628 (1946).

[8] R. SPEISER and C. R. EDDY, *J. Amer. chem. Soc.* **68**, 287 (1946).

[9] B. VOLLMERT, *Makromol. Chem.* **5**, 110 (1950).

[10] Data of S. SÄVERBORN, quoted after GREENWOOD. [6]

(f/f_0, see chapt. 3) in all instances were found high — between 3·5 and 7·4. The axial ratios, assuming a cylindrical shape of the macromolecules, seem to be between about 50 and 150,[7] as computed from viscosity data. The solutions of the pectins are extremely viscous, and they become birefringent on streaming. Since the pectins are polyelectrolytes, the viscosity is dependent not only on the length of the chain but also on the degree of ionization (see chapt. 4). The intrinsic viscosity of pectinic acid increases upon neutralization of the carboxyl groups, since a higher degree of ionization results in an increased repulsion between the segments of the chain, followed by stretching.[11]

Gelation of Pectin

Pectins are most remarkable with their jelly-forming capacity. This is important not only for their application in food product industry but also in the general understanding of the mechanism of gelation. The change of consistency is especially important for a better understanding of the protoplasmic processes in cells and tissues. The mechanism of gelation is still obscure, not only in such complex systems as protoplasm but even in the relatively much simpler high polymers. One may, for instance, ask the question, why the dilute solutions of starch or cellulose derivatives do not set, and why the pectin solutions do.

The factors which influence the gelation of pectin have been studied by several authors, notably in the Western Regional Research Laboratory in Albany, California,[12] and in Zurich, Switzerland.[11] It has been established that the longer the chains the greater the capacity of gel formation, which is measured either by determining the minimum concentration which enables gelation or by measuring the firmness of the jellies of identical pectin concentration. (In all such comparative studies the measurements are made at a constant temperature, since gelation depends on temperature.) The acidity of the solutions, the presence of inorganic cations, and especially the degree of esterification of the carboxyl groups are other factors to be considered. The case is relatively simple and understandable in the instance of calcium pectate gels, since it can be assumed that the calcium (or other polyvalent cations) are interlinking the chains by ionic bonds, viz.:

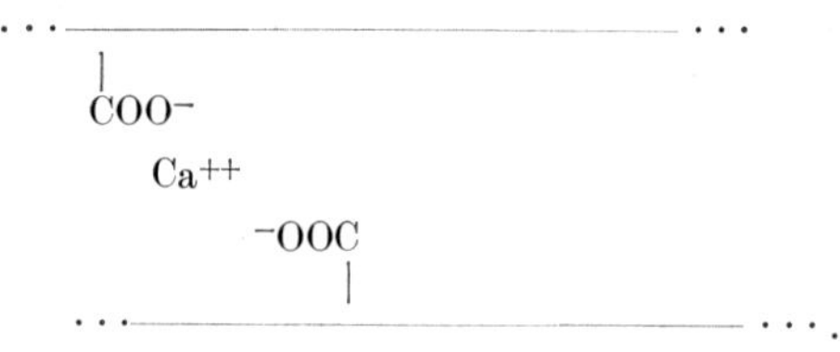

[11] H. Deuel, J. Solms and H. Altermatt, *Vierteljahresschrift d. Naturforsch. Gesellschaft in Zürich* **48**, 49 (1953).

[12] E. L. Pippen, T. H. Schultz and H. S. Owens, *J. Colloid Sci.* **8**, 97 (1953); H. S. Owens, H. A. Swenson and T. H. Schultz, in *Natural Plant Hydrocolloids* p. 10, Amer. Chem. Soc. publication, Washington D.C., 1954.

In this instance a high degree of esterification of the carboxyls is unfavorable for the gelation, since only the free carboxyl groups can participate in such ionic interlinking. It may seem, however, somewhat surprising that in the absence of calcium a high rather than a low degree of esterification favors gel formation.[12] It is assumed that in this instance the gelation is due to the *hydrophobic* property of the ester groups which tend to associate themselves. Since the chains are relatively rigid, this association cannot readily occur between the segments of the same chain but rather between the neighbor chains which happen to collide in the solution. The gelation process thus is relative to crystallization. This analogy, of course, is rather crude, since in a gel the large fibrous macromolecules are contacted only in a few points thus forming a loose meshwork which holds the whole of the solvent. This explanation is supported by the following facts: (1) gelation is facilitated by addition of acid, (2) it is facilitated by addition of sugar or glycerin, and (3) the solutions set at 25 °C more rapidly than at a lower temperature of 10 °C. Addition of acid results in a decrease of ionization of the free carboxyl groups; this favors the contact formation between the fibrous macromolecules, since the negatively charged carboxyl ions will cause repulsion. Addition of sugar or glycerin probably causes some dehydration of the pectin thus favoring the association of the segments. Finally, a moderate temperature facilitates the interchain contacting, since at a too low temperature the molecular movement is too sluggish. (A too high temperature naturally inhibits gelation.) The question of the effect of the degree of esterification on gelation is not completely solved, since the effects depend on many factors, and there is some discrepancy between the conclusions as made by different authors.[11,12] It seems that most favorable for the gelation of pectin–sugar systems is an esterification degree of about 50%. While the onset of gelation is facilitated by a still higher degree of esterification, the rigidity of the 40–60%-ester pectin gels is higher than that of 70–80%-ester jellies.[13] This indicates that the rigidity may be determined by the hydrogen bonding between the hydroxyl groups and the free carboxyl groups. It is also noteworthy that the solutions of sugar-beet pectin do not set, and that gelation can be achieved only after the removal of the acetyl groups which are present in this pectin.[13] The interfering effect of the bulky acetyl groups indicates the necessity of some smoothness of the chain which should facilitate the alignment of the segments and a close contacting of the groups involved in the bonding. If the pectin specimens have not been carefully liberated from calcium and other polyvalent cations, the results certainly will be affected also by these impurities.

The intrinsic viscosity of a pectin which was 98% esterified with diazomethane at −23° was found to be 3·1 dl/g, while a 58% esterified product yielded a higher intrinsic viscosity of 4·2 dl/g.[12] The number-average molecular weight of this preparation was 39,000. Higher intrinsic viscosities of

[13] F. A. HENGLEIN, *Forschungen u. Fortschr.* **26**, 184 (1950).

6·2–7·1 were reported by the same authors for 70–80% esterified specimens with a number-average molecular weight of 45,000. The viscosity depends on both acidity and ionic strength, besides the chain length and degree of esterification. The high intrinsic viscosity values of 3–7 have been found either in acid solutions of low ionic strength or in nearly neutral solutions of moderate ionic strength of 0·1–0·2 (see also chapt. 4).

Enzymic Modification of Pectins [14]

The esters of the naturally occurring pectins or pectinic acids can be modified not only by chemical methods of saponification, methylation, and hydrolysis, but also by certain enzymes. The existence of at least two enzymes has been ascertained: the *pectinesterase* and the *polygalacturonase*. Pectinesterase catalyzes the saponification of the methyl ester groups, whereas polygalacturonase facilitates the hydrolytic cleavage of the 1,4-glucosidic linkages of the chain. Both enzymes have been purified and well characterized, and found to be highly specific. While pectinesterase is widely distributed in higher plants, polygalacturonase is found only in bacteria and fungi, as well as in snails. These facts are of considerable interest if one thinks of the metabolic pathways of these substances. Since there are no enzymes in higher plants which cleave the macromolecules, they probably cannot be rebuilt into other polysaccharides or used as food reserve. Only some bacteria, fungi, and the snails are able to degrade the pectin chains and utilize the degradation products. It is also interesting that the enzymic breakdown of the pectin is facilitated by the removal of the methyl ester groups, i.e. a highly methylated pectin is attacked by the enzyme less vigorously than a demethylated pectin. The enzymic degradation *in vitro* is accompanied by an increase in reducing groups, a decrease in viscosity, and in a decrease in optical rotation.

The presence of pectinesterase in plant tissues indicates that the esterification reactions are important for the metabolism of the plant, probably by changing the number of ionogenic groups and thus the electrical charge density. Demethylation experiments *in vitro* have shown that enzymic demethylation differs from chemical saponification in that the latter is at random, whereas the enzyme sweeps off the methyl groups at certain sections of the chain leaving other sections intact. [15] The enzymically demethylated pectinic acids are attacked by the chain-cleaving enzyme more readily than the chemically saponified pectins. [15a]

Araban and Galactan

Most of the acid or aqueous plant extracts which contain pectinic acid are contaminated with araban and galactan. These polysaccharides can be removed from impure pectin by extraction with 70% alcohol, or by fractional

(14) H. Lineweaver and E. F. Jansen, *Adv. Enzymol.* **11**, 267 (1951).
(15) E. F. Jansen and L. R. MacDonnell, *Arch. Biochem.* **8**, 97 (1945).
(15a) H. Deuel and E. Stutz, *Adv. Enzymol.* **20**, 341 (1958).

precipitation of the pectinic acid with 50–55% alcohol. Since araban is very sensitive to hydrolytic cleavage with acids, it can be removed by treating the specimens with dilute hydrochloric acid. Only L-arabinose is obtained on complete hydrolysis of araban which seems to be a rather low-molecular polymer composed of arabofuranose residues. Since araban is strongly levorotatory (—160° with sodium light), it affects the optical rotation of the dextrorotatory pectin considerably. The galactans are slightly levorotatory, and the moderately long chains of this polysaccharide are built of the pyranoid rings of the D-anhydrogalactose units which are linked by β-1,4 glucosidic linkages. Large amounts of complex arabans and galactans have been isolated from wood, for example from larch.[16] D-galactose was found as the major hydrolysis product of this polysaccharide. The arabo–galactans found in wood are very heterogeneous. They find some application as paper pulp sizes, as thickening agents in drilling muds, etc. Other galactans will be mentioned in the following chapter.

[16] F. C. Peterson, A. J. Barry, H. Unkauf and L. E. Wise, *J. Amer. chem. Soc.* **62**, 2361 (1940); L. E. Wise and E. C. Jahn, *Wood Chemistry* 2nd ed., Vol. I and II, Reinhold, New York, 1952.

CHAPTER 10

GUMS AND MUCILAGES. SEAWEED POLYSACCHARIDES

> The plant gums have been thought to represent a protective mechanism by which the injured parts of the plant are sealed off and thereby protected from the attack of microorganisms. The complicated structure of these gums should certainly afford a good protection, since very special enzymes would be necessary to break them down.
>
> LUIS F. LELOIR [1]

THE VARIETY of the naturally occurring polysaccharides is not even nearly exhausted by the examples described in previous chapters. Yet, there is a simple pattern in this variety in that all the most important macromolecules are composed of the pyranoid six-rings linked through oxygen. The variety is caused chiefly by the differences in the spatial arrangement of the line-up of the rings and their structural elements, on substitution at the rings, and on the branching of the chains. Polysaccharides with the furanoid fiverings are relatively insignificant, and they are of a comparatively low molecular weight of several thousands. Inulin is an example of such polysaccharides; it is found e.g. in the roots of chicory, in artichoke, or in dahlia tubers. More information on these substances can be found in texts on carbohydrates. [2]

Plant gums and mucilages are macromolecular polysaccharides yielding on hydrolysis hexoses, pentoses, and their derivatives. The chemical composition and constitution of these polysaccharides is usually much more complex than in the previously described instances. There will be no attempt to give a complete systematic survey of the whole field, but only some of the most important examples will be mentioned.

Gum Arabic [3]

Gum arabic is an exudate from the bark of acacia trees, especially the species which grow in Sudan and other parts of North Africa and Near East.

(1) L. F. LELOIR, *Currents in Biochemical Research* p. 585; quoted from pp. 607–608 (D. E. GREEN, ed.), Interscience, New York, 1956.

(2) W. PIGMAN (ed.), *The Carbohydrates: Chemistry, Biochemistry, Physiology* Academic Press, New York, 1957; R. L. WHISTLER and CH. L. SMART, *Polysaccharide Chemistry,* Academic Press, New York, 1953; F. SMITH and R. MONTGOMERY, *Chemistry of Plant Gums and Mucilages* Reinhold, New York, 1959; R. L. WHISTLER and J. N. BEMILLER, *Industrial Gums, Polysaccharides and their Derivatives* Academic Press, New York, 1959.

(3) C. L. MANTELL, *The Water-Soluble Gums* Reinhold, New York, 1947; *Natural Plant Hydrocolloids* p. 20, *Amer. chem. Soc. Publ.*, Washington D. C., 1954.

This is one of the oldest known adhesives and thickening agents, and its importance has not much decreased in the modern competition with the various other natural and synthetic high polymers. The annual production of gum arabic is estimated at about 50 million pounds.

The gum is soluble in warm water, and it can be purified by reprecipitation with alcohol. The aqueous solution of the gum is acid (pH 2–3), and the natural acidity is sufficient to promote a slow autohydrolysis, especially on long heating. On a mild hydrolysis, L-arabinose is the first monose liberated from the macromolecules, and it is followed by L-rhamnose, D-galactose, and D-glucuronic acid. According to Hirst, [4] the macromolecules are branched, and the various anhydromonoses are linked by 1,3, 1,4, and 1,6 glucosidic bonds, as shown in the scheme:

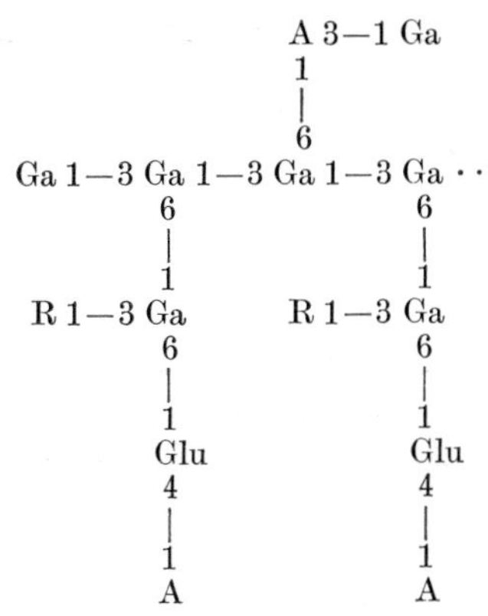

A: **L**-arabofuranose, Ga: **D**-galactopyranose, Glu: **D**-glucuronic acid, R: rhamnopyranose

Gum arabic is a polyelectrolyte, and its solutions are highly viscous. The adhesive properties of the gum seem to be related to the highly branched structure of the macromolecules, a correlation which holds also for the ramified amylopectin. The solutions of gum arabic are levorotatory (specific rotation −20 to −30° with sodium light). Molecular weights between 200,000 and 250,000 have been found from osmotic pressure data, [5] and 250,000–300,000 by sedimentation and diffusion. [6] Higher values of about 1,000,000 have been obtained in more recent studies on the light scattering of the solutions of the high polymer. [7] The gum is completely amorphous. The macromolecule, according to the light scattering studies, [7] appears to be a stiff coil, a conclusion which is in agreement with the chemical data on branching and inflexibility of the branches. The dimensions of the coil vary from 1000 Å

(4) E. L. HIRST, *J. chem. Soc.* 70 (1942).

(5) H. B. OAKLEY, *Trans. Faraday Soc.* **31**, 136 (1935); **32**, 1360 (1936); **33**, 372 (1937).

(6) E. C. DODDS and R. T. M. HAINES, *Biochem. J.* **28**, 499 (1934); D. R. BRIGGS, *J. Phys. and Colloid Chem.* **52**, 76 (1948); S. SÄVERBORN, quoted after *Chem. Abstr.* **39**, 1345 (1945).

(7) A. VEISS and D. N. EGGENBERGER, *J. Amer. chem. Soc.* **76**, 1560 (1954).

at zero charge to 2400 Å at maximum ionization. This is in agreement also with the results on the flow properties of the solutions. The intrinsic viscosity of the solutions containing uncharged macromolecules was found 0·33 dl/g, and a complete dissociation of the carboxyls resulted in a viscosity rise up to 2·2 dl/g.

Tragacanth, Karaya, and other Gums

Gum tragacanth, like gum arabic, is one of the first natural polymers the early technologist and druggist has used. It is an exudate of the shrubs belonging to the genus *Astragalus* which belong to the leguminoses. Like gum arabic, it oozes from the wounds inflicted in the bark of the plant. Asia Minor and Iran are the chief producers of this gum.

Gum tragacanth is a horny light colored material which swells and partially dissolves in water. The soluble part is called tragacanthin or tragacantic acid, and the insoluble portion is termed bassorin. The soluble tragacanthin can be purified by precipitating from water with alcohol or acetone. Tragacanthin is a highly viscous polyelectrolyte, and the viscosity depends on pH and ionic strength. Molecular weight of 840,000 has been found for the soluble gum by the sedimentation method. [8]

The chemical structure of the macromolecules of this gum has not been fully established. The soluble tragacanthin yields chiefly glucuronic acid and L-arabinose. The acid part seems to be built of chains of the D-anhydrogalacturonic acid units. Some of the carboxyls of the acid are methylated, and some L-fucopyranose and D-xylopyranose residues also are attached to the main chain. [9] Aside of galacturonic acid, D-xylose, L-fucose, D-galactose, and L-arabinose are found in the hydrolysis products of the polysaccharide.

Gum tragacanth is produced in considerable amounts, and it is widely applied as thickening and emulsifying agent, as a base for cosmetic and pharmaceutical creams and pastes, as a stabilizer in food product industry, etc.. [10]

Gum karaya is a more recent addition to the commercially important series of gums. It originates from the tropical *Sterculia urens* tree which grows chiefly in India. Gum karaya is now widely used in food products industry, as a laxative drug, etc.. [11] Gum karaya is a high-molecular weakly acid polysaccharide of a very complex structure which is not yet fully disclosed. Quantitative chromatographic analysis of the hydrolysis products has revealed the presence of D-galacuronic acid (43 parts), D-galactose (14 parts), and L-rhamnose (15 parts). [12] A similar study on a highly purified karaya gum from *Sterculia setigera* yielded somewhat different results, viz.: D-galacturonic

(8) N. Gralèn and M. Karrholm, *J. Colloid Sci.* **5**, 21 (1950).
(9) E. L. Hirst and J. K. N. Jones, *Research.* **4**, 411 (1951).
(10) D. C. Beach in *Natural Plant Hydrocollids* p. 38, ACS publ., Washington D.C., 1954.
(11) A. M. Goldstein, in *Natural Plant Hydrocolloids* p. 33.
(12) L. Beauquesne, *Compt. rend.* **222**, 1056 (1946).

acid (8 parts), D-galactose (5 parts), L-rhamnose (5 parts), and D-tagatose (1 part).[13] This is the first instance when tagatose has been found in a natural product. The carboxyl groups of the polysaccharide are partially neutralized, and some of the alcoholic hydroxyls are esterified with acetyl groups. Molecular weight of about 9 million has been reported (from sedimentation data).[14] Like tragacanth, karaya swells in water yielding a translucent gel. A complete dissolution occurs on boiling, and probably is associated with a partial hydrolysis.

Gums are produced not only by the mentioned tropical or subtropical plants but also by our cherry and plum trees. These gums are soluble in water, they are levorotatory, and resemble more or less the earlier described polysaccharides. The chemical composition and structure has been studied by Hirst, Jones, and their associates.[15] Damson gum, for example, seems to have a highly branched structure in which many relatively short side chains are attached to one main chain. L-arabinose, D-galactose, D-glucuronic acid, and other constituents have been found in the hydrolysis products. Hydrolysis of methylated gums yields relatively large amounts of dimethyl monoses, an indication of branching.[15,16] The carboxyl groups of these polysaccharides in the native gums are neutralized with inorganic bases which can be removed by adding acid to an aqueous solution of the gum, and precipitating the gum with alcohol.

Mucilages

The term "mucilage" usually is applied to denote the complex polysaccharides which are isolated from seeds, stalks, and other parts of plants, and it is impossible to draw a strict borderline between gums and mucilages. The latter usually are completely soluble, and the solutions do not set readily, although the viscosity of the solutions is high. Chemically, the mucilages differ from gums in that the latter are highly charged polyelectrolytes, while the former may be devoid of carboxyl groups. The mucilages from locust beans and from guar[17] are noteworthy. The locust beans are obtained from the brown pods (St. John's bread) of the *Ceratonia siliqua* L. tree which grows in the Mediterranean region. Guar is a legume resembling the peanut plant, and it is cultivated in India and in the southern states of U.S.A. The polysaccharide is extracted from ground starting material with water, and can be purified by reprecipitation with 40% alcohol. Fractionation experiments have led to the conclusion that the polysaccharide is relatively homogeneous,[18] and chemical studies indicate that it is a galactomannan. Hydro-

(13) E. L. Hirst, L. Hough and J. K. N. Jones, *J. chem. Soc.* 3145 (1949).
(14) J. V. Kubal, *J. Colloid Sci.* **3**, 457 (1948).
(15) E. L. Hirst and J. K. N. Jones, *J. chem. Soc.* 506 (1946).
(16) F. Brown, E. L. Hirst and J. K. N. Jones, *J. chem. Soc.* 1757 (1949).
(17) R. L. Whistler, in *Natural Plant Hydrocolloids* p. 45, ACS publ., Washington D.C., 1954.
(18) E. Heyne and R. L. Whistler, *J. Amer. chem. Soc.* **70**, 2249 (1948).

lysis of the locust bean polysaccharide yields 80% D-mannose and 20% D-galactose, while guar gum produces 65% mannose and 35% galactose.[17] According to Whistler,[17,18] the mannopyranose rings constitute the main chain, and the galactose units are attached to this main chain as short limbs, the whole macromolecule thus resembling something like a centipede. "The protruding D-galactose units on the D-mannose chain allow the molecule to become highly hydrated by associating itself with a large envelope

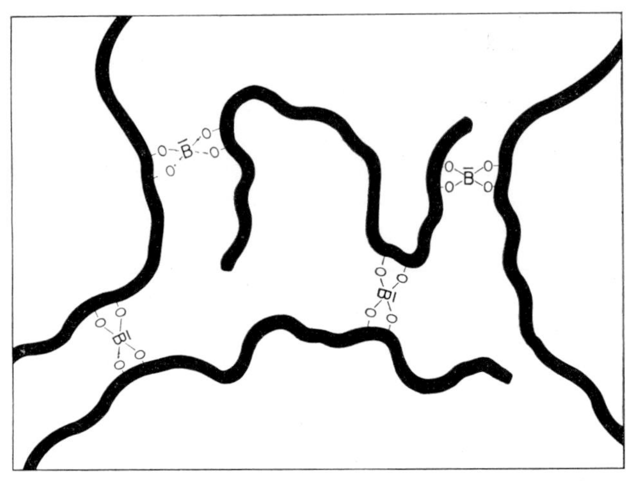

FIG. 61a. Linking of polysaccharide chains by complexing with borate ions, according to Deuel

of water molecules. Complete association between the guaran molecules over an extensive portion of their chains as to produce an aggregating particle which would bring about precipitation is prevented by the protruding D-galactose units which tend to fend off one molecule from another or at least produce such irregularities that extensive interchain association cannot take place. Thus, disperse molecules remain stable and a highly viscous solution results" (ref. 17, p. 48). The molecular weight of these substances ranges in several hundred thousand.[17]

The practical applications of the polymeric branched galactomannans are based on the fact that they are able to raise the viscosity of the system without causing gelation. However, the solutions of these polymers set when a small amount of borax is added to the solution. According to Deuel *et al.*, this is due to complex formation between the borate and two pairs of hydroxyl groups — in cis configuration — of two chains,[19] as illustrated in Fig. 61a.

The mucilages extracted from other sources, such as flax seeds, are mixtures of several complex polysaccharides. D-galacturonic acid, L-galactose, L-rhamnose, and D-xylose are the monosaccharides obtained on total hydrolysis

(19) H. DEUEL and H. NEUKOM, *Makromol. Chem.* **3**, 13 (1949).

of flaxseed mucilage. A somewhat similar constitution can be presumed for a mucilage extracted from the inner bark of the slippery elm tree. The viscid mucilage of okra (*Hibiscus esculentus*) also consists of galactose, galacturonic acid and rhamnose units.[20]

Agar and other Seaweed Polysaccharides

Marine algae contain a number of interesting polysaccharides which are not found in terrestial plants. In addition to ordinary cellulose, the red algae contain large amounts of sulfur-containing polysaccharides of acid nature, notably *agar* (also called agar-agar) and *carrageenin*. The bulk of commercial agar comes from Japan, where several sorts of agar and other seaweed polysaccharides are important food products. After soaking and washing, the agar-containing seaweeds are boiled with water for 2 hr, followed by heating with dilute sulfuric acid at 80° for 14 h (pH 5–6), and bleaching with sulfite. The liquid is filtered and the gel obtained on cooling is cut to pieces, frozen, and thawed; upon thawing the gel partially disintegrates, and a large part of the liquid soaks away, carrying with it the water-soluble impurities.[21] Further purification can be achieved by repeating this freezing–thawing procedure which is followed by thorough washing with cold water. Reprecipitation with water-miscible organic solvents from warm aqueous solutions, and dialysis may be applied. Dried agar is a quite tough stringy material which swells in cold water and dissolves on boiling. These solutions are very viscous and they possess a remarkable tendency to set. Firm gels are obtained with 1–2% agar, but gelation is observed even with 0·2–0·3% of the polysaccharide, and many applications of agar are based on this property. According to chemical studies, D- and L-galactose are the chief constituents of the linear macromolecules, and several of the alcoholic hydroxyls of the chain are esterified with sulfuric acid. It is also ascertained that the latter is not introduced in the course of isolation, since sulfate groups are found even when sodium carbonate or acetic acid is used in extraction and the bleaching performed with chlorine or hydrogen peroxide. Neither the structure nor size and shape of the macromolecules of agar have been fully elucidated. One sulfate group seems to appear only for every 10–50 galactose units which appear to be linked chiefly by 1,3-glucosidic linkages. The high tendency to congeal can be explained by chain cross-linking through the sulfate groups and polyvalent cations, such as calcium, viz.:

$$-\overset{|}{\underset{|}{C}}-O-SO_3-Ca-O_3S-O-\overset{|}{\underset{|}{C}}-$$

Agar is a typical polyelectrolyte. The viscosity can be studied only at relatively high temperatures of about 50 °C, and the viscosity is affected strongly by electrolytes (see chapt. 4).

(20) R. L. WHISTLER and CH. L. SMART, *Polysaccharide Chemistry* p. 333, Academic Press, New York, 1953.

(21) T. MORI, *Adv. Carbohydr. Chem.* 8, 315 (1953).

Carrageenin is isolated from red algae (chiefly *Chondrus crispus*, sometimes called "Irish moss") of the North American and European coastal zones. About 80% of the dry weight of the seaweed is carrageenin which in this instance replaces cellulose as structural material to a great extent. Pure carrageenin is a white powder, it is soluble in hot water, and the solutions have a lesser tendency to set than agar solutions. This may be explained by the high sulfate content; the macromolecules are composed of galactose residues linked at 1,3 carbons as in agar, but the sulfate content is much higher than in agar; the protruding bulky sulfate groups can hamper the chain association by steric reasons and electrostatic repulsion. The solutions of carrageenin are dextrorotatory, while those of agar are levorotatory. Carrageenin is strongly polymolecular, and the molecular weights found by various methods differ considerably. Light scattering data have given the highest values of over one million, [22] while sedimentation-diffusion and osmotic pressure measurements rendered lower values of several hundred thousand. [23] Light scattering disymmetry studies indicate that the macromolecules resemble rods of an average length of 3700 Å. [22]

Algin is one of the commercially most important seaweed polysaccharides. [24] It is found in various species of brown algae, notably in kelp (*Macrocystis pyrifera*) from which it is extracted by means of sodium carbonate. Algin is the sodium salt of alginic acid which, in the form of mixed salts of calcium, magnesium, and other bases, makes up a large portion of cell walls. Recent chemical studies [25] confirm earlier work that the linear macromolecules of alginic acid are built of β-D-anhydromannuronic acid residues linked at the 1,4 carbon atoms. *X*-ray studies on algin fibers are in general agreement with chemical data and indicate that the anhydromannose units have the pyranoid ring structure. [26] The macromolecules of alginic acid and algin thus resemble pectin (chapt. 9). However, the solutions of algin, although very viscous, are less prone to gelation than those of pectin. Although the algin solutions precipitate or set on addition of acid or calcium salts, they are not used as jellying agents but chiefly as stabilizers and thickening agents. Especially suitable for this purpose is the propylene glycol alginate, since it does not precipitate in acid solutions. [24] Propylene glycol alginate is nontoxic, and it is used extensively as stabilizer for ice cream, orange juice concentrates, salad dressings, custard-type puddings, cheeses, and similar food products. It improves the foam stability of beer. Algin or propylene glycol

[22] D. A. I. GORING, *Canad. J. Chem.*. **31**, 1078 (1953).

[23] C. R. MASSON and G. W. CAINES, *Canad. J. Chem.* **32**, 57 (1954); C. T. GREENWOOD, *Adv. Carbohydr. Chem.* **11**, 389 (1956).

[24] A. B. STEINER and W. H. MCNEELY, *Natural Plant Hydrocolloids* p. 68, ACS publ., Washington D. C., 1954.

[25] S. K. CHANDA, E. L. HIRST, E. G. V. PERCIVAL and A. G. ROSS, *J. chem. Soc.* 1833 (1952).

[26] W. T. ASTBURY, *Nature* **155**, 667 (1945); K. J. PALMER, *J. Appl. Phys.* **17**, 405 (1946).

alginate is used as a hydrophilic ingredient in medical and cosmetic ointment bases, tablets, as well as in dental impression materials. Other applications of algin involve adhesives, printing inks, textile fibers, paper pulp sizing, textile printing, rubber latex creaming, etc.

Sedimentation and diffusion studies have shown that algin is polymolecular, and that the molecular weights are about 47,000–370,000. [27] The molecular weight can be computed also from viscosity measurements, as it has been established that the relationship

$$|\eta| = 7{\cdot}5 \cdot 10^{-5}\, M$$

holds in this case. [27] The flow properties, moreover, indicate that the macromolecules are highly asymmetric. Sodium alginate is a highly charged polyelectrolyte, as illustrated below.

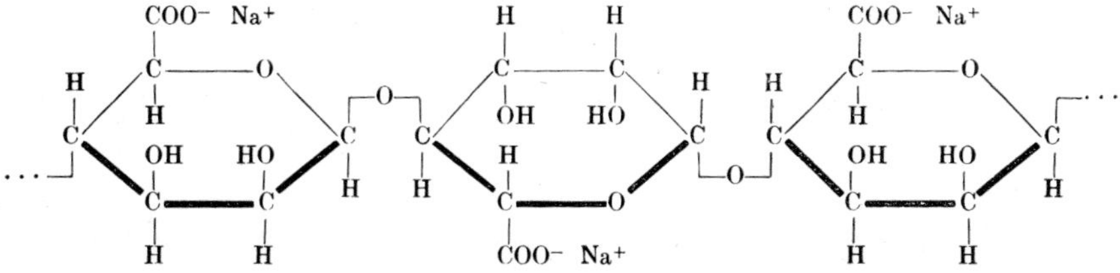

The polyelectrolyte nature of algin, agar, and carrageenin indicates that they are not simply passive structural materials of the marine plant tissues but also participate in important cellular functions. The negatively charged carboxyl groups attract oppositely charged cations, and the polsaccharide thus acts as an ion exchanger. Interactions with the nitrogen containing organic bases thereby may be even more important than the interactions with inorganic cations.

Dextrans [28]

The dextrans represent one of the many types of polysaccharides synthesized by micro-organisms. Only a few other polysaccharides have been as thoroughly investigated as these dextrans, and there are several reasons for this. First, certain fractions of partially hydrolyzed dextran are suitable as blood plasma substitutes (volume expanders). Second, they are readily available in pure state, and are easy to handle. The strains of *Leuconostoc mesenteroides* and similar microbes can be readily cultivated in sucrose solutions containing other nutrients, and they synthesize a formidable spectrum of giant molecules of uniform structure. Cell-free enzymes also have been prepared, and the mechanism of the enzymic synthesis has been disclosed

(27) W. H. Cook and D. B. Smith, *Canad. J. Biochem. Physiol.* **32**, 227 (1954).

(28) A. Gronwall, *Dextran and its Use in Colloidal Infusion Solutions* Academic Press, New York, 1957.

to a certain extent.[29] The macromolecules of dextran are built of anhydroglucose which is linked through α-1,6 glucosidic linkages, as shown below. The chains are branched, and on the average one branch occurs for every 10–12 glucose residues. Since the solutions are highly viscous, exhibit double refraction of flow, and dextran shows fibre diagrams on examination with X-rays, the macromolecules must be highly asymmetric. It can then be assumed that the structure may resemble a comb rather than a ramified bush. Dextrans are strongly dextrorotatory (+200 to +240° with sodium light), and the specific rotation decreases on degradation.

```
· · —Glu, 1—6, Glu, 1—6, Glu, 1—6, Glu, 1—6, Glu, 1—6, Glu— · ·
      |
      4
      |
     Glu
      |
      :
```

Glu — anhydroglucopyranose residue.

The molecular weight of various fractions of partially hydrolyzed dextrans has been determined with various methods, and it was found that the weight-average molecular weights are much higher than the number-averages, an indication of polymolecularity.[30,31] Light scattering measurements of the less degraded fractions have rendered values as high as 12 to even 600 million,[32] and Elias recently reported molecular weights of 10^8–10^9;[33] the scattering effects of such giant molecules, however, are complicated and difficult to evaluate. According to Wales *et al.*,[30] the simple relation

$$|\eta| = 10^{-3} \cdot M^{\frac{1}{2}}$$

holds in the molecular weight range 20,000–250,000. The square root molecular weight–intrinsic viscosity relationship indicates that the macromolecules of dextran are strongly coiled, and that they are flexible.

(29) E. J. Hehre, *Science* **93,** 237 (1941); *Trans. N. Y. Acad. Sci.* **10,** 188 (1948). E. J. Hehre, *Adv. Enzymol.* **11,** 297 (1951).

(30) M. Wales, P. A. Marshall and S. G. Weissberg, *J. Polymer Sci.* **10,** 229 (1953).

(31) F. R. Senti, N. N. Hellman, N. H. Ludwig, G. E. Babcock, R. Tobin, C. A. Glass and E. L. Lamberts, *J. Polymer Sci.* **17,** 527 (1955).

(32) L. H. Arond and H. P. Frank, *J. physic. Chem.* **58,** 953 (1954).

(33) H.-G. Elias, *Makromol. Chem.* **27,** 192 (1958); see also: F. A. Bovey, *J. Polymer Sci.* **35,** 167 (1959).

CHAPTER 11

LINEAR POLYSACCHARIDES OF ANIMAL ORIGIN

By 1949, it had become apparent that the mucopolysaccharides differed not only in quantity but that there existed qualitative differences in various tissues. In fact, at least some tissues possess distinct and unique patterns of mucopolysaccharides.

KARL MEYER [2]

APART from the earlier mentioned glycogen, there is a great variety of polysaccharides in animal tissues. "At present it is impossible to state how many distinct mucopolysaccharides are contained in connective tissue. We have demonstrated three sulfate-free mucopolysaccharide acids — hyaluronic acid, chondroitin, and an acid which appears to be related to heparin. We have three chondroitin sulfates which we designate *A*, *B*, and *C*. In addition, *A* and *C* occur in various stages of sulfation. We further have isolated from two tissues a uronic acid-free polysaccharide which we named keratosulfate". [1] The mucopolysaccharides are aminodeoxypolysaccharides, i.e. they contain nitrogen. The monose residues are usually different, and there may be substituted sulfate and carboxyl groups present. The blood group polysaccharides contain even some amino acids, thus representing *a bridge between polysaccharides and proteins.*

Chitin

"There are two principal skelatal systems which support the cellular structure of animal tissues, and they may be described as the collagenous and the chitinous skeleton". [2] The collagenous skeleton dominates in mammals and other higher animals the collagen there being supported by calcium phosphate deposits, whereas chitin is very abundant in lower animals, such as crustaceans and insects, where the chitinous structures are hardened by calcium carbonate deposits. Other nitrogen containing polysaccharides, such as the chondroitin sulfates and hyaluronates are closely associated with the skeletal materials. Collagen is a protein, and the collagenous skeleton is of

[1] KARL MEYER, *The Harvey Lectures* ser. 51, p. 88, quotation from p. 92, Academic Press, New York, 1957.

[2] K. M. RUDALL, Symp. Soc. Experim. Biol., IX, *Fibrous Proteins and their Biological Significance* p. 49, Academic Press, New York, 1955.

internal mesodermal origin, whereas chitin is of ectodermal origin and forms chiefly the external shells, cuticles, etc. It must, however, be pointed out that the total encrusting substance of the arthropods (insects, crustaceans) is not pure chitin–calcium carbonate but represents complex structures. While the outer layer of these cuticles is more or less pure chitin–calcium carbonate (containing pigments and small amounts of other organic substances), the inner layers of the cuticle contain also protein. Furthermore, not all lower animals contain exclusively chitinous skeletons; chitin is abundant, for example, in hydrozoan polyps but not in hydrozoan medusae [(2)] where collagen dominates. There also seem to be several types of slightly different chitins. In cephalopods (molluscs, squids, octopuses) an α- and a β-chitin can be distinguished in different parts of the bodies. The α-chitin replaces collagen, while the β-chitin is found in association with collagenous structures. [(2)] Chitin is found also in lower plants, such as the mycelia and spores of fungi, and the presence of chitin or cellulose in the cell walls is taken as criterion for establishing philogenetic relations between the species of these organisms.

Chitin is prepared most conveniently from crab or lobster shells which contain 20–25% chitin and about 70% of calcium carbonate. The shells are cleaned, washed, dried, and ground. The calcium carbonate then is removed by a treatment with dilute hydrochloric acid, and the residual chitin washed with alkali and water. Pigments may be removed by bleaching agents, and lipophilic impurities by washing with alcohol and ether. Since chitin is a fibrous material, the removal of the last traces of impurities is a difficult task. Especially difficult is the removal of the protein impurities tightly associated with the polysaccharide. Repeated treatment with alkali and dilute acid, or a treatment with proteolytic enzymes, can be considered. However, in all these procedures a partial degradation of the polysaccharide is unavoidable. This is demonstrated e.g. by measuring the optical activity or viscosity of the freshly prepared solutions of chitin in concentrated hydrochloric acid: the initially observed weak levorotation slowly changes in the positive direction as the hydrolysis proceeds. Purified chitin is a white material resembling paper pulp. It is insoluble in the ordinary mild solvents, except some saturated salt solutions, although it is difficult to prove that a complete dissolution has occurred. Chitin is soluble also in concentrated mineral acids upon partial degradation, and in anhydrous formic acid. There are no reliable molecular weight data available for this high polymer. [(3)]

Total acid hydrolysis of chitin yields D-glucosamine and acetic acid in molar ratio 1 : 1, and isolation of N-acetyl-D-glucosamine upon milder acid or enzymic hydrolysis indicates that the chains are composed of these N-acetyl-

(3) See e.g. L. ZECHMEISTER and G. TOTH, *Fortschr. d. Chem. org. Naturstoffe* **2**, 212 (1939); R. L. WHISTLER and CH. L. SMART, *Polysaccharide Chemistry* p. 395, Academic Press, New York, 1953.

D-glucosamine units. Other chemical and physical evidence leads to the conclusion that the units are linked by the β-1,4 glucosidic linkages, viz.:

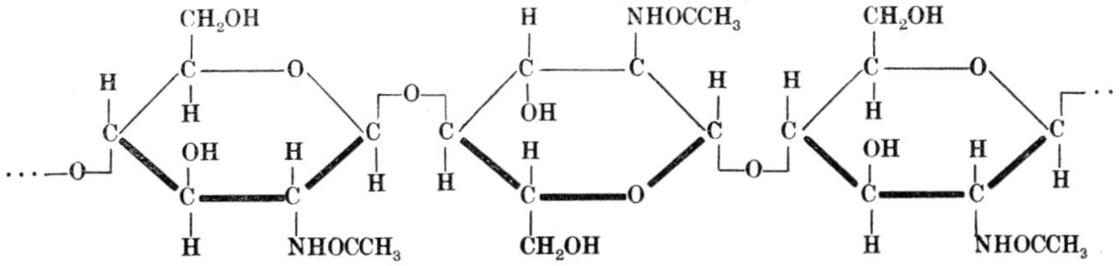

Examination of chitin specimens with X-rays yields good fiber diagrams which show a striking resemblance between chitin and cellulose. According to Meyer and Pankow, [4] the unit cell contains eight acetylglucosamine units, and the fiber period is 10·46 Å long. The X-ray diagrams of oriented chitin, e.g. the chitin from rock lobster tendon, indicate that the well oriented fibrous macromolecules are very long, and that they are uniform. Fungal chitin showed essentially the same X-ray diagram as crustacean chitin; [5] although this does not definitely prove identity, it ascertains the presence of a chitin in the fungi. Differences in chitins isolated from various sources are substantiated in more recent X-ray studies which have revealed the β-chitin e.g. in the skeletal pen of squids. [2,6]

The enzymes which enable hydrolytic decomposition of chitin are found in certain bacteria and molds found in marine sediments, soil, in the intestines of marine animals, and in snails.

The Chondroitin Sulfates

Chondroitin sulfates are acid mucopolysaccharides found in various animal tissues, such as cartilage, growing bone, tendon, heart valves, blood vessels, and skin. The nasal septum cartilage is known to be one of the richest sources of the polysaccharide (20–40%), but the isolation of pure native chondroitin sulfate is not an easy task, since it involves separation of two fibrous high polymers — chondroitin sulfate and collagen. The best method seems to be extraction with a concentrated solution of potassium chloride; the extract is slightly acidified with acetate buffer, the impurities are removed by adsorption on kaolin, and the filtrate containing the polysaccharide is dialyzed; the dialyzed clear solution is again buffered with a mixture of acetic acid and acetate, and treated with kaolin; the filtrate then is evaporated in vacuum, and a white chondroitin sulfate is precipitated by pouring the con-

[4] K. H. MEYER and G. W. PANKOW, *Helv. Chim. Acta* **18**, 589 (1935); K. H. MEYER, *Natural and Synthetic High Polymers* p. 450, Interscience, New York, 1950; G. L. CLARK and A. F. SMITH, *J. physic. Chem.* **40**, 863 (1936).

[5] G. VAN ITERSON, JR., K. H. MEYER and W. LOTMAR, *Rec. Trav. chim. Pays-Bas* **55**, 61 (1936).

[6] W. LOTMAR and L. E. R. PICKEN, *Experientia* **6**, 58 (1950).

centrated solution in alcohol. A crystalline calcium chondroitin sulfate also could be isolated. [7] Since the chondroitin sulfates have higher charge density and higher mobility than the protein impurities, preparative electrophoresis also can be used for purification. [8] Chondroitin sulfate appears homogeneous in eletrophoresis tests. [9]

Complete hydrolysis of chondroitin sulfate yields D-glucuronic acid, sulfuric acid, acetic acid, and 2-deoxy-2-amino-D-galactose (chondrosamine). This is the composition of the ordinary hyaline cartilage, while the chondroitin sulfate *B*, according to Karl Meyer *et al.*, [1] contains the L-iduronic acid, instead of glucuronic acid. It has been found that the acetic acid results from the N-acetyl group of the chondrosamine, but the location of the sulfate is not quite well established. Moreover, the quantity of sulfate may vary in different preparations. [1] The structure of the macromolecular chain also is not completely settled, and branched or linear chains have been proposed. [10] According to Karl Meyer *et al.*, the chain must be linear, and the sugar units are joined by 1,3-glucosidic linkages, viz.: [11]

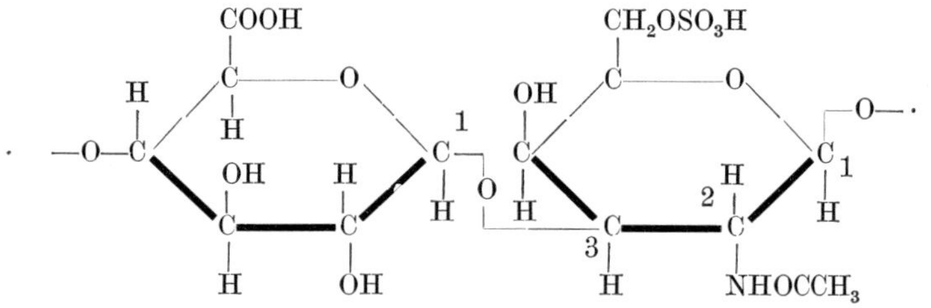

COOH CH_2OSO_3H
H C O OH C O
H 1 —O—·
·—O—C OH H C— C C 1
O H
H H 2
C C C C H
3
H OH H NHOCCH$_3$

According to Wolfram *et al.*, the chain is essentially linear, i.e. it can be but slightly branched. [9] As indicated before, some structural variety has been ascertained, and the most essential differences between the various chondroitin sulfates are summarized in Table 16. The above formula represents a small part of the macromolecular chain in the acid form which, due to the sulfate groups, must be a strong acid. In the tissues the acid groups are neutralized by either inorganic cations or by the basic amino groups of proteins, especially the collagen. The possibility of extracting the sulfates by means of potassium chloride, however, indicate that the linkages with the proteins are not strong.

While the sulfates *A* and *C* differ relatively little from each other, the chondroitin sulfate *B* is structurally very different. This polysaccharide is found chiefly in skin, also in abdominal aorta, in tendons, heart valves, and

(7) J. Einbinder and M. Schubert, *J. biol. Chem.* **185**, 725 (1950); **191**, 591 (1951).

(8) S. Gardell, A. H. Gordon and S. Aquist, *Acta Chem. Scand.* **4**, 907 (1950).

(9) M. L. Wolfrom, R. K. Madison and M. J. Cron, *J. Amer. chem. Soc.* **74**, 1491 (1952).

(10) H. G. Bray, J. E. Gregory and M. Stacey, *Biochem. J.* **38**, 142 (1944).

(11) E. A. Davidson and K. Meyer, *J. Amer. chem. Soc.* **77**, 4796 (1955).

TABLE 16
COMPARISON OF THE PROPERTIES OF CHONDROITIN SULFATES *A*, *B*, AND *C* (according to Karl Meyer [1])

Property	*A*	*B*	*C*
Specific rotation $[\alpha]_D$	—28° to —32°	—55° to —63°	—16° to —22°
Ethanol concentration precipitating Ca salt	30–40%	18–25%	40–50%
Hydrolysis by testicular enzyme	+	—	+
Hexosamine	Chondrosamine	Chondrosamine	Chondrosamine
Uronic acid	D-glucuronic	L-iduronic [12]	D-glucuronic
Reducing sugar equivalent after 1 hr hydrolysis with 1 N H_2SO_4 at 100°	15	32	22
Repeating unit in chain	N-acetyl-chondrosin 6(?) sulfate		N-acetyl-chondrosin 6(?) sulfate

in minute amount in other tissues. [1,13,14] The embryonic skin of pigs contains only a small amount of chondroitin sulfate *B*, but the amount increases in the course of growth, and adult pig skin contains about 64% chondroitin sulfate *B* from the total polysaccharide substance. [15] Chondroitin sulfate *B* differs from the other sulfates also in its slight antithrombic activity thus resembling closely the so-called heparin *B* isolated from beef lungs. [16] Most interesting, however, is the occurrence of this polysaccharide in blood vessels and heart valves. The constitutional similarity between the ascorbic acid and one of the constituting units — the L-iduronic acid — is noteworthy. "If the identity of the uronic acid is substantiated, it probably will be found that ascorbic acid is the precursor of this uronic acid. One of the known properties of ascorbic acid is its essentiality for the maintenance and repair of connective tissue. Ascorbic acid in this reaction would not be a vitamin but an essential nutrient" (1, quoted from p. 110). This finding thus would render an interesting basis in explaining the well known beneficial effects of ascorbic acid in the treatment of connective tissue disorders, and it indicates the importance of this vitamin also for the circulatory system. *

(12) A. LINKER, K. MEYER and P. HOFFMAN, *J. biol. Chem.* **219**, 13 (1956); F. SHAFIZADEH and M. L. WOLFROM, *J. Amer. chem. Soc.* **77**, 2568 (1955).

(13) K. MEYER, E. DAVIDSON, A. LINKER and P. HOFFMAN, *Biochim. Biophys. Acta* **21**, 506 (1956).

(14) W. P. DEISS and A. S. LEON, *J. biol. Chem.* **215**, 685 (1955).

(15) G. LOEWI and K. MEYER, *Biochim. Biophys. Acta* **27**, 453 (1958).

(16) R. MARBETH and A. WINTERSTEIN, *Experientia* **8**, 41 (1952).

* According to Karl Meyer (a personal communication), the presence of L-iduronic acid in the chondroitin sulfate B has been established; however, the guess that L-ascorbic acid might be the precursor of L-iduronic acid could not be substantiated by preliminary *in vivo* experiments with labeled ascorbic acid which was injected into scorbutic guinea pigs. The chondroitin sulfate B isolated after five days from the skin of the animals had practically no radioactivity.

The polyelectrolyte nature of chondroitin sulfuric acid and its salts has been well demonstrated by Mathews.[17] These experiments, moreover, strongly suggest that the macromolecules are linear. The reduced specific viscosity of pure chondroitin sulfuric acid in the absence of electrolytes is very high (6–18, and higher), and it increases with increasing dilution (see chapt. 4). In the presence of 0·02–0·2 M sodium phosphate and chloride, however, the reduced specific viscosity is only about 0·5–1·0, and it does not vary much with the concentration of the polyelectrolyte (see Fig. 41).

The molecular weight of chondroitin sulfuric acid and its salts has been determined by several authors, and the results have been very different, depending on the preparation and method of study. Recent light scattering studies on well defined preparations of the mucopolysaccharide showed that the molecular weight depends strongly on the presence or absence of contaminating protein. When the preparation is carefully liberated from protein, by the very mild treatment with proteolytic enzymes, the molecular weight

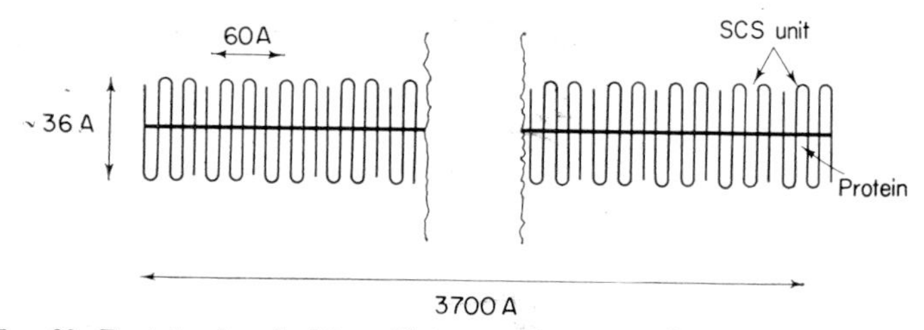

FIG. 62. Protein-chondroitin sulfate complex, according to Mathews and Lozaityte[19]

of the pure chondroitin sulfate is about 50,000.[18] This was obtained on a preparation of sodium chondroitin sulfate isolated from bovine hyaline cartilage. If, however, the accompanying protein is not removed, very high molecular weight of 4,000,000 is obtained.[19] The light scattering study on such preparation, moreover, led to the conclusion that the particles in solution are of rod-like shape, and that the length of these rods is 3 700 Å. According to Mathews *et al.*,[19] the protein moiety should be thought as a thin core of the rod-shaped particle, and that the sodium chondroitine sulfate units, each of the molecular weight of 50,000, are hanging on this central core as illustrated in Fig. 62. Each of the chondroitin units is linear, and retains its flexibility which allows an increase in average lateral chain extension with decrease in salt concentration.[19] Aggregates of these basic units are possibly formed by linear end to end or lateral hydrogen-bonded association which probably involves also some additional protein; the "molecular weight" or relative particle weight of these aggregates ranges to about 50 million.

(17) M. B. MATHEWS, *Arch. Biochem. Biophys.* **43**, 181 (1953).
(18) M. B. MATHEWS, *Arch. Biochem, Biophys.*, **61**, 367 (1956).
(19) M. B. MATHEWS and I. LOZAITYTE, *Arch. Biochem. Biophys.* **74**, 158 (1958).

The keratosulfate of cornea [1,20] appears to be composed of N-acetyl-glucosamine, galactose, and sulfate, and it can hardly be classified as belonging to the chondroitin sulfate family, since it does not contain any uronic acid.

Hyaluronic Acid and other Mucopolysaccharides

Hyaluronates, the salts of hyaluronic acid, are important components of the ground substance, i.e. the jelly-like matrix holding and cementing together the fibers and cellular structures. Hyaluronates have been isolated, for example, from skin, tendons, vitreous humor, umbilical cord, and cock's comb. [21] The ground substance is important not only as a structural component but also as a medium regulating the spreading of metabolically important substances in the tissues. This spreading can be greatly facilitated by injecting the hyaluronidases, i.e. the enzymes that are able to promote the hydrolysis and disintegration of the macromolecular skeleton of the jelly-like matrix (see chapt. 26).

Various methods have been used for the isolation and separation of the hyaluronates and other acid mucopolysaccharides. [13] Minced tissue can be extracted with dilute alkalies, also with trichloroacetic acid, or with phenol solution. The polysaccharides are fractionally precipitated from the extracts by alcohol or by ammonium sulfate. Ion exchange resins also have been used. The protein impurities are removed by enzymic digestion with proteolytic enzymes.

Complete hydrolytic degradation of hyaluronic acid yields D-glucosamine, D-glucuronic acid, and acetic acid; and additional chemical studies have led to the conclusion that N-acetyl-D-glucosamine and D-glucuronic acid represent the units in the linear chain. The exact mode of linking the units is not quite established, the β-1,3 and β-1,4 linkages being considered. Important information on the structure was obtained also by analyzing the enzymic degradation products of the hyaluronates. It was found that there are two major types of enzymes attacking the polysaccharide chains: the testicular and the bacterial hyaluronidases. The thermostable testicular hyaluronidase yields tetrasaccharides as major hydrolysis products, while bacterial hyaluronidase produces chiefly disaccharides. The fundamental disaccharide unit in the macromolecules seems to be N-acetyl-glucuronido glucosamine which could be isolated from the products of enzymic hydrolysis. The enzymes are able to cleave not only the hyaluronates but also the chondroitin sulfates and similar polysaccharides, although the sulfate groups cause some steric hindrance. [22] Moreover, the hyaluronidases act not only as hydrolases but also as trans-

(20) K. MEYER, A. LINKER, E. A. DAVIDSON and B. WEISSMANN, *J. biol. Chem.* **205**, 611 (1953).

(21) K. MEYER, *Physiol. Rev.* **27**, 335 (1947); K. MEYER and M. RAPPORT, *Adv. Enzymol.* **13**, 199 (1952); see also ref. 13.

(22) J. C. HOUCK and R. H. PEARCE, *Biochim. Biophys. Acta* **25**, 555 (1957).

glucosidases (see chapt. 8, p. 154), and they seem to be able not only to degrade but also link the fragments together. Various hybrid oligosaccharides have been produced by incubating mixtures of hyaluronates and chondroitin sulfates with testicular hyaluronidase.[23] Unsaturated disaccharides have been isolated by enzymic hydrolysis using bacterial hyaluronidases.[24]

The hyaluronates are levorotatory (−70°, sodium light), the solutions are highly viscous, and they become birefringent on flow. As expected, the viscosity decreases upon enzymic degradation of the polysaccharide. Furthermore, the viscosity of highly dialyzed solutions is much higher than the viscosity of salt-containing solutions that is in accord with the polyelectrolyte nature and linear shape of the macromolecules. However, the subject is complicated by the fact that the viscosity and similar properties depend on the method of preparation of the polysaccharide[25] as well as on the presence of a protein component. It is then difficult to account for what is the effect of the protein and what is the effect of degradation. According to Ogston and Stanier,[26] complete removal of the protein without degrading the polysaccharide is impossible, and we are faced with the old problem of preserving nativity in a thorough purification (see chapt. 2). The hyaluronate-protein complex isolated from the synovial fluid of ox had particles with the relative weight of about 8,000,000, and the dispersion was very viscous. The complex contained 30% protein which is bound to the hyaluronate by hydrogen bonds and by salt linkages between the carboxyl ions of the hyaluronate and the basic sites of the protein. More highly purified preparations of the hyaluronates (about 90% pure) which were isolated from cattle eye vitrous tissue possessed a somewhat lower viscosity than that found for other hyaluronates (e.g. those from umbilical cord). The number-average molecular weight of these hyaluronates was found to be 270,000,[27] and weight-average molecular weights of 340,000–500,000 are reported for somewhat similar preparations by light scattering.[28] The same method has yielded also higher values for other preparations, and it indicated that the particles have the shape of stiff coils several thousand Angstrom units in diameter.[29] In the electron microscope, however, were observed fibrous bodies.[30] The hyaluronate–protein complex of synovial fluid could be partially cleaved by a proteolytic enzyme (papain), whereby the particle weight decreased about five-fold.[31] It has been ascertained that the hyaluronates are polymolecular, but it is

[23] P. Hoffman, K. Meyer and A. Linker, *J. biol. Chem.* **219**, 653 (1956).
[24] A. Linker, K. Meyer and P. Hoffman, *J. biol. Chem.* **219**, 13 (1956).
[25] Z. Hadidian and N. W. Pirie, *Biochem. J.* **42**, 260 (1948).
[26] A. G. Ogston and J. E. Stanier, *Biochem. J.* **46**, 364 (1950); **49**, 585 (1951).
[27] J. A. Christiansen and C. E. Jensen, *Acta Chem. Scand.* **9**, 1405 (1955).
[28] T. C. Laurent, *J. biol. Chem.* **216**, 262 (1955).
[29] T. C. Laurent and J. Gergely, *J. biol. Chem.* **212**, 325 (1955).
[30] J. W. Rowen, R. Brunish and F. W. Bishop, *Biochim. Biophys. Acta* **19**, 480 (1956).
[31] B. S. Blumberg and A. G. Ogston, *Biochem. J.* **66**, 342 (1957).

very difficult to assess how much this inhomogeneity depends on the method of isolation and what is the chain length of a hyaluronate in living tissue. It is possible that the macromolecules of different tissues are of different length, but it is not easy to prove this. It is even more difficult to ascertain whether the protein component is a native satellite or whether it has joined the polysaccharide in the process of isolation.

The *biosynthesis* of hyaluronic acid has been studied recently to a considerable extent and it is established that the chain is built in step by step incorporation of preformed D-glucuronic acid and N-acetyl-D-glucosamine units. [32] The preformed glucuronic acid and glucosamine units are assembled in strictly alternating order by a mechanism not yet fully understood. More data are available on the formation of the glucuronic acid and glucosamine, but these reactions are outside the scope of this survey. It will suffice to mention that D-glucose is the chief starting material, and that the syntheses involve phosphorylation.

Several polysaccharides resembling hyaluronic acid have been described. For example, a mucopolysaccharide isolated from stomach wall is composed of N-acetyl-D-glucosamine, D-glucuronic acid, and sulfuric acid. It seems to represent a hyaluronate some hydroxyls of which are esterified with sulfuric acid.

Heparin [33,34]

Heparin, as the name indicates, is found in liver which is one of the best starting materials, although it contains only about a hundred milligrams of this polysaccharide per kilogram tissue. Lung, spleen, thymus, and muscle are the other organs containing small amounts of it, while the heparin content of blood is much lower than in the mentioned organs. Heparin is a powerful anticoagulant of blood thus being of great importance in preventing clot formation. It seems to be formed in the mast cells generally located in the connective tissues in the vicinity of capillaries, and in the walls of blood vessels.

Heparin is extracted from tissues by an alkaline solution of ammonium sulfate, and the protein-containing heparin is precipitated with acid. The precipitate is treated with alcohol, dissolved in very dilute alkali, and the protein is removed by digestion with trypsin. After the removal of all the micromolecular impurities, the heparin is precipitated by acetone or alcohol, and the precipitate is further purified by reprecipitation, etc. The final stages of purification involve precipitation with glacial acetic acid, redissolving in water and crystallization in the presence of barium acetate and acetic acid. This microcrystalline derivative represents the purest form of heparin, and it was used for the structural studies. This crystallized heparinate appeared

[32] R. L. Whistler and E. J. Olson, *Adv. Carbohydr. Chem.* **12**, 299 (1957).

[33] E. Jorpes, *Heparin* 2nd ed., Oxford Univ. Press, London, 1946.

[34] A. B. Foster and A. J. Huggard, *Adv. Carbohydr. Chem.* **10**, 336 (1955); L. Velluz, *Bull. Soc. chim. Biol.* **41**, 415 (1959).

to be homogeneous on both electrophoresis and countercurrent distribution, while the noncrystalline commercial heparins are inhomogeneous. The molecular weight of pure heparin is about 20,000, i.e. much lower than the molecular weight of the previously mentioned polysaccharides. The specific rotation of pure heparinates has been found between $+36°$ and $+56°$ (Na-light).

The chemical structure of heparin has been elucidated by Jorpes and his associates,[33] by Charles and Todd,[35] and most of all by Wolfrom *et al.*.[36] The hydrolysis products of heparin include D-glucuronic acid, D-glucosamine, and sulfuric acid. One of the acid functions of the sulfuric acid appear to be esterified with some of the hydroxyls or bound to the amino groups of the glucosamine residues. Since only one of the acid functions is neutralized in this bond, and since most of the pyranoid units contain two ionogenic sulfate groups, the polysaccharide has an extremely high electrical charge density. This seems to be one of the factors which endows this substance with the anti-clotting potency, though it is established that this is not the only requirement. Structural factors and configuration of the macromolecules also is important for this function, since semi-synthetic highly sulfated polysaccharides of similar charge density and molecular weight possessed only a weak anti-clotting activity.[37] Moreover, heparin can be inactivated without the loss of its charge density.

A section of the heparin chain, according to Wolfrom *et al.*,[36] can be represented by the following formula (free acid form):

The barium salt contains one barium atom for a pair of the monobasic sulfate groups, while the carboxyl groups are free. In blood and tissues, sodium, potassium, calcium, and other ions replace the acid hydrogen ion, and the acid polyelectrolyte interacts also with proteins. The above formula, however, is only a tentative one, since it is not unequivocally proven and does not explain all factual data. Very little is known about the configuration of the chains. Since heparin can be inactivated, i.e. lose its anti-clotting capacity, without notable change in composition and molecular weight, it has been assumed that the active form contains a few intramolecular sulfate bridges of the type[34]

$$\cdots-\overset{\displaystyle H}{\underset{|}{\overset{|}{C}}}-NH-SO_2-O-\overset{|}{C}H-\cdots.$$

[35] A. F. Charles and A. R. Todd, *Biochem. J.* **34**, 112 (1940).

[36] M. L. Wolfrom, R. Montgomery, J. V. Karabinos and P. Rathgeb, *J. Amer. chem. Soc.* **72**, 5796 (1950); see also ref. 34.

[37] K. H. Meyer, R. P. Piroue and M. E. Odier, *Helv. chim. Acta* **35**, 574 (1952).

Inactivation by acetic acid then could be envisaged as a hydrolytic cleavage of these bridges. Now, it is interesting that the sedimentation constant increases (from 2·0 to 2·7) and the frictional ratio (see chapt. 3) falls (from 2·5 to 1·8) on inactivation; [38] and, since the molecular weight does not change, the inactivation would be explained by a change in molecular shape. [34] It is, however, not quite clear what kind of change this might be. Inactivation apparently is associated with a transformation into a more compact configuration than that of the native state, but the mechanism of this change is altogether obscure. A cleavage of intramolecular bridges in linear macromolecules usually leads to a higher asymmetry, i.e. higher frictional ratio and lower sedimentation constant which would be contrary to the facts observed in this case. It also has been pointed out [34] that there are alternate α-1,3 and α-1,4 glucosidic linkages in the heparin chain, and that such chains have the tendency to assume a helical configuration. [34] The intramolecular sulfate bridges may stabilize this highly asymmetric helical configuration thus ensuring a higher asymmetry than in the randomly coiled inactivated or "denatured" state. The extremely high charge density and inflexibility of the polysaccharide chain, however, throws doubt on such explanation. Further studies should clarify this challenging and interesting problem.

Several other native mucopolysaccharides are known to be endowed with the anti-clotting capacity, although to a lesser degree than heparin. Most important of these is chondroitin sulfate *B*. [1,13,39] The latter was isolated recently from bovine aorta by zone electrophoresis and column chromatography, and it could be shown that it is identical with the so called β-heparin. [39] Thus the inhibition of clotting apparently is regulated by several substances present in blood and blood vessel walls.

Blood Group Polysaccharides [40]

"The term blood group substances refers to any of a number of substances on or in the surface of erythrocytes which are present in certain individuals of a species and lacking in others. These substances are antigens, i.e. they can induce the formation of antibodies when erythrocytes containing the particular blood group substance are injected into an individual of the same species but lacking this particular blood group substance . . ." (40, p. 1). A more detailed account on this subject will be given in chapt. 23, while in this section only the chemistry of these substances will be briefly described.

Since these macromolecular substances are in blood and tissues in low concentrations, and since they are associated with other large and small molecules, the isolation is a difficult task. This difficulty is enhanced by the

(38) R. Jensen, O. Snellman and B. Sylven, *J. biol. Chem.* **174**, 265 (1948).

(39) G. S. Berenson, *Biochim. Biophys. Acta* **28**, 176 (1958).

(40) E. A. Kabat, *Blood Group Substances, Their Chemistry and Immunochemistry* Academic Press, New York, 1956; G. E. W. Wolstenholme and M. O'Connor (ed), *Chemistry and Biology of the Mucopolysaccharides* Little and Brown, Boston, 1958.

very intricate composition and structure of these macromolecules. It has not been ascertained as yet that the best preparations of these substances are free of any extraneous material, and they certainly are polymolecular. Strangely enough, the richest source of the so called *A*-substance is not erythrocyte but ovarian cyst fluid. Another convenient source of the blood group sub-

TABLE 17

PHYSICOCHEMICAL DATA OF BLOOD GROUP SUBSTANCES
(from Kabat, ref. 40)

	Substances from ovarian cyst fluid					Substances from hog mucin
	A	*B*	*B*'	0 (*H*)	*Le*	*A* + 0 (*H*)
Sedimentation constant $s_{20} \cdot 10^{13}$ at $c = 0{\cdot}5\%$	6·7	11·9	8·3	6·6	6·7	
Ditto, at $c = 1{\cdot}0\%$	5·4	7·2	6·2	5·2	5·4	
Diffusion constant $D_{20} \cdot 10^7$	1·7	0·56	1·2	1·2	1·3	1·1
Partial specific volume V = ml/g	0·63	0·60	0·60	0·64	0·64	0·66
Mol. wt. $\overline{M}_w$ from s and D	260,000	$1{\cdot}8 \cdot 10^6$	$4{\cdot}6 \cdot 10^5$	$3{\cdot}2 \cdot 10^5$	$2{\cdot}7 \cdot 10^5$	
$\overline{M}_w$ from light scatter						$9 \cdot 10^7 - 1{\cdot}1 \cdot 10^6$
$\overline{M}_w$ from diffusion and viscosity						10^6
$\overline{M}_n$ from osmotic pressure						200,000($\pm$30,000)
Frictional ratio f/f_0	3·2	5·7	3·9	4·2	4·8	

stances is gastric juice. One of the best methods of isolation consists in extraction of lyophilized starting material with 90% phenol, precipitation with ethanol, and further fractional reprecipitation from formamide or glycol with ethanol. The purified preparations appear to be complicated mucopolysaccharides containing in addition about 10% of amino acids. The polysaccharides are composed of N-acetylhexosamine, D-galactose, and L-fucose. The N-acetylhexosamine may be in the form of either N-acetylglucosamine or N-acetylgalactosamine. The hexosamine content in the various preparations was found to vary between 20 and 37%, the acetyl content between 6–11%, the glucosamine 8–22%, galactosamine 4–13%, and methylpentose (fucose) 2–20%. The amino acids are integral constituents of the macromolecules, e.g. a preparation isolated from hog gastric mucosa, and showing both *A* and *O* group activity, contained 3·3% proline, 1·9% serine, 1·6% glycine, 1·3% glutamic acid, 1·0% lysine, and smaller amounts of several other amino acids. Most of the preparations have been found to be levorotatory, although low positive optical activity also has been reported. The chemical differences between the substances of the various blood types (*A*, *B*, *O*, etc.) are very small and the data are ill reproducible. Some physicochemical data are presented in Table 17.

CHAPTER 12

THE STRUCTURE AND CONFIGURATION OF NATIVE AND DENATURED PROTEINS

> The studies have gone far enough, however, to indicate that every protein behaves in an individual way towards various agents which cause configurational change. As a result, it may well be that different proteins possess a compact configuration for quite different reasons.
>
> CHARLES TANFORD [1]

Classification

Proteins can be defined as macromolecular substances yielding amino acids as major products of total hydrolysis. According to this definition, any micromolecular peptides or polypeptides of the molecular weight as low as 500–5 000 are not proteins. (The lower limit for the molecular weight of a macromolecular substance is somewhere near 10,000, but in the realm of proteins it seems to be useful to lower this limit to about 5 000, since the chemical molecular weight of insulin is just above this value.) Furthermore, many different α-amino acids, such as alanine, leucine, lysine, phenylalanine, tryptophan, etc. must be found in the hydrolysis products, and these must comprise the major portion of the products; the other minor components may include some carbohydrates, lipids, porphyrins, etc. All of the α-amino acids isolated from the hydrolysis products of proteins, except glycine, are optically active and of the same L-configuration.

A complete exact classification of proteins is very difficult. The old classifications were based on either chemical composition or solubility behavior, and they never have been satisfactory. More modern classifications include such characteristics as molecular shape and electrophoretic mobility. In reality, the variety in chemical composition, structure, and configuration is so great that any classification covers only part of this variety. Moreover, the structure and configuration of many proteins is little investigated, and it is quite possible that many difficulties in classification, as well as about the general behavior of these macromolecules, will be solved when chemists will know more about structure and configuration. So much, however, is already known about the macromolecular morphology that one can classify all proteins into *globular* (also called corpuscular or sphero-proteins) and *fibrous* (linear)

(1) CHARLES TANFORD in *Symposium on Protein Structure* p. 45 (A. NEUBERGER, ed.), Methuen, London, Wiley, New York, 1958.

proteins. In cells and tissues, the former serve either as vehicles (e.g. serum albumin, hemoglobin), or as active enzymes and hormones, while fibrous proteins serve as structural materials. It may be useful at this moment to forget about the structural proteins and to concentrate attention to the globular proteins. These may be further classified into sub-groups according to their molecular weights, chemical composition, or functions. The electrophoretic mobility also is a useful criterion for classification, if the conditions of electrophoresis are specified. The following scheme, which certainly is crude and incomplete, may be helpful in distinguishing some of the major groups:

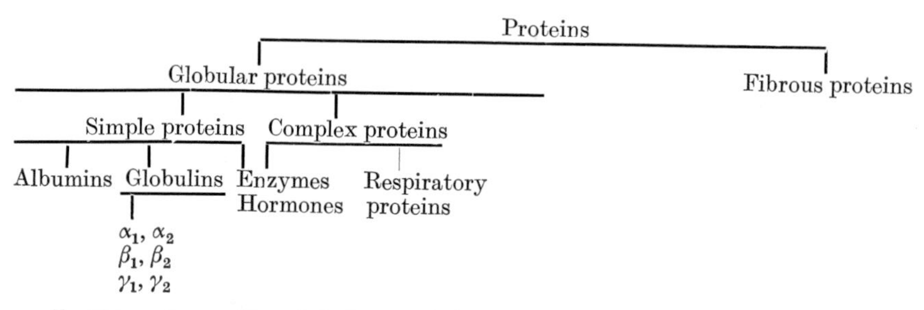

In this scheme the globular proteins are subdivided into simple and complex proteins the former yielding only amino acids on hydrolysis, while the latter contain a certain portion of other constituents. However, some albumins, e.g. the albumin from egg white, contain some carbohydrate, as do some globulins. The albumins differ from globulins chiefly in the electrophoretic mobility, as well as in solubility. The globulins are classified according to electrophoretic mobility into the α, β, and γ groups, and sometimes also in euglobulins and pseudoglobulins; the former are soluble only in dilute salt solutions not in pure water, while the latter are soluble also in water. The enzymes may be either simple or complex proteins. The group of the complex proteins includes many other types of proteins not mentioned in the scheme, e.g. the lipoproteins containing a lipid component. The mucoproteins and nucleoproteins are very complex macromolecules, and they are asymmetric. The mucoproteins contain a large carbohydrate component, while the nucleoprotein represents a compound of nucleic acids with several proteins. The casein of milk and phosvitin of egg yolk contain phosphoric acid. The hemoglobins, myoglobin, and certain other proteins contain a colored porphyrin group (hem), and many enzymes contain a small but metabolically very important active nonprotein component.

Terminal Groups and Amino Acid Sequence in the Polypeptide Chain

The basic principles about the chemical structure of proteins have been established by Emil Fischer and his school about 50 years ago. It is well known that the amino acids are linked by peptide bonds —CO—NH— in which the carbonyl part —CO— comes from the carboxyl group of the one amino acid and the imino group —NH— from the amino group of another amino acid. Meantime many small peptides have been isolated from partial hydrolysis products of proteins, and the identity of these peptides has been established by syntheses from amino acids and their derivatives.[1,2,3,4] Especially important were the facts that both natural and synthetic peptides were attacked by proteolytic enzymes, while several other structures proposed by some authors were resistant to enzymes. The presence of peptide bonds in proteins and polypeptides was ascertained also by physical chemical studies, such as *X*-ray structural analysis and infrared spectroscopy.[5]

In spite of these achievements, there were no methods available which could reveal the amino acid sequence in the macromolecules of proteins, i.e. establish the detailed primary structure of the polypeptide chain. Big strides toward this goal were made only in the late forties when Sanger introduced his method of dinitrophenylation of the N-terminal amino acids, and when the sensitive chromatographic micromethods (Martin, Synge, *et al.*) were available for the identification. At about the same time great progress was made in the understanding of the chain configuration. Methods appeared also for unraveling the sequence at the other end of the chain — the C-terminal. The chain can be envisaged as follows:

$$\underset{\text{N-terminal}}{NH_2{-}CH(R){-}CO}\,\vdots\,NH{-}CH(R_1){-}CO{-}NH{-}CH(R_2){-}CO{-}\cdots{-}NH{-}CH(R_n){-}CO\,\vdots\,\underset{\text{C-terminal}}{NH{-}CH(R_m){-}COOH}$$

It must, however, be realized that the protein molecules are so large and relatively unstable that it is virtually impossible to unravel the whole sequence by simply nibbling the chain from both ends. It appears expedient to chop the chain to smaller fragments (polypeptides), to study their sequence, and then to try to envisage the order of the fragments in the chain. This has been accomplished thus far only with insulin,[6] while several other small proteins, notably ribonuclease[7] and lysozyme[8] are still studied extensively, and

[2] H. Neurath and K. Bailey (ed.), *The Proteins* Academic Press, New York, Vol. I A and B, 1953, Vol. II A and B, 1954.

[3] H. D. Springall, *The Structural Chemistry of Proteins* Butterworth, London, 1954.

[4] M. Goodman and G. W. Kenner, *Adv. Protein Chem.* **12**, 465 (1957).

[5] C. H. Bamford, A. Elliott and W. E. Hanby, *Synthetic Polypeptides* Academic Press, New York, 1956.

[6] F. Sanger, in *Currents in Biochemical Research* p. 434 (D. E. Green, ed.), Interscience, New York, 1956; A. P. Ryle, F. Sanger, L. F. Smith and R. Kitai, *Biochem. J.* **60**, 541 (1955).

[7] C. H. W. Hirs, W. H. Stein and S. Moore, in *Symposium on Protein Structure* p. 211 (A. Neuberger, ed.), Methuen, London, Wiley, New York, 1958; also: C. B. Anfinsen, *ibid.*, p. 223.

[8] P. Jollès, J. Jollès-Thaureaux and C. Fromageot, in *Symposium on Protein Structure* p. 277, 1958.

their amino acid sequence probably will be fully established in the near future.*

The fluorodinitrophenyl method or dinitrophenylation method (*DNP method*) of Sanger [9] is illustrated in the following reaction scheme:

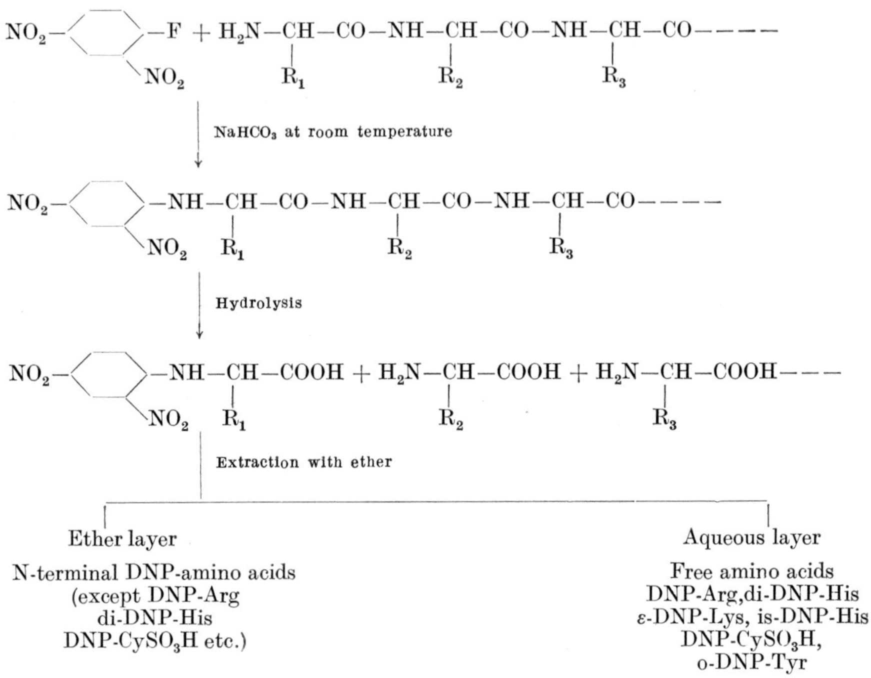

$$NO_2-C_6H_3(NO_2)-F + H_2N-\underset{R_1}{CH}-CO-NH-\underset{R_2}{CH}-CO-NH-\underset{R_3}{CH}-CO----$$

$$\downarrow \text{NaHCO}_3 \text{ at room temperature}$$

$$NO_2-C_6H_3(NO_2)-NH-\underset{R_1}{CH}-CO-NH-\underset{R_2}{CH}-CO-NH-\underset{R_3}{CH}-CO----$$

$$\downarrow \text{Hydrolysis}$$

$$NO_2-C_6H_3(NO_2)-NH-\underset{R_1}{CH}-COOH + H_2N-\underset{R_2}{CH}-COOH + H_2N-\underset{R_3}{CH}-COOH---$$

Extraction with ether

Ether layer	Aqueous layer
N-terminal DNP-amino acids (except DNP-Arg di-DNP-His DNP-$CySO_3H$ etc.)	Free amino acids DNP-Arg,di-DNP-His ε-DNP-Lys, is-DNP-His DNP-$CySO_3H$, o-DNP-Tyr

In the first step, the protein is treated with fluorodinitrobenzene, whereby the terminal amino group (and other active groups of the side chains R) reacts forming a dinitrophenyl derivative of the protein. In the following step, this derivative is hydrolyzed, and the hydrolysis products are separated and identified by chromatography. For this purpose, of course, a complete set of the DNP-amino acids to be expected in the protein must be at hand. The N-terminal amino acids of many proteins have been determined by this method.

* *Note added in proof.* During the years 1958—61 the complete sequence in ribonuclease, tobacco mosaic virus proteins, as well as in some relatively small hormones has been clarified.

(9) F. SANGER, *Biochem. J.* **39**, 507 (1954); *Adv. Protein Chem.* **7**, 1 (1952).

Another widely applicable method for the study of the N-terminal sequence is the phenylthiocarbamyl (PTC) method of Edman [10] illustrated below:

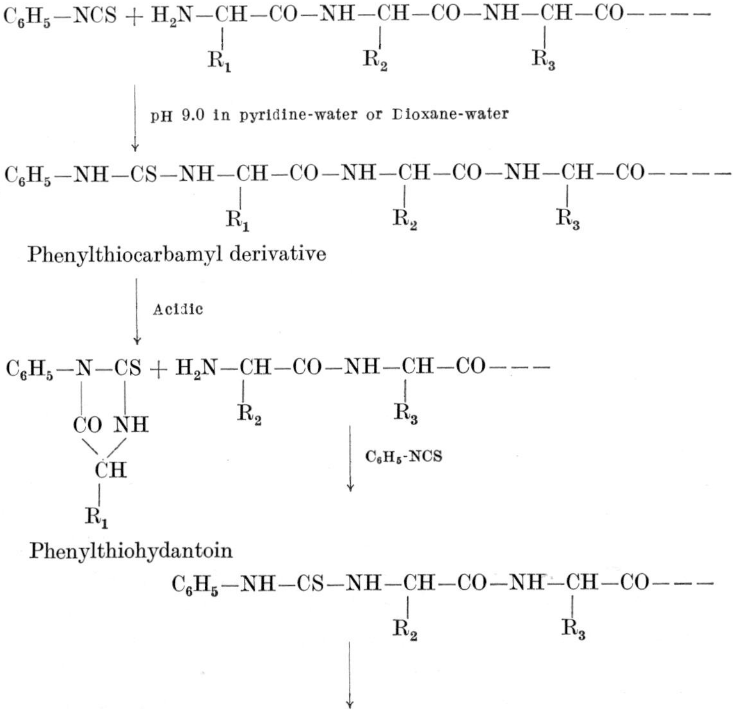

$$C_6H_5{-}NCS + H_2N{-}\underset{R_1}{CH}{-}CO{-}NH{-}\underset{R_2}{CH}{-}CO{-}NH{-}\underset{R_3}{CH}{-}CO{-}{-}{-}{-}$$

↓ pH 9.0 in pyridine-water or Dioxane-water

$$C_6H_5{-}NH{-}CS{-}NH{-}\underset{R_1}{CH}{-}CO{-}NH{-}\underset{R_2}{CH}{-}CO{-}NH{-}\underset{R_3}{CH}{-}CO{-}{-}{-}{-}$$

Phenylthiocarbamyl derivative

↓ Acidic

$$C_6H_5{-}N{-}CS + H_2N{-}\underset{R_2}{CH}{-}CO{-}NH{-}\underset{R_3}{CH}{-}CO{-}{-}{-}$$

(ring: N—CS, CO NH, CH, R_1)

Phenylthiohydantoin

↓ C_6H_5-NCS

$$C_6H_5{-}NH{-}CS{-}NH{-}\underset{R_2}{CH}{-}CO{-}NH{-}\underset{R_3}{CH}{-}CO{-}{-}{-}$$

↓

The phenylthiohydantoins formed in the reaction with the N-terminal amino acids are identified by chromatography. In favorable cases, not only the terminal but also the next (second, third, etc. up to about seventh) amino acid can be identified.

The *C-terminal* amino acids could be determined in some cases by reduction with lithium-aluminium hydride $LiAlH_4$, whereby the C-terminal amino acid is reduced to the corresponding amino alcohol. [11] Better results have been achieved by the hydrazinolysis method of Akabori. [12] Degradation of the protein with hydrazine converts all amino acids into hydrazides, except the C-terminal amino acid. The following steps involve aldehyde treatment, and extraction and identification of the C-terminal amino acid in the form of

(10) P. Edman, *Acta. Chem. Scand* **4**, 283 (1950); **7**, 700 (1953).

(11) C. Fromageot and M. Jutisz, in *The Chemical Structure of Proteins* p. 82 (G. E W. Wolstenholme and M. P. Cameron, ed.), Little and Brown, Boston, 1953.

(12) S. Akabori, K. Ohno, T. Ikenaka, Y. Okada, H. Hanafusa, I. Haruna, A. Tsugita, K. Sugae and T. Matsushima, *Bull. chem. Soc. Japan* **29**, 507 (1956); see also: G. Braunitzer, *Angew. Chem.* **69**, 189 (1957); C. I. Niu and H. Fraenkel-Conrat, *J. Amer. chem. Soc.* **77**, 5882 (1955).

its DNP-dervative by chromatography, as briefly shown below:

$$\cdots -NH-\underset{R_{n-2}}{CH}-CO-NH-\underset{R_{n-1}}{CH}-CO-NH-\underset{R_n}{CH}-COOH$$

$$\downarrow NH_2\text{-}NH_2 \; 100°C$$

$$NH_2-\underset{R_{n-2}}{CH}-CONHNH_2 + NH_2-\underset{R_{n-1}}{CH}-CONHNH_2 + NH_2-\underset{R_n}{CH}-COOH$$

$$\downarrow \text{Aldehyde treatment } (+C_6H_5CHO)$$

$$NH_2-\underset{R_{n-2}}{CH}-CONHN{=}CHC_6H_5 + NH_2-\underset{R_{n-1}}{CH}-CONHN{=}CHC_6H_5 + NH_2-\underset{R_n}{CH}-COOH$$

$$\downarrow \text{Dinitrophenylation}$$

$$DNP-NH-\underset{R_n}{CH}-COOH$$

Another important way to study the amino acid sequence from the C-terminal is the *carboxypeptidase method.* [13] Carboxypeptidase is a proteolytic enzyme which attacks a peptide or protein gradually from the chain end that contains the free carboxyl group. The released amino acids then are determined by paper chromatography, either as free acids or their DNP-derivatives. After a certain time of digesting the protein, the C-terminal amino acid is found in the highest concentration, the next one in a smaller concentration, and so on.

Each of these methods have their imperfections and pitfalls which we cannot discuss here in detail. For example, the carboxypeptidase is unable to release proline if this amino acid happens to be the C-terminal. Also one has to be certain that the carboxypeptidase used does not contain some other proteolytic enzymes which may chop off larger pieces of the chain, and the C-terminals of which then would be attacked by the carboxypeptidase, thus producing erroneous results.

A step-wise degradation from both the N- and C-terminal, however, cannot reveal the whole long sequence of the chain, especially of the long chains; which are often therefore intentionally split to shorter fragments, as indicated before. Enzymic hydrolysis is often used for this purpose, taking advantage of the fact that certain proteolytic enzymes preferentially attack certain amino acid pairs. Chymotrypsin, for example, preferentially attacks the peptide bonds in which the carbonyl group belongs to either phenylalanine, tyrosine, tryptophan, or methionine, while trypsin hydrolyzes the bonds in which the carbonyl belongs to either lysine or arginine (see the following scheme). This has been established by enzymic hydrolysis studies on small

[13] H. Fraenkel-Conrat, J. I. Harris and A. L. Levy, in *Methods of Biochemical Analysis* Vol. II, p. 359 (D. Glick, ed.), Interscience, New York.

well investigated peptides. It is then easy to see that this approach should help considerably in finding out the correct arrangement of the fragments in the chain.

Specificity of Proteinases

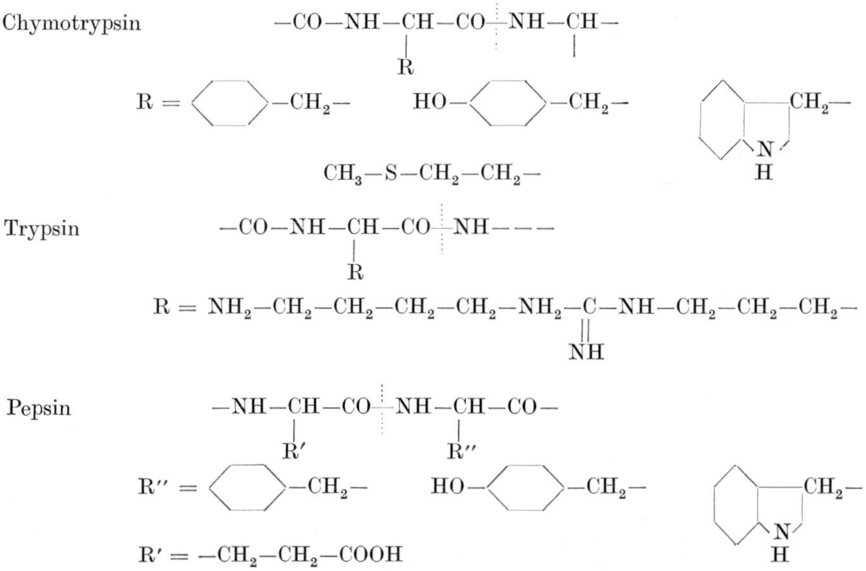

Chymotrypsin —CO—NH—CH(R)—CO ⋮ NH—CH—

R = C_6H_5—CH_2— HO—C_6H_4—CH_2— (indolyl)—CH_2—

CH_3—S—CH_2—CH_2—

Trypsin —CO—NH—CH(R)—CO ⋮ NH———

R = NH_2—CH_2—CH_2—CH_2—CH_2— NH_2—C(=NH)—NH—CH_2—CH_2—CH_2—

Pepsin —NH—CH(R′)—CO ⋮ NH—CH(R″)—CO—

R″ = C_6H_5—CH_2— HO—C_6H_4—CH_2— (indolyl)—CH_2—

R′ = —CH_2—CH_2—COOH

Some of the well established sequences in the most important proteins will be presented in the following chapters. For a biologist, most interesting are the differences found in the same protein of various species. Differences have been found not only in terminal groups but also somewhere in the middle of the chain,[14] as it has been found e.g. with the insulins, hemoglobins, and cytochrome-*c*. "Biologists should realize that before long we shall have a subject which might be called 'protein taxonomy' — the study of the amino acid sequences of the proteins of an organism and the comparison of them between species. It can be argued that these sequences are the most delicate expression possible of the phenotype of an organism and that vast amounts of evolutionary information may be hidden away within them".[15]

The Number of Polypeptide Chains in the Macromolecules of Proteins

A macromolecule of a simple protein may be built of either one or more chains. In order to determine the number of chains, two sorts of data are needed: (1) quantitative data on terminal amino acids, and (2) molecular

[14] H. TUPPY, in *Symposium on Protein Structure* p. 66 (A. NEUBERGER, ed.), Methuen, London, Wiley, New York, 1958.

[15] F. H. C. CRICK, in *The Biological Replication of Macromolecules* p. 142 (Soc. for Experim. Biol. Symposia), Academic Press, New York, 1958.

weight. When one mole of a terminal amino acid is found per one mole of protein, there is only a single polypeptide chain in each molecule. When several N- or C-terminal amino acids have been found by means of the DNP- and hydrazinolysis methods, the molecule probably contains more than one chain. If, for example, six DNP-amino acids are found in equal amounts by the Sanger method for one mole of protein, it is very probable that there are six chains. If, however, one of the DNP-amino acids is found in the amount of nearly one mole per mole protein and the other DNP-amino acids only in small amounts, i is well possible that the protein used has not been homogeneous but contained small amounts of other proteins. Ribonuclease is an one chain protein, whereas the insulin molecule is composed of two chains. The macromolecules of horse hemoglobin contain six chains (see chapt. 14).

Intra- and Inter-chain Bonding and Configuration of Proteins

Amino acid residues in a polypeptide chain are linked by primary covalent bonds. However, we have thus far completely disregarded the side groups (R) hanging at the main chain. The basic amino acids, such as lysine, contain a free basic amino group, while aspartic and glutamic acid have each one free carboxyl group. The possibility of intra- or inter-chain salt bond formation between these free basic and acid groups must be considered. Another possibility would be a cross-reaction between the hydroxy groups of the hydroxy amino acids and the carboxyl groups. Although such intra- and inter-chain bonding has been frequently considered, there is no definite proof that such salt or ester bridges really exist in proteins. There is, however, a third type of covalent intra- and inter-chain bonding which has been experimentally established — the *disulfide* linking. The disulfide bridges can be thought to originate either by polycondensation at all four functional groups of cystine (2 amino and 2 carboxyl) groups or by oxydation of two adjacent sulfhydryl (thiol) groups —SH. The bridge can be visualized as follows:

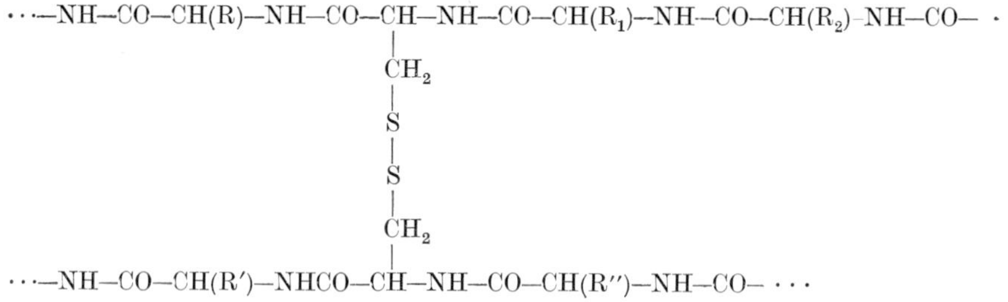

```
···—NH—CO—CH(R)—NH—CO—CH—NH—CO—CH(R1)—NH—CO—CH(R2)—NH—CO— ·
                       |
                       CH2
                       |
                       S
                       |
                       S
                       |
                       CH2
                       |
···—NH—CO—CH(R′)—NHCO—CH—NH—CO—CH(R″)—NH—CO— ···
```

The disulfide bridges can be broken without any damage to the other covalent bonds by either oxidation at low temperature with performic acid [16] or by

[16] C. H. W. Hirs, *J. biol. Chem.* **219**, 611 (1956).

reduction. [17] In this oxidation each disulfide is converted into two $-SO_3H$ groups, and the reaction is irreversible, viz.:

$$\cdots -CH_2-S-S-CH_2- \cdots \xrightarrow{+O} 2 \cdots -CH_2-SO_3H.$$

Upon reduction, each disulfide bond is converted into two —SH groups, and the reaction may be reversible, viz.:

$$\cdots -CH_2-S-S-CH_2- \cdots \underset{+O}{\overset{+H}{\rightleftarrows}} 2 \cdots -CH_2-SH.$$

In order to prevent the reoxidation, the reduction is immediately followed by a treatment with iodoacetic acid, viz.:

$$\cdots -CH_2-SH + ICH_2COOH \rightarrow \cdots -CH_2-SCH_2COOH.$$

The reduction is usually carried out with thioglycolic acid, and the reduction and carboxymethylation of the reduced protein is accomplished under a nitrogen atmosphere.

The oxidative cleavage of disulfide bridges has rendered invaluable service in the structural studies on insulin and ribonuclease. If the oxidation is carried out at a sufficiently low temperature, hydrolysis of the peptide bonds can be avoided, and this possibility of hydrolysis can always be tested by determining the terminal amino acids of the oxidized protein. Now, if the protein in question is composed of two polypeptide chains bound through disulfide bridges, the molecular weight after oxidation or reduction will decrease; while in the case of a disulfide loop at a single chain the molecular weight will not be affected by either oxidation or reduction. A complete hydrolysis of the oxidized protein yields a certain amount of cysteic acid $HOOC-CH(NH_2)CH_2SO_3H$ which can be determined by chromatographic methods.

According to Linderstrom-Lang, [18] the covalent linkages of the peptide chain as well as the disulfide bridges represent what is called the *primary structure* of the protein. It is obvious that in the case of a single chain the disulfide bridges can only form rings or loops at the chain, as it is actually known to happen in several instances. In the instances of two- or poly-chain structure the disulfide bridges usually link the chains. Branching of the chains also can be envisaged, e.g. when the polycondensation occurs at three functional groups of either cystine or such three-functional amino acids as lysine or glutamic acid.

Now, it is important to bear in mind that the primary bonds alone do not determine the configuration of the chains, but that very important are also the secondary interactions between the polar groups, especially the oxygen of the carbonyl —CO— and the hydrogen of the imide —NH—. Hydrogen bonding between these groups within the same chain or between adjacent chains is known to be important in stabilizing the configuration. It has been assumed that in certain instances the chain assumes the shape of a spiral

[17] M. Sela, F. H. White and C. B. Anfinsen, *Science* **125**, 691 (1957); *Biochim. Biophys. Acta* **31**, 417 (1959).

[18] K. Linderstrom-Lang, *Proteins and Enzymes* p. 58, Lane Medical Lectures, Stanford University Press, Stanford, Calif., 1952.

or helix, and the configuration is stabilized by intramolecular hydrogen bonding between those carbonyl and imino groups which happen to come close to each other on this twisting. This represents the so called *secondary structure* of the protein.

The helical configuration of the chains has been established in a few linear proteins, such as collagen (see chapt. 17), while hydrogen bonding between adjacent chains appears to be important in such fibrous proteins as silk.[5,19] The problems of the structure and configuration of the globular proteins, however, require additional considerations, since the chain or chains must be folded in order to have a compact globular shape. The number of chains in globular proteins usually is very small, thus they must be folded many times. This leads to the question on the folding or *tertiary* structure of the chains. First of all, there are reasons to believe that the folding in each globular protein is specific and different. Only by assuming a unique folding in each case can be understood the high specificity of antibodies (chapt. 23) and the specificity of proteolytic enzymes (chapt. 15). It is inconceivable that the folding is at random; it must have a specific pattern in each case. What these patterns are in each case is not known. For example, we do not know how the single chain of serum albumin or pepsin is folded. The most powerful method from which the answers are expected is the X-ray structural analysis, and it has given some encouraging results with myoglobin (see chapt. 5). It has been established that the chain of this small protein of molecular weight about 17,000 is folded several times, but it is impossible to see the exact configuration at the points of folding; nor is it possible yet to allocate the various side groups R_1, R_2, ...[20] Moreover, it is not altogether certain that the macromolecules of the myoglobin in a crystal have the same configuration as in solution. It has been pointed out that the chain in a globular protein may turn at the loci containing proline, since in this case both the basic N (in this instance devoid of H) and carboxyl group belong to a ring, viz.:

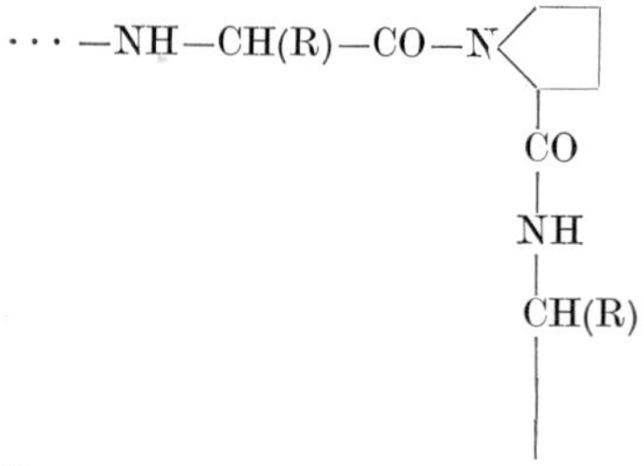

```
· · · —NH—CH(R)—CO—N<  ring
                    |
                    CO
                    |
                    NH
                    |
                    CH(R)
                    |
```

There is, however, no direct proof that proline is responsible for the folds; on the contrary, collagen and gelatin, although rich in proline, do not fold but are known as fibrous proteins.

[19] F. H. C. Crick and J. C. Kendrew, *Adv. Protein Chem.* **12**, 134 (1957); M. L. Huggins, *J. Polymer Sci.* **30**, 5 (1958); L. Pauling and R. B. Corey, *Proc. Nat. Acad. Sci.* **37**, 205, 235 (1951).

[20] J. C. Kendrew, *Nature* **182**, 764 (1958); Kendrew *et al.*, *Nature*, **185**, 422 (1960).

What then causes the chains to fold and assume these unique globular configurations? This question has been asked by many investigators but a definite answer has not been given as yet.[21] Tanford showed that there are several factors to consider, and that different proteins possess a compact configuration probably for quite different reasons.[1] First of all, Tanford points out that primary bonds alone, such as disulfide bridges or salt bonds (intramolecular ion pairs), cannot be responsible for folding. This is demonstrated by the facts that many globular proteins contain less disulfide than it would be necessary for the formation of a cross-linked unit. For example, egg albumin ($M = 44{,}000$) contains only two disulfide bridges, yet its macromolecules are almost perfectly spherical. Bacterial amylase is devoid of cystine, i.e. disulfide bridges, yet this protein ($M = 68{,}000$) is a typical globular protein.[22] It is also perfectly clear that the hydrogen bonds alone cannot be made responsible for the folding. First, there is intramolecular hydrogen bonding also in fibrous proteins. Second, in an aqueous solution, the hydrogen bonding between the solvent and the active hydrogen and oxygen of the protein may well overweigh the intramolecular H-bonding so that unfolding rather than folding might be expected.[23] The other factors to be considered for this folding are: the *hydrophobic groups* of the protein, and *electrostatic forces*. The latter were emphasized by Tanford;[1] the free energy was calculated for several models of charge distribution at the isoelectric condition, and it could be shown that this factor may be important for the stability of compact configurations. The importance of hydrophobic groups for the folding has been considered by several authors, notably by Kauzmann.[21] Since many of the hydrophobic groups of the hydrocarbon side chains of proteins (e.g. $R = C_6H_5-$ of phenylalanine or $(CH_3)_2CHCH_2CH$ of leucine) have no affinity to water they must tend to avoid it. They must therefore assemble into a compact unit, as the hydrophobic "tails" of soap do in aqueous solution. In other words: the H-bonded polar water pushes out the hydrophobic segments of the peptide chain which thus is forced to assume a more compact configuration. How complete this folding can be, at what points the chain folds, and how the folds align themselves, will be determined from the composition and primary structure of the chains.*

While the *peptide bonds* and *disulfide* bonds are definitely established in proteins, several other types of primary bonds have been suspected or proven to exist in some special instances. First, the electrovalent *salt bonds* between

[21] W. Kauzmann, in *The Mechanism of Enzyme Action* p. 70 (W. D. McElroy and B. Glass, ed.), J. Hopkins Press, Baltimore, 1954.

[22] S. Akabori, Y. Okada, S. Fujiwara and K. Sugae, *J. Biochem.* (*Tokyo*) **43**, 741 (1956); K. Kuratomi, K. Ono and S. Akabori, *ibid.* **44**, 183 (1957).

[23] W. F. Harrington and J. A. Schellman, *Compt. rend. trav. lab. Carlsberg* **30**, 21 (1956).

* *Note added in proof.* The importance of hydrophobic bonds has been ascertained recently by several authors; see e. g. Tanford *et al.*, *J. Amer. chem. Soc.* **82,** 6028 (1960); B. Jirgensons, *Arch. Biochem. Biophys.* **94,** 59 (1961).

the free carboxyl groups of the aspartic and glutamic acid residues and the basic side chains of lysine or arginine are very probable, although their importance has not been sufficiently verified. Second, *ester bonds* between the free carboxyls and the alcoholic OH-groups of serine, threonine and hydroxyproline have been considered. Their presence has been demonstrated recently in collagen and gelatin,[23a] and it is possible that these bonds play important parts in all proteins which are rich in hydroxyamino acids, such as certain virus proteins, the γ-globulins, and Bence–Jones proteins. Also the proteins which contain in their macromolecules a carbohydrate component as an integral part, may be linked with the carbohydrate by ester bonds. In the macromolecule of pepsin, phosphoric acid forms a diester link between two hydroxyamino side groups in the single chain of pepsin (see chapt. 15).

An excellent review on the primary structure of globular proteins, in connection with problems of configuration and biological activity, has been provided by Anfinsen and Redfield.[24]

Denaturation of Proteins

Denaturation is usually defined as distortion of the secondary and tertiary structure (configuration) of a protein without affecting the primary structure. It may be added that any minor chemical changes, such as acetylation, deamination, salt formation, etc. is not called denaturation, provided that the *configuration** of the chain, remains unaltered. Likewise any disaggregation into subunits or association into larger units is not denaturation, although there is not a complete agreement between protein chemists on this point. There is also some controversy about the disulfide bridges: the reductive or oxidative cleavage of these may or may not be denoted as denaturation. It would be correct to desist from applying this term in those cases when the disulfide bonds are broken without affecting the configuration of the macromolecule. Hydrolytic degradation, either partial or complete, is not denaturation.

Various criteria have been used and are used to assess denaturation, i.e. change of the unique native configuration. Loss of biological activity, loss of solubility, increase in reactivity, and increase in viscosity have been the chief criteria up to the last decades. The first criterion is applicable only to biologically active proteins, such as enzymes, hormones, or antibodies. Moreover, it is not always the most sensitive one, since cases are known where alteration in configuration does not affect enzymic activity. Furthermore, the biological activity in certain instances may be lost without affecting the configuration, e.g. when only the enzymically important coenzyme compo-

[23a] P. M. Gallop, S. Seifter and E. Meilman, *Nature* **183**, 1659 (1959).

[24] C. B. Anfinsen and R. R. Redfield, *Adv. Protein Chem.* **11**, 1 (1956).

* The term "conformation" has been proposed recently for the spatial arrangement of large segments, and term "configuration" is restricted for such cases as L- and D-isomers.

nent is affected. The solubility criterion has its limitations too. Proteins can be precipitated without change in their native state (see chapt. 2), and proteins can be denatured without losing their solubility. In fact, many globulins are highly soluble in the presence of certain denaturing agents, such as urea or guanidine salts. If this criterion is used, the denaturing agent must be removed and the protein solution brought to the isoelectric state. The increase in reactivity is often used as a criterion for biologically inactive proteins such as various albumins and globulins. It is obvious that an unfolded macromolecular chain will be more readily attacked by various reagents than a compactly coiled chain, since some of the reactive groups may be hidden in the interior of the coil and thus be inaccessible to the reagents. Thus denatured proteins are more readily digested by proteolytic enzymes than native proteins. Estimation of denaturation by titration of free sulfhydryl groups (—SH) is another widely applied criterion.[25] Again, its applicability is by no means universal, since in certain instances there is no difference in the reactivity of these groups between the native and denatured state. This obviously is then when the sulfhydryl is on the surface of the native protein. Moreover, many proteins do not contain any free —SH groups at all.

The *increase in viscosity* is a very important criterion, since it clearly indicates the change in gross configuration.[26,27,28,29] However, in this method too the interpretation of the results is not always unequivocal. First, it is conceivable that the first stage of the unfolding of the coils may be followed by a second stage in which the chains refold into even more compact configurations than before. The first stage may be so short that it can be missed entirely, and the refolded unnatural configuration is mistaken for the native configuration. Second, native globular macromolecules, without losing their original secondary and tertiary structure, may polymerize forming linear aggregates exhibiting high viscosity.[30] And, finally, the viscosity may not be sensitive enough if the gross configuration (molecular asymmetry) remains the same, and only some subtle changes in the configuration occur within the large molecule. Generally, the viscosity indicates any changes only in the mechanical properties of the solution, and, even if a definite rise in viscosity is established (without any side effects of aggregation), the actual change of configuration is not easy to assess. This is due to the fact that either

[25] H. NEURATH, J. P. GREENSTEIN, F. W. PUTNAM and J. O. ERICKSON, *Chem. Rev.* **34**, 157 (1944).

[26] W. KAUZMANN *et al.*, *J. Amer. chem. Soc.* **75**, 5139–5171; *J. Cell. Comparat. Physiol.* **47**, 113 (1956).

[27] K. STRACHITSKII and K. FIRFAROVA, *Biokhimiya* **18**, 235 (1953).

[28] M. STERMAN and J. FOSTER, *J. Amer. chem. Soc.* **78**, 3652 (1956).

[29] B. JIRGENSONS, *J. Polymer Sci.* **5**, 179 (1950); *Makromol. Chem.* **18/19**, 48 (1956); **24**, 159 (1957); *Arch. Biochem. Biophys.* **48**, 154 (1954); **71**, 148 (1957).

[30] E. BARBU and M. JOLY, *Discuss. Faraday Soc.* **13**, 77 (1953); M. JOLY, *Progr. Biophysics and Biophys. Chem.* **5**, 168 (1955).

isometric swelling or more or less complete unfolding of the chain may produce the same viscosity effect. Additional light scattering and streaming birefringence studies often are helpful in solving these problems. Tanford recently compiled some illustrative viscosity data of native proteins in comparison to the viscosity for solutions containing either compact spheres, randomly coiled threads, or helical rods. [1] These data, supplemented by a few data on denatured globular proteins, are presented in Table 18.

TABLE 18
INTRINSIC VISCOSITIES OF PROTEINS IN AQUEOUS SOLUTIONS

	Molecular weight	Intrinsic viscosity, dl/g
Rigid impenetrable spheres, density 1·33	any	0·019
Random coil	50,000	0·47
Helical rod	66,000	0·45
Ribonuclease, native, isoelectric	13,680	0·033
Myoglobin, native, isoelectric	17,000	0·031
β-Lactoglobulin, native, isoelectric	35,000	0·034
Pepsin, native	35,000	0·034
Ovalbumin, native, isoelectric	44,000	0·043
Serum albumin, native, isoelectric	65,000	0·037
Serum albumin, acid, pH 2·5	65,000	0·20
Serum albumin, unfolded	65,000	0·22–0·40
Hemoglobin, native, isoelectric	67,000	0·036
Conalbumin, native, isoelectric	77,000	0·038
γ-Globulin, native, isoelectric, pH 6–7	160,000	0·05–0·07
γ-Globulin, pH 10·7	160,000	0·13
γ-Globulin, pH 11·6	160,000	0·22
γ-Globulin, heated with 3 M guanid. HCNS	160,000	0·23

The data for the denatured proteins are from partially unpublished results of the author. The rather wide limit of 0·22–0·40 of the unfolded serum albumin seems to indicate different degrees of unfolding. The highest values for the intrinsic viscosity were obtained with specimens of oxidized albumin in 4 *M* guanidine thiocyanate. The disulfide bridges were broken by oxidation with performic acid at a low temperature, and it was shown that no hydrolytic cleavage of the chain thereby occurred. The oxidized albumin was then purified and dissolved in a guanidine salt solution. [31] Since unoxidized albumin in the same solvent gave lower intrinsic viscosity values of 0·26, the disulfide bridges apparently link some distant part of the chain, and they are partially responsible for the globular configuration. However, it is also obvious that their role is not decisive, since denaturation of the unoxidized albumin with the same reagent produced an increase of the in-

[31] B. JIRGENSONS and T. IKENAKA, *Makromol. Chem.* **31**, 112 (1959).

trinsic viscosity from 0·037 of the native state to 0·26 of the denatured state. Moreover, it was found in this laboratory that bacterial amylase, a protein of the same size as serum albumin but devoid of any disulfide bridges, [22] rendered in 4 *M* guanidine thiocyanate the same intrinsic viscosity of 0·40 as the unfolded serum albumin. According to the data presented in Table 18 by Tanford, this value is close to both the random coil and helical rod values. Which one of these configurations is present is difficult to decide from viscosity data alone, but optical rotation studies indicate that random coil is the actual configuration (see next section).

There are several other criteria for the native state and denaturation of proteins. It is known that denatured proteins do not crystallize; hence, when a protein can be crystallized, it very probably is in a native state. This criterion, however, cannot always be applied. First, when a protein is not in a crystalline state it does not mean that it is denatured, e.g. the many immunochemically active γ-gobulins do not crystallize. Second, one should suspect that crystallinity is not the most senstive criterion for the native state. The only requirement for crystallization is a ertain regular shape of the macromolecules, and it is conceivable that minor alterations inside these macromolecular bodies may not hamper crystallization.

Several other important aspects of denaturation have been discussed in recent reviews. [32] These aspects include the kinetics and thermodynamics of the process, the reversibility, and possibility of steps, as well as the individual behavior of various proteins toward different denaturing agents. The equilibrium constant and standard free energy change, as well as the entropy of the process have been determined in a few instances of reversible denaturation. The conclusions about reversibility are subject to doubt, because in none of these cases has the reversibility of denaturation been fully established. Usually only one or two criteria for estimating the denaturation have been applied. While one criterion may indicate reversibility, two usually show some difference. The writer usually applies three or four criteria, and only in a few cases could he find a complete reversibility. It is also very unlikely that a chain which has unfolded and taken a random coil configuration would refold back into the unique regular native state. A reversible transformation, however, is conceivable in those instances when only the chain ends have unfolded, or when the macromolecule had just swollen (see Fig. 63). This leads to the problem of *gradual* or step-wise denaturation. The problem is relatively simple in such disulfide cross-linked proteins as serum albumin (chapt. 13) which can be reversibly denatured by acid or guanidine salts if the disulfide bridges remain intact. The globular macromolecule can just swell, and only the chain ends can unfold, and there must be unlimited inter-

[32] F. W. PUTNAM, in *The Proteins* Vol. I B, 1953, p. 807 (H. NEURATH and K. BAILEY, ed.), Academic Press, New York; S. W. FOX and J. F. FOSTER, *Protein Chemistry* chapt. 17, p. 304, Wiley, New York, 1957.

mediate stages. For multi-chain proteins such as hemoglobin, or for one chain proteins without any or only a few disulfide bridges, the problem is more complex. The problem is often obscured also by the *inhomogeneity* of the protein. When several types of macromolecules are present, the one component may be denatured more readily than the others, and the experimentally observed "steps" then may indicate just the presence of different components reacting differently toward a denaturing agent. Some authors have pointed

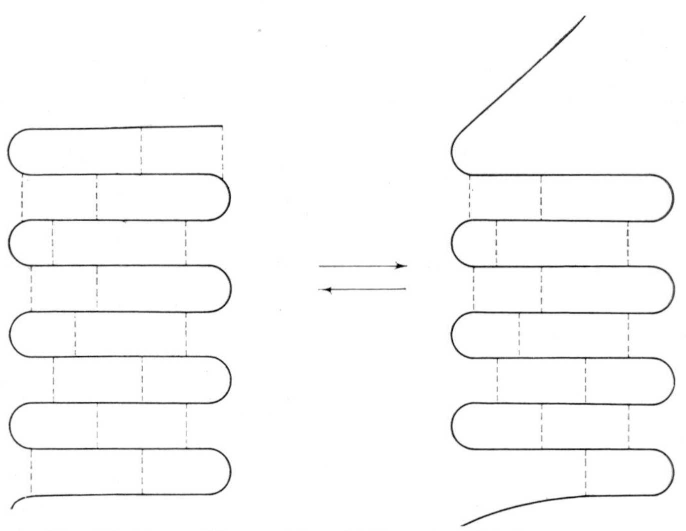

FIG. 63. Reversible partial unfolding of a globular protein

out that a reversible swelling and shrinking of the macromolecules is associated with a considerable change in hydration.[33,34] It also has been suggested that these reversible changes should not be called denaturation, and that this term should be used only for irreversible configurational changes.

The *stability* of various proteins toward *different denaturing agents* shows a bewildering variety. The small proteins, such as ribonuclease and lysozyme are generally more stable than the large proteins (γ-globulin, fibrinogen). However, exceptions from this rule are not uncommon; e.g. the Bence–Jones proteins are smaller than the albumins and γ-globulins yet they are denatured by guanidine salts more readily than the albumins or γ-globulins. Some medium size proteins, such as pepsin, are extremely sensitive to weak alkali (pH 7·5–8, and higher), while most other proteins are quite stable in weak alkali. The stability toward organic solvents and heat also is very different, and it should be remembered that coagulation on heating and denaturation are not exactly the same things. Many proteins, e.g. serum albumin, can be

(33) I. M. KLOTZ, *Science* **128**, 815 (1958).
(34) J. STAUFF and J. RASPER, *Kolloid-Z.* **159**, 97 (1958).

heated up to 70–80 °C without being flocculated if the solution contains a sufficiently high concentration of certain salts (e.g. sodium thiocyanate). The protein is denatured, though it does not coagulate, due to the protective effect of the salt, since coagulation occurs upon dialysis. The aggregation and flocculation effects in heat denaturation are *secondary* processes which follow the actual distortion of the configuration by the thermal bombardment. Moreover, as mentioned in chapt. 2, proteins can be safely precipitated without denaturation if the temperature is low enough. Interesting changes in configuration occur upon spreading a protein solution on surfaces, [35] when the macromolecules seem to be flattened out. These facts about surface denaturation substantiate the concept that the tendency of the lyophobic groups to escape the polar water is the chief force which is responsible for the globular configuration. Denaturation can occur also under various other physical effects, such as irradiation with ultraviolet light. [36]

Optical Rotation and Configuration of Proteins

Optical rotation is one of the most sensitive criteria for denaturation, and it is treated in a special section because the most important work in this field has been done in the last decade, and no recent reviews are available. The usefulness of this approach for the study of the configuration of organic macromolecules in general has already been mentioned in chapt. 5. Most of the work has been done by Doty *et al.*, [37] Kauzmann *et al.*, [21,26] Schellman, [38] and the writer. [29,31,39,40] It has been found that the *specific rotation of globular proteins becomes more negative on denaturation,* and this change has been explored in many ways, e.g. the change was measured at various time intervals, thus studying the course (kinetics) of the process. [21,26] Some of the studies have also been done at various temperatures, thus learning something about the thermodynamics of unfolding (e.g. [21,38]). The *negative shift* of the specific rotation on unfolding or expansion seems to be a general property, although the correlation between this shift and actual change in configuration is by no means a simple one. [41] This is because the rotation depends not only on the folding of the chain but also on the specific contributions of the many asymmetry centers, and on their interactions. This is demonstrated best by the facts that reduction or oxidation of the highly levorotatory cystine residues ($[\alpha]_D = -214$ °C in acid solution) results

[35] H. B. Bull, *Adv. Protein Chem.* **3**, 95 (1947); J. T. Davies, *Biochim. Biophys. Acta* **11**, 165 (1953); D. F. Cheesman and J. T. Davies, *Adv. Protein Chem.* **9**, 439 (1954).

[36] A. D. McLaren, *Adv. Enzymol.* **9**, 75 (1949).

[37] P. Doty and R. D. Lundberg, *Proc. Nat. Acad. Sci.* **43**, 213 (1957); J. T. Yang and P. Doty, *J. Amer. chem. Soc.* **79**, 761 (1957).

[38] J. A. Schellman, *Compt. rend. trav. lab. Carlsberg* **30**, 363, 395, 415, 429, 439, 450; Ch. Schellman and J. A. Schellman, *ibid.* p. 463ff.

[39] B. Jirgensons, *Arch. Biochem. Biophys.* **74**, 57 (1958).

[40] B. Jirgensons, *Arch. Biochem. Biophys.* **78**, 235 (1958); *Makromol. Chem.* **44-46**, 123 (1961).

[41] W. Kauzmann, *Ann. Rev. Phys. Chem.* **8**, 413 (1957).

in a small change of the specific rotation on denaturation. Oxidative [31,42] or reductive [43] cleavage of the disulfide bridges of serum albumin should result in a strong negative shift, if the rotation depended only on unfolding. In reality, the shift upon oxidation or reduction is smaller than on denaturation without oxidation or reduction. This seems to be due to the fact that conver-

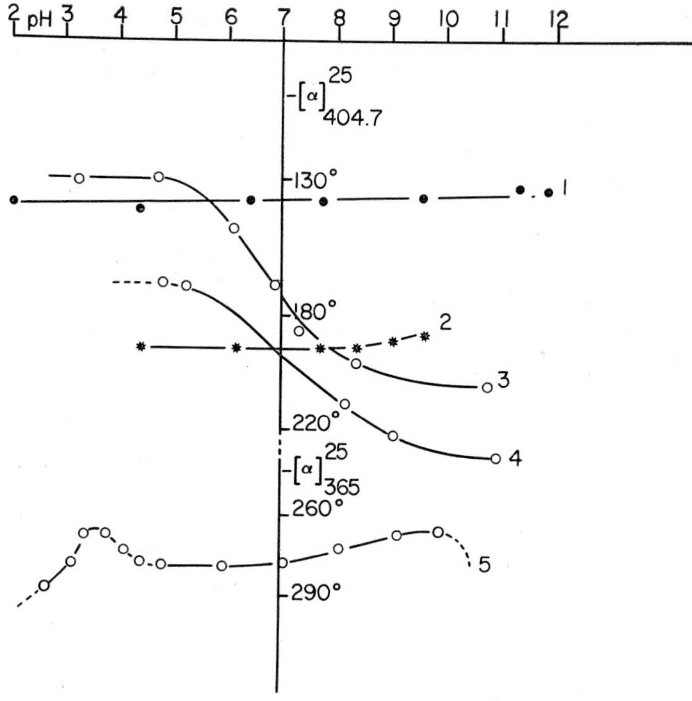

FIG. 64. The change of specific rotation with pH for lysozyme (1), ribonuclease (2), phosvitin (3), pepsin (4), and bovine serum albumin (5). Data of the author

sion of the cystine disulfide into either cysteic acid (on oxidation) or cysteine (on reduction) is associated with an opposite — positive — shift of rotation.

Specific rotation values for several native and denatured proteins are compiled in Table 19.

Fig. 64 demonstrates examples of the dependence of the specific rotation on pH. It is obvious that in the instance of lysozyme, ribunoclease, and serum albumin, there is relatively little change in the specific rotation when the pH of the solutions is varied between 4 and 10, whereas in the instances of phosvitin and pepsin the changes are quite conspicuous. The strong negative shift upon the increase of alkalinity in these two cases is due to changes in

(42) J. E. TURNER, R. T. BOTTLE and F. HAUROWITZ, *J. Amer. chem. Soc.* **80**, 4117 (1958); see also: F. HAUROWITZ, *Progress in Biochemistry since* 1949 p. 204ff., Interscience Publ., New York, London, 1959.

(43) G. MARKUS and F. KARUSH, *J. Amer. chem. Soc.* **79**, 134 (1957).

molecular conformation. Both phosvitin and pepsin are strongly anionic proteins, and the charge density increases considerably when the acid groups react with the added alkali. It can be assumed that this increase in charge density causes the expansion of the macromolecules.

The optical *rotatory dispersion*, i.e. dependence of the specific rotation on the wave length of light also has been employed for the study of the secondary and tertiary structure of proteins.[31, 37, 38, 39, 40] It is noteworthy that the

TABLE 19

SPECIFIC ROTATION OF SOME NATIVE AND DENATURED PROTEINS

(Data of the first section of the Table ($\lambda = 546$ mμ) are from our laboratory; those of the second section are data of Schellman and Schellman,[38] and those in the bottom section are from K. Imahori, E. Klemperer and P. Doty (*Abstracts, Amer. chem. Soc. Nat. Meeting, Miami, Florida*, p. 54 C, April, 1957)

	$[\alpha]_{546}$, native	$[\alpha]_{546}$, denatured
Albumin, serum	−78°	−105° to −115°
β-Globulin, metal binding	−56°	− 88°
γ-Globulin, serum	−66°	−110°
Bence–Jones proteins	−41° to −67°	− 60° to −147°
Amylase, bacterial	−32°	− 77°
Amylase, taka	−15°	− 75°
Pepsin	−79°	− 99°
	$[\alpha]_D$, native	$[\alpha]_D$, in 8–9 *M* urea
Albumin, serum (bovine)	−59°	−108°
Albumin, egg white	−30°	− 98°
β-Lactoglobulin	−28°	−117°
α-Chymotrypsin	−66°	−111°
Chymotrypsinogen	−78°	−116°
Insulin	−30°	− 88°
Ribonuclease	−74°	−108°
Insulin	−36°	− 69° (in 8 *M* urea)
Ovalbumin	−31°	−106°
Myoglobin	−15°	− 71°
Histone, calf thymus	−38° (pH 12)	− 81°
Ribonuclease	−72°	− 94°
Tropomyosin	−16°	−110° (in 10 *M* urea)

dispersion constants (λ_c or λ_0) of the linear proteins have been found about 210 mμ,[44, 37] while the constants of the globular proteins usually are found higher (230–290 mμ). When these globular proteins are denatured, their dispersion constants attain the values of denatured proteins. This has been observed e.g. with egg albumin, serum albumin, and the metal-binding β-globulin. Unfortunately this rule cannot be generalized, since in several

[44] K. LINDERSTROM-LANG and SCHELLMAN, *Biochim. Biophys. Acta* **15**, 156 (1954); C. COHEN, *J. Biophys. Biochem. Cytol.* **1**, 203 (1955); C. COHEN and A. G. SZENT-GYORGYI, *J. Amer. chem. Soc.* **79**, 248 (1957).

instances the dispersion constants of native globular proteins are in the low range (200–220 mμ, and even lower), and they may increase on denaturation. This has been observed, for example, with crystallized pepsin, and with the γ-globulins and Bence–Jones proteins.[40] The dispersion constants of several well investigated globular proteins are compiled in Table 20. Very important is also the finding that in all instances of native and denatured globular or linear proteins the rotatory dispersion follows the linear one-term

TABLE 20

OPTICAL ROTATORY DISPERSION CONSTANTS OF SOME NATIVE AND DENATURED PROTEINS
(The data of the first section of the Table are obtained by the author, those of the second section are from Schellman and Schellman[33])

	Dispersion constant, λ_0, mμ, of native protein	Dispersion constant, λ_0, mμ, of denatured protein
Albumin, serum	265 (± 3)	228–240 (± 3)
Albumin, serum, oxidized		218
Albumin, serum, reduced		229
β-Globulin, serum, metal bind.	242	217
γ-Globulin, serum	*205–217*	*220*
α-Amylase, pancreatic	243	
α-Amylase, taka	271	212
α-Chymotrypsin	229–235	218
Aldolase	277	232
Carboxypeptidase	255	
Lactic acid dehydrogenase	264	210
Papain	231	
Pepsin	*212–216*	*224*
Trypsin	235	220
Trypsin, inhibitor, soy bean	*210*	*223*
Rennin	*210*	*222*
Bence–Jones proteins	*175–208*	*216–223*
Albumin, serum, bovine	265 (± 5)	221 (± 5)
Albumin, egg white	266	226
α-Chymotrypsin	241	220
Chymotrypsinogen	239	224
Insulin	261	220
β-Lactoglobulin	245	225
Ribonuclease	233	220
Oxidized ribonuclease		228

Drude equation* (see p. 110, chapt. 5). Now, it was very interesting to learn that the rotatory dispersion of certain synthetic polyamino acids, notably poly-γ-benzyl-L-glutamate, was the same as that of proteins in those solvents in which the macromolecules were known to be random coils.[45] In certain

* This statement is valid for the wave length range of 350—700 mμ.

[45] P. DOTY, J. H. BRADBURY and A. M. HOLTZER, *J. Amer. chem. Soc.* **78**, 947 (1956); P. DOTY and J. T. YANG, *ibid.* **78**, 498 (1956); P. DOTY and R. D. LUNDBERG, *Proc. Nat. Acad. Sci.* **43**, 213 (1957).

other solvents the same polyamino acid assumed the configuration of helical rods showing a more complex rotatory dispersion behavior. Since everybody wanted to believe that all proteins must be helical, great efforts have been made to reconcile these findings by preserving the helical concept for globular proteins. These attempts have not been very successful, and many questions have not been answered as yet. This is partially due to the difficulties in the theoretical concepts which could be used as basis for correlating rotatory dispersion with configuration.[46,47] According to Yang and Doty,[37] about 10–30% of the chain in a macromolecule of a native globular protein is helical, while the rest is disordered. The macromolecules of denatured proteins definitely seem to be random coils, as indicated by both rotatory dispersion and light scattering data. It is well possible that ordered configurations other than helical are present in native globular proteins.[48]

(46) D. D. Fitts and J. G. Kirkwood, *J. Amer. chem. Soc.* **78**, 2650 (1956).

(47) W. Moffitt, *J. chem. Physics* **25**, 467 (1956).

(48) See a review of S. J. Leach, *Revs. Pure and Applied Chem.* (*Melbourne, Australia*) **9**, 33 (1959); also: A. Elliott, W. E. Hanby and B. R. Malcolm, *Discuss. Faraday Soc.* **25**, 167 (1958); B. Jirgensons, *Makromol. Chem.* **44–46**, 123 (1961).

See also: A. Todd in A Laboratory Manual of Analytical Methods of Protein Chemistry (P. Alexander and R. J. Block, eds), vol. II, *Pergamon Press*, London, 1960; B. Jirgensons, *Tetrahedron* **13**, 166 (1961); J. T. Yang, ibid. p. 143.

CHAPTER 13

ALBUMINS AND GLOBULINS IN ANIMALS AND PLANTS

> Some may perhaps ask how far we should go in our demands as to the purity of proteins, and if there is not a danger that we might become protein "purists", interested in purity for its own sake. Such an argument neglects, however, several facts of importance in protein research to-day. One is that the very character of the modern sequence analysis methods, developed by Sanger, assumes a high degree of homogeneity. It would be an almost hopeless task to fit the puzzle of peptide fragments together, if these residues come from more than one homogeneous protein.
>
> A. TISELIUS [1]

THE MOST important albumins and globulins are relatively large proteins. Rigorous purity and homogeneity tests for such proteins are difficult, and inhomogeneity has been ascertained in many cases. Because of the large molecular size, very little is known about the structure of these proteins, although a considerable progress has been made in learning something about the chemical and physical properties of these macromolecules. The terminal amino acids also are known, and interesting species differences in chemical and physical properties have been established. Since it is impossible to describe in this book all the albumins and globulins thus far studied, only some of the most important examples will be discussed in the following sections.

Serum Albumin [2]

Human and bovine serum albumins have been studied more thoroughly than the albumins from other species. They have been highly purified and crystallized, and they were found to contain 16·0% nitrogen and 1·9% sulfur. Serum albumin is the major protein in blood plasma or serum, and it can be isolated by various methods, such as salting out, fractional precipitation of the plasma proteins with alcohol and certain ions, also by preparative electrophoresis, and by ion exchange chromatography. The salting out procedures are the oldest ones. Most of the other proteins of plasma or serum are salted out first, i.e. by a lower degree of saturation than albumin. After the

[1] A. TISELIUS, in *Symposium on Protein Structure* p. 93 (A. NEUBERGER, ed.), Methuen, London, Wiley, New York, 1958.

[2] W. L. HUGHES, in *The Proteins* Vol. II B, p. 663 (H. NEURATH and K. BAILEY, ed.), Academic Press, New York, 1954; J. F. FOSTER in F. W. PUTNAM (ed.), *The Plasma Proteins*, vol. I, Academic Press, 1960.

removal of the various globulins, albumin is salted out at 0·60–0·62 saturation, i.e. 2·56 *M* ammonium sulfate. Thus precipitated albumin always contains globulins, as can be found most readily by paper electrophoresis. Purer albumin preparations can be isolated by cold ethanol fractionation after Cohn *et al.*,[3] and several fractionation systems have been proposed. For example, according to Cohn's method 10, the albumin is precipitated (from the solutions from which the globulins already removed) with ethanol and zinc acetate in a slightly acid solution. [4] Preparative zone electrophoresis of albumin is based on its high mobility in comparison with the globulins. This is important also for the analytical testing of purity. In the commonly used barbiturate buffer of pH 8·3–8·6 and ionic strength 0·1 the mobility of albumin is −6·0 Tiselius units, [5] while all the globulins remain behind albumin. No carbohydrate should be present in a pure albumin. The ion exchange chromatography, especially on the anion exchanger diethylaminoethyl (DEAE) cellulose, also has been found suitable for the separation and purification of albumin. [6] In all these procedures, including fractionation by organic solvents, electrophoresis, or chromatography, cooling to possibly low temperatures is essential in order to avoid denaturation. The cold alcohol fractionation methods of Cohn *et al.* yield about 95–97% pure albumin, and the traces of globulins can be removed quite conveniently by means of the DEAE–cellulose column fractionation. Crystallized serum albumin, although devoid of carbohydrates and globulin impurities, contains small amounts of bound micromolecular impurities, such as the fatty acids and heavy cations. The ionic impurities can be removed by a mixed bed anion–cation exchanger, according to Dintzis. [7] Several layers of resin are packed in the column: the small bottom layer is an acid form cation exchanger, next is packed the mixed bed cation (H-form) and anion (OH-form) exchanger and on the top is placed a layer of acetate form anion resin and another layer of ammonium form cation exchanger (Fig. 65). When an albumin solution which contains various ionic impurities is poured on the resin, all anions and all cations in the two upper layers are exchanged for acetate and ammonium by maintaining a nearly neutral reaction. In the major mixed-bed middle layer, acetate and ammonium ions too are removed, and a nearly isoelectric pure albumin solution is obtained. Removal of nonionic micromolecular impurities is possible by dialysis, if the contaminating substance in not strongly adsorbed

[3] E. J. Cohn, L. E. Strong, W. L. Hughes, Jr., D. J. Mulford, J. N. Ashworth, M. Melin and H. L. Taylor, *J. Amer. chem. Soc.* **68**, 459 (1946).

[4] E. J. Cohn, F. R. N. Gurd, D. M. Surgenor, B. A. Barnes, R. K. Brown, G. Derouaux, J. M. Gillespie, F. M. Kahnt, W. F. Lever, C. H. Liu, D. Mittelman, R. F. Mouton, K. Schmid and E. Uroma, *J. Amer. chem. Soc.* **72**, 465 (1950).

[5] S. H. Armstrong, Jr., M. J. E. Budka and K. C. Morrison, *J. Amer. chem. Soc.* **69**, 416 (1947).

[6] H. A. Sober, F. J. Cutter, M. M. Wyckoff and E. A. Peterson, *J. Amer. chem. Soc.* **78**, 756 (1956).

[7] H. M. Dintzis, Thesis, Harvard University, 1952.

at the macromolecule. Certain lipids, such as cholesterol, are very difficult to remove. Extraction at a low temperature with lipid solvents may be used, followed by removal of the solvent by evaporation in high vacuum at a low temperature. It is noteworthy that albumin has a considerable affinity to various ionic, polar, and non-polar substances. The ionic and polar impurities are bound at the ionic and polar sites of the macromolecule, while the lipids and other nonpolar substances are adsorbed at the hydrocarbon side chain loci. Since the hydrophobic groups of the macromolecule must be located mostly in the interior of it, the binding of such hydrophobic substances as testosterone [8] indicates a considerable flexibility of configuration.

Albumin is denatured by heating at 70 °C and higher, as well as by alcohols and similar organic substances at room temperatures. The protein is hydrolytically degraded by various proteolytic enzymes, as well as by boiling with acids and alkalies. Amino acid analysis of the digestion products is now accomplished most conveniently by ion exchange chromatography according to Moore and Stein,[9] and the amino acid composition of human and bovine serum albumins, as well as of the oxidized human serum albumin, is presented in Table 21. In comparison, in the same Table are given the older data of Brand [10] for human albumin, and recently published data of Sorm[11] obtained by a paper chromatography method. The amino acid composition was calculated in numbers of

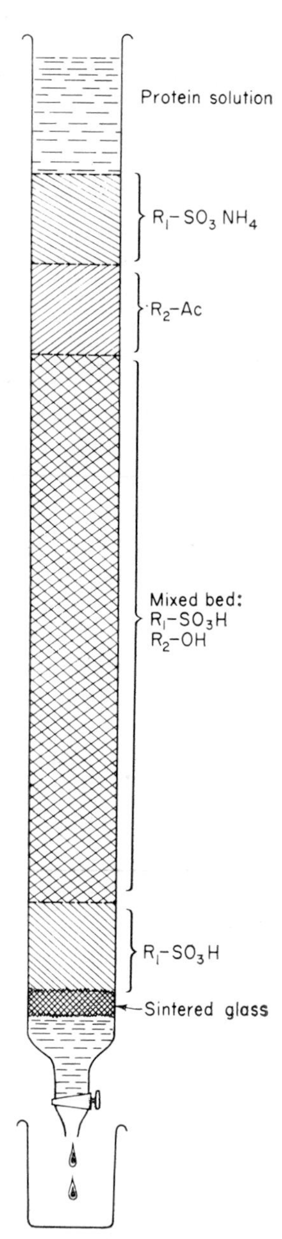

FIG. 65. A multilayer ion exchange column for the deionization of proteins, according to Dintzis

[8] J. A. SCHELLMAN, R. LUMRY and L. T. SAMUELS, *J. Amer. chem. Soc.* **76**, 2808 (1954); B. H. LEVEDAHL and R. PERLMUTTER, *Arch. Biochem. Biophys.* **61**, 442 (1956).

[9] S. MOORE and W. H. STEIN, *J. biol. Chem.* **192**, 663 (1951); **178**, 53 (1949); *Anal. Chem.* **30**, 1185 (1958).

[10] E. BRAND, *Ann. N. Y. Acad. Sci.* **47**, 187 (1946).

[11] F. SORM, in *Symposium on Protein Structure* p. 77 (A. NEUBERGER, ed.), Methuen, London, Wiley, New York, 1958; B. KEIL, *ibid.*, p. 90.

residues per mole protein assuming a molecular weight 65,000, according to the suggestion of Hughes.[2] If a is the percentage of the amino acid, and A the molecular weight of it, the number of residues per mole of albumin can be calculated according to:

Number of residues per mole $= 65{,}000\, a/100\, A$.

TABLE 21

AMINO ACID COMPOSITION (number of residues per mole) OF BOVINE (BA) AND HUMAN SERUM ALBUMIN AND OF OXIDIZED HUMAN SERUM ALBUMIN (OHA)

Amino acid	BA	HA (Sorm)	HA (Brand)	OHA *
Cysteic acid, CysA		24		31 †
Aspartic acid, Asp	50	58	48	48
Threonine, Thr	32	21	25	28 **
Serine, Ser	26	22	20	20
Glutamic acid	75	76	75	72
Proline, Pro	27	26	29	28
Glycine, Gly	17	14	14	13
Alanine, Ala	46	60	—	60
Cystine, Cys/2	34	—	34	—
Cysteine	1	—	1	—
Valine, Val	33	43	43	30
Methionine, Met	4	6	6	—
Isoleucine, Ileu	13	75 (Ileu + Leu)	8	8
Leucine, Leu	61		54	52
Tyrosine, Tyr	18	13 (18)	17	16
Phenylalanine, Phe	26	32	31	31
Histidine, His	17	66 (His + Lys)	15	15
Lysine, Lys	55		55	55
Arginine, Arg	22	23	23	20
Tryptophan, Try	2	2–3	1	—
Amide N	(36)	—	(41)	(40)

* B. JIRGENSONS and T. IKENAKA (unpublished results).
† Cysteic acid determined from oxidized albumin.
** This value includes the methionine sulfone formed on oxidation.

The data presented in Table 21 deserve some comments. First, certain differences between the human and bovine albumins are established, e.g. bovine albumin contains more glycine, serine, and threonine, and less alanine than human serum albumin. Second, it is obvious that different methods yield different results. These differences may be due either to errors and inadequacies of the methods or to inherent individual differences in composition of the albumins themselves. This could be solved by determining the amino acid composition of the same specimens by various methods, and by analysing various individual specimens of human or bovine albumins by exactly the same method. The defects of the methods are clearly indicated, e.g. by the case of tyrosine content, as the 13 residues accounted by paper chromatography seem to be too low (16–18 found by other methods). Likewise, the

24 cysteic acid residues found in Sorm's laboratory seem to be due to incomplete oxidation of the disulfide and sulfhydryl groups. Our results on glutamic acid, valine and arginine may be too low. In our laboratory, work is in progress about amino acid composition of individual specimens of human serum albumin using in all instances the same method of isolation and purification and

TABLE 22

AMINO ACID COMPOSITION OF SERUM ALBUMINS FROM FIVE SPECIES (according to Sorm [11])

Amino acid	Ox	Man	Horse	Duck	Sheep
Cysteic acid	6·5 ± 0·3	6·3 ± 1·1	7·6 ± 0·6	6·9 ± 0·2	6·1 ± 0·28
Lysine + histidine	16·8 ± 0·05	15·3 ± 0·19	17·05 ± 0·18	13·3 ± 0·3	17·1 ± 0·28
Arginine	5·2 ± 0·82	6·25 ± 0·30	5·2 ± 0·21	5·4 ± 0·16	5·6 ± 0·14
Aspartic acid	10·9 ± 0·3	11·9 ± 0·0	10·2 ± 0·1	13·1 ± 0·2	11·6 ± 0·25
Serine	4·2 ± 0·12	3·53 ± 0·4	4·18 ± 0·22	6·1 ± 0·12	4·3 ± 0·12
Glycine	1·8 ± 0·05	1·62 ± 0·05	2·34 ± 0·14	2·5 ± 0·14	2·5 ± 0.16
Glutamic acid	16·5 ± 0·3	17·2 ± 0·0	16·65 ± 0·48	16·1 ± 0·22	15·33 ± 0·36
Threonine	5·8 ± 0·5	3·93 ± 0·36	3·6 ± 0·26	4·1 ± 0·12	5·2 ± 0·12
Alanine	6·25 ± 0·08	8·2 ± 0·2	7·85 ± 0·45	6·6 ± 0·15	6·7 ± 0·07
Proline	4·7 ± 0·0	4·6 ± 0·0	4·3 ± 0·0	{10·8 ± 0·15	9·3 ± 0·3
Tyrosine	5·0 ± 0·1	3·75 ± 0·8	3·88 ± 0·02	{	
Methionine	0·8 ± 0·03	1·77 ± 0·12	—	4·5 ± 0·2	1·0 ± 0·09
Valine	5·9 ± 0·35	7·76 ± 0·3	4·0 ± 0·23	4·2 ± 0·26	6·8 ± 0·23
Phenylalanine	6·6 ± 1·02	8·1 ± 0·87	8·25 ± 0·77	6·6 ± 0·36	9·0 ± 0·57
Leucine + isoleucine	14·8 ± 0·42	15·18 ± 0·5	15·10 ± 0·77	11·3 ± 0·39	14·6 ± 0·26
Methionine	0·76	1·14	0·46	1·14	0·81
Tyrosine	5·62	5·20	4·43	5·66	5·67
Tryptophan	1·43	0·88	1·08	0·62	1·11

the same amino acid analysis method. Since only small differences could be found between the human and bovine albumins, the differences within the same species may be even smaller, if any, and the present methods may not be good enough to ascertain any possible very small differences. The reproducibility of the determinations by running parallel samples and repetition has been tested in Professor Sorm's laboratory; moreover, the Czech investigators compared the amino acid composition of serum albumins from five different species. Their results are presented in Table 22. [11] The figures denote grams of amino acid per 100 g of protein, and they are average values of 6–8 independent determinations. The probable errors also are indicated. Methionine, tyrosine, and tryptophan were determined also by different colorimetric methods (last three lines).

The results presented in Table 22 show that the amino acid composition of the albumins from the five species is similar, yet some small differences seem to be ascertained. The albumin from duck blood serum, the most distant species from the others, has less lysine + histidine and leucine + isoleucine, and more aspartic acid, serine, and methionine than the albumins of the mammals. The good agreement between the results of Table 22 on bovine albumin and those of Moore and Stein (with the exception of tyrosine and tryptophan) is noteworthy. The albumin of man has a slightly higher content of arginine, glutamic acid, and alanine, and a very slightly lower glycine and serine content than the other mammals. It is also obvious that a higher accuracy would be very desirable. Especially difficult is the problem on the number of residues of the amino acids which are found in a very low concentration. Tryptophan cannot be determined in the acid hydrolyzate, since it is decomposed*, and it must be determined separately, e.g. from alkaline hydrolyzates. The methods for its determination are not sensitive enough considering the low concentration of it.

If the exact number of the tryptophan residues per mole could be established, this would provide an additional criterion for the *homogeneity* and calculation of the exact *chemical molecular weight*. More accurate results for methionine also would be important for the same purpose. Thus far only the exact number of cysteine is known, although not from amino acid analysis but from quantitative studies about the reaction of albumin with mercury compounds.[2,12] It must be pointed out that the residue number 1 for cysteine in Table 21 pertains not to the total albumin but to the *mercaptalbumin subfraction* of bovine or human albumin. It is now established that 60–70% of all macromolecules of these albumins contain one free sulfhydryl belonging to cysteine, while the rest of the macromolecules are devoid of this —SH group.[7,12] The mercaptalbumin component is isolated as the mercaptalbumin Alb—SH mercury dimer by means of the reaction

$$2\,\text{Alb—SH} + \text{HgCl}_2 \rightarrow \text{Alb—S—Hg—S—Alb} + 2\,\text{HCl}.$$

The reaction is slow and partially reversible, since it proceeds in two steps, viz.:

$$\text{Alb—SH} + \text{HgCl}_2 \rightleftharpoons \text{Alb—S—Hg—Cl} + \text{HCl, and}$$

$$\text{Alb—S—Hg—Cl} + \text{Alb—SH} \rightleftharpoons \text{Alb—S—Hg—S—Alb} + \text{HCl}.$$

Ten times recrystallized bovine mercaptalbumin mercury dimer is now commercially available.

The 34 half-cystine groups found in bovine or human albumins belong to 17 cystine residues which form 17 disulfide bridges between various parts of the polypeptide chain. It seems likely that the heavier component observed in sedimentation experiments in some albumin solutions (especially old pre-

* Tryptophan reacts with the traces of carbohydrate present in the protein, and also with the hydroxyamino acids (serine and threonine) releasing ammonia and forming dark insoluble "humin". The directly found serine and threonine content thus may be a little too low.

[12] W. L. Hughes, *Cold Spring Harbor Symp. Quant. Biol.* **14**, 79 (1950).

parations) is formed in a peculiar polymerization involving the sulfhydryl and disulfide bonds, viz: [13]

$$R_1{-}SH + \begin{matrix} S \\ | \\ S \end{matrix}\!\!>R_2 \rightarrow R_1{-}S{-}S{-}R_2{-}SH,$$

and more molecules can be added to the dimer in a further similar reaction. As indicated in chapt. 12, the positions of the disulfide bridges in the macromolecules is not known but it is likely that some of the 17 bridges link some distant parts of the chain.

The N- and C-terminal amino acids have been determined in albumins of several species, [14] and data are presented in Table 23. The presence of histidine as the third amino acid from the N-terminal of human albumin was established in our laboratory by Dr. T. Ikenaka. [15] While the N-terminal amino acid in all thus far studied species is the same, differences were found already between the second residues. The differences at the C-terminal also are interesting, especially the fact that with respect to the terminal amino acids human serum albumin is more relative to the albumin of dog and rabbit than to ox, cow, or sheep. The finding that valine is the C-terminal in the turkey instead of the alanine found in hens and ducks albumin also is noteworthy. The C-terminal groups of the albumins of the bird species have been determined by both the hydrazinolysis and carboxypeptidase method, and both methods yielded identical results. [16]

TABLE 23
SPECIES DIFFERENCES IN TERMINAL AMINO ACIDS OF ALBUMINS

	N-terminal	C-terminal
Human	Asp-Ala-His- . . .	Leu- . . .
Cow, ox	Asp-Thr- . . .	Ala- . . .
Sheep	Asp-Thr- . . .	Ala- . . .
Horse	Asp-Ala- . . .	Ala- . . .
Pig	Asp-Ala- . . .	Ala- . . .
Dog	Asp-Ala- . . .	Leu- . . .
Rabbit	Asp-Ala- . . .	Leu- . . .
Hen	Asp- . . .	Ala- . . .
Duck	Asp- . . .	Ala- . . .
Turkey	Asp- . . .	Val- . . .

The best values for the molecular weight of serum albumin range between 65,000 and 70,000, and the lower value is now considered to be the more reliable. [17] Since all of the macromolecules are supposed to have the same

(13) C. HUGGINS, D. F. TAPLEY and E. V. JENSEN, *Nature* **167**, 592 (1951).

(14) E. O. P. THOMPSON, *J. biol. Chem.* **208**, 265 (1954); see also: *Symposium on Chemical Structure of Proteins* Tokyo, 1957.

(15) T. IKENAKA, *J. Amer. chem. Soc.* **82,** 3180 (1960).

(16) T. PETERS, A. C. LOGAN and C. A. SANFORD, *Biochim. Biophys. Acta* **30,** 88 (1958).

(17) B. W. LOW, *J. Amer. chem. Soc.* **74,** 4830 (1952); J. M. CREETH, *Biochem. J.* **51,** 10 (1952); V. L. KOENIG and J. D. PERRINGS, *Arch. Biochem. Biophys.* **41,** 367 (1952).

weight, there should not be any difference between the values obtained e.g. by the osmotic pressure method and sedimentation–diffusion technique (see chapt. 3). If a preparation contains some polymerized material, this will strongly affect the light scattering; such material can always be revealed by the sedimentation test in the analytical ultracentrifuge. The exact molecular size and asymmetry (shape) is more difficult to assess than the molecular weight. The intrinsic viscosity of native isoelectric serum albumin is 0·037 dl/g (Table 18, chapt. 12), while compact spherical macromolecules should yield a value near 0·020. This indicates that the macromolecules of albumin are either asymmetric or non-compact, or both. The reduced specific viscosity of albumin increases moderately with concentration (see Table 6, chapt. 4), a fact indicating asymmetry and certain flexibility of the molecules. There is some evidence that the axial ratio may be about 1 : 3 or 1 :4, but a fully spherical shape is not excluded. Since the macromolecules definitely are not quite rigid, it can be assumed that the molecular volume and shape can be different, depending on the interacting medium and physical conditions. This is demonstrated by the effect of acidity and salt concentration on the sedimentation, viscosity, and optical rotation of serum albumin. The macromolecule contains about 100 carboxyl groups and 58 amino groups, and an albumin solution acts as a buffer. Moreover, the amphoteric nature of it is affected by the 19 phenolic (acid), 16 imidazole, and 22 guanidyl groups (both basic). When an acid is added, ionization of the acidic groups is suppressed and ionization of the basic groups promoted. In the native state, i.e. in blood plasma, the macromolecules carry a surplus of negative charge, since most of the free carboxyls are neutralized by inorganic bases. Addition of acid results in a decrease of this surplus, and at a certain point the number of the negative and positive charge units will be equal. In this *isoelectric state* the macromolecules will not move if direct current is applied to the solution, and the pH of this state is about 4·8–5·0. In the pH limits 4·0–8·0 there is practically no change in the physical or chemical properties, except that at a pH lower than the isoelectric state the macromolecules have a surplus positive charge, and they move to the negative pole in electrophoresis. Human albumin does not differ from bovine albumin in this respect.

Interesting changes, however, occur when the acidity of the albumin solution is raised to pH 3·0–3·5: (1) the sedimentation constant decreases, (2) the viscosity increases, (3) the specific rotation changes, (4) the electrophoretic pattern changes. The effects are reversible, and they depend on the ionic strength, i.e. salt concentration. The change of the sedimentation constant [(18)] and viscosity [(19,20)] indicates expansion of the macromolecules, and

[(18)] P. A. Charlwood and A. Ens, *Canad. J. Chem.* **35**, 99 (1957).
[(19)] J. T. Yang and J. F. Foster, *J. Amer. chem. Soc.* **76**, 1588 (1954).
[(20)] Ch. Tanford and J. G. Buzzell, *J. physic. Chem.* **60**, 225 (1956); Ch. Tanford, J. G. Buzzell, D. G. Rands and S. A. Swanson, *J. Amer. chem. Soc.* **77**, 6421 (1955).

only small differences could be found in this respect between human and bovine albumins. These changes are much larger than those observed with egg albumin or ribonuclease, and the changes can be suppressed to a great extent by adding a neutral salt. This is demonstrated in Fig. 66 which illustrates the behavior of bovine serum albumin at various ionic strength, and ribonuclease also is presented for comparison. The viscosity of the albumin in-

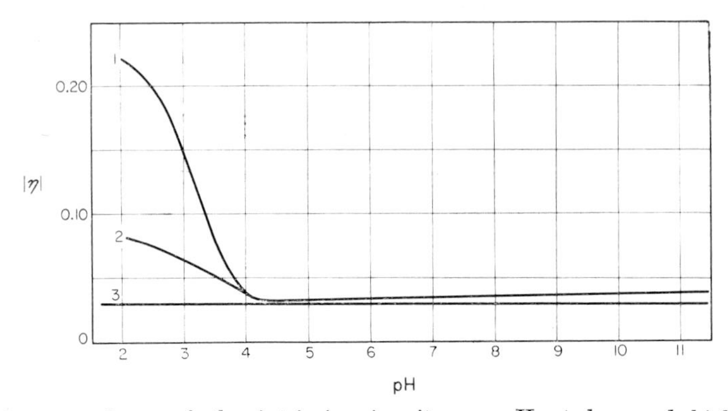

FIG. 66. Dependence of the intrinsic viscosity on pH at low and high ionic strength. Curve 1, serum albumin at low ionic strength of 0·01; curve 2, serum albumin at high ionic strength of 0·15; curve 3, ribonuclease at ionic strength ranging from 0·02 to 0·25

creases with increasing acidity the more the lower the ionic strength, while the viscosity of the ribonuclease practically does not change either with acidity or ionic strength. In electrophoresis experiments, a second component appears under certain conditions in acid solutions, and this has been interpreted as a *structural change — isomerization.* [21] This seems to be substantiated also by optical rotation measurements which, among other things, demonstrate a significant difference between human and bovine albumins. [22] The effects are not observable by using the conventional sodium light; they are indicated by using the more effective blue light, and they can be demonstrated conclusively by working with ultraviolet light. The specific rotation is constant in the pH range 4–8; at pH 3·7–3·9 and at pH 8·0–9·5 is observable a positive shift; the latter can be demonstrated with human albumin even with the sodium light. [23] The positive shift at pH 3·7–3·9 is quite explicit with crystallized (or non-crystallized) bovine albumin but it is very weak with pure crystallized human albumin. The results obtained with deionized crystallized bovine and human albumins are shown in Fig. 67. The peak in the curves at pH 3·5 can be explained as being caused by the interplay

(21) J. T. YANG and J. F. FOSTER, *J. Amer. chem. Soc.* **76**, 1588 (1954); J. R. CANN, *J. Amer. chem. Soc.* **80**, 4263 (1958); K. AOKI, *J. Amer. chem. Soc.* **80**, 4904 (1958).

(22) B. JIRGENSONS, *Arch. Biochem. Biophys.* **78**, 227 (1958).

(23) B. JIRGENSONS, *Arch. Biochem. Biophys.* **59**, 420 (1955); G. MARKUS and F. KARUSH, *J. Amer. chem. Soc.* **79**, 3264 (1957).

of two effects: *isomerization* and *molecular expansion.* The positive shift of the rotation is caused by isomerization which predominates at pH 3·5–4, because the expansion which is associated with an opposite rotational effect — negative shift — is still weak at this pH. At a higher acidity of pH 2–3

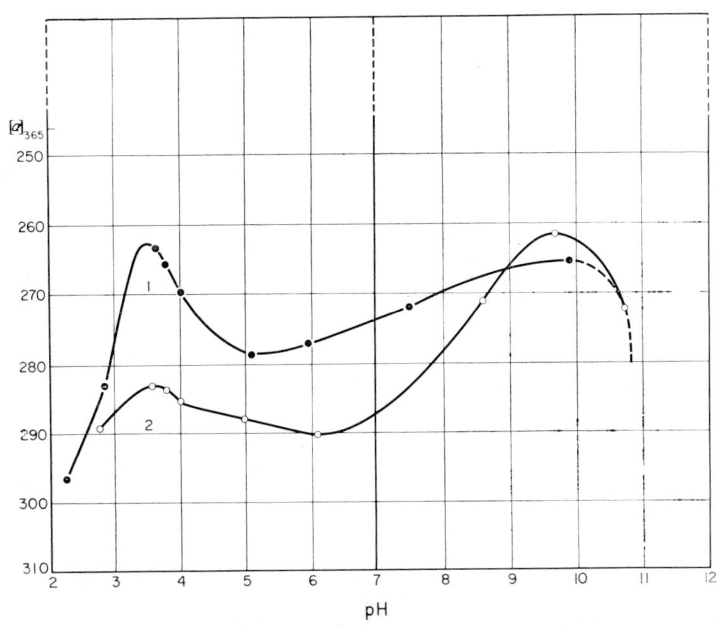

FIG. 67. Dependence of the specific rotation (measured with ultraviolet light of $\lambda = 365$ mμ) on pH for deionized bovine (curve 1) and human (curve 2) serum albumins

the expansion predominates, and the albumin becomes more and more levorotatory with increasing acidity. The difference between the human and bovine albumins seems to be due to the fact that the human albumin expands more readily than bovine, hence the expansion effects overshadow the isomerization, and nothing much of a peak is formed. The flat plateau of the curves at pH 8–10 probably can be explained in an analogous fashion, although these changes are not so well reflected in the electrophoretic behavior as those in acid solutions. In weakly alkaline solution, the levorotation of the human albumin changes more with pH than that of the bovine albumin. In more strongly alkaline solution (pH 11–12 and higher), the macromolecules strongly expand, the viscosity increases, and the specific rotation strongly shifts toward the negative direction. Very interesting optical rotation changes and differences between bovine and human albumins have been observed also under the influence of certain anionic azo dyes. [(24)] These observations are in accord with the outlined concept on the flexibility and configurational

(24) G. MARKUS and F. KARUSH, *J. Amer. chem. Soc.* **80**, 89 (1958).

adaptability of serum albumin. Since the effects caused by the dyes are reversible, the rather bulky molecules of the dye apparently can penetrate deep into the macromolecule causing some change in the secondary and tertiary structure, and after the removal of the intruder the macromolecule is able to return to its native state.

Of a considerable interest are also the findings that sodium caprylate and similar salts of the fatty acids are able to stabilize serum albumin against coagulation by heating.[25] When human blood plasma containing 0·04 *M* caprylate is heated to 70 °C, only the globulins precipitate and the albumin remains in solution. According to Luck *et al.*, the caprylate anions combine with the albumin, and like protective braces tighten the segments of the folded chain thus stabilizing the macromolecule against unfolding. These views have been challenged recently by Loseva and Tsyperovich[26] who claimed that the caprylate and similar surface active anions do not protect albumin from denaturation proper but only from flocculation. As a criterion for denaturation these authors used precipitation at the isoelectric point. They heated the albumin solutions containing the fatty acid salts at 50 °C or 70 °C (or higher), and adjusted the pH after cooling to the isoelectric pH; they found that more albumin is precipitated from the aliquots containing the surface active salts than from the blanks which did not contain them. On the basis of these findings, the quoted authors concluded that the caprylate protects albumin only from flocculation but not from denaturation proper, and that in reality the fatty acid sensitizes the macromolecules to denaturation. These phenomena were reinvestigated in our laboratory by using sodium caprylate as well as a series of other surface active salts with large lyophobic anions (detergents). Denaturation was checked by three criteria: optical rotation, viscosity, and isoelectric precipitation. It was found that there is no denaturation if albumin is heated only to 50° in the presence of various surface active ions. Flocculation at the isoelectric point takes place only at a high concentration of the caprylate, and it is due to the combination of the negatively charged micelles of the detergent with the positively charged loci of the albumin. Heating to 70 °C, however, results in a slight denaturation, while heating to 80 °C caused a complete denaturation. These results indicate that surface active anions scarcely protect albumin at 70° to denaturation. In fact, this binding of the surface active molecules at the macromolecule causes some change in the secondary and tertiary structure. This is reflected also in the optical rotation properties. While the dispersion constant is not affected by this binding, the specific rotation is somewhat shifted toward the positive direction.[27] The albumin solutions which are heated to 70 °C for several hours, in the presence

[25] G. A. Ballou, P. D. Boyer, J. M. Luck and F. G. Lum, *J. Clin. Investig.* **23**, 454 (1944); P. D. Boyer, F. G. Lum, G. A. Ballou, J. M. Luck and R. G. Rice, *J. biol. Chem.* **162**, 181 (1946); J. D. Teresi and J. M. Luck, *J. biol. Chem.* **194**, 823 (1952).

[26] A. L. Loseva and A. S. Tsyperovich, *Kolloidny Zhurnal* (*Russ.*) **19**, 222 (1957).

[27] B. Jirgensons, *Texas Reports Biol. Med.* **17**, 106 (1959).

of caprylate or other detergent, precipitate at the isoelectric point, and this precipitation occurs even at such low detergent concentration at which no micelles of the detergent are formed. It could not be proved that the detergents actually sensitized albumin to denaturation, but it was ascertained that this treatment at 70° resulted in some slight configurational change. Detailed general reviews on the binding of various substances at proteins in general [28] and also specifically on reactions with detergents [29] are available. The binding of detergents and similar molecules containing ionic and nonpolar sites is determined by both ionic (electrostatic) and cohesive interaction (adsorption).

Serum albumin interacts not only with small molecules but also with other proteins, and these interactions are known to be determined chiefly by the acidity of the solutions. These interactions are especially pronounced with the proteins whose isoelectric point differs much from the isoelectric point of albumin, such as lysozyme. The isoelectric point of the latter is at pH 10·5, and at pH 6 or 7 this protein is positively charged, whereas albumin is negative; the proteins form reversibly dissociable compounds in neutral solutions. [30] A weak interaction between albumin and the γ-globulins occurs at pH 5·9–5·5, since the isoelectric point of these globulins is at 6–8, and at pH below 6 they are weakly positively charged.

The γ-Globulins of Serum [2,31]

Electrophoresis of blood serum or plasma produces separation of the various electrically charged components. The highly mobile albumin is followed closely by the α_1 globulins, these being followed by the α_2, β_1, β_2, and finally the most slowly migrating γ-globulins. The mobility depends on the pH of the buffer used for dilution of the serum. In a weakly alkaline buffer of pH 8·4–8·6 all of the γ-globulin is shifted a short distance toward the positive electrode, while at pH 6·5–7 some of the components migrate a little toward the negative pole. The mobility distribution peak showing the quantity of the globulin at a certain distance is flat indicating considerable heterogeneity with respect to electrophoresis. The amount of the total γ-globulin comprizes about 11% of the total serum proteins. A lesser degree of heterogeneity appears in sedimentation in the analytical ultracentrifuge. The major peak in the sedimentation diagram is quite symmetric indicating a relatively high degree of homogeneity with respect to molecular weight, and usually a small faster component also is observed. The sedimentation constants for the major component range between 6·5–7 S, and they are 9–11 S for the heavier com-

(28) I. M. Klotz in *The Proteins* Vol. I B, p. 727 (H. Neurath and K. Bailey, ed.), Academic Press, New York, 1953).

(29) F. W. Putnam, *Adv. Protein Chem.* **4**, 80 (1948).

(30) R. F. Steiner, *Arch. Biochem. Biophys.* **47**, 56 (1953).

(31) W. C. Boyd, in *The Proteins* Vol.II B, p. 755 (H. Neurath and K. Bailey, ed.), Academic Press, 1954.

ponent. The molecular weight of the major component is close to 160,000, and the macromolecules seem to be moderately asymmetric.[32] According to recent low angle X-ray diffraction studies, the length of the macromolecules was calculated to be 230–240 Å, and the axes of the assumed elliptical cross section 57 Å and 19 Å respectively.[33] Other authors have arrived at somewhat different dimensions, e.g. 274 Å for the long axis and 37 for the short axis.[34]

The γ-globulins have deserved special interest due to the fact that the *antibodies* belong to this group of globulins; and since there are many specific antibodies there are many different proteins in the group named γ-globulins. The whole γ-globulin fraction can be separated relatively easily from serum or plasma, for example, by one of the fractionation methods of Cohn and colleagues.[3,4] The γ-globulin thus isolated appears to be 95–98% pure, as judged from electrophoresis experiments. Further subfractionation of the protein can be achieved in various ways. First, there is the old classical method of separating the *eu-globulin* subfraction from the *pseudoglobulin.* If a solution of γ-globulin is dialyzed, the less soluble component, called euglobulin, precipitates when most of the ions have left the solution, while the pseudoglobulin subfraction remains in solution. This separation, however, is not sharp and the solubility differences do not correspond to significant other chemical, physical or biological differences. More revealing have been found other methods of subfractionation, such as *immunochemical precipitation* of a certain antigen with an antibody,[2,31] *electrophoresis convection,*[35] or *chromatography.*[6] The first method has been found suitable for the isolation of specific antibodies, since these reactions with the antigen are extremely specific; after precipitation the antibody can be eluted from the washed precipitate by a treatment with salt solutions. The electrophoresis convection method (see chapt. 2) also was applied successfully for the isolation of highly purified antibodies and subfractions of the γ-globulins. Chromatographic subfractionation has yielded many components, and some of them were immunochemically indistinguishable. In a multicolumn modification of the method, the γ-globulins were separated from a hyperimmune serum first from the bulk of the serum by passage through a short anion exchange DEAE–cellulose column; this was followed by chromatography on a carboxymethyl cellulose cation exchange column, and resulted in separation in many com-

[32] J. L. Oncley, G. Scatchard and A. Brown, *J. Phys.. Colloid Chem.* **51,** 184 (1947).

[33] O. Kratky, G. Porod, A. Sekora and B. Paletta, *J. Polymer Sci.* **16,** 163 (1955).

[34] S. Filitti-Wurmser, G. Aubel-Lesure and R. Wurmser, *J. Chim. physique* **50,** 236 (1953).

[35] J. R. Cann, J. G. Kirkwood, R. A. Brown and O. J. Plescia, *J. Amer. chem. Soc.* **71,** 1603 (1949); J. G. Kirkwood, J. R. Cann and R. A. Brown, *Biochim. Biophys. Acta* **5,** 301 (1950); J. R. Cann, *J. Amer. chem. Soc.* **75,** 4213 (1953).

ponents with various serological activity.[36] Since the γ-globulins are sensitive to denaturation, the subfractionation sometimes may result in artifact formation; in order to avoid it, greatest care should be observed in any of these isolation and subfractionation procedures (see also chapt. 2).

The differences in some physical properties of γ-globulins from various sources have been studied in this laboratory to a considerable extent. The differences found in sedimentation constants of various pooled preparations were found to be statistically not significant.[37] The intrinsic viscosity of various individual and pooled preparations was found to vary between 0·048–0·083 dl/g (at ionic strength 0·1 and pH near the isoelectric point of 6–7·7).[38] This is a quite large range of variation, but the interpretation of the significance of it is difficult. The viscosity of various γ-pseudoglobulin samples was found to be generally the same as the viscosity of the whole γ-globulin fraction. The reproducibility of the data obtained by investigating the *same* isolated specimen was very good; it was, however, much poorer by comparing the viscosity of *two* specimens isolated by possibly identical procedures from the *same* blood plasma specimen. For example, the intrinsic viscosities of 0·0614 and 0·0727, and the slope constants of 0·016 and 0·0097 respectively were found for two preparations isolated on two different occasions from the same plasma specimen by possibly identical procedures. The purity in both instances was near 97%, and the traces of impurities could not be made responsible for the differences. This indicates that the viscosity differences, at least partially, may be due to some artifact formation, e.g. a slight denaturation or partial aggregation which cannot be completely avoided in the course of isolation. However, the possibility of genuine individual differences is not at all excluded, especially when one considers individual specimens isolated from healthy and sick (especially immunized) individuals. Certain antibodies are known to possess larger molecular weights than the average 160,000, and it is quite possible that the larger components are also more asymmetric and thus could produce a higher viscosity than the common intrinsic viscosity of about 0·06 dl/g.[31]

Although the macromolecules of the γ-globulins have a lesser affinity to dyes and other small molecules than serum albumin, they are quite flexible. This is demonstrated in Fig. 68 showing the dependence of the intrinsic viscosity and optical activity of γ-globulins on pH.[39] Both intrinsic viscosity and levorotation increase symmetrically on both sides of the isoelectric point which is near 6·5–7·5, an indication of expansion. The changes produced by

[36] A. Sober, M. M. Wyckoff and E. A. Peterson, *Abstracts, Amer. chem. Soc. Natl. Meeting, Miami, Florida*, p. 670, April, 1957.

[37] J. A. Cooper, L. Straumanis and B. Jirgensons, *Makromol. Chem.* **26**, 167 (1958).

[38] B. Jirgensons and E. C. Adams, *Makromol. chem.* **24**, 159 (1957).

[39] B. Jirgensons, *Arch. Biochem. Biophys.* **48**, 154 (1954); **71**, 148 (1957); see also ref. 1.

weak acid or alkali are reversible, while the γ-globulin which was exposed to stronger acid (pH 1·8–2·2) or stronger alkali (pH 11·6–12) could not be fully reconverted to native state on neutralization.

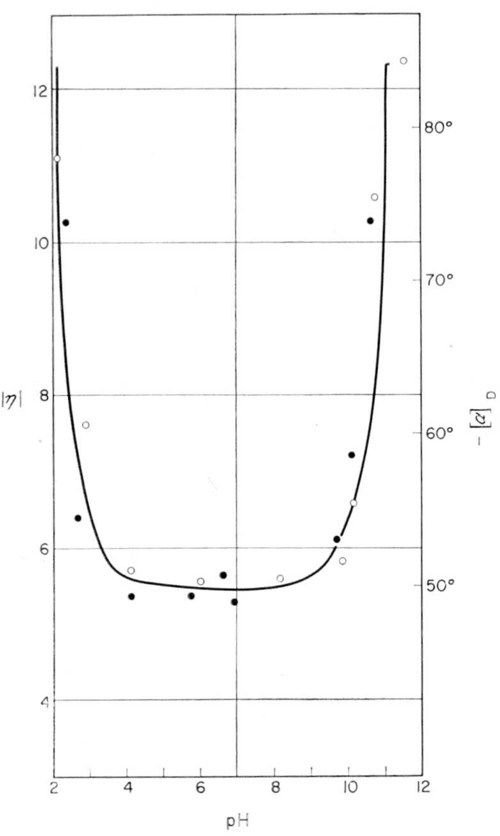

FIG. 68. Dependence of the intrinsic viscosity and specific rotation of γ-globulin on pH. Open circles represent viscosity, discs the specific rotation

The amino acid composition of the γ-globulins has been determined in several laboratories by various methods,[40] and some of the results are presented in Table 24. Examination of this Table shows that the amino acid composition is not too different from the amino acid composition of serum albumin, with the exception of the hydroxyamino acids serine and threonine which are found in the γ-globulins in unusually high concentrations. Moreover, the γ-globulins contain small amounts of bound carbohydrate, viz. about 1·2% hexose and 0·5% hexosamine.

If one includes our alanine data in the Tristram's list, all of the nitrogen is accounted for, and it appears that 100,000 g of the protein contain nearly 900 moles of the various amino acids. A macromolecule of the $M = 160{,}000$ thus contains e.g. 22 tryptophan residues, 9 methionine residues, and an unusually large number of about 174 serine groups. The differences in the electrophoretic mobility of the various components in the γ-globulin fraction can be explained by a slight variation in the number of the free carboxyls (aspartic acid, glutamic acid) and the number of the basic amino acid residues (lysine, histidine, arginine). Several terminal amino acids have been found, and differences between various preparations also have been ascertained in

[40] G. R. TRISTRAM, in *The Proteins* Vol. I A, p. 215, Academic Press, New York, 1953; G. R. TRISTRAM, *Adv. Protein Chem.* **5**, 83 (1949).

this respect.[41] This is not surprising if one considers the heterogeneity of these proteins. The macromolecules of these globulins are large and the preparations so heterogeneous that nothing yet is known about the number of peptide chains in a macromolecule or about the primary structure.

Some interesting observations have been made about the secondary and tertiary structure of the γ-globulins. Only one of the several cysteine —SH

TABLE 24

AMINO ACID COMPOSITION OF HUMAN γ-GLOBULIN (N content 16·0%)

	g amino acid per 100 g protein (data of our lab.) *	g amino acid per 100 g protein (Tristram, ref. 40)	Number of residues per 10^5 g protein (Tristram)
Alanine	5·3	—	—
Glycine	5·1	4·2	56·0
Valine	7·0	9·7	83·0
Leucine	8·6	9·3	71·0
Isoleucine	2·0	2·7	20·6
Proline	9·0	8·1	70·5
Phenylalanine	6·0	4·6	27·9
Tyrosine	7·1	6·8	37·6
Tryptophan	—	2·9	14·2
Serine	13·4	11·4	108·8
Threonine	10·5	8·4	70·6
Cystine/2	—	2·4	19·9
Cysteine	—	0·7	5·8
Methionine	0·8	1·1	7·3
Arginine	4·4	4·8	27·9
Histidine	2·9	2·5	16·1
Lysine	7·2	8·1	55·5
Aspartic acid	8·9	8·8	66·2
Glutamic acid	11·5	11·8	80·4
Amide N	1·2	1·1	(79·5)

groups is reactive. The disulfide bonds of the cystine can be reduced, especially in the presence of surface active detergents which denature the macromolecules, and a maximum of about 17 disulfide bonds per mole are reduced.[42] Contrary to albumin, however, the intrinsic viscosity or optical rotation of the protein solution is little affected by this breaking of the —S—S— bonds,[42] and it is was concluded that in the case of γ-globulin the disulfide bridges are unimportant for the configuration. The disulfide bridges, however, probably link several chains in the macromolecule of these globulins, since reduc-

[41] F. W. PUTNAM, *J. Amer. chem. Soc.* **75**, 2785 (1953); E. L. SMITH *et. al.*, *J. biol. Chem.* **216**, 601, 621 (1955); WOO-POK LAY and W. J. POLGLASE, *Canad. J. Biochem. Physiol* **35**, 39 (1957).

* The amino acid composition was determined according to MOORE and STEIN by Dr. T. IKENAKA.

[42] G. MARKUS and F. KARUSH, *J. Amer. chem. Soc.* **79**, 134 (1957).

tion with β-mercaptoethylamine hydrochloride in 6 M urea yielded subunits of molecular weight about 48,000.[42a] Thus the role of the disulfide bonds in the structure and configuration of the macromolecules of the γ-globulins is not clear, and requires a more detailed study. Another interesting observation was made with respect to the optical rotatory dispersion of the γ-globulins:[43] they possess unusually low dispersion constants which, contrary to the albumin, *increase* on denaturation (see Table 20, chapt. 12). This may be due to the extremely high hydroxyamino acid content that probably results in some unusual bonding between the OH-groups of the serine and threonine residues and the carboxyl groups. Another possibility would be that these OH-groups have a specific effect on the folding of the chain because of steric reasons. The reasoning that the hydroxyamino acids are responsible for these effects is supported by the facts that similar anomalies in the optical rotatory dispersion are observed also with pepsin and the Bence–Jones proteins[43] which also have a high hydroxyamino acid content.

The immunochemical properties and reactions of the γ-globulins as antibodies will be discussed in chapt. 23.

The Albumins and Globulins of Birds' Eggs[44,45]

The avian egg has attracted the interest of investigators for two main reasons: (1) as a closed system containing all the components needed for the development of a highly developed organism, and (2) as an important nutritional item. In addition to the various membranes, the avian egg has two major parts — the white and yolk. The chicken egg has been much better investigated than the eggs of other birds, and excellent reviews on the egg proteins are available.[44,45,46] Chicken egg white contains 88% water, and the various proteins comprise 10·6% of the white, i.e. almost all of the solids of the white; the yolk contains 49% water, 33% fat and lipid, and 16% protein.

The *proteins of the white* are characterized best by electrophoresis, and the components can be isolated by fractional precipitation, centrifugation, dialysis, and preparative electrophoresis. Analytical electrophoresis reveals in chicken egg white between 6 and 8 components. The major component is egg *albumin* (65% of total protein) the others being *conalbumin* (14%), *ovomucoid* (13%), the *globulins* G_1, G_2, G_3, *ovomucin*, and *avidin*. The globulin G_1 is an enzyme called *lysozyme*, while ovomucoid inhibits the proteolytic activity of trypsin. Ovomucin and avidin also are physiologically active, i.e. avidin combines with biotin thus inactivating it and causing certain deficiencies.[47]

[42a] G. M. Edelman, *J. Amer. chem. Soc.* **81**, 3155 (1959).
[43] B. Jirgensons, *Arch. Biochem. Biophys.* **74**, 57 (1958); **78**, 235 (1958); **85**, 89 (1959).
[44] H. L. Fevold, *Adv. Protein Chem.* **6**, 187 (1951).
[45] R. C. Warner, in *The Proteins* Vol. II A, p. 435, Academic Press, New York, 1954.
[46] A. L. Romanoff and A. J. Romanoff, *The Avian Egg.* Wiley, New York, 1949.
[47] R. E. Eakin, E. E. Snell and R. J. Williams, *J. biol. Chem.* **140**, 535 (1941).

Electrophoretic analyses of the components in other bird species have revealed considerable differences in the composition.[48] Albumin was present in all instances but in a few species it was not the major component. The metal-binding conalbumin was present in all species.

Egg albumin has been isolated in a highly purified state, and recrystallized albumin has been often thoroughly studied in many laboratories. The electrophoretic mobility peak of the albumin, either of the native white or isolated albumin, is asymmetric and suggests the presence of several components. The sedimentation peak in the ultracentrifuge, however, is symmetric and indicates homogeneity with respect to the molecular weight which is close to 45,000. Since the intrinsic viscosity of the solutions is very low, the macromolecules are globular and compact. The high consistency of fresh egg white is not caused by albumin but by the asymmetric ovomucin; however, the hardening of the white upon boiling is due to unfolding and aggregation of the unfolded macromolecules of the albumin and other proteins of the white. There is a great difference between the various proteins of the white in respect to their stability to heat denaturation and flocculation. While albumin is readily denatured and precipitated on heating, ovomucoid and lysozyme are stable. Albumin is denatured even by shaking the solution, i. e. by contacting the macromolecules with the surface, while ovomucoid, lysozyme and conalbumin are very little affected by shaking.

Egg albumin differs from serum albumin in amino acid composition quite considerably. The sulfur content in both proteins is nearly the same but the sulfur distribution is different. In serum albumin most of the sulfur forms disulfide bridges, in egg albumin most of the sulfur is in the methionine residues. There are only one or two disulfide bridges in a macromolecule of egg albumin, and there are 4 or 5 free cysteine sulfhydryl groups. Moreover, the macromolecule of egg albumin contains a carbohydrate component of the molecular weight 1200, and one or two atoms of phosphorus. The amino acid composition is presented in Table 25. Nothing much is known as yet about the amino acid sequence in the macromolecule. There seems to be only one polypeptide chain, the N-terminal being masked with the carbohydrate component.[49] The C-terminal is proline. Since the macromolecule is compact, the chain must be folded many times, and the one or two disulfide bridges cannot be the only reason for the compact configuration.

From the nutritional point of view, the high content of the essential amino acids methionine, isoleucine, leucine, lysine, phenylalanine, and valine is noteworthy. Conalbumin also contains all essential amino acids, notably 10% lysine, 6% threonine, and 8% valine. The ovomucoid contains about 25% of a carbohydrate component containing mannose and glucosamine.

[48] J. A. Bain and H. F. Deutsch, *J. biol. Chem.* **171**, 531 (1947).
[49] C. B. Anfinsen and R. R. Redfield, *Adv. Protein Chem.* **11**, 1 (1956).

Egg yolk contains a variety of intersetting proteins, but they have been thus far insufficiently purified and characterized. The water-soluble components of low phosphorus content are designated as *livetins*; several electrophoretic components have been found in this fraction which also possesses various kinds of enzymic activities. Thus most of the enzymes of the egg seem to

TABLE 25

AMINO ACID COMPOSITION AND RESIDUE WEIGHT OF EGG ALBUMIN (44)

Component	Per cent of egg albumin	Number of residues per mole	Residue weight	Total residue weight
Alanine	5·8	28	71	1988
Arginine	5·9	15	156	2340
Aspartic acid	9·4	32	115	3680
Cystine	0·52 *	1	222	222
Cystine + cysteine	1·80			
Cysteine	1·28	5	103	515
Glutamic acid	16·9	52	129	6708
Glycine	3·2	19	57	1083
Histidine	2·3	6	137	822
Isoleucine	7·7	26	113	2938
Leucine	10·1	33	113	3729
Lysine	6·6	20	128	2560
Phenylalanine	7·8	21	147	3087
Methionine	5·4	16	131	2227
Proline	4·0	16	97	1552
Serine	10·3	43	87	3741
Threonine	4·1	16	101	1616
Tryptophan	1·2	3	186	558
Tyrosine	3·9	10	163	1630
Valine	7·1	28	99	2772
Carbohydrate		1	1200	1200
Phosphorus	0·12	2	(H_2PO_3) 81	162
Total		393		45,130

belong to this fraction. *Vitellin* and *vitellenin* are lipoproteins, i.e. proteins containing a fat or lipid as integral part of the macromolecule. The lipid of these proteins is a phospholipid (or phospholipids), hence these components are rich in phosphorus (vitellin contains 1%, vitellinin 0·3% of phosphorus). Vitellin contains 1% sulfur, and it has a somewhat unusually high arginine content of about 8%. The highest phosphorus content, however, has been found in another protein of egg yolk — *phosvitin.* (50) This water-soluble protein contains 9·7% phosphorus and only 11·9% nitrogen, and it is inhomogeneous in both sedimentation and electrophoresis. Due to the presence of the large number of the highly charged phosphate groups, the properties

* By difference from cystine + cysteine sulfur minus the sulfur of sulfhydryl groups.
(50) D. K. MECHAM and H. S. OLCOTT, *J. Amer. chem. Soc.* **71**, 3670 (1949).

of the macromolecules in the solution depend to a great extent on the pH of the solution. The specific rotation of phosvitin at pH 4·7 was found −129° (with the wave length 404·7 mμ), and it was −204° at pH 10·7. The dispersion constant changed from 225 mμ at pH 4·7 to 207 mμ at pH 10·7.[51]

Albumins and Globulins in Plants

There is very little protein in the stalks, leaves, fruits, and other parts of plants except the *seeds*. Amino acids and other micromolecular substances are transported from the synthesizing organs of the plant to the ripening seed, where they are converted to different proteins. The major part of this protein is stored as reserve substance, and only a small part of it goes to the embryo in the form of various enzymes. The amino acids of the reserve protein are used for synthesizing nucleoproteins and enzymes needed for the developing new plant. The amount of total protein in various cereals is between 7 and 18% of dry grain, while it may be as high as 50% in certain dicotyledonous seeds, such as hazel or soybean.[52] Common wheat grain contains 10–15%, rice 8–10%, corn 7–13%, soybean 30–50% of protein. Most of the seed proteins are polymolecular *globulins* which are extracted from ground seeds with a dilute sodium chloride solution,[53] and are precipitated on dialysis of the extract. Only a small portion of these proteins is

TABLE 26

PHYSICAL CONSTANTS OF SOME SEED PROTEINS
(from Brohult and Sandegren[52])

	Sediment. const. (s_{20} in S)	Diffusion const. (D_{20})	Mol. wt.	Isoelectric point
α-globulin from barley	2·5	$7{\cdot}4 \cdot 10^{-7}$	29,000	5·0
β-globulin from barley	6·2	4·9	110,000	4·9
Albumin from barley	4·5	6·5	54,000	5·7
Gliadin from wheat	2·1	6·7	28,000	
Zein from corn	1·9	4·0	51,000	
Legumin from pea	12·6	3·5	330,000	
Vicilin from pea	8·1	4·2	186,000	
Edestin from hemp seed	12·8	3·9	310,000	
Excelsin from Brazil nut	13·3	4·2	295,000	

water-soluble. The so-called *prolamines* of various cereals, such as the *gliadin* of wheat, are soluble in 50–90% alcohol. Some of the most important physical constants of some of these proteins are compiled in Table 26. It must, however, be emphasized that the macromolecules of several of these proteins,

[51] B. JIRGENSONS, *Arch. Biochem. Biophys.* **74**, 70 (1958).

[52] S. BROHULT and E. SANDEGREN, in *The Proteins* Vol. II A, p. 487, Academic Press, New York, 1954; H. B. VICKERY, *Physiol. Rev.* **25**, 347 (1945).

[53] T. B. OSBORNE, *The Vegetable Proteins* 2nd ed., Longmans, Green, London, 1924.

such as the arachin of peanut, are composed of sub-units. The macromolecules of arachin dissociate readily into halves of greater asymmetry depending on pH and on the salt concentration. [54]

Some of the protein systems appear to be very complex, e.g. the conarachin fraction of the peanut protein is a reversibly-dissociating system composed of six or seven components with sedimentation constants from 2 to 50 *S* units.[55]

TABLE 27 [52]

AMINO ACID COMPOSITION (g per 100 g PROTEIN) OF SEVERAL SEED PROTEINS

	Gliadin	Zein	β-globulin (barley)	Arachin
Glycine	1	0	4·2	3·7
Alanine	2·0	11·5	6·5	5
Serine	4·8	7·8	4·3	5·3
Threonine	2·1	3·0	5·9	2·6
Valine	2·6	3·0	9·5	4·5
Leucine	6·7	24·0	11·0	7·8
Isoleucine	(5·1)	7·4	3·2	7·6
Methionine	1·6	2·3	3·2	0·7
Cystine + cysteine	2·5	1·0	9·4	1·5
Proline	13·2	10.5	13.3	7
Phenylalanine	6·3	6·5	4·7	6·3
Tryptophan	0	0	3·8	1·0
Tyrosine	3·3	5·3	8·5	5·5
Histidine	2·3	1·7	1·7	2·2
Arginine	2·7	1·8	2·7	14·0
Lysine	1·2	0	2·1	4·6
Aspartic acid	3·6	5·7	8·8	(16·0)
Glutamic acid	47.0	27·0	17·8	23·8

The amino acid composition of the seed proteins has been extensively studied chiefly because of the importance of the protein in human and animal nutrition. Generally, some of the essential amino acids are either in very small amounts or even completely missing in these proteins. Data on some of the most important examples are presented in Table 27. Some of the proteins are extremely rich in glutamic acid, proline, and leucine; zein is devoid of the important tryptophan and lysine, and gliadin is deficient in these essential amino acids. According to Table 27, the nutritionally most valuable of these plant proteins are arachin of the peanut and β-globulin of barley.

Since none of these proteins have been crystallized and otherwise characterized as pure substances, nothing is known about the amino acid sequence and the number and configuration of the polypeptide chains in the macromolecules.

[54] P. JOHNSON and E. M. SHOOTER, *Biochim. Biophys. Acta* **5**, 361 (1950).
[55] P. JOHNSON and W. E. F. NAISMITH, *Discuss. Faraday Soc.* **13**, 98 (1953).

The proteins found in tubers and leaves also have been studied, but these proteins are even less characterized as chemical individuals than the seed proteins.[56,57] Only inhomogeneous preparations have been isolated. With respect to the amino acid composition, the cytoplasmic proteins are distinguished by their high content in arginine (12–15%) and lysine. The protein of potato tubers is somewhat exceptional in that it contains all essential amino acids in reasonable amounts (e.g. 3·3% lysine, 3·3% tryptophan, and 3·9% phenylalanine.

(56) F. C. STEWARD and J. F. THOMPSON, in *The Proteins* Vol. II A, p. 513, Academic Press, New York, 1954.

(57) J. BONNER, *Plant Biochemistry*, chapt. 17, Academic Press, New York, 1950. A. C. CHIBNALL, *Protein Metabolism in Plant*, Yale University Press, 1939.

CHAPTER 14

THE HEMOGLOBINS AND OTHER RESPIRATORY PROTEINS

> Chemical studies on hemoglobins A (normal) and S (sickle-cell) enable us to say that there is a difference in amino acid composition and that this involves a charged carboxyl group and thus explains the electrophoretic behavior. The polypeptide chains of the two hemoglobins differ in only one amino acid residue; one of the glutamic acid residues of hemoglobin A had changed to valine, a neutral group, in hemoglobin S. No other changes could be detected.
>
> V. M. INGRAM [1]

RECENT advances in disclosing differences between certain hemoglobins have provided new hope that some of the most difficult problems of life will be solved in the near future. One of such problems is the relationship between genetic factors as they are reflected in the structure of proteins. Although the structure of the large hemoglobin molecule is far from being completely solved, chemical differences between the hemoglobins of various species, as well as between individual hemoglobins within the same species, have been fully established.

In the course of evolution, the hemoglobins and similar conjugated proteins have been mighty factors in the victorious march of Life toward higher forms. With hemoglobin the organisms obtained new tools for the efficient utilization of the free chemical energy not only from the organic nutrients but also from the oxygen of the air. It is conceivable that the development of *muscle* was associated with the development of the *respiratory system* of fast oxygen transfer, since motion requires a steady and very efficient supply of energy.

The Hemoglobins [2,3]

The hemoglobins are complex or conjugated proteins which, as well as the amino acid residues, contain a *ferroporphyrin* component. The latter comprises only a small portion of the macromolecule. The physical molecular weight of mammalian hemoglobin is very close to 68,000 (see chapt. 3), and the macromolecule contains four ferroporphyrin or *hem* groups. The chemi-

[1] V. M. INGRAM, *Abstracts, Amer. chem. Soc. Nat. Meeting, Boston* p. 38 C, April, 1959.

[2] F. HAUROWITZ and R. L. HARDIN, in *The Proteins* Vol. II A, p. 279 (H. NEURATH and K. BAILEY, ed.), Academic Press, New York, 1954.

[3] H. A. ITANO, *Adv. Protein Chem.* **12**, 215 (1957).

cal molecular weight, based on iron analyses, is 17,000, thus the macromolecule seems to be composed of four subunits. The way of linking these, as well as the linkage of the hem to the protein or globin component is not known. The macromolecule dissociates into halves of $M = 34{,}000$ under the influence of concentrated solutions of urea or certain salts; the same happens upon spreading hemoglobin on surfaces. This indicates that the four subunits may be chemically linked into two pairs of $M = 34{,}000$ each, and that these two halves are held together by some weak secondary bonds. The true molecular weight of hemoglobin thus may be either 34,000 or 17,000, and a definite answer will be possible only after working out the detailed structure of the units. According to the X-ray diffraction studies of Perutz *et al.*,[(4,5)] the 68,000 unit is composed of two identical halves (not four identical quarters) which are joined to a roughly spherical unit with the dimensions 70 · 55 · 55 Å. The hem groups must be flat on the surface of the macromolecule since all four of them react readily with oxygen, carbon monoxide, and other substances. The hem can be split off by a treatment with acid, and by keeping the temperature low enough the globin component is not denatured. The study of hemoglobin and its derivatives is facilitated by its intense color, i.e. absorption of light in the visible spectrum. This absorption is due to the hem, its linking to the globin, and the groups linked with the iron atom in the porphyrin complex.

The red blood cells contain about 32% of hemoglobin which is released by hemolysis, e.g. by dilution with water or by adding a surface active substance which damages the red cell membrane. The cellular fragments (stroma) can be removed by high speed centrifugation or adsorption to alumina, and crystallization of hemoglobin is achieved e.g. by addition of alcohol at a low temperature. The hemoglobins of various animal species have different solubilities, i.e. different tendency to crystallize, and the crystal forms too are different. The molecular weight of the hemoglobins of mammals and most other vertebrates is 68,000, while smaller and much higher values for the physical molecular weight have been reported for various invertebrate hemoglobins; e.g. 31,000 for the hemoglobins of some insects, 1,300,000 for the hemoglobins from leeches (planorbis), and 2,750,000 for the pigment isolated from earth worms.[(6)] The isoelectric point of human and other hemoglobins from mammals is near pH 7, while the isoelectric point of the hemoglobins from the lower species is shifted to lower pH values.

While no significant differences can be detected between the X-ray diffraction spectra or molecular weights of hemoglobins isolated from the blood of

[(4)] M. F. Perutz, *Endeavour* **17**, 190 (1958).

[(5)] A. F. Cullis, H. M. Dintzis and M. F. Perutz, *Conference on Haemoglobin* Washington, Nat. Acad. Sci. and Nat. Res. Counc. Publ. 557, 1957.

[(6)] T. Svedberg and I.-B. Ericksson-Quensel, *J. Amer. chem. Soc.* **56**, 1700 (1934); see also: T. Svedberg and K. O. Pedersen, *The Ultracentrifuge* p. 360, Clarendon Press, Oxford, 1940.

various mammals, the *amino acid composition* of hemoglobins from various sources is different. Apart from the subtle differences between the normal and sickle-cell human hemoglobins mentioned in the introduction of this chapter, the hemoglobins of normal *adult* blood differ from the hemoglobin isolated from *embryonal* blood. The amino acid composition is presented in Table 28.

TABLE 28

AMINO ACID COMPOSITION OF HEMOGLOBINS AND MYOGLOBINS
(residues per mole)

	Human fetal hemoglobin (3,7)	Normal human globin	Adult hemoglobin	Horse hemoglobin (9)	Horse myoglobin (9)	Human myoglobin (8)
		a (3,7)	*b* (3,8)			
Alanine	74	78	75	54	15 (60)	11 (44)
Glycine	41	41	39	48	13 (52)	13 (52)
Valine	55	64	64	50	6 (24)	6 (24)
Leucine	79	79	77	75	22 (88)	18 (72)
Isoleucine	10	2	0	0	—	6 (24)
Proline	25	29·5	30	22	5 (20)	8 (32)
Phenylalanine	33	32·5	39	30	5 (20)	8 (32)
Tyrosine	13	16·5	11	11	2 (8)	2 (8)
Tryptophan	—	—	7	5	2 (8)	2 (8)
Serine	45	36	33	35	6 (24)	7 (28)
Threonine	42	35	34	24	7 (28)	4 (16)
Cysteine	6	6	5	5·5	0	0
Methionine	9	7	5·5	4·5	2 (8)	3 (12)
Arginine	13	13	14	14	2 (8)	2 (8)
Histidine	33	37	37	36	9 (36)	8 (32)
Lysine	49	49	49·5	38	18 (72)	22 (88)
Aspartic acid	54	54	51	51	10 (40)	10 (40)
Glutamic acid	35	33	34	38	19 (76)	19 (76)
Amide groups	44	44	45	36	8 (32)	13 (52)

It is recommended first to compare the values under the headings *a* and *b* of normal adult human hemoglobins since they represent results obtained in two laboratories with similar methods of ion exchange chromatography. The differences are considerable in the instance of tyrosine, isoleucine, phenylalanine, and methionine, and they may indicate differences in the preparations of hemoglobin used for the analyses. The differences between human fetal and adult hemoglobins however are much greater than between those

(7) P. C. VAN DER SCHAAF and T. H. J. HUISMAN, *Biochim. Biophys. Acta* **17**, 81 (1955).

(8) A. ROSSI-FANELLI, D. CAVALLINI and C. DE MARCO, *Biochim. Biophys. Acta* **17**, 377 (1955)

(9) G. R. TRISTRAM, in *The Proteins* Vol. I A, p. 215, Academic Press, New York, 1953.

under *a* and *b*. The fetal (embryonal) hemoglobin contains less valine, proline, and histidine, and more isoleucine, serine, and threonine than adult hemoglobin. The amino acid composition of horse hemoglobin differs from that of the human hemoglobins. The myoglobins will be discussed later in the next section.

The hemoglobin macromolecule is devoid of disulfide bridges, and the six sulfhydryl groups of cysteine are of various reactivity. According to Ingram, [10] these groups occur as three pairs. In horse hemoglobin four of the groups are directly titratable and require only two moles of mercuric binding reagent, while the two others react only after denaturation and also require two moles of bivalent mercury. Thus there are two easily accessible pairs, and two separate masked —SH groups. The reactive surface —SH groups make hemoglobin prone to aggregation by the formation of intermolecular disulfide bonds. [11] This may be one of the reasons that hemoglobin becomes more inhomogeneous on repeated crystallization or treatment on ion exchange resins.

Four polypeptide chains have been found in human hemoglobin. The N-terminal amino acid is *valine*, and 4 moles of valine are recovered from one mole of hemoglobin ($M = 68,000$). The second amino acid from N-terminal in human hemoglobin is leucine. Carboxypeptidase digestion studies on adult and fetal human hemoglobins, as well as on sickle-cell hemoglobin, indicated that the C-terminal in all these hemoglobins is the same and that one mole of tyrosine and one mole of histidine were released from one mole of hemoglobin ($M = 68,000$). Since carboxypeptidase hydrolyzes the peptide bonds between various terminal amino acids at various rates, and since less than four moles of terminal amino acids were found, the question on the C-terminal groups remains unsettled. The N-terminal groups of hemoglobins from other species have been determined by Ozawa *et al.*, [12] and the results are presented in Table 29. It is interesting that the hemoglobins from dog, horse, hog, and guinea pig contain *six* terminal groups per mole, i.e. the macromolecule ($M = 68,000$) in these species is composed of 6 chains. The hemoglobins of cow, goat, and sheep contain 4 terminal groups but only two of them are valine groups while the two others are methionine groups. Three different penultimate residues were found in the hemoglobins of dog, horse, hog, and guinea pig respectively. Much more biologically interesting information can be expected on further study of the amino acid sequence of the hemoglobins of various species.

The polypeptides obtained on partial hydrolysis of the macromolecule also have been studied, and interesting differences have been found in the

(10) V. M. Ingram, *Biochem. J.* **59**, 653 (1955).

(11) A. F. Riggs and R. A. Wolbach, *J. Gen. Physiol.* **39**, 585 (1956).

(12) H. Ozawa, T. Okuyama, M. Ohashi, S. Sasagawa and K. Satake, *Symp. on Chemical Struct. of Proteins, Tokyo* 1957, p. 1; see also ref. (19).

amino acid composition of one of the middle fragments of normal human adult, the sickle cell, and the C-disease hemoglobins [1,13] viz.:

Normal Hemogl. · · · —Val—Leu—Leu—Thr—Pro—*Glu*—Glu—Lys— · · ·
Sickel-cell hem. · · · —Val—Leu—Leu—Thr—Pro—*Val*—Glu—Lys— · · ·
C disease hemogl. · · · —Val—Leu—Leu—Thr—Pro—*Lys*—Glu—Lys— · · ·

TABLE 29
THE N-TERMINAL SEQUENCE OF SEVERAL HEMOGLOBINS [12]

Animal	Number of N-terminal groups per mole	N-terminal and penultimate residues
Dog	6	Val-Leu- . . . Val-Gly- . . . Val-Asp- . . .
Horse	6	Val-Leu- . . . Val-Gly- . . . Val-Glu- . . .
Hog	6	Val-Leu- . . . Val-Gly- . . . Val-Glu- . . .
Guinea pig	6	Val-Leu- . . . Val-Ser- . . . Val-Asp- . . .
Cow	4	Val-Leu- . . . Met-Gly- . . .
Goat	4	Val-Leu- . . . Met-Gly- . . .
Sheep	4	Val-Leu- . . . Met-Gly- . . .
Rabbit	4	Val-Leu- . . . Val-Gly- . . .
Snake	4	Val-Leu- . . . Val-Gly- . . .

The physiological function of hemoglobin is to bind oxygen of the air and to carry it to various parts of the body. The oxygenated hemoglobin is called *oxyhemoglobin*. One molecule of oxygen is bound at each of the bivalent iron atoms reversibly, thus, if Hb denotes hemoglobin, the reaction can be expressed by the equation

$$\mathrm{Hb} + 4\,\mathrm{O_2} \rightleftarrows \mathrm{Hb(O_2)_4}.$$

Although this change is reflected in the absorption spectrum and some other physical properties, it does not much affect the macromolecular properties. The same can be said about the poisoning of hemoglobin with carbon monoxide or nitric oxide. The preparations of oxyhemoglobin are less stable than those of hemoglobin, since the oxygen slowly interacts with the bivalent iron oxidizing it irreversibly to trivalent level; some other changes, such as oxidation of the freely accessible sulfhydryl groups also occur. The hemoglobin modifi-

[13] V. M. INGRAM, *Nature* **180**, 326 (1957); J. A. HUNT and V. M. INGRAM, *ibid.* **181**, 1062 (1958).

cation containing trivalent iron is called *methemoglobin* or *ferrihemoglobin.* It can be prepared by oxidizing hemoglobin or oxyhemoglobin with ferricyanide, permanganate, and other oxidizing agents. The acid solutions of methemoglobin are brown and the alkaline solutions are red. While the hem (ferroporphyrin) portion of hemoglobins from various species is the same, the spectra and affinity to oxygen differ. This indicates that the atomic groups of the protein (globin) component of the macromolecule have some effect on these properties, and these groups in the various species certainly are different.[14]

The change of the single glutamic acid residue to the neutral valine results in the loss of one negatively charged carboxyl group in the macromolecule, and this is sufficient to affect the electrophoretic mobility so that the difference can be detected experimentally with sufficient degree of precision. The exchange of the glutamic acid of normal hemoglobin to lysine in the hemoglobin C changes the mobility even more in the same direction.[3]

The differences between fetal and adult hemoglobins have been found not only in human hemoglobins but also in other species. These differences are not confined only to amino acid composition but extend to many other properties,[15] such as: crystallographic differences, solubility differences, immunological specificity, stability toward denaturation by alkali, rate of spreading of surface films, differences in electrophoretic mobility, in absorption of light in the ultraviolet region of the spectrum, and in oxygen–hemoglobin dissociation curves. The anodic mobility of adult human hemoglobin is greater than that of fetal hemoglobin at both pH 7·1 and 8·0. These electrophoretic studies have shown[16] that 6% of adult hemoglobin is present at 20 weeks fetal age, that this amount increases to 20% at birth, to 50% in two months and to 80–90% at four months after birth. The differences between the reaction rates in alkali denaturation of the adult and fetal hemoglobins are striking. Fetal hemoglobin is so much more stable toward the denaturing effect of alkali that it is possible to find conditions at which in a mixture of both, the adult hemoglobin is fully denatured and the fetal remains in the native state.[15] This difference in the stability to alkali has not been explained in terms of macromolecular structure.

The Myoglobins

The myoglobins have been mentioned in chapt. 5, since the configuration of this protein has been partially solved by means of *X*-ray diffraction studies.[17] The macromolecule of myoglobin is four times smaller than that of

(14) A. C. Redfield, *Quart. Rev. Biol.* 8, 31 (1933); F. J. W. Roughton and J. C. Kendrew (ed.), *Hemoglobin* T. Thornton Butterworth, London, 1949.

(15) J. C. White and G. H. Beaven, *J. Clin. Pathol.* **7**, 175 (1954).

(16) G. H. Beaven, H. Hoch and E. R. Holiday, *Biochem. J.* **49**, 376 (1951).

(17) J. C. Kendrew, *Nature* **182**, 764 (1958); F. H. C. Crick and J. C. Kendrew, *Adv. Protein Chem.* **12**, 133 (1957); J. C. Kendrew *et al.*, Nature **185**, 422 (1960).

hemoglobin, and contains only one hem and one bivalent iron atom. The amino acid composition of human and horse myoglobins is presented in Table 28, and the numbers in parentheses indicate the number of residues in four molecules in order to get a better comparison with the hemoglobins. It is obvious that there is only a small difference in the composition of horse and human myoglobins, while the difference between the composition of the myoglobins differs strongly from that of the hemoglobins. This is particularly clear in the instances of valine, cysteine, arginine, lysine, and glutamic acid. Data are available also on the myoglobin of whale, [18] and it is noteworthy that this myoglobin is quite similar in its amino acid composition to human and horse myoglobins. Thus the myoglobins of the various species are more similar than the larger and more complicated molecules of the hemoglobins.

The red myoglobin is sometimes called the hemoglobin of the muscle, and the flesh of diving animals, such as the whale, is dark red due to its high myoglobin content. The physiological function of this relatively small protein is about the same as that of hemoglobin — to supply and store oxygen in the muscle. Myoglobin actually transmits the oxygen from hemoglobin to the oxidizing sites of the muscle cells. Each macromolecule of myoglobin is able to carry one molecule of oxygen, but the affinity of myoglobin for oxygen is higher than that of hemoglobin, hence upon collision of an oxyhemoglobin molecule with myoglobin the oxygen is transferred to myoglobin. The relatively small myoglobin then carries the oxygen to the metabolic sites of the muscle cell where free oxygen is required.

The N-terminal amino acid of horse myoglobin is glycine, [19] and in whale myoglobin it is valine. [18] There is only one polypeptide chain in the macromolecules of myoglobin, since one mole of terminal amino acid is found per one mole protein. Since the viscosity of the solutions is very low, the macromolecule is compactly folded, and the way of chain folding is now well revealed by recent analysis of the X-ray diffraction data. [17] There are no disulfide bridges which might link the folds, hence the folding must be due to other reasons which have not been fully explained as yet. The forces causing this folding have been discussed in chapt. 12, and a more detailed treatment of the problem can be found in the publications of other authors. [20,21]

The conviction that crystallized myoglobin of mammalian blood is a homogeneous protein has been subjected to doubt by recently published experiments. [22] It has been found that crystalline human myoglobin can be separated in three components with somewhat different electrophoretic mobilities.

[18] K. Schmidt, *Nature* **163**, 481 (1949).

[19] R. R. Porter and F. Sanger, *Biochem. J.* **42**, 287 (1948).

[20] W. Kauzmann, in *The Mechanism of Enzyme Action* p. 70 (W. D. McElroy and B. Glass, ed.), Hopkins Press, Baltimore, 1954.

[21] Ch. Tanford, in *Symposium on Protein Structure* p. 35 (A. Neuberger, ed.), Methuen, London, Wiley, New York, 1958.

[22] A. Rossi-Fanelli and E. Antonini, *ibid.* p. 140.

Apart from the major component which comprizes 74% of the total, two subfractions (19% and 7% respectively) were found. The second component (19%) was found to be identical with the major fraction in such properties as absorption spectrum, and reversible combination with oxygen.

While the myoglobins of the mammals differ very little in their physical and chemical properties, the myoglobins of the lower species exhibit more variety. Thus a very interesting myoglobin has been isolated recently from the muscles of Mediterranean molluscs.[23] The molecular weight of this myoglobin was found to be near 20,000, and the isoelectric point near pH 4·5, while the mammalian myoglobins have isoelectric point at pH 6·5–7. The amino acid composition of the mollusc myoglobin differs strongly from the amino acid composition of human, horse, or whale myoglobins. Thus, according to the Italian researchers,[23] the mollusc myoglobin contains only 1·2% histidine and 6·9% lysine, while 7·8% histidine and 19·1% lysine were found in human myoglobin. This low content of the basic amino acids in the myoglobin of mollusc is responsible for the shift of the isoelectric point to the acid side. There are large differences also in the content of proline, alanine, and serine. The ferroporphyrin component, however, was found the same as in the mammalian myoglobins.

The Variety of Respiratory Proteins in the Lower Species

In addition to hemoglobin and myoglobin, many other respiratory proteins have been described in the literature.[2,6,24] Some of the respiratory proteins contain copper instead of iron, while some others have iron without the porphyrin. This variety is especially pronounced in the lower species, and in several instances it is impossible to distinguish these oxygen carriers from enzymes of similar composition. Thus the cytochromes contain a ferroporphyrin complex very similar to that of the hemoglobins, and then we have in the green plants the chlorophylls with magnesium in the porphyrin complex which is not directly attached to a protein but is linked to a small lipophylic chain. It is noteworthy that complex proteins closely resembling hemoglobins have been found in the root nodules of legumes. This vegetable "hemoglobin" contains 0·34% iron, has a spectrum resembling the spectrum of hemoglobin, and can be converted into a methemoglobin-like modification.[25] Its functions in the plant have not been fully explained.

Considering this variety in the lower species from the evolutionary point of view, one has to acknowledge that from the unwieldy multitude of substances available to the primitive organisms many have been tried as oxygen carriers for the purpose of respiration. It is well conceivable that many diffe-

[23] A. Rossi-Fanelli, E. Antonini and D. Povoledo, *ibid.* p. 144.

[24] J. Roche, *Pigments Respiratoires*, Masson, Paris, 1935; H. Benard, *Hemoglobine et Pigments Apparentées*, Paris, Masson, 1950.

[25] H. Sternberg and A. Virtanen, *Acta Chem. Scand.* **6**, 1342 (1952).

rent metals were combined with porphyrin-like and protein-porphyrin compounds, but not all of these were suitable as oxygen carriers or catalysts. Many protein–metal chelates devoid of porphyrin also were formed, and some of them have survived as suitable respiratory proteins in the lower species of animals up to our time. The absence of these respiratory proteins in the vertebrates, however, indicates that these macromolecules are less efficient than the hemoglobin–myoglobin system.

The *chlorocruorin* type respiratory proteins are green pigments found in certain species of marine worms. It resembles the various red pigments of

TABLE 30

MOLECULAR CONSTANTS OF HEMOCYANINS ACCORDING TO ERIKSSON-QUENSEL AND SVEDBERG

Species	pH	S	$D_{20} \cdot 10^7$	M (from sedim. velocity	M from sed. equil.
Palinarus	6·8	16·4	3·4	446,000	447,000
Helix pomatia	9·7	12·1	2·23	502,000	
Busycon	9·6	13·5	3·29	379,600	
Eledone	11·6	10·6	2·16	457,000	
Homaris vulg.	6·8	22·6	2·78	752,000	803,000
Helix pomatia	8·6	16·0	2·06	719,000	797,000
Octopus vulgaris	6·8	49·3	1·65	2,785,000	
Eledone	6·8	49·1	1·64	2,791,000	
Rossia owenii	6·8	56·2	1·58	3,316,000	
Helix pomatia	6·8	98·9	1·38	6,630,000	6,680,000
Busycon	6·8	101·7	1·38	6,814,000	

invertebrates (*erythrocruorins*) in that all of them contain a ferroporphyrin component, although the details of composition and structure are little investigated. The iron content of chlorocruorin is higher than that of hemoglobin, and it is possible that some of the iron, besides that present in the ferroporphyrin, is directly bound to the globin. The isoelectric point of chlorocruorin is at pH 4·3, and its particle weight is very high (over 2 million).

The brown *hemerythrins* are found in the annelids and related species, and they represent a class of iron-containing respiratory proteins devoid of porphyrin. The capacity of these proteins to combine with oxygen is much lower than that of mammalian hemoglobins. The molecular weight of these proteins, however, is in the hemoglobin range.

The *hemocyanins* represent a large group of copper containing respiratory proteins found in such lower species as snails, various crustaceans (crabs, clams, etc.), spiders, scorpions, octopuses etc. The proteins are devoid of any porphyrin, and the copper forms a kind of chelate with the protein. The copper content of the hemocyanins varies between 0·17% and 0·26%, depending on the source of the pigment. The oxygen-binding capacity is lower than that of the hemoglobins of mammals. Extensive studies on the molecular weights of these proteins have been done by Svedberg *et al.*, and some of the results are presented in Table 30. The molecular weights of the preparations are very high, and it is interesting that many hemocyanins dissociated reversibly upon the variation of the acidity of the medium. In several instances, the larger particles appeared to be associations of 2, 4, or 8 smaller units which thus formed paucidisperse solutions, i.e. systems containing several homogeneous components the larger being simple multiplies of the smaller units.[(26)]

The isoelectric points of the various hemocyanins were found to be in the pH range between 4·4 and 5·8, and the particles did not dissociate if the pH was altered between 4 and about 8, with a few exceptions of higher or lesser stability. The particle weight of the hemocyanin from snail (*Helix pomatia*) was 6·6 million between pH 4·5 and 7·5; it decreased to 719,000 at pH 8·6, and further down to 502,000 at pH 9·7. This indicates that the larger units, whose molecular weight is measured in millions, definitely are not macromolecules but associations of several macromolecules. The chemical molecular weight of these smaller macromolecules, however, is not known. It is noteworthy that in spite of the extremely high particle weight the solutions of the hemocyanins are not highly viscous. This indicates that the particles are globular and compact (corpuscular).

(26) T. Svedberg and K. O. Pedersen, *The Ultracentrifuge* p. 369, Clarendon Press, Oxford, 1940.

CHAPTER 15

ENZYMES, AND ENZYMIC ACTIVITY

> The reactions of proteins — most of which seem to be enzymes — are fundamental for biological life, since they play a primary role in both of its essential features: reproduction and metabolism.
>
> H. THEORELL [1]

ENZYMES are catalytically active proteins which have a high degree of specificity and a tremendous efficiency resulting in the quick and well co-ordinated processes of living cells. "Hundreds and thousands of enzyme proteins play their parts in each vital process, let alone metabolism as a whole. Each can catalyze only one or a very limited number of reactions, and it is only when taken together, when their actions are unified in a definite way, that they constitute the orderly sequence of phenomena which forms the foundation for the process of life". [2] Enzymes are involved not only in such relatively simple processes as fermentation or digestion of food but also in the *building* of the various extremely complicated macromolecules essential for life. How do the enzymes themselves evolve from the germ cell? How are enzymes themselves synthesized, and how do they promote the reduplication of the other cellular elements? These questions have not been answered yet. But it is hoped that a better understanding of the ontogenic evolution of the organism will shed new light also on the *origin of enzymes* in the early stages of evolution. It is well known what enzymes are, since many have been isolated in a pure state, but very little is known about their synthesis, and much is to be learned also about the mechanism of their action. While the mechanism of some isolated systems is relatively well investigated, the harmonious *co-ordinated* actions of the many enzymes in a living cell is little understood.

The boundless multitude of enzymes must be *classified*, and there are several principles of classification. First, according to their *chemical composition*, all enzymes can be divided in *simple enzyme proteins* and *complex* or *conjugated proteins*. The former yield only amino acids on complete hydrolysis, while the latter contain a nonprotein prosthetic group called *co-enzyme*. Pepsin and ribonuclease are examples of simple enzyme proteins, whereas catalase or the various dehydrogenases are examples of enzymes containing

[1] H. THEORELL, in *Currents in Biochemical Research* p. 275 (D. E. GREEN, ed.), Interscience Publ., New York, 1956.

[2] A. I. OPARIN, *The Origin of Life on the Earth* 3rd ed., p. 374 (transl. by A. Synge), Oliver and Boyd, Edinburgh, London, 1957.

prosthetic groups. Most enzymes, however, have not been isolated yet in a pure state, although a great deal is known about their functions and mode of action. The enzymic action actually has been observed and even utilized for centuries for various practical purposes, such as fermentation, without knowing much about what is happening in terms of chemical changes. Later in the nineteenth century the chemists learned how to concentrate enzymes and obtain very active concentrates, though the chemical nature of these specific catalysts was not clear at all. For this reason, the old classification based on the function of the enzyme rather than chemical composition is still prevailing. According to this classification, we have *hydrolytic enzymes*, *redox enzymes*, phosphorylases, decarboxylases, hydrases, and various transferring, condensing, and isomerizing enzymes, and this does not include all of the variety. The *hydrolytic* enzymes represent one of the largest and best investigated class, and one finds here such important groups as the *esterases*, *carbohydrases*, and *proteases* or *proteolytic enzymes*. The esterase group can be subdivided further into such subgroups as the lipases, the phosphatases, sulfatases, nucleases, etc. To the large carbohydrase group belong the various glucosidases, the amylases, the cellulose-splitting cellulase. To the relatively well studied group of proteolytic enzymes belong such proteins as pepsin, trypsin, chymotrypsin, carboxypeptidase, and many others. The important domain of enzymes has attracted the interest of so many researchers, and the literature on enzyme chemistry and enzymic action is so voluminous that there is reason to regard enzymology as a special branch of biochemistry. [(3)] In this treatise we are interested in the enzymes as macromolecules, and we shall have to desist from a detailed discussion of enzyme kinetics and the metabolic reactions they catalyze. It has been established that the rate of reactions catalyzed by enzymes depends on various factors, such as enzyme–substrate ratio, temperature, pH, and the presence of other micromolecular and macromolecular substances. Certain common cations, such as magnesium, may act as *activators*, while other substances may *inhibit* an enzymic reaction. This inhibition may be brought about in several ways, e.g. by inactivating the active group of the enzyme or by blocking the active site of the substrate. A great deal of information has been obtained by using relatively simple *synthetic substrates*; e.g. the specificity and mechanism of the action of proteolytic enzymes has been studied in great detail by using various simple di- and tripeptides and other small amino acid derivatives; by testing the hydrolysis of these simple and well defined compounds, it was possible to find out

[(3)] J. B. Sumner and K. Myrbäck, *The Enzymes* Vol. I and II (each in 2 parts), Academic Press, New York, 1950–52; S. P. Colowick and N. O. Kaplan, *Methods in Enzymology* Vol. I–IV, Academic Press, New York, 1955–57; M. Dixon and E. C. Webb, *Enzymes* Academic Press, New York, 1958; J. B. Neilands and P. K. Stumpf, *Outlines of Enzyme Chemistry* Wiley, New York, 2nd ed., 1958; P. D. Boyer, H. Lardy and K. Myrbäck (ed.), *The Enzymes*, Vol. I, Academic Press, New York, 1959; Vol. II and III, 1960.

much about the *specificity* of the various enzymes [4,5] (see also chapt. 12). The enzymic activity of several enzymes participating in the metabolism of polysaccharides was mentioned in chapt. 8.

Proteolytic Enzymes [6,7]

An exact study on the chemical nature of proteolytic enzymes begins in 1930 when Northrop isolated *crystalline pepsin* and showed that this preparation was more active than the noncrystalline concentrates. [6] In the following decades many more crystallized proteolytic enzymes were isolated from animal tissues and plants, and it was established that they all are proteins. It was also established that pepsin and several other proteolytic enzymes are formed from *precursors* or *zymogens* either autocatalytically or catalytically under the influence of other enzymes. Several precursors also have been isolated and crystallized, and the mechanism of activation has been explained in chemical terms. Thus the molecular weight of *pepsinogen* of stomach is 42,500, whereas the molecular weight of pepsin is 35,000. Activation of pepsinogen occurs under the influence of pepsin in that the latter splits off certain peptides from the macromolecule of the precursor. It is noteworthy that pepsin is a very acid protein of a very low basic amino acid content and that the peptides split off on activation are basic.

The amino acid composition of pepsin, carboxypeptidase, and papain is presented in Table 31. All determinations were made by the precise chromatographic methods.

Since all of the enzymes mentioned in the Table contain a small amount of certain amino acids (arginine and histidine in pepsin, methionine in carboxypeptidase, and histidine in papain) it is easy to calculate the chemical molecular weight from the amino acid content. This chemical molecular weight agrees closely with the best physical values thus ascertaining the chemical homogeneity and macromolecular nature of the enzymes. According to the rigorous homogeneity tests of constant solubility and electrophoresis however, pepsin is not quite homogeneous. It is not clear whether the inhomogeneities found in isolated crystallized pepsin preparations are caused by the procedures of isolation or if they are genuine. Considering the *in vivo* conditions in the stomach, where pepsin is formed from pepsinogen by gradual cleavage of a polypeptide chain, there seems to be little sense to speak about homogeneity of the enzyme in the organism.

(4) M. Bergmann and J. S. Fruton, *Adv. Enzymol.* **1**, 63 (1941); M. Bergmann, *ibid.* **2**, 49 (1942).

(5) E. L. Smith, *Adv. Enzymol.* **12**,, 191 (1951).

(6) J. H. Northrop, M. Kunitz and R. M. Herriott, *Crystalline Enzymes* 2nd ed., Columbia Univ. Press, New York, 1948.

(7) N. M. Green and H. Neurath, in *The Proteins* Vol. II B, p. 1057 (H. Neurath and K. Bailey, ed.), Academic Press, New York, 1954; K. Okuhuki in *Analytical Methods of Protein Chemistry* (P. Alexander and R. J. Block, eds), Vol. I, Pergamon Press, London, 1961.

TABLE 31

AMINO ACID COMPOSITION IN RESIDUES PER MOLE OF SOME PROTEOLYTIC ENZYMES

	Pepsin [8]	Carboxypeptidase [9]	Papain [10]
Alanine	18	20	13
Glycine	38	23	23
Valine	21	16	15
Leucine	28	25	9
Isoleucine	27	20	9
Proline	15	11	9
Phenylalanine	14	15	4
Tyrosine	18	20	17
Tryptophan	6	6	5
Serine	44	33	11
Threonine	28	27	7
Cystine/2	6	(4)	(6)
Methionine	5	1	0
Arginine	1	10	9
Histidine	1	8	1
Lysine	1	18	8
Aspartic acid	44	30	17
Glutamic acid	27	26	17
Amide	(36)	(19)	(19)
Molecular weight	35,000	34,400	20,300
Isoelectric point at pH	1–2	6	8·7

Pepsin is isolated either directly from gastric juice or prepared by activation of pepsinogen obtained from gastric mucosa. It can be precipitated with concentrated magnesium sulfate, and it is recrystallized usually from 20% ethanol. As a protein, pepsin is stable in acid solutions of pH 4–5, and it is quickly denatured in neutral and alkaline solutions. Inhomogeneity (in a physical sense) may arise from denaturation, but chemical and physical inhomogeneity may be due also to *autodigestion* in acid solution, especially at a pH below 4. Pepsin is a "cannibal", i.e. the macromolecules tend to digest each other under certain suitable conditions. Some genuine chemical inhomogeneity is suggested by the amino acid analyses of Blumenfeld and Perlmann [8] in which a very small concentration of hydroxyproline was found in the hydrolyzates of pepsin. This amounts to only 0·1 residues of hydroxyproline per mole of pepsin, indicating that one molecule of ten contains this residue.

The macromolecule of pepsin consists of a *single* polypeptide chain which is folded and cross-linked by three disulfide bridges and one phosphate–diester bridge. [11] The N-terminal amino acid in pepsin is isoleucine, and the penultimate residue is glycine; the C-terminal is valine, and the C-terminal

[8] O. O. BLUMENFELD and G. E. PERLMANN, *J. Gen. Physiol.* **42**, 553 (1959).
[9] E. L. SMITH and A. STOCKELL, *J. biol. Chem.* **207**, 501 (1954).
[10] E. L. SMITH, A. STOCKELL and J. R. KIMMEL, *J. biol. Chem.* **207**, 551 (1954).
[11] G. E. PERLMANN, *J. Gen. Physiol.* **41**, 441 (1958).

sequence probably is Val-Leu-Ala- . . . Pepsinogen has the same C-terminal sequence as pepsin, but the N-terminal of pepsinogen is leucine followed by another leucine. About 10 basic lysine residues are in the peptides split off the N-terminal tail of pepsinogen on activation. [12] There are no free sulfhydryl groups in pepsin or pepsinogen, and the latter has the same disulfide and phosphate–diester bridges as pepsin. [11]

A great deal of work has been done on the enzymic activity of pepsin as depending on its structure and configuration. First, it is known that denaturation of pepsin by alkali is associated with a loss of enzymic activity. While the molecular weight does not change on this denaturation, the viscosity increases. This indicates that inactivation and denaturation are associated with an expansion of the macromolecule. [13,14] The specific rotation thereby is shifted to the negative direction. The rotatory dispersion constant of enzymically active native pepsin is low, and it somewhat increases on denaturation with alkali or other denaturing agents. [14] It must be pointed out that this abnormality arises not from the abnormality of the denatured state but from the abnormality of the *native* state. The dispersion constants of the various denatured pepsins were found to be 220–224 mμ which are the ordinary values for denatured proteins, whereas the low value of 212–214 mμ for the native pepsin is abnormal. On what structural features this abnormality depends, is not known. [14a] The acid nature of the enzyme cannot be made responsible for this, since some less acid proteins (serum γ-globulin) behave similarly. It is also doubtful that the single phosphate–diester bridge could be made responsible for this, since the other proteins which show similar abnormalities do not contain such bridges. The only possible reason seems to be in the extremely high *hydroxyamino acid* (serine and threonine) content which is common to the proteins which show an abnormal increase of the dispersion constant on denaturation.

With respect to enzymic activity, Gertrude Perlmann has shown that the interesting *phosphate–diester bridge* is not essential for enzymic activity. With the aid of a phosphodiesterase from snake venom, only one of the phosphate ester bonds was hydrolyzed, and the phosphate, now with two free acid functions, still remains attached to the macromolecule. It is split off by a second stage treatment with prostate monophosphorylase. Although the proteolytic activity is not inhibited by this destruction of the bridge, the enzyme is now more labile to autodigestion than the native pepsin. A similar step-wise breakage of the phosphate–diester bridge was accomplished with pepsinogen, and it was found that this change does not adversely affect the conversion of pepsionogen to pepsin. [11] Reduction of one of the *disulfide* bonds does not affect much the activity of the enzyme, whereas breakage of

[12] C. B. Anfinsen and R. R. Redfield, *Adv. Protein Chem.* **11**, 1 (1956).
[13] H. Edelhoch, *J. Amer. chem. Soc.* **79**, 6100 (1957).
[14] B. Jirgensons, Arch. Biochem. Biophys. **74**, 70 (1958); **78**, 235 (1958).
[14a] See also: G. Perlmann, *Proc. Nat. Acad. Sci.* **45**, 915 (1959).

the other two disulfide bridges results in a decrease of the activity. Since the alkali-inactivated enzyme is more or less expanded and unfolded, it is possible that the globular configuration is essential for the activity, and that two of the three disulfide bridges are linking distant parts of the single chain. On the basis of these findings, the structure of the macromolecule of pepsin can be crudely illustrated as follows:

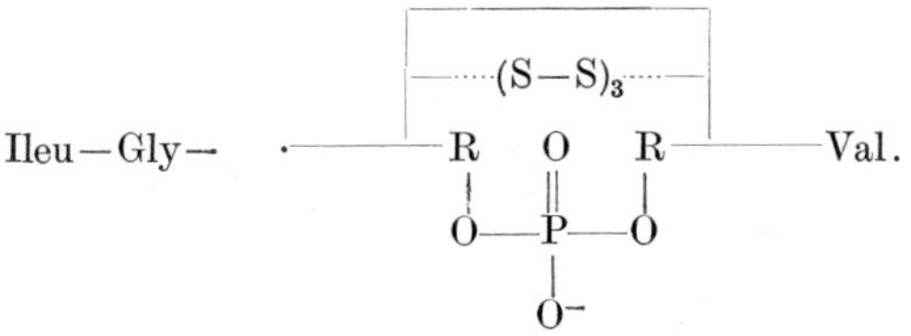

```
                          ┌──────────────────┐
                          │·····(S—S)₃·······│
Ileu—Gly—    ·────────────R      O      R────┴────────Val.
                          |      ‖      |
                          O──────P──────O
                                 |
                                 O⁻
```

In contrast to several other enzymes, pepsin is not extremely specific in its catalytic action in hydrolyzing the peptide bonds between various amino acid residues. The most rapidly affected are the peptide bonds which are between two aromatic residues, e.g. between phenylalanine and tyrosine, but others, such as the leu-val, leu-tyr, and leu-glu bonds also are attacked quite rapidly, while the phe-val, tyr-glu, and several others are affected slowly. The mechanism of these catalytic effects is unknown. It can be speculated that the catalytic activity is associated with the *peculiar folding* due to the high amount of hydroxyamino acids and carboxyl groups of the macromolecule, and that such configuration is favorable for the attack on the peptide bonds. The parallelism between inactivation and expansion in neutral and weakly alkaline solution indicates that *ionization of the carboxyls is the cause of expansion, and that such highly charged and expanded macromolecule is unable to catalyze hydrolysis of peptide bonds.* The highly active macromolecule in an acid solution of pH 1·5–2·5 is strongly shrunk and devoid of the high charge density. Hydrogen bonded structures between the unionized carboxyls and the carboxyls and hydroxyl groups of the tyrosine, serine, and threonine residues, aside of the peculiar configuration, may be important in the enzymic activity.

Trypsin and the *chymotrypsins* are the best investigated pancreatic enzymes. Both trypsin and the chymotrypsins are formed from enzymically inactive precursors called *trypsinogen* and *chymotrypsinogen* respectively. All are simple proteins in the molecular weight range 20,000–27,000, and their isoelectric points are near neutrality or somewhat on the alkaline side at about pH 8. The enzymes are stable in weakly acid solutions, and they are maximally active between pH 7–9. The mechanism of activation of the zymogens (precursors) and the specificity of the enzymes has been extensively studied, and excellent reviews are available on this subject.[7,15] It is known

[15] H. NEURATH and W. SCHWERT, *Chem. Rev.* **46**, 69 (1950); H. NEURATH, *Adv. Protein Chem.* **12**, 319 (1957).

that trypsinogen can be activated either by another enzyme (enterokinase) in weakly acid solution of pH 5·2–6 or by trypsin itself autocatalytically at pH 7–9. The autocatalytic activation is especially efficient in the presence of calcium ions, while in the absence of calcium a portion of trypsinogen is converted into an enzymically inert protein. Chymotrypsinogen can be activated catalytically by trypsin; if only a trace of trypsin is present, the zymogen is converted into the so called α-chymotrypsin, which may be converted further into the β- and γ-chymotrypsins in an autolytic reaction. Only a small peptide is split off the chain in the activation process of trypsinogen, while the chemical changes in the activation of chymotrypsinogen are somewhat obscure. The macromolecules of trypsinogen and trypsin contain only one polypeptide chain which is folded in an unknown manner and cross-linked by several disulfide bridges. The N-terminal amino acid of trypsinogen is valine, and the N-terminal group of trypsin is isoleucine. The C-terminal groups could not be well identified, and it can be assumed that either the carboxyl group is in amide form or that there is a cyclic structure (in both instances the C-terminal would escape detection by both the carboxypeptidase or hydrazinolysis methods). According to Neurath *et al.*, [15,16] the splitting of the peptide from the N-terminal of the chain during activation results in the removal of structural rigidity; the macromolecule becomes more flexible at the N-terminal, and the tail assumes a more nearly helical configuration. The active center of the enzyme is near the N-terminal; apart from the terminal isoleucine and penultimate valine, it contains a histidine in juxtaposition with a serine from one of the middle folds of the single chain. Optical rotation data also have been invoked for the support of this idea. It is noteworthy that the specific rotation of both trypsinogen and chymotrypsinogen is more negative than of the corresponding enzymes. Since the expanded flexible proteins are more levorotatory than the compact native proteins, this rotational shift indicates, contrary to the conclusion of Neurath, a change to a more rigid configuration on activation of the zymogens. However, Neurath's views are supported by the facts that the specific rotation of both trypsinogen and chymotrypsinogen is independent of pH, whereas the rotation of the enzymes becomes more negative the more distant the pH value of the solution from the isoelectric point of the enzyme. [17] Thus the problem is far from being solved. A more complete elucidation of the amino acid sequence and mode of folding of the chain will facilitate solution of the problem.

The same pertains to the activation and structure of chymotrypsinogen and the chymotrypsins. Half-cystine has been found as the N-terminal of chymotrypsinogen, while isoleucine and alanine, in addition to half-cystine,

[16] J. F. PECHÈRE and H. NEURATH, *Symposium on Protein Structure* p. 169 (A. NEUBERGER, ed.), Methuen, London, Wiley, New York, 1958.

[17] H. NEURATH, J. A. RUPLEY and W. J. DREYER, *Arch. Biochem. Biophys.* **65**, 243 (1956).

were found in some of the chymotrypsins. No C-terminal residues could be found in the zymogen, but leucine and tyrosine appeared in the α-chymotrypsin. All this evidence seems to indicate that chymotrypsinogen represents a cyclic macromolecule, and that the closed structure is opened on activation. The amino acid sequence on some segments of the cycles has been established, and it also is known that the chain is looped by four disulfide bridges. The activation involves several steps which include opening of the closed chain, first, between isoleucine and arginine residues which results in the so-called π-chymotrypsin. In the fast activation with large amount of trypsin, this π-chymotrypsin is converted further to the δ-chymotrypsin, in that seryl-arginine is split off from he newly formed C-terminal. In a slow activation, another dipeptide threonylasparagine is liberated by opening another segment of the closed structure near the half-cystine N-terminal. Thus the active α-chymotrypsin contains three N-terminal and two C-terminal groups, the N-terminal groups being half-cystine, isoleucine, and alanine, and the C-terminal groups leucine and tyrosine. Much more work, however, will be needed in order to establish the complete sequence, the position of the disulfide bridges, and the active center of the enzyme.

The specificity of trypsin is narrower than that of pepsin, since trypsin affects only those peptide bonds in which the carbonyl group is contributed by arginine or lysine. The chymotrypsins are less specific than trypsin.[(7)] The effect of chemical modification of the enzymes on their specificity and activity also has been studied, and it is surprising to learn that rather drastic treatment, such as acetylation of 75% of the free amino groups of trypsin affects its enzymic activity very little.[(18)] Iodination, reduction and diazotization also affected trypsin but little, whereas formaldehyde was found as a strong inactivator[(18)] for trypsin. α-chymotrypsin also was found to be relatively resistant to several rather drastic treatments.[(19)] The enzymic activity of trypsin is inhibited by a number of various proteins which combine with the enzyme, forming well defined compounds. Ovomucoid, a carbohydrate-containing protein of egg white ($M = 28{,}000$), and the soy bean inhibitor ($M = 16{,}000$), are the best investigated trypsin inhibitors. The isoelectric point of the soy bean trypsin inhibitor is at pH 4·5, hence it is a slightly acid protein, and the interaction with the slightly basic trypsin is of ionic nature.[(19a)]

Carboxypeptidase is another interesting enzyme found in pancreatic juice. Since this protein crystallizes readily, it is obtainable in a highly purified

(18) H. Fraenkel-Conrat, R. S. Bean and H. Lineweaver, *J. biol. Chem.* **177**, 385 (1949).

(19) E. F. Jansen, A. L. Curl and A. K. Balls, *J. biol. Chem.* **189**, 671 (1951).

(19a) M. Laskowski and M. Laskowski, Jr., *Adv. Protein Chem.* **9**, 203 (1954); B. Jirgensons, T. Ikenaka and V. Gorguraki, *Makromol. Chem.* **39**, 149 (1960).

state, and many times recrystallized carboxypeptidase is homogeneous in both electrophoresis and sedimentation. The molecular weight of this enzyme is 34,000, and the physical molecular weight agrees closely with the chemical molecular weight calculated from amino acid composition (Table 31). Carboxypeptidase has a single polypeptide chain with asparagine as the N-terminal and serine as the penultimate residue.[20] Moreover, it is interesting that 0·18% of zinc has been found in the enzyme, this amount corresponding to one atom zinc per molecule.[21] Carboxypeptidase is stable in neutral and weakly alkaline solution, also with respect to autodigestion, but it is unstable at pH below 6 and above 10. The enzyme is formed from a precursor — *procarboxypeptidase,* which is a much larger protein (M = 95,000) than carboxypeptidase,[15] by the catalytic influence of trypsin. Activation studies indicate that the activation involves splitting of many peptide bonds and release of enzymically inactive components. Since the zymogen appears to be not a complex but a real macromolecule, the potential enzyme in this instance comprises about a third of this unit, and the activation is quite different from that of the previously mentioned cases.

Carboxypeptidase has acquired especially great attention chiefly due to the fact that it is now an indispensible tool in the study of amino acid sequence. The enzyme is specific in the sense that it attacks only those peptide bonds which have an adjacent *free carboxyl group,* whereas pepsin or trypsin attack the peptide bonds anywhere in the middle of the chain. Carboxypeptidase and similarly acting enzymes are denoted as *exo*peptidases, in contrast to such *endo*peptidases as pepsin. Incubation of a protein with carboxypeptidase (at pH 7–8) results in a gradual digestion of the protein from its C-terminal. Analysis of the liberated amino acids, e.g. by paper chromatography, gives information about the C-terminal sequence. The C-terminal amino acid is found in the largest amount followed by smaller amounts of the amino acids that follow in the chain. Carboxypeptidase is not extremely specific with respect to what residues it is able to chop off the chain. However, it is known that it will not attack an amidated carboxyl or terminal proline, probably also not cystine and cysteine. Moreover, the hydrolysis rates are different with various amino acids so that the quantities of the liberated amino acids sometimes do not reflect exactly their order in the chain.[22,23]

(20) E. O. P. Thompson, *Biochim. Biophys. Acta* **10,** 633 (1953).

(21) B. L. Vallee, *Adv. Protein Chem.* **10,** 317 (1955); see also: H. Neurath, J. A. Rupley and B. L. Vallee, *Abstracts, Amer. chem. Soc. Nat. Meeting* p. 44 C, Atlantic City, Sept. 1959.

(22) J. A. Gladner and H. Neurath, *J. biol. Chem.* **205,** 345 (1953).

(23) J. I. Harris, *J. Amer. chem. Soc.* **74,** 2944 (1952); see also: T. Ikenaka and B. Jirgensons, *Abstracts, Amer. chem. Soc. Nat. Meeting, Atlantic City,* Sept., 1959, p. 1 C. T. Ikenaka, *J. Amer. chem. Soc.* **82,** 3180 (1960).

Papain is the best investigated plant proteinase.[24] It is isolated from the tropical papaya (*Carica*), particularly from the latex vessels of the leaves and fruit, and it was first obtained in pure crystalline form by Balls *et al.*[25] The molecular weight of papain is near 20,000, its isoelectric point is at pH 8·7, and its amino acid composition (see Table 31) agrees well with the physically determined molecular weight. The macromolecule contains only one polypeptide chain which has isoleucine at the N-terminal. One of the sulfhydryl groups of the macromolecule is more active than the others, since it reacts readily with mercury, and the well defined mercuripapain contains two moles of the enzyme per one gram-atom mercury ($M = 41{,}400$). A large part of the macromolecule could be split off without much affecting the specificity and enzymic activity, and Smith *et al.* conclude: "In essence, these results support the view, expressed earlier, that substrate specificity and catalytic effectiveness are part of the same phenomenenon, namely, that each locus of interactions, on the enzyme which contributes to the specificity, plays a role in the catalytic transformation of the substrate"[24] (p. 199 of this ref.). The active sulfhydryl appears to be essential for the enzymic activity, and this —SH group seems to be participating in a high energy bond with one of the carboxyl groups of the enzyme. The enzyme is readily inactivated by oxidizing agents and heavy metal ions, but the mercury compound is stable, and the enzyme can be recovered from it and activated by means of chelating agents and cysteine.

It is noteworthy that the enzymic activity of the catalysts mentioned in this section is not limited to hydrolysis of peptide bonds. First, it is known that the same enzymes which catalyze hydrolysis of the peptide bonds may, under certain conditions, catalyze the *synthesis* of peptides and proteins. This certainly happens *in vivo*, and such syntheses have been demonstrated also in isolated tissue slices.[26] It is much more difficult to demonstrate such synthesis with isolated pure enzymes, all this indicating that efficient protein synthesis requires the presence of an *organized system of many catalysts* and modifiers. Second, it is interesting that several proteolytic enzymes may act not only on peptide bonds but also on ester bonds. And finally, some proteolytic enzymes seem to be able to catalyze transpeptidation, i.e. replacement of one participant in a peptide bond by a related compound. All this leads to the conclusion that a macromolecule of a certain enzyme may be endowed with a variety of functions which probably depend on the presence of other enzymes, substrates, ions, etc., and also on the available sources of energy.

(24) E. L. Smith, R. L. Hill and J. R. Kimmel, in *Symposium on Protein Structure* p. 182 (A. Neuberger, ed.), Methuen, London, Wiley, New York, 1958. J. R. Kimmel and E. L. Smith, *Adv. Enzymol.* **19**, 267 (1957).

(25) A. K. Balls and H. Lineweaver, *J. biol. Chem.* **130**, 669 (1939).

(26) H. Tarver, in *The Proteins* Vol. II B, p. 1199 (H. Neurath and K. Bailey, ed.), Academic Press, New York, 1954.

Ribonuclease [27,28,29]

Ribonuclease is a very important and well investigated enzyme which is able to split (and probably also to catalyze the synthesis) of the ribonucleic acid of cells. In crystalline form, ribonuclease was first isolated by Kunitz (in 1939), and it also was found that the enzyme is a relatively stable simple protein.[6] One of the best sources for the isolation of this enzyme is bovine pancreas. Most of the enzyme is found in the ammonium sulfate precipitation fraction which is soluble in 0·6 saturated ammonium sulfate and insoluble at 0·8 (or 80%) saturation. The enzyme is purified by recrystallization from ammonium sulfate and dilute alcohol, and by electrophoretic and chromatographic methods. Pure ribonuclease does not have any proteolytic activity but it acts as an esterase splitting the sugar–phosphoric acid bonds and liberating mononucleotides.[30]

Pure ribonuclease is a homogeneous protein of relatively low molecular weight of 13,500. The very slight inhomogeneity detected on electrophoresis has been explained as being due to a single amide group (free or blocked carboxyl), while the enzymic activity and general structure of both components is the same.[31] Various physical methods for molecular weight determination have rendered values between 13,000 and 15,000. According to chemical data, the lower value of 13,400–13,500 is the most correct one. The intrinsic viscosity of the solutions of ribonuclease is very low, viz. 0·032–0·035 dl/g, depending on ionic strength and pH, and the viscosity varies only slightly with pH.[31a] These data indicate that the macromolecule of this enzyme is symmetric and compact, and that there is practically no expansion on ionization of the free carboxyl and amino groups. The isoelectric point of the enzyme is a little above pH 9·4, somewhere between pH 9·4–9·6, i.e. there are excessive basic groups in the macromolecule. The crystals have been analyzed by means of *X*-ray diffraction methods, but relatively little new structural information thus far was provided by this approach. Molecular weight of 13,400 was calculated from the dimensions of the volume of the unit cell obtained from *X*-ray diffraction data, in close agreement with the chemical molecular weight.[32] More information about the actual configuration and folding of

[27] C. H. W. Hirs, W. H. Stein and S. Moore, in *Symposium on Protein Structure* p. 211 (A. Neuberger, ed.), Methuen, London, 1958.

[28] C. B. Anfinsen, in *Symposium on Protein Structure* p. 223 (A. Neuberger, ed.), Methuen, London, 1958; see also ref. 12.

[29] C. H. W. Hirs, W. H. Stein and S. Moore, *J. biol. Chem.* **221**, 151 (1956).

[30] R. Markham and J. D. Smith, *Biochem. J.* **52**, 552, 558, 565 (1952).

[31] Ch. Tanford and J. D. Hauenstein, *Biochim. Biophys. Acta* **19**, 535 (1956).

[31a] J. G. Buzzell and Ch. Tanford, *J. physic. Chem.* **60**, 1204 (1956).

[32] F. H. C. Crick and J. C. Kendrew, *Adv. Protein Chem.* **12**, 133 (1957); most of the work on *X*-ray diffraction of ribonuclease crystals has been done by D. Harker.

the polypeptide chain of the macromolecule is expected from the isomorphous replacement method. Heavy metal atoms are attached to the macromolecules of the crystallized enzyme, and the *X*-ray diagrams are analyzed.[(32)]

The chemical-structural studies on ribonuclease have been very successful, so that the structure of the whole macromolecule is almost fully established. The basis of these achievements was rendered by the very accurate and complete amino acid analyses of Hirs, Stein, and Moore.[(29)] First of all, since some of the amino acids, such as methionine and phenylalanine, appeared only in very small amounts, it was possible to compute the chemical molecular weight quite accurately. The next important step was to ascertain the fact that there is only one polypeptide chain in the macromolecule. Lysine was found as the N-terminal group, and valine as the C-terminal residue. The molar ratios corresponded exactly to one mole N-terminal lysine and one mole C-terminal valine for one mole of the enzyme. The enzyme moreover distinguished with its high content of lysine, serine, and threonine; the content of the aspartic and glutamic acid also was found to be high, but the acidity is moderated by the amidation of many of the carboxyl groups of these dicarboxylic acids. No free sulfhydryl groups could be detected, and the cystine content indicated the presence of four disulfide bridges in the macromolecule.

The amino acid sequence studies were undertaken on a large scale chiefly in two laboratories: in the Rockefeller Institute for Medical Research, New York, by Hirs, Moore, and Stein, and at the National Heart Institute, National Institutes of Health, Bethesda, under the leadership of Anfinsen. Both groups applied independently the classical methods of terminal sequence studies, the study of partial degradation products (polypeptides) obtained by means of different enzymes, and both investigated also the properties of oxidized and reduced ribonuclease. The sequence at the N-terminal was unraveled chiefly by the Edman phenylisothiocyanate method, and the sequence at the C-terminal by the carboxypeptidase method. The latter enzyme released first valine which was followed by serine, alanine, aspartic acid, and phenylalanine. The sequence of the bulk of the chain was elucidated by partial digestion with various enzymes, such as pepsin, trypsin, chymotrypsin, and subtilisin (a proteinase from *bacillus subtilis*). The peptides were separated, and the amino acid sequence in the various peptides was determined. An attempt was made to assemble the pieces on the basis of the well known specificity of the various enzymes (chapt. 12). A similar partial enzymic cleavage was accomplished with oxidized ribonuclease in which the original cystine residues yielded cysteic acid, and the methionine residues the sulfone.

The tentative sequence of the residues in ribonuclease is illustrated below. The parts in parentheses are not fully clarified with respect to the sequence. The position of the amides is not indicated (altogether 14–17 carboxyls of the aspartic and glutamic acids are in amide form). The cystine bridges are indicated by vertical bars. Some of the places attacked by pepsin are denoted by P, those by trypsin with T, and those by chymotrypsin by Chy.

NH_2—Lys. Glu. Thr. Ala. Ala. Ala. Lys. Phe. Glu. Arg. Ser. Thr. Ser. Ser. Asp. His. Met.-
P P T Chy T

Glu. Ala. Ala. Ser. Ser. Asp. Ser. Tyr. Cys. Asp. Glu. Met. Met. Lys. Ser. Arg. Asp. Leu.-
Chy T

Thr. Lys. Asp. Arg. (Cys. Asp. Val. Pro. Thr. Lys.). Phe. (Glu. Val. Leu. Ser. His. Asp.-
T T P

Glu. Ala. Val. Cys. Glu. Ala. Val. Ser.). Lys. Asp. Val. Ala. Cys. Lys. Asp. Gly. Thr. Asp.-
T T

Glu. Cys. Tyr. Glu. Ser. Tyr. Ser. Thr. Met. Ser. Ileu. Thr. Asp. Cys. Arg. Glu. Ser. Thr.-
Chy Chy T

Ser. Gly. Lys. Tyr. Pro. Asp. Ala. Cys. Tyr. Lys. Thr. Thr. Asp. Glu. Ala. Lys.(Val. Ileu.-
T P Chy T T

Ileu. His. Cys. Asp. Glu. Gly. Ala. Pro. Tyr. Val. Pro. His.). Phe. Asp. Ala. Ser. Val—COOH
Chy P

Altogether there are 124 amino acid residues in the chain which is cross-linked by four disulfide bridges forming one small and three large loops, as indicated in the following scheme:

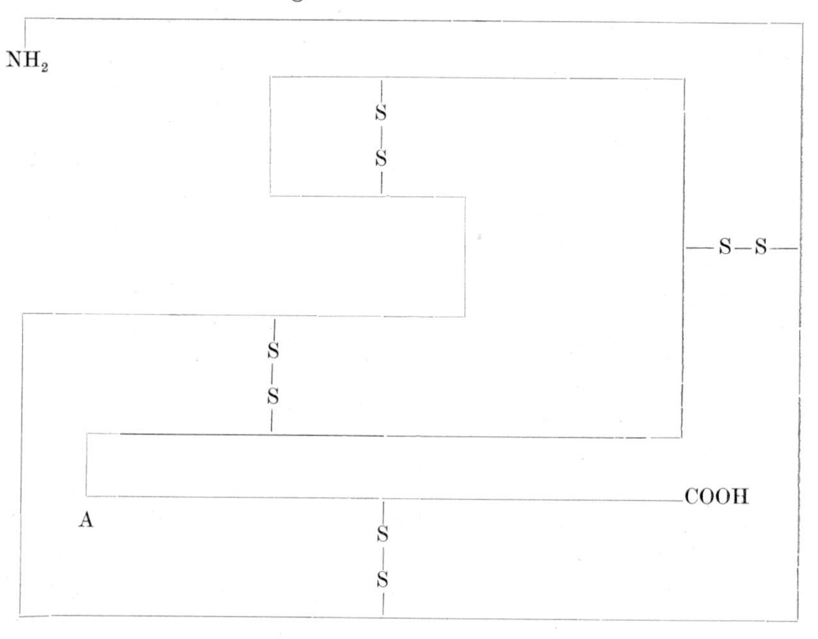

Since the viscosity of the solutions is so very low, the peptide chain in the macromolecule must be folded many more times than shown in the scheme, and the model of course must be three-dimensional. More exact information on the exact way of folding, including the presence and extent of the possible helical configuration in the segments, can be expected from further studies on X-rays diffraction.[32]

Extensive studies have been carried out also on the importance of the folded configuration and certain parts of the macromolecule for the enzymic activity of ribonuclease.[32a] It has been found that the enzymic activity is not lost in 8 M urea, and Anfinsen concludes that "enzymatic activity in this protein is not dependent upon an intact system of hydrogen bonds".[28] The reduced specific viscosity of the enzyme in 8 M urea is 0·085, i.e. higher than that of ribonuclease in water; hence the macromolecules may undergo a considerable expansion without losing their enzymic capacities. It also has been found that a partial disruption of the disulfide bridges does not much affect the enzymic activity, while a complete oxidative or reductive cleavage of the cross-links leads to inactivation. Furthermore, clipping off the free hanging tails at both the N- or C-terminal only little affects the enzymic functions. Thus neither the entire chain nor its specific configuration are strictly essential for the enzymic activity.[28] However, the macromolecule seems to have an active center which probably is located in the loop A near the C-terminal tail.[32a] The disulfide-stabilized configuration of this part, and especially the hydrogen-bonded tyrosine residues of this part of the macromolecule, seem to be essential for the activity of this enzyme.[28] The importance of the hydrogen-bonded tyrosine residues was assumed on the basis of the fact that inactivation is associated with a strong change of the light absorption at 285 mμ.

Very recent studies in both the Rockefeller Institute and National Institutes of Health have yielded a more accurate picture of the structure of ribonuclease, and the results are summarized in the two-dimensional illustration as shown in Fig. 69*. In reality the macromolecule, of course, is folded in three dimensions, but the exact way of folding is not yet known. Also some portions in the chain are not fully elaborated. Definite differences in the amino acid sequences have been found in different species, and the difference between the ribonucleases of beef and sheep pancreas is illustrated in Fig. 70.

It is interesting that there is some similarity between ribonuclease and pepsin both in the amino acid composition, macromolecular structure, and the effects of configurational changes on certain physical properties and enzymic acitivity as well. The content of hydroxyamino acids (serine and threonine) in both enzymes is unusually high. The single polypeptide chain in both enzymes is looped by several bridges. In both instances considerable

[32a] A recent discussion presented by F. M. Richards and P. J. Vithayathil, *Abstracts, Amer. chem. Soc. Nat. Meeting, Atlantic City* p. 23 C, Sept. 1959.

* An in the illustration denotes asparagine, Gn-glutamine. The cross-hatched sections of the chain are not definitely determined.

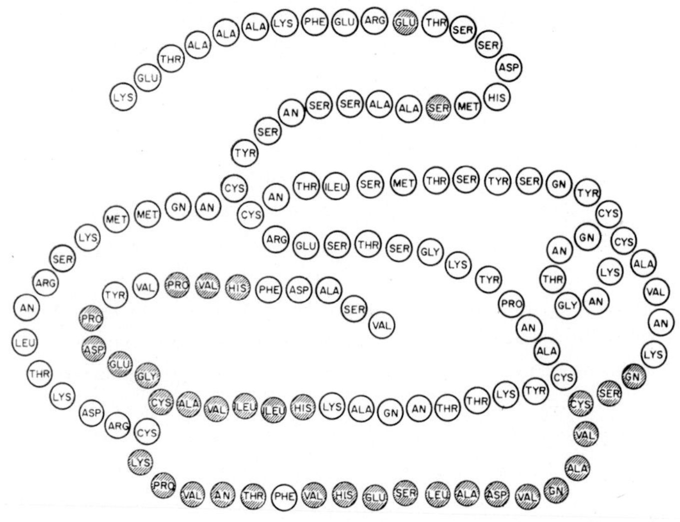

FIG. 69. The structure of ribonuclease according to Hirs, Moore, Stein, Spackman, Bailey, Redfield, Cooke, Ryle, and Anfinsen. The sequence of the cross-hatched residues is not yet fully established (by *Courtesy* of C. B. Anfinsen)

Differences in structures of bovine and ovine pancreatic ribonucleases

Beef Lys . Glu . Thr . Ala . Ala . Ala . Lys . Phe . ------

Sheep Lys . Glu . Ser . Ala . Ala . Ala . Lys . Phe . ------

Trypsin Pepsin

1 2 3 4 5 6 7 8

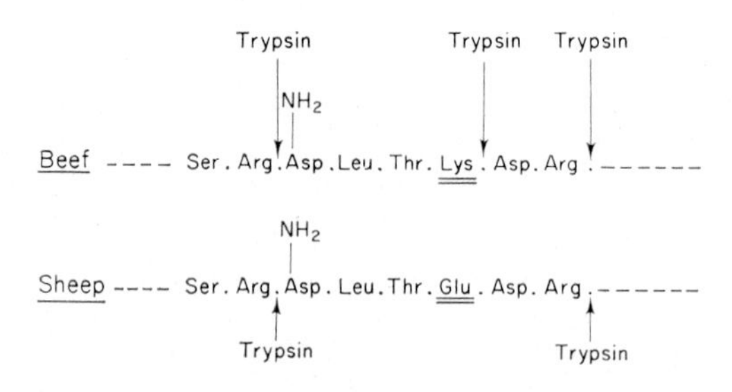

FIG. 70. Differences in structures of bovine and ovine ribonucleases, according to Anfinsen *et al.*

chemical and configurational modification is possible without the loss of enzymic activity. In both instances the macromolecules are compactly folded (low viscosity); in both cases the specific rotation is strongly negative and the dispersion constants are low. In both cases the dispersion constants change but little on denaturation. Thus, according to Anfinsen, [28] the dispersion constant of the completely unfolded oxidized, enzymically inactive ribonuclease is 226 mμ, while that of the native enzyme is 230 mμ. The rotatory dispersion constant of native pepsin is 213 mμ, and it increases somewhat on denaturation and inactivation of pepsin. [14] This seems to indicate that in both these enzymes there is little if any helical configuration in the straight segments of the polypeptide chain, and that the mechanism of action in both instances may be similar. [32b]

The Redox Enzymes [33,34]

The class of redox enzymes contains a variety of substances. Many of these have been isolated in pure state, crystallized, and analyzed. They all participate in some kind of oxidation–reduction reactions occurring in living tissues, and sometimes are classified further into the hydrogen transferring dehydrogenases and the oxidases. It has been suspected long ago that the mechanism of biological oxidation is very complex, and that a whole series of enzymes participate in the metabolism of such simple substances as glucose or glycerin. The life work of many biochemists has been devoted to unraveling this mechanism; they have attempted to isolate the various enzymes and to reproduce the reactions *in vitro*. Good exhaustive treatises and review articles are available on the subject. [3,33,34]

From the chemical point of view, it is interesting to note that the redox enzymes generally are more complex than the previously described proteinases and esterases. The molecular weight of most of the dehydrogenases is higher than that of the ribonuclease, trypsin, or pepsin. Moreover, the redox enzymes contain a nonprotein group, the so called prosthetic group or coenzyme, or at least one or more heavy metal atoms in the macromolecule. Examples of the latter are: ascorbic acid oxidase and phenol oxidase. The former can be isolated from summer squash; the macromolecule of the $M = 146{,}000$ contains six copper atoms per molecule, but no prosthetic group. The phenol oxidase of mushrooms is a somewhat similar protein, and it contains four copper atoms per molecule ($M = 100{,}000$). [21]

The hydrogen transferring enzymes may contain various prosthetic groups some of which contain a heavy metal atom. In some cases, as in cytochrome-*c*, the prosthetic group or coenzyme is firmly bound to the protein moiety,

[32b] See W. F. HARRINGTON and M. SELA, *Biochim. Biophys. Acta* **31**, 427 (1959).

[33] E. BALDWIN, *Dynamic Aspects of Biochemistry* 3rd ed., Cambridge Univ. Press, 1957.

[34] T. P. SINGER and E. B. KEARNEY, in *The Proteins* Vol. II A (H. NEURATH and K. BAILEY, ed.), Academic Press, New York, 1954.

while in many other instances the coenzyme is readily dissociable. The protein moiety in such complex enzymes is designated as *apoenzyme*, and the whole enzyme (coenzyme + apoenzyme) as *holoenzyme.* In several instances, the coenzyme portion of these enzymes is a simple derivative of some of the B-group vitamins. For example, the "old yellow enzyme" of Warburg and Christian[35] contains lactoflavin phosphoric acid as the prosthetic group. The latter is weakly bound to the apoenzyme, and the holoenzyme may dissociate reversibly. Full enzymic activity is exhibited only by the holoenzyme. Diphosphothiamine is another coenzyme found in several oxidizing enzymes. The various dehydrogenases contain pyridine nucleotides as prosthetic groups in which nicotinamide is one of the essential constituents. For example, in diphosphopyridine nucleotide (DPN) one finds one mole of nicotinamide, two moles of D-ribose, one mole of pyrophosphate, and one mole of adenine. The pyrophosphate is in the middle linking through ester bonds the sugar groups which at the other ends are holding the bases, viz.:

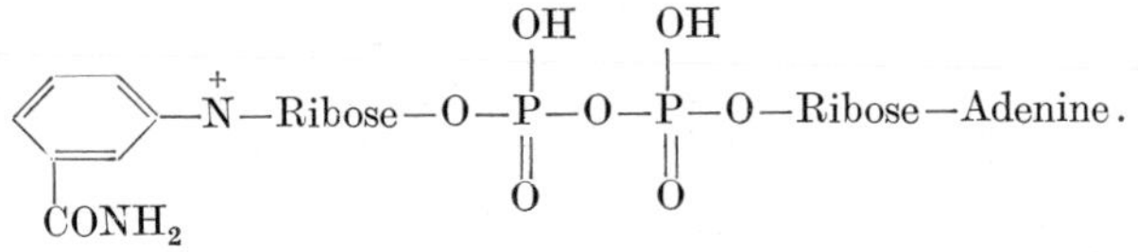

$$\text{(C}_5\text{H}_4\text{)(CONH}_2\text{)}-\overset{+}{N}-\text{Ribose}-O-\underset{\underset{O}{\|}}{\overset{\overset{OH}{|}}{P}}-O-\underset{\underset{O}{\|}}{\overset{\overset{OH}{|}}{P}}-O-\text{Ribose}-\text{Adenine}.$$

DPN is the coenzyme of such enzymes as e.g. the glyceraldehyde-3-phosphate dehydrogenase, lactic dehydrogenase of muscle, and alcohol dehydrogenase. In the instance of the glyceraldehyde-3-phosphate dehydrogenase, which has been isolated in pure crystalline state from rabbit muscle,[36] two moles of DPN are firmly bound to one mole of protein,[37] and the molecular weight of the enzyme was found to be 140,000 by the method of light scattering.[38] There is very little information on the amino acid sequence and configuration of the apoenzyme portions of these enzymes.

Very important in this group are also the enzymes which contain a porphyrin as the prosthetic group. This subgroup is characteristic with its very wide size range of the catalysts. One of the largest is the catalase of liver which has a molecular weight of 225,000–250,000, and contains four ferriporphyrin groups per molecule.[39] Recent sedimentation studies have shown[40] that dissociation into subunits which are two or four times smaller than the native macromolecule results in inactivation. Each of the subunits seems to contain one single polypeptide chain. The macromolecules of catalase are globular, and they are so large as to be made visible in the electron

(35) O. WARBURG and W. CHRISTIAN, *Biochem. J.* **258**, 496 (1933).

(36) G. T. CORI, M. W. SLEIN and C. F. CORI, *J. biol. Chem.* **173**, 605 (1948).

(37) J. F. TAYLOR, S. F. VELICK, G. T. CORI, C. F. CORI and M. W. SLEIN, *ibid.* **173**, 619 (1948); S. F. VELICK, J. E. HAVES, Jr. and J. HARTING, *ibid.* **203**, 527 (1953).

(38) W. B. DANDLIKER and J. B. FOX, Jr., *J. biol. Chem.* **214**, 275 (1955).

(39) H. THEORELL, *Adv. Enzymol.* **7**, 265 (1947); *Experientia* **4**, 100 (1948); B. CHANCE, *Acta Chem. Scand.* **1**, 235 (1947).

(40) CH. TANFORD and R. E. LOVRIEN, *Abstracts, Amer. chem. Soc. Nat. Meeting*, p. 14 C, Boston, April, 1959.

microscope.[41] A much smaller protein in the porphyrin enzyme subgroup is the peroxidase from horseradish. Its molecular weight is 44,000, and there is only one porphyrin prosthetic group in the molecule. The apoenzyme in this instance is rich in carbohydrate.

Cytochrome-*c* is the smallest of all porphyrin-containing enzymes, as its molecular weight is only 13,200. The fact is noteworthy that this enzyme is most universally distributed, and it has been isolated not only from various tissues of mammals but also from fishes, insects, birds, and even yeasts. Not only the structure of the iron-containing prosthetic group but also the way of linking that group to the protein, as well as the amino acid sequence of a part of the macromolecule, have been well investigated.[1,42] Moreover, very interesting differences in the amino acid sequence in the essential protein moiety have been found in cytochromes-*c* from various species. The cytochrome peptides of the part of the macromolecule at which the porphyrin is attached could be isolated in pure state by chromatography and other methods, and it could be shown that the cytochrome peptides isolated from the tissues of various mammals and fish (salmon) were structurally identical. The structure is illustrated in the scheme below:

· · · —Val.—Glu.(NH_2)—Lys.—Cys.—Ala.—Glu.(NH_2)—Cys.—His.—Thr.—Val.—Glu.—Lys. · · ·

S S

Hem (porph.) Fe

In the cytochrome-*c* peptide which was obtained in partial digestion of chicken cytochrome, however, the alanine residue was exchanged for serine, whereas in the cytochrome of the silk spinning *Bombyx mori* the lysine residue is exchanged for arginine.[42,43] Even more different is the composition of a peptide obtained on partial digestion of yeast cytochrome-*c*,[44] viz.:

Salmon: · · · —Val. Glu.(NH_2)Lys. Cys. Ala. Glu.(NH_2). Cys. His. Thr. Val. Glu.— · · ·
Chicken · · · —Val. Glu.(NH_2)Lys. Cys. Ser. Glu.(NH_2). Cys. His. Thr. Val. Glu.— · · ·
Bombyx m:· · · —Val. Glu.(NH_2). Arg. Cys. Ala. Glu(NH_2). Cys. His. Thr. Val. Glu.— · ·
Yeast: · · · —Phe—Lys—Thr. Arg. Cys. Glu. Leu. · · · Cys. His. Thr. Val. Glu.— · · ·

The porphyrin group, however, in all instances is the same, and also in all cytochromes-*c* the hem is linked to the protein by the strong thioether bridges, as well as by a secondary bond to the imidazole of the histidine residue. The mentioned similarities and differences between the cytochromes, of course, are by no means exhaustive, since other differences may be found in other parts of the apoenzyme, when the amino acid sequence in the whole macromolecule will be fully established.

(41) C. E. Hall, *J. biol. Chem.* **185**, 749 (1950).

(42) H. Tuppy, in *Symposium on Protein Structure* p. 66 (A. Neuberger, ed.), Methuen, London, 1958.

(43) H. Tuppy and S. Paleus, *Acta Chem. Scand.* **9**, 353 (1955); H. Tuppy, *Z. Naturforsch.* **12 b**, 784 (1957).

(44) H. Tuppy and K. Dus (see ref. 42).

CHAPTER 16

PROTEIN HORMONES

> These observations provide an additional instance of the fact that somatotropin molecules from various species differ completely from one another with respect to chemical and structural characteristics. The hormones from all species are equally active, however, in promoting growth in rats, whereas only monkey and human hormones are effective in man.
>
> C. H. Li [1]

THE CHEMISTRY of protein hormones has advanced in the last decade so rapidly that most of the reviews which were written a few years ago became rather obsolete during the time of publication. Certain facts, however, are now so well established that there is very little possibility of any further revolutionary changes. The situation with the protein hormones is just about the same as with many other large molecules: the chemical structure in some cases is better known than the configuration, and the latter is better known than the mechanism of action in living tissues.

The hormone field is so broad that only an incomplete review is possible in this kind of treatise. First, the well investigated small (micromolecular) peptide hormones, such as vasopressin and oxytocin, will be only mentioned. Also some of the larger hormones, which are thus far little investigated, will be omitted. A brief survey will be given only on insulin, adrenocorticotropic hormone, prolactin, and growth hormone.

The Structure of Insulin [2,3,4]

The gigantic undertaking of Sanger and his colleagues of solving the chemical structure of insulin was successfully completed in 1956, a brilliant achievement which can be justly regarded as a milestone in protein chemistry. In spite of the fact that the insulin molecule is smaller than that of e.g. ribonuclease, many years were required in order to establish the amino acid sequence, the position of the amide groups, and the position of the disulfide

[1] C. H. Li, in *Symposium on Protein Structure* p. 302 (quotation from p. 236) (A. NEUBERGER, ed.), Methuen, London, J. Wiley, New York, 1958.

[2] F. SANGER, in *Currents in Biochemical Research* p. 434 (D. E. GREEN, ed.), Interscience, New York, 1956.

[3] A. P. RYLE, F. SANGER, L. F. SMITH and R. KITAI, *Biochem. J.* **60**, 541 (1955).

[4] F. SANGER and H. TUPPY, *Biochem. J.* **49**, 463, 481 (1951); **53**, 366 (1953); F. SANGER, *Science* **129**, 1340 (1959) — the Nobel Prize lecture, delivered in Stockholm, on 10 Dec. 1958.

bridges. The problem could be tackled only with the aid of the modern chromatographic micromethods which enabled the separation and identification of the various peptides, amino acids, and their derivatives with a sufficiently high degree of reliability. An important new tool in this work was Sanger's new method of dinitrophenylation of proteins and peptides by means of fluorodinitrobenzene (see chapt. 12). Since a direct determination of the sequence from both the N- and C-terminal groups does not lead very far, most of the chain sequence was elaborated by an extensive study of the many peptides obtained in partial digestion of the protein. Of great help in putting the peptide pieces together were earlier data on the specificity of the various proteolytic enzymes (see chapt. 12), and much new experience was gained here with respect to this specificity of the enzymes which were applied.

The structure of beef insulin is illustrated schematically as follows:

```
                       NH2   ┌──────S────S──────┐               NH2         NH2            NH2
                        |    |                  |                |           |              |
Gly–Ileu–Val–Glu–Glu–Cys–Cys–Ala–Ser–Val–Cys–Ser–Leu–Lys–Glu–Leu–Glu–Asp–Tyr–Cys–Asp
                              |                                                 |
                              S                                                 S
                              |                                                 |
        NH2 NH2               S                                                 S
         |   |                |                                                 |
Phe–Val–Asp–Glu–His–Leu–Cys–Gly–Ser–His–Leu–Val–Glu–Ala–Leu–Tyr–Leu–Val–Cys–Gly–Glu
                                                                                     |
                                     Ala–Lys–Pro–Thr–Tyr–Phe–Phe–Gly–Arg
```

```
        ┌─────────────────────┐
Beef   –Cys–Cys–Ala–Ser–Val–Cys–

Pig    –Cys–Cys–Thr–Ser–Ileu–Cys–

Sheep  –Cys–Cys–Ala–Gly–Val–Cys–

Horse  –Cys–Cys–Thr–Gly–Ileu–Cys–

Whale  –Cys–Cys–Thr–Ser–Ileu–Cys–
```

Altogether there are 51 residues which are arranged in two chains, A and B. The N-terminal amino acid of the A chain is glycine, and the C-terminal of it is asparagine. The N-terminal group of the B-chain is phenylalanine, and the C-terminal is alanine. The chains are linked by two disulfide bridges. Moreover, there is another disulfide loop at the A-chain which is of the same size as the rings in oxytocin and vasopressin. [(5)]

Slight differences were found in the A chain by comparing the insulins of beef, hog, sheep, horse, and whale pancreas. In this section of the chain, which comprises part of the 20-atom ring, the section -Ala-Ser-Val- of beef insulin may be exchanged for -Thr-Ser-Ileu- in hog insulin, etc., as shown in the formulae. These changes are found at R 1, R 2, and R 3, in the more

[(5)] V. DU VIGNEAUD, C. RESSLER and S. TRIPPETT, *J. biol. Chem.* **205**, 949 (1953); V. DU VIGNEAUD, H. C. LAWLER and E. A. POPENOE, *J. Amer. chem. Soc.* **75**, 4880 (1953); M. F. BARTLETT, A. JÖHL, R. ROESKE, R. J. STEDMAN, F. H. C. STEWART, D. N. WARD and V. DU VIGNEAUD, *J. Amer. chem. Soc.* **78**, 2905 (1956).

complete illustration of the structure of this part of the insulin, viz.: [6]

```
· · · —NH—CH—CH2—S—S—CH2—CH—CO— · · ·
          |                 |
          CO                NH
          |                 |
          NH                CO
          |                 |
 —S—CH2—CH                  CH—R3
          |                 |
          CO                NH
          |                 |
          NH-CH--CO—NH—CH—CO
               |        |
               R1       R2
```

The uncompleted -S-S- bridge leads to the B-chain which thus far has been found identical in all insulins. The constituents in the oxytocin and vasopressin rings are exactly the same, while the side chains differ strongly, e.g. one finds tyrosine instead of the cystine bridge leading to the B-chain, and asparagine at R 3, instaed of the valine or isoleucine of the insulins. Interesting speculations have been made on the question of the dependence of the biological function on the structure of this ring. The mechanism of the hormone action, however, is so incompletely elucidated that the time is not ripe yet for a plausible theory.

The molecular weight of insulin has been a subject of controversy for quite a long time. Various physical methods rendered values of 48,000, 36,000, and 12,000, [7] and it seemed that the latter value may represent the true chemical molecular weight. Sanger himself, in the first period of his structural studies, calculated the numbers of amino acid residues assuming a M of 12,000. The still lower value of 6000 was first suggested by Harfenist and Craig [8] who studied the countercurrent fractionation of partially dinitrophenylated insulin. It was found that the *mono* DNP-insulin, the compound closest in its phase distribution properties to insulin, contained one DNP group per 6000 unit of protein, a di-DNP-insulin contained two DNP groups per 6000, etc., and there was no compound with one DNP per 12,000. This strongly indicated that the chemical molecular weight of insulin is 6000 instead of 12,000, as it was later ascertained also by physicochemical measurements of specifically treated insulin (see chapt. 3). Summation of the atomic weights of the 51 amino acid unit of beef insulin yields a value of 5733, while the directly determined physicochemical values range between 6000–6500. [9] These higher values can be explained as being due to bound water and some binding of the chemical agents used for disaggregation of the larger units.

[6] J. I. Harris, F. Sanger and M. A. Naughton, *Arch. Biochem. Biophys.* **65**, 427 (1956).

[7] H. Gutfreund, *Biochem. J.* **42**, 544 (1948).

[8] E. J. Harfenist and L. C. Craig, *J. Amer. chem. Soc.* **74**, 3087 (1952).

[9] E. Fredericq, *Nature* **171**, 570 (1953); D. W. Kupke and K. Linderstrom-Lang, *Biochim. Biophys. Acta* **13**, 153 (1954).

The role of zinc found in crystallized insulin is not fully clarified as yet. There is usually one atom zinc per 12,000 equivalent weight of protein, and the metal is bound rather firmly, probably at the imidazole groups of the histidine residues.[10]

Insulin, like ribonuclease, lysozyme, and other small proteins, is a relatively stable substance. It can be heated in acid solution of pH 2·5 at 50° for a long time without losing its physiological activity as a hormone. The isoelectric point of insulin is near pH 5·3, and its solubility at this pH is very low, except in the presence of such salts as the thiocyanates. Heating of insulin in an acid solution of pH 2 at 90–100° results in a very interesting reversible aggregation which has been studied in great detail, especially by Waugh.[11] The solution is transformed upon such treatment into a birefringent thixotropic gel which contains long fibrils of the protein. Electron microscopic studies have revealed that these fibrils are over one hundred Å units wide and about 16,000 Å long, hence they are formed in linear as well as lateral aggregation of the original units. The hormone can be reactivated from these fibrils by a treatment with weakly alkaline solution, whereby the double refraction of flow and high viscosity are lost, and the fibrils are disaggregated. Shorter fibrils could be demonstrated also in the precipitates formed near the isoelectric point in unheated solutions, and of some practical importance was the finding of Waugh that seeding of a trace of the fibrillary polymer in a dilute solution of the hormone resulted in a quantitative removal of the solute; the fibrils simply act as crystallization centers on which the solute precipitates, and this "pseudocrystallization" is promoted by heating. Waugh comes to the conclusion that no denaturation or covalent bond involvement occurs at this aggregation, since the insulin which was regenerated from the fibrils could be crystallized, and was physiologically active. Hence, according to Waugh, the aggregation is due to the weak cohesive forces acting between the nonpolar groups of the hormone molecules. The low solubility of insulin in water is due to its low content of free acid carboxyls and free basic groups, and a relatively high content of cystine and the non-polar side groups. Heating in acid results in some slight transient spatial adjustment and contacting of the groups of the colliding units so that they pack together into larger aggregates. The repulsive effects which are caused by the ionization of the free carboxyl groups upon addition of alkali are sufficient to disintegrate the aggregate. The plausibility of this explanation was ascertained by the facts that an increased tendency to reversible association is obtained, and depolymerization is hampered, when additional non-polar groups are introduced, e.g. by azo coupling.

These problems bring us back again to the general problem of configuration, and the reasons why the polypeptide chains assume in aqueous solutions a

[10] CH. TANFORD and J. EPSTEIN, *J. Amer. chem. Soc.* **76**, 2163 (1954).
[11] D. F. WAUGH, *Adv. Protein Chem.* **9**, 325 (1954).

globular configuration (see chapt. 12). One of the reasons that the insulin chains are not extended may be the same which is involved in the aggregation, viz. the *hydrophoby* of the nonpolar groups. Since these groups tend to escape water, the molecule will shrink in a way similar to that of detergent micelle formation. [12] The three other factors would be: [13] hydrogen bonding between the —CO— and —NH— groups of the peptide bonds, repulsion and attraction between the charged groups, and the disulfide bridges. The latter impose restrictions on all of the configurations which might be formed due to the display of the other factors, e.g. the hydrogen bonding, so that in several parts of the molecule the much discussed α-helix with its 3·7 amino acid residues per turn is impossible. The involvement of the hydrogen bonds, however, is indicated by the fact that the 12,000 double-unit dissociates under the influence of such hydrogen bond cleavers as the guanidine salts. This then seems to indicate that the hydrogen bonds may be important also in maintaining the folded configuration within each of the $M = 6000$ unit. A more direct evidence of this is provided by the deuterium exchange method of Linderstrom-Lang and Hvidt. [14] It was found that the exchange in general occurs readily in the end groups and side groups, while the peptide bond hydrogen of the backbone exchanges at various rates, depending on the configuration. In the case of insulin, all the peptide hydrogens in the tails of the chains are easy exchangeable, whereas those belonging to the middle portion, are exchanged more slowly. This then is interpreted as a proof that the hydrogen atoms in the middle sections are involved in hydrogen bonds, while the hydrogen atoms of the NH groups in the tails are free of such involvement. On the other hand, the α-helix is impossible near the disulfide bridges, and one might expect that the hydrogens of the 20-member disulfide ring should not be H-bonded and readily exchangeable, whereas in fact they are quite stable. [14] Moreover, considering the thermodynamic stability of protein α-helices in aqueous solution in general, and using as an experimental basis data on ribonuclease and oxidized ribonuclease, Harrington and Schellman have shown that "a simple α-helix supported by no other forces than hydrogen bonds must be abandoned as a model for a protein in aqueous solution". [15] This is due, briefly, to the fact that the competition between formation of such intramolecular bonds and formation of hydrogen bonds between the same groups and water molecules largely reduces the importance of such bonds for the stabilization of any folded structure. [13] One might then conclude that the particular globular configuration of insulin is secured chiefly by the

[12] B. JIRGENSONS, *Organic Colloids* chapt. 5 and 34, Elsevier, Amsterdam, D. VAN NOSTRAND, Princeton, 1958.

[13] CH. TANFORD, in *Symposium on Protein Structure* p. 35 (A. NEUBERGER, ed.), Methuen, London, 1958.

[14] A. HVIDT and K. LINDERSTROM-LANG, *Biochim. Biophys. Acta* **14**, 574 (1954); **16**, 168 (1955); A. HVIDT, *ibid.* **18**, 306 (1955).

[15] W. F. HARRINGTON and J. A. SCHELLMAN, *Compt. rend. trav. lab. Carlsberg* **30**, 21 (1956).

following factors: (1) the disulfide bridges, (2) the amount and distribution of the hydrophilic polar groups interacting with the water, and (3) the amount and distribution of the nonpolar side groups tending to escape water and thus causing contraction of the extended configuration.

Important information on the structure of insulin crystals and the macromolecules themselves can be expected from further studies on X-ray diffraction. Molecular models of insulin have been built in which the B-chain was assumed to be a straight α-helix, [16] and the model seems to be in a reasonable agreement with crystallographic and other data. However, it must be borne in mind that the configuration of the macromolecule in solution may be not the same as in a crystal.

Since the structure of insulin is completely established, it is worthwhile to consider the structure also in connection with the optical rotatory properties of the solutions of this protein. The work has been carried out chiefly by Schellman [17] who found that native insulin possesses a "normal" dispersion constant of native globular proteins, viz. 265 mμ, whereas denatured insulin had a value of 220 mμ, and both native and denatured insulin follow the simple one-term Drude rule. Thus insulin behaves in the same way as most of the other globular proteins, and this is in agreement with the previously made conclusion that there cannot be much of a hydrogen bonded α-helical configuration in the macromolecules of dissolved native insulin. The question why insulin in its rotatory dispersion properties is closer to serum albumin than to ribonuclease cannot be answered yet.

It is surprising that both the physicochemical studies on configuration as well as the purely chemical sequence studies have not revealed any simple periodicity in the molecules of insulin, and the same seems to be true for all other proteins. The arrangement of the amino acid residues in insulin is *irregular* in the sense that certain residues do not appear at regular intervals or in ordered groups, yet the arrangement is *definite*, i.e. *the same* irregular sequence appears in all molecules of the hormone (in the same species). "It follows that the extremely uneven but strictly determined sequences of amino acid residues in the polypeptide chain, which are to be found in any proteins which have been isolated from living bodies, arise as a result of a pre-existing organization of their protoplasm. This applies even more forcibly to the three-dimensional structure of corpuscular proteins, which clearly requires for its development a certain spatial organisation". [18] It is clear, that there must be a *definite* spatial organization or configuration, but, like the irregular amino acid sequence, it is *not a simple one* (e.g. α-helical). Future research should disclose this organization and its importance in the physiological functionation of the hormone.

[16] H. LINDLEY and J. S. ROLLETT, *Biochim. Biophys. Acta* **18**, 183 (1955).

[17] J. A. SCHELLMAN, *Compt. rend. trav. lab. Carlsberg* **30**, 415 (1958).

[18] A. I. OPARIN, *The Origin of Life on the Earth* 3rd ed., p. 260, transl. by A. SYNGE, Oliver and Boyd, Edinburgh, London, 1957.

The Adrenocorticotropic Hormone (ACTH) [1,19,20]

The adrenocorticotropic hormone, also called corticotropin or simply ACTH, is one of the many hormones produced by the pituitary gland. ACTH is released into blood in the anterior lobe of the gland, and it affects the adrenal cortex, i.e. the production of corticosteroids.

Pure ACTH was isolated a few years ago by several groups of investigators from the pituitary glands of swine, sheep, and bovine sources, [21,22,23] and further studies showed that e.g. the α-ACTH from sheep [19,20] is an open chain long polypeptide or small protein. The chain contains 39 amino acid residues with serine as the N-terminal and phenylalanine as the C-terminal group. The chemical molecular weight of the hormone is 4541, as found by summation of the weights of the 39 residues, whose sequence also has been established, as follows:

NH_2Ser. Tyr. Ser. Met. Glu. His. Phe. Arg. Try. Gly. Lys. Pro. Val. Gly. Lys. Lys. Arg.-Arg. Pro. Val. Lys. Val. Tyr. Pro. Ala. Gly. Glu. Asp. Asp. Glu. Ala. Ser. Glu(NH_2).-Ala. Phe. Pro. Leu. Glu. PheCOOH.

The chain does not contain any cystine, threonine, and isoelucine, and it is abundant in basic amino acids (lysine and arginine) and dicarboxylic acids. Also it is noteworthy that there is a cluster of the basic amino acids Lys. Lys.-Arg. Arg. in the middle of the molecule, and a cluster of dicarboxylic acids Glu. Asp. Asp. Glu. The sequence was established by analyzing the peptides obtained in partial disgestion of the hormone, and the task of the assembly of the fragments was greatly facilitated by the experience already available from the insulin studies. Countercurrent distribution was extensively applied in the isolation and characterization studies. [24]

It is interesting to note that considerable differences have been found in the amino acid sequence and certain physical properties not only between the corticotropins isolated from various species but also between the preparations isolated from the same species by different methods by different investigators. [1,19] For example, the sequence of the residues No 25–33 in the α-ACTH of sheep (Li *et al.*) is Ala. Gly. Glu. Asp. Asp. Glu. Ala. Ser. Glu(NH_2), it is Asp. Gly. Ala. Glu. Asp. Glu(NH_2). Leu. Ala. Glu in the ACTH-A of pig pituitary, [24] while another sequence of Gly. Ala. Glu. Asp. Asp. Glu. Leu. Ala. Glu was found by another group of researchers for the same section

(19) C. H. Li, *Adv. Protein Chem.* **11**, 101 (1956).
(20) O. K. Behrens and W. W. Bromer, *Ann. Rev. Biochem.* **27**, 57 (1958).
(21) W. F. White, *J. Amer. chem. Soc.* **75**, 503 (1953).
(22) C. H. Li, I. I. Geschwind, A. L. Levy, J. I. Harris, J. S. Dixon, N. G. Pon and J. O. Porath, *Nature* **173**, 251 (1954).
(23) P. H. Bell, *J. Amer. chem. Soc.* **76**, 5565 (1954).
(24) R. G. Shepherd, K. S. Howard, P. H. Bell, A. R. Cacciola, R. G. Child, M. C. Davies, J. P. English, B. M. Finn, J. H. Meisenhelder, A. W. Moyer and J. van der Scheer, *J. Amer. chem. Soc.* **78**, 5051 (1956).

of the chain of pig pituitary ACTH. Since all of the preparations possessed about the same hormonal activity, it seemed likely that the part near the C-terminal may not be essential for the hormone activity. Indeed, a limited peptic hydrolysis could be applied for the release of 11 amino acid residues from the C-terminal without loss of adrenal-stimulating activity.[25] In this then ACTH differs strongly from insulin which appears much more uniform than the ACTH. According to Li,[1,19] the 39-amino acid chain should be regarded rather as a *prohormone*, and that the real hormonal activity resides in only a part of the molecule. Attempts are in progress to synthesize the active part, and some positive results have already been announced by Boissonnas *et al.*[26] It seems noteworthy that the nonessential part of the chain near the C-terminal is more acidic than the essential part which contains an excess of the basic amino acids.

The Lactogenic Hormone[1,20,27]

The pituitary hormone which stimulates the mammary gland is designated as lactogenic hormone or prolactin. Contrary to ACTH, it is a real protein of molecular weight 24,100. Most of the chemical and physical studies have been done on the hormone preparations which were isolated from sheep or beef pituitary glands, and no significant differences thus far could be found between the hormones from these two species. Some of the essential data of this protein are compiled in Table 32.

TABLE 32

SOME PHYSICAL AND CHEMICAL DATA ON PROLACTIN FROM SHEEP[1]

Molecular weight	
from sedimentation and diffusion data	24,200
from osmotic pressure	26,500
from chemical data (amino acid analysis)	24,100
Diffusion coefficient (in 0·1 M $NaHCO_3$ solution)	$8{\cdot}44 \cdot 10^{-7}$
Sedimentation constant ($s_{20,w}$) in S	2·19
Isoelectric point (in acetate buffer, 0·05 M)	5·7
Specific rotation	−40·5°
N-terminal amino acid	Threonine
C-terminal group	None

The amino acid composition of the lactogenic hormone is presented in Table 33.[27]

[25] C. H. Li, I. I. Geschwind, R. D. Cole, I. D. Raacke, J. I. Harris and J. S. Dixon, *Nature* **176**, 687 (1955); W. F. White and W. A. Landmann, *J. Amer. chem. Soc.* **77**, 1711 (1955).

[26] R. W. Boissonnas, S. Guttmann, J. P. Waller and P. A. Jaquenoud, *Experientia* **12**, 446 (1956).

[27] C. H. Li, *Adv. Protein Chem.* **12**, 269 (1957).

TABLE 33

AMINO ACID COMPOSITION OF LACTOGENIC HORMONE (LI [27])

	Grams of amino acid per 100 g protein	Number of residues per mole (M = 24,200)
Alanine	4·07	11
Arginine	7·95	11
Cystine	2·99	3
Aspartic acid	10·50	19
Glutamic acid	13·43	22
Glycine	3·74	12
Histidine	4·51	7
Leucine + isoleucine	20·15	37
Lysine	6·07	10
Methionine	4·33	7
Phenylalanine	5·48	8
Proline	6·69	14
Serine	7·85	18
Threonine	5·44	11
Valine	5·83	12
Tyrosine	5·26	7
Tryptophan	1·69	2
Amide		17
Total	115·98	211

The amino acid sequence at the N-terminal was studied by the Edman method, and in both sheep and bovine prolaction the same sequence of Thr. Pro. Val. Thr. Pro. . . has been found. The C-terminal group could not be detected either by the carboxypeptidase or hydrazinolysis methods. It also could be ascertained that the molecular weight of prolactin did not change upon oxidative cleavage of the cystine disulfide bonds by means of performic acid, and that no new terminal amino groups appeared on such treatment. From this it was concluded [1] that there is only one single polypeptide chain in the macromolecule, and that the three cystine residues form loops on the chain, viz.:

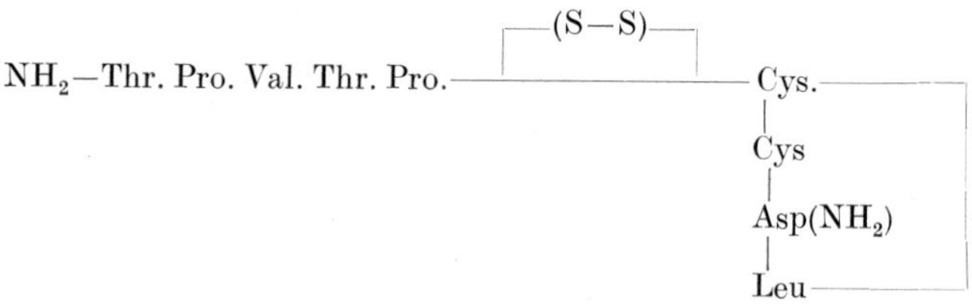

```
                                      ┌──(S—S)──┐
NH2—Thr. Pro. Val. Thr. Pro.──────────┴─────────┴── Cys.──────────┐
                                                     |             |
                                                    Cys            |
                                                     |             |
                                                   Asp(NH2)        |
                                                     |             |
                                                    Leu────────────┘
```

According to Li, [1] one of the cystine disulfide bridges is part of the large loop which conceals the C-terminal. Cysteine has been identified as a C-terminal after reductive cleavage of the bridge by reduction with mercapto-ethanol in an alkaline 10 M urea solution of the hormone.

The Growth Hormones [1,19,20]

The growth hormone or somatotropin originates in the anterior lobe of the pituitary gland, and it exerts a variety of functions in promoting growth. The experiments are made with young animals which are hypophysectomized; the observed disturbances in the body then are tried to remedy by the injection of the hormone preparations. Somatotropin is known as a stimulant of protein synthesis; it also affects the growth of bone tissue, as well as the metabolism of carbohydrates and fats. It has been shown that growth hormone affects also the development of malignant tumors in the liver. [28]

The growth hormones from various species have been isolated in pure state, and the best preparations appeared to be homogeneous by various criteria, including sedimentation, electrophoresis, and chromatography. Comparison of the physical and chemical properties of the somatotropins from various species disclosed important species differences, some of which are compiled in Table 34.

TABLE 34

DATA ON GROWTH HORMONES FROM VARIOUS SPECIES [1]

	Beef	Sheep	Whale	Monkey	Human
Sedimentation constant $s_{20,w}$ (in S)	3·19	2·76	2·84	1·88	2·47
Diffusion constant $D_{20,w} \times 10^7$	7·23	5·25	6·56	7·20	8·88
Partial specific volume	0·76	0·73	0·73	0·72	0·73
Molecular weight	45,000	47,800	39,900	25,400	27,100
Frictional ratio f/f_0	1·31	1·68	1·45	1·57	1·23
Isoelectric point	6·8	6·8	6·2	5·5	4·9
Cystine, resid./M	4	5	3	4	2
N-terminal groups	Phe Ala	Phe Ala	Phe	Phe	Phe
C-terminal residue	Phe	Phe	Phe	Phe	Phe

Most surprising are the species differences in the molecular weights and cystine content of the hormones. The frictional ratio, which indicates molecular asymmetry, also differs considerably. The differences in the isoelectric points are not so serious, as they may be due to a small difference in the number of amides at the free carboxyls of the dicarboxylic acids. Moreover, it is noteworthy that two N-terminal amino acids have been found in beef and sheep somatotropins, whereas only one N-terminal phenylalanine was found in the hormones isolated from whale, monkey, and human pituitary glands. While the C-terminal group is the same in all species, the sequence at the C-terminal was found different, e.g. in the monkey hormone it is . . . -Ala.

(28) C. H. ROBERTSON, M. A. O'NEAL, H. L. RICHARDSON and A. C. GRIFFIN, *Cancer Res.* **14**, 549 (1954).

Gly. PheCOOH, whereas in human hormone it was found to be . . . -Tyr. Leu. PheCOOH. In spite of these differences, the human and monkey hormones are more similar than e.g. the human and bovine hormones.[29] This is supported by the fact that only human and monkey hormone is active in man, whereas the somatotropins of the more distant species are inactive in man. All of the mentioned hormones (sheep, beef, whale, monkey and man) are equally active in promoting growth in rats, while the hormone from such distant species as fish was found inactive in rats or other mammals. According to Li, this indicates that there is a considerable variety in this group of hormones, and that *only a part* of the macromolecule of the hormone is *biologically* active. For instance, a molecule of the monkey somatotropin contains 4 cystine residues and 6 methionine residues, whereas the human hormone has only 2 cystine and 4 methionine groups, yet the activity is very similar. Moreover, all somatotropins could be partially digested without a loss of their growth-stimulating potencies, and the small human somatotropin was the most resistant to such partial digestion, while the large bovine hormone released more readily its inactive portion.[1]

The chain structure of the growth hormones has been little investigated. According to Li, the bovine growth hormone has a branched chain with four disulfide loops, while the whale, monkey, and human somatotropins are single chain macromolecules. The latter two can be schematically illustrated as follows:

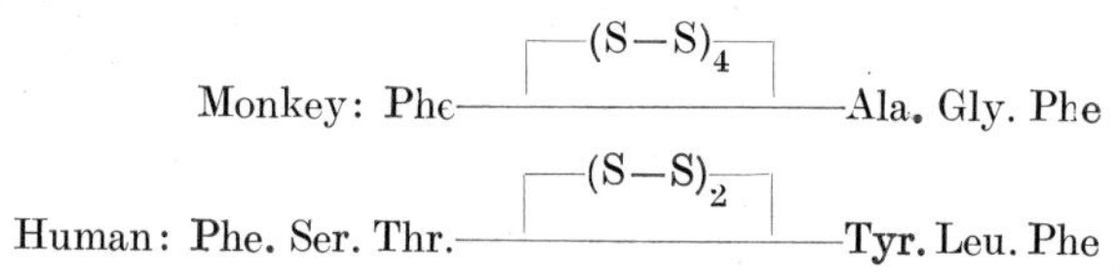

Further studies on the amino acid sequence, configuration, and physiological functioning of these hormones should reveal more about the subtle equilibration of the metabolic processes exerted by these substances. Also these studies are expected to shed more light on the phylogenetic relationships between the higher species.

[29] C. H. Li and H. Papkoff, *Science* **124**, 1293 (1956).

CHAPTER 17

THE FIBROUS STRUCTURAL PROTEINS

> A study of the various sequences recorded in this article reveals no general law or principle which conditions the order or position in which amino acids are laid down in protein chains. It would seem rather that each protein has its own unique arrangement of amino acids, an arrangement which is conditioned not by any simple theory but rather by the limitations of the synthetic mechanism whereby it is produced and by the nature of the biological role that it has to perform.
>
> F. SANGER [1]

IN MOST of the recent reviews and studies on fibrous structural proteins the physical aspects have been treated preferentially, while the chemistry of these important macromolecules has been more or less neglected. This is due to the fact that the physical approach (*X*-ray diffraction, infrared spectra, etc.) is the easiest one, since most of these structural proteins are insoluble. The very nature of these fibrous structural proteins is such that isolation without degradation may be an insoluble task, at least in some instances. In spite of these difficulties, a considerable progress has been made in the chemistry of these substances. Recent amino acid analyses and sequence studies have fully substantiated Sanger's statement [1] that there are no simple periodic sequences. This conclusion, which was so well demonstrated in the previous chapter with several well investigated polypeptide chains in the hormones, is applicable also to the fibrous proteins.

The scope of this chapter includes such fibrous proteins as the silks, the keratins and epidermin, the collagens and elastins, as well as the linear proteins of muscle. The fibrinogen–fibrin systems and problems on blood clotting will be left for chapt. 23. In spite of the progress in the chemistry of fibrous proteins, much of the classical knowledge on the structural principles of these substances is based on the interpretation of their *X*-ray diffraction spectra. (Recently this information has been supplemented by other physical data, e.g. the infrared spectra and electron microscopy.) The general structural principles and the more or less accepted structural models will be discussed briefly in the following section.

[1] F. SANGER, in *Fibrous Proteins and their Biological Significance* p. 10 (IX Symp. of the Soc. for Exp. Biology), Academic Press, New York, 1955; quotation from p. 298.

General Structural Principles

The first X-ray diffraction spectra of protein fibers were obtained about forty years ago (R. Herzog, W. Janke, R. Brill, K. H. Mayer, H. Mark, and others), and shortly afterwards various speculations on the possible structures were published. Especially important contributions were rendered in the early thirties by Astbury *et al.* in Leeds, [2] and later in the forties by R. S. Bear (in the Massachusetts Institute of Technology, Boston), M. L. Huggins, and later by L. Pauling and R. B. Corey. The earlier work in this field is well reviewed in several books and review articles. [3,4,5,6]

It must be emphasized in the very beginning that the X-ray diagrams of the fibrous proteins are much poorer than the diagrams of the monocrystals of globular proteins, hence the protein fibers are partially amorphous. Consequently, no detailed information about the location of atomic groups is possible on the basis of these data. The now more or less generally accepted principles about the configuration of the chains in a protein fiber of a particular kind have not been deduced from the fiber diagrams but they have emerged on the basis of our general knowledge about protein structure. In addition to this, the configurations of simple crystalline peptides and amino acids were calculated from X-ray spectroscopic data, and this experimental material proved to be of great value in assessing the configurations of the larger molecules. And finally, the X-ray fiber diagrams are used for checking the structural models which are conceived from time to time for the various protein fibers. The structures and configurations of amino acids and simple peptides have been analyzed chiefly by Corey [7] and Mizushima. [8]

The general principles of structure of linear proteins had been formulated by Huggins as early as 1943, [5] and they have been valid up to the present time. [9] According to these principles, (1) only long polypeptide chains are assumed, (2) only levo orientation at the α-carbon atoms is present, (3) the distances and angles of bonds in the proteins are approximately the same as in comparable small molecules, (4) hydrogen bonds are formed whenever possible, (5) like atomic groups tend to be surrounded by close neighbors in a like manner, and (6) atoms and groups tend to pack as closely as possible.

(2) W. T. Astbury, *Fundamentals of Fibre Structure* Oxford, 1933.

(3) K. H. Meyer, *Natural and Synthetic High Polymers* 2nd ed., p. 520ff., Interscience, 1950.

(4) H. D. Springall, *The Structural Chemistry of Proteins* Butterworths, London, 1954

(5) M. L. Huggins, *Chem. Rev.* **32**, 195 (1943).

(6) J. C. Kendrew, in *The Proteins* Vol. II B, p. 846ff. (H. Neurath and K. Bailey, ed.), Academic Press, New York, 1954; H. Zahn and H. Dietrich in *Analytical Methods of Protein Chemistry* (P. Alexander and R. J. Block, eds), Vol. II. Pergamon Press, London, 1961.

(7) R. B. Corey, *Adv. Protein Chem.* **4**, 385 (1948); R. B. Corey and L. Pauling, *Proc. Roy. Soc.* B **141**, 10 (1953).

(8) S. Mizushima, *Adv. Protein Chem.* **9**, 299 (1954); *Structure of Molecules and Internal Rotation* Academic Press, New York, 1954.

(9) M. L. Huggins, *J. Polymer Sci.* **30**, 5 (1958); *Physical Chemistry of High Polymers* Wiley, New York, 1958.

It is easy to see that while these principles place certain restrictions on any configurations which can be envisioned, they are very general and thus provide plenty of space for a certain variety of models.

Two major types of configurations have emerged on the basis of these principles: (1) the *pleated sheet model*, and (2) the *helical configuration*. "Many chain polymers in the crystalline state have spiral structures, resulting from the interaction between adjacent units in the chains or between neighboring chains. Spiralling of polypeptide chains permits N—H . . . O hydrogen-bonding between consecutive turns: *intra*molecular hydrogen-bonding, rather than the *inter*molecular hydrogen-bonding in the sheet structures".[9] In the pleated sheet models the polypeptide chains are highly extended, whereas in the helical configurations they are thought to be coiled into spirals or helices. Certain types of *X*-ray spectra of the fibers then could be correlated with certain of the basic configurations, viz., the *α-type* indicates the presence of helices and the *β-type* the sheet structure. The major subgroups in the α-class are the α-keratins, epidermin, myosin, and fibrin, which all are believed to be helical, whereas the silks and β-keratins comprise the β-protein class. The collagens and elastins represent a special type of spectrum corresponding to a different kind of helical configuration. It is interesting to note that the more or less crystalline synthetic polypeptides which are composed of only one kind of amino acid residues also may appear in either the α- or β-configuration.[10] It is surprising that the *X*-ray spectra of certain kind of silks and of the

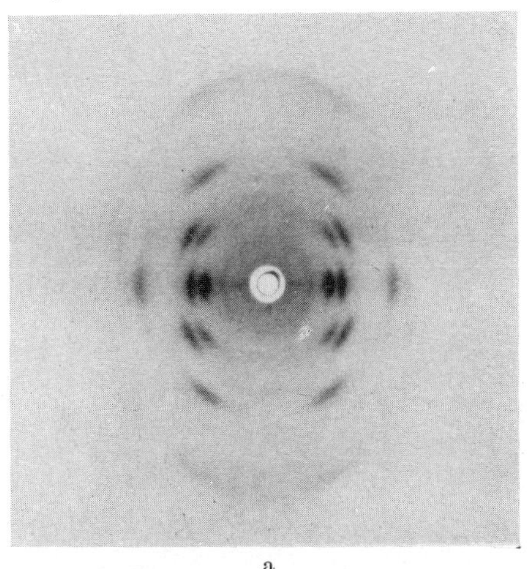

a

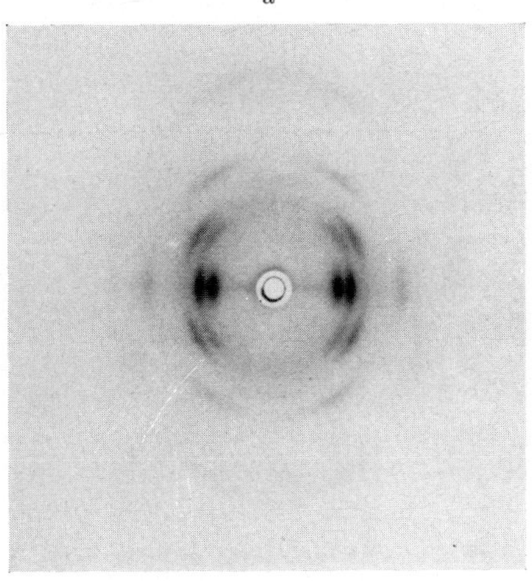

b

FIG. 71. X-ray diffraction spectra of β-poly-L-alanine (above and tussah silk belon) (by *Courtesy* of C. H. Bamford)

[10] C. H. BAMFORD, A. ELLIOTT and W. E. HANBY, *Synthetic Polypeptides*, Academic Press, New York, 1956.

crystalline polyalanine are so very similar as demonstrated in Fig. 71. The positive conclusion from this similarity is that both substances possess a similar configuration of their crystalline portions. However, this conclusion must be supplemented with the remark that the X-ray method is insensitive

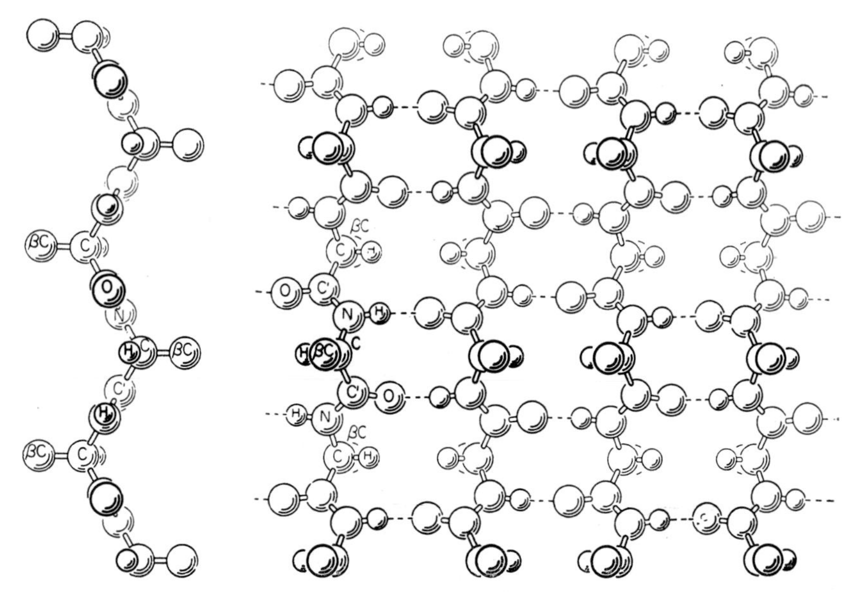

Fig. 72. The anti-parallel-chain pleated sheet structure according to Pauling and Corey

in revealing differences between preparations, since the silk contains a large portion of other amino acid residues beside alanin (see next section).

Two major types of chain arrangements have been considered for the pleated sheet or β-configurations: the chains can run parallel or anti-parallel (see Fig. 72). The first possibility is considered chiefly for the stretched β-keratins, while the latter seems to fit better for the more highly crystalline silks. [9] For the α-spectral type fibrous proteins the α-helix of Pauling and Corey (see Fig. 73) has gained wide acceptance.[11] In this model there are approximately 3·7 amino acid residues per turn, and the structure is stabilized by hydrogen bonding between the CO and NH groups of the residues in consecutive turns. "The rough agreement between equatorial intensities of the X-ray diagram of proteins of the α-keratin type and those predicted for the α-helix supports the assignment of this configuration to the α-keratin proteins". [12] While the α-helical configuration seems likely also in several rod-shaped macromolecules of certain synthetic polypeptides, its presence in the

[11] L. Pauling, R. B. Corey and H. H. Branson, *Proc. Nat. Acad. Sci.* **37**, 203, 729 (1951); L. Pauling and R. B. Corey, *ibid.* **37**, 235 (1951); L. Pauling and R. B. Corey, *Fortschr. Chem. org. Naturstoffe* **8**, 310 (1954).

[12] L. Pauling and R. B. Corey, *Proc. Roy. Soc.* B **141**, 21 (1953).

globular proteins is less important. Moreover, it is possible that even in the α-spectral type fibrous proteins some other types of configuration may be present.

The Fibrous Proteins in Silk [13]

The term "silk" can be used either in a narrow or in a broad sense. In the latter instance the term covers not only the common silk produced by the silk moth *Bombyx mori* but also a whole series of more or less similar fibrous materials spun by other families and species of insects; moreover, an even broader application of this term would include here also the proteinous fibers of spider webs. The common silk larvae are raised best on mulberry leaves, and at a certain stage of development the larvae start to produce long silken filaments to form ovoid cocoons in which they pupate.

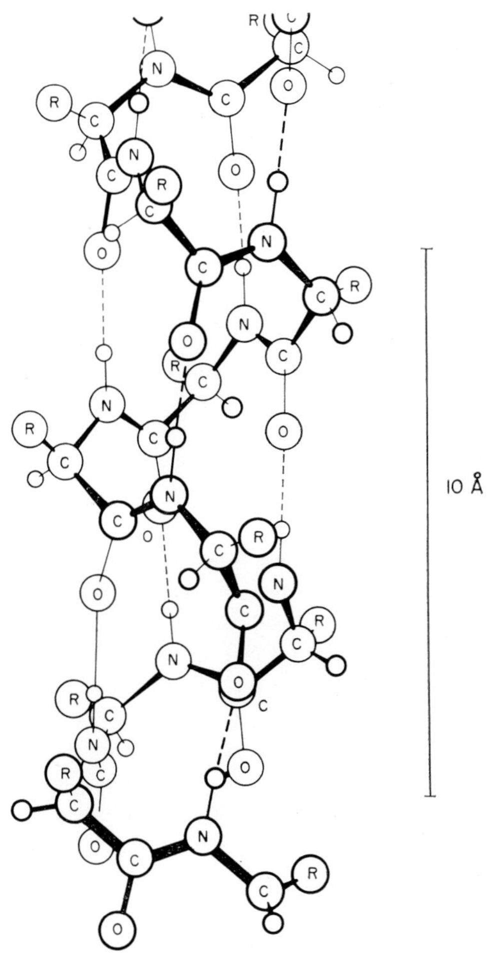

Fig. 73. The α-helix of Pauling and Corey

The fibrous material of the cocoon is not a homogeneous substance but it is composed of at least two proteins (in addition to small amounts of other impurities, such as colored materials): *sericin* and *fibroin*. Sericin is an amorphous coating of the more or less crystalline core of fibroin. This sticky coating is not easy to remove from the fibers, since it cannot be removed mechanically, and a chemical treatment is associated with a hydrolytic degradation of the components. This is just one special case which well illustrates the difficulties in the isolation of fibrous proteins in general; it is very difficult, and sometimes quite impossible, to separate two kinds of interwoven fibers. It is fortunate that in the instance of sericin–fibroin separation the sericin component is on the surface of the fiber and that the macromolecules of the sericin

(13) F. Lucas, J. T. B. Shaw and S. G. Smith, *Adv. Protein Chem.* **13**, 107 (1958).

are less fibrous than those of the fibroin. Because of this, at least the outer layer of the sericin can be removed more or less easily without degrading the fibroin. Several methods are used in silk industry and research laboratories for removing the undesired sericin from the fibers. One of the mildest methods is treatment of the material with hot water. Sericin, like gelatin, dissolves in hot water, and the solution becomes very viscous on cooling; it may even set, when the concentration of the protein is high enough. However, it could be shown that a mere washing with hot water does not remove all of the sericin, while a prolonged boiling adversely affects the mechanical properties of the silk. Another method employs treatment of the raw silk with solution of soap and other detergents. Hot diluted alkalies or soap solutions remove sericin more completely than water, but a complete removal of the sericin without affecting the fibroin is questionable. The same pertains to the third method — removal of the sericin coating by a treatment with proteolytic enzymes, e.g. papain. Since the fibroin itself is a protein, and thus subject to the attack of the enzyme, this method does not automatically guarantee success, as was shown in several experimental studies.(13) This method would be successful only if it were possible to find conditions at which a proteolytic enzyme specifically attacks some bonds of the sericin but leaves the fibroin intact.

There is no doubt that the sericin component differs from fibroin not only in solubility but also in amino acid composition. Although there is a considerable difference between the composition of the sericins from various sources, they are all rich in aspartic acid, serine, arginine, and glutamic acid, in addition to glycine, alanine, threonine, tryptophan, and other common constituents, while the fibroin is composed chiefly of glycine, alanine, and serine. Since these proteins do not represent definite chemical compounds, the amino acid composition data are less meaningful than in the instance of the homogeneous crystallized proteins. Some analytical data on fibroins from various sources are presented in Table 35.

TABLE 35. AMINO ACID COMPOSITION OF VARIOUS FIBROINS (data of Lucas, Shaw and Smith, quoted from ref. 10); grams amino acid N per 100 g protein N

	Antherea pernyi (tussah)	*Anaphe moloneyi*	*Anaphe infracta*	*Bombyx mori*	*Nephila* (spider)
Glycine	24·0	41·7	28·3	44·1	35·3
Alanine	37·9	52.1	53·2	29·7	27·9
Serine	10·2	0·8	2·1	12·4	3·7
Tyrosine, phenylalanine, leucine, isoleucine, valine	4·9	1·7	2·7	7·5	5·2
Aspartic and glutamic ac.	7·3	0·7	3·0	3·6	10·9
Threonine	0·8	0·6	0·6	1·2	0·9
Arginine	10·5	2·1	4·1	1·5	8·5
Tryptophan	2·6	0·2	2·1	0·5	

Examination of these data shows that there are great differences in the amino acid composition, in spite of the fact that glycine and alanine are the major constituents in all fibroins. However, these vary considerably even in the same genus (*Anaphe*). Complete amino acid analysis on highly purified common (*Bombyx mori*) and tussah fibroins also are available [14]. Since the molecular weight of fibroin is unknown, the number of residues in such instances is calculated per 10^5 g protein. According to these determinations, there are 567·2 g mole glycine per 10^5 g *Bombyx mori* fibroin and 318 g mole glycine in the same amount of tussah silk. The alanine content is nearly reversed, viz. 385·7 in *Bombyx* and 529·5 in tussah. Large differences were found also in valine (26·7 in *Bombyx* and 7·4 in tussah), threonine, arginine, histidine, and tryptophan. Some amino acids are found in trace amounts, but it is impossible to determine the chemical molecular weight from these data, because the chemical homogeneity cannot be ascertained.

Silk fibroin can be dissolved in concentrated solutions of certain lithium salts, such as lithium iodide or thiocyanate (LiCNS), or in copper ethylenediamine solutions. It is difficult to prove that this dissolution has occurred without some hydrolytic degradation, since the solutions of the lithium salts are somewhat acid due to hydrolysis, and the copper complex solutions are alkaline. Molecular weight determinations by various methods have given values that vary in a very wide range of about 30,000–300,000, and this is the best sort of evidence that the entities present in the solution depend on the method of dissolution and handling. Although there is no doubt that the macromolecules in the fibers are linear, their length is not known. [15] The solutions of fibroin have been used also with the purpose of attempting fractionation. No evidence of any homogeneous fractions, however, could be presented by the researchers who have studied them. Amino acid sequence studies on the partial degradation products have rendered some information about the sequences, and it appears that the sequence X. Gly. Ala. Gly. Ala. Gly may be common in the major fraction, [13] in *Bombyx mori* (X denoting serine or any other amino acid residue).

Structural studies by means of *X*-rays have revealed valuable information about the configuration of the chains in the crystalline portions of the fiber, whereas practically nothing is known about the less oriented sections of the fiber. The *X*-ray fiber diagrams of the various fibroins, as can be expected, differ considerably, as demonstrated in Fig. 45, which shows the spectrum of the *Bombyx mori* fibroin, and Fig. 71 showing the diagram of the tussah fibroin. It is generally assumed that the chains in both instances are arranged in the "pleated sheets", [16] but not much is known about any structural details. The contention that the hydrogen bonds are directed parallel to the fiber axis is supported by the study of the infrared spectra of the fibroins. [10]

[14] W. A. Schroeder and L. M. Kay, *J. Amer. chem. Soc.* **77**, 3908 (1955).

[15] G. Braunitzer and D. Wolff, *Z. Naturforsch.* **10** b, 404 (1955).

[16] R. E. Marsh, R. B. Corey and L. Pauling, *Biochim. Biophys. Acta* **16**, 1 (1955).

"Whenever the silk proteins are considered, it is important to remember their biological function. They are proteins designed for specific structural purposes; the silk proteins of the cocoon, fibroin and sericin, must together produce a structure with resilience, a measure of rigidity, strength to resist tearing, insulation against shock and changes of temperature, and resistance to microbiological attack. Such characteristics are provided to a high degree by the combination of silk proteins, to which sericin contributes insulation and rigidity and the fibroin framework beneath ensures the other requirements" (from p. 235 of ref. 13).

Keratin and Epidermin [6,,17,18]

Keratin is found not only in hair, wool, horn, nails, claws, beaks, and scales but also in the membranes of egg shells and even in the nerve tissues. A great variety of keratins, both with respect to chemical composition and physical

TABLE 36
AMINO ACID COMPOSITION OF SOME KERATINS [19]

Hair (hog)			Wool		Feather keratin	
	% amino acid	g-moles per 10^5 g	% amino acid	g-moles in 10^5 g	% amino acid	g-moles in 10^5 g
Alanine			4·14	46·4		
Glycine			6·53	87·0		
Valine	5·9	50·4	4·64	39·7	8·3	71·0
Leucine	8·3	63·5	11·3	86·3	8·0	61·1
Isoleucine	4·7	35·9			6·0	45·9
Proline	9·6	83·6	9·5	82·6	8·8	76·5
Phenylalanine	2·7	16·4	3·65	22·1	5·2	31·3
Tyrosine	3·5	19·3	4·65	25·7	2·2	12·2
Tryptophan			1·8	8·8		
Serine	7·6	72·5	10·01	95·4	10·2	97·1
Threonine	6·3	52·9	6·42	53·9	4·4	37·0
Cystine/2	14·4	119	11·9	98·9	8·2	68·0
Methionine	0·5	3·4	0·7	4·7	0·5	3·35
Arginine	10·9	62·6	10·4	59·7	7·5	43·1
Histidine	1·1	7·1	1·1	6·83	0·4	2·58
Lysine	3·8	26·1	2·76	18·9	1·3	8·9
Aspartic acid	8·0	60·3	7·2	54·1	7·0	52·6
Glutamic acid	17·9	121·8	14·1	96·0	9·7	66·0
Amide N			1·17	(83·2)		
Per cent N	16·6		16·3		15·0	
Per cent S	3·85		3·3		2·3	

[17] H. ZAHN, *Das Leder* **1**, 222, 265 (1950); **2**, 8 (1951).
[18] W. H. WARD and H. P. LUNDGREN, *Adv. Protein Chem.* **9**, 243 (1954).
[19] G. R. TRISTRAM, in *The Proteins* Vol. I A, p. 220 (H. NEURATH and K. BAILEY, ed.), Academic Press, New York.

properties, thus can be expected. Indeed, the keratin of birds' feathers, for instance, is highly crystalline and exhibits an X-ray β-spectrum, whereas most of the other keratines yield α-type diagrams. Also there are large differences in the amino acid composition between the various keratins. The keratin of skin is called epidermin. The keratins, like the silk proteins, occur in complicated fibrous structures, e.g. a wool fiber is composed of several layers which are difficult to separate. Moreover, like the silk fibroins, the keratins are insoluble without degradation, hence a fractionation and isolation of homogeneous components is impossible. A piece of horn is actually a space polymer of indefinite molecular size, since the fibrous polypeptide chains are all interlinked by many disulfide bridges. Dissolution thus can be accomplished only after reductive or oxidative breakage of these bridges. Chemically the keratins differ from the other fibrous structural proteins chiefly by their *high cystine content.* Sequence studies on partial degradation products have revealed a great variety of sequences without any preferable grouping or periodicity. The amino acid composition of a few keratins is presented in Table 36. [19]

The keratins thus contain all of the common amino acids, and an exceptionally high amount of cystine. The Table also shows that the keratins of hog hair and sheep wool differ less from each other than from the feather keratin. The differences are even greater when such more distant keratins are compared as the epidermin of skin with sheep wool, or the keratin of finger nails with neurokeratin. Some data are presented in Table 37. [20]

TABLE 37
LYSINE, ARGININE, AND CYSTINE CONTENT IN VARIOUS KERATINS
(according to Block, ref. 20)

	Lysine (%)	Arginine (%)	Cystine (%)	Molecular ratio lysine/arginine
Human hair	2·5	8·0	16·5	5:14
Finger nails	2·4	8·4	12·0	3:15
Sheep wool	2·3	7·8	10·0	4:14
Egg shell membrane	2·1	7·4	6·4	5:15
Goose feathers	1·0	4·8	6·4	4:14
Snake epidermis	1·4	5·4	5·3	3:12
Quills, porcupine	2·2	7·3	7·8	4:11
Human skin epidermis	4·7	5·9	3·8	3:3
Neurokeratin	2·7	3·8	3·4	3:3

Table 37 shows some interesting relationships between the chemical composition and origin of the various keratins. In the highly differentiated species of the mammals one finds the true keratins which are very rich in cystine, and the different (pseudo-) keratins of the epidermis and nerve tissue. In a less differentiated species (snake) are found epidermis keratins which are

[20] R. J. BLOCK, *J. biol. Chem.* **121**, 761 (1937).

chemically in between the nail–hair keratin and the skin epidermin. It is also noteworthy that the keratins of egg shell membrane and feathers are similar. Some interesting data on mammalian epidermin can be found in a review by Rudall.[21]

The macromolecular network of a keratin which is cross-linked by many disulfide bridges can be dissolved only after the cleavage of these bridges and disruption of the hydrogen bonds. A milder treatment results in swelling, whereby maximum swelling is obtained when both disulfide and hydrogen bond cleaving agents are used. Various sulfides, sulfites, and cyanides can be used for disrupting the —S—S— bridges, and concentrated guanidine salts are employed as the hydrogen bond cleaving agents[22]. A more or less complete dissolution of wool can be accomplished by heating with sodium sulfide, saturated lithium thiocyanate, ir on mixtures of detergents and reducing agents[23]. Water–alcohol mixtures containing salts and reducing agents also can be used for the same purpose[23]. The molecular weight of the keratins which were dissolved by reductive or oxidative cleavage of the disulfide bridges and breaking of the hydrogen bonds have been found in a wide range of about 10,000–70,000.[24,25,26] The solutions are very viscous, an indication of the presence of linear macromolecules.

The keratins of wool and hair show the α-type X-ray spectra. Upon softening the fiber in hot water or dilute alkali, the keratinous fiber can be stretched considerably, and the stretched fiber exhibits a β-spectrum. If hair is steamed for a short period in stretched state, it contracts after the removal of the stress to a length shorter than the original length. A similar result can be achieved by a treatment of the extended fiber with mild reducing agents, while a more drastic treatment may cause a loss of the elasticity. This is explained as being due to a gradual breakage of the weaker bonds. Removal of a small portion of the cross-links renders the keratin fiber rubber-like, i.e. the chains can slip along each other more readily than before, and they tend to assume a maximum disordered state due to the second principle of thermodynamics. A more drastic treatment results in the formation of new bonds ("permanent set") between the segments of the chains. These considerations are of great practical importance in the treatment of wool, as well as in the waving of hair.

There is strong evidence that the polypeptide chains in the keratins have assumed a helical configuration, and the α-helix of Pauling and Corey[12] seems to explain most of the experimental data reasonably well. In order to

(21) K. M. Rudall, *Adv. Protein Chem.* **7**, 253 (1952).
(22) O. Ripa, *Textile Res. J.* **23**, 776 (1953).
(23) H. P. Lundgren, *Adv. Protein Chem.* **5**, 305 (1949).
(24) P. Alexander and C. Earland, *Nature* **166**, 396 (1950).
(25) E. H. Mercer and B. Olofsson, *J. Polymer Sci.* **6**, 671 (1951).
(26) A. M. Woodin, *Biochem. J.* **57**, 99 (1954); I. J. O'Donnell and E. F. Woods, *J. Polymer Sci.* **31**, 397 (1956).

explain some of the X-ray reflections, Pauling and Corey have made further assumptions that the helices in the keratinous fibers (α-keratins) are wound around each other thus forming compound helices. These problems have been treated recently also by Huggins.[27] It must, however, be emphasized that all these discussions about the configuration of the chains are largely bold speculations. The X-ray diagrams of the α-keratins are even poorer than those of the silks, and do not permit any detailed predictions about the positions of the atomic groups in the fiber. The same X-ray diagrams also indicate that there is a very low degree of crystallinity, and it is even not known whether this means a uniform semicrystalline state throughout the whole fiber or the presence of crystalline and amorphous portions. Due to the presence of the strong interchain bonding, and to the presence of many polar side groups, it is very probable that the helices must be strongly distorted, and that several types of folding are present in the fibers.

The Collagens and Elastins [6,28,29,30]

The collagens and elastins comprise a very important class of structural proteins. Collagens are found in bone, cartilage, tendons, skin, and in many other tissues, and they are characterized by their chemical, mechanical, and structural properties. Chemically the collagens are characteristic with their high content of glycine, proline, and hydroxyproline; the arginine content also is high. Mechanically, the native collagen fiber is characteristic with its low extensibility, and with its shrinkage on warming. The general structural features are revealed by X-ray diffraction and electron microscopy. X-ray diffraction studies have shown that native collagen fibers possess a certain degree of orientation of the macromolecular chains, and that the patterns differ from both the α- and the β-keratin patterns. The elastins are practically amorphous and elastic, and they differ from the collagens also in amino acid composition in that they are poor in the polar side groups and rich in nonpolar residues.[31] This may well be the reason that the fiber is elastic, i.e. that the chains can reversibly coil up. At the same time, this indicates that the low elasticity of native collagen is due to strong interchain bonding. The chains in the case of collagens, however, are not interlinked by disulfide bridges, since these proteins are devoid of cystine; hence the interchain bonding probably is due to hydrogen bonds. Salt bridges between the polar groups of the basic and acidic residues, and ester bonds between the hydroxils of the hydroxy-amino acids and carboxyl groups of aspartic and glutamic acids, also have

(27) M. L. Huggins, *Proc. Nat. Acad. Sci.* **43**, 204 (1957).

(28) K. H. Gustavson, *The Chemistry and Reactivity of Collagen* Academic Press, New York, 1956.

(29) J. T. Randall (ed.), *Nature and Structure of Collagen* Academic Press, New York, Butterworth Publ., London, 1953.

(30) R. S. Bear, *Adv. Protein Chem.* **7**, 68 (1952).

(31) R. E. Neuman, *Arch. Biochem.* **24**, 289 (1949).

been considered. According to recent determinations of Grassmann *et al.*,[32] a collagen from beef hide contained 25% glycine (in per cent nitrogen from total nitrogen), 8·7% the dibasic aspartic and glutamic acids, 10·2% proline, 7% hydroxyproline, and 15·7% arginine. The concentration of the nonpolar side groups (valine and the leucins) was low, while alanine amounted to 8·4%. Earlier determinations have yielded approximately the same values,[13] with the exception of arginine which was found less than by Grassmann *et al.* Comparative amino acid analyses on collagens from various species have been made recently by means of the most accurate chromatographic methods,[32a] and the results are compiled in Table 37a. Most striking is the uniformly high glycine content in all instances and the differences in the content of some amino acids, such as alanine, hydroxyproline, and lysine.

TABLE 37 a

THE AMINO ACID COMPOSITION OF SOME VERTEBRATE AND INVERTEBRATE COLLAGENS
(number of residues per 1000 total residues)

	Steer skin	Shark elastoidin	Thyone body wall	Metridium tissue	Physalia float	Spongin A	Spongin B
Glycine	334	319	306	311	307	315	323
Alanine	105	123	113	70	66	56	95
Leucine	25	19	22	37	31	28	24
Isoleucine	11	18	13	23	22	24	17
Valine	19	17	30	34	26	29	24
Proline	131	119	109	63	83	78	73
Hydroxyproline	91	72	60	49	61	108	94
Phenylalanine	13	15	8·9	12	11	9·3	10
Tyrosine	4·7	9·2	7·9	7·9	5·6	4·7	4·0
Serine	38	42	43	54	47	38	24
Threonine	17	23	35	39	33	43	27
Methionine	6·6	13	2·2	8·8	5·8	4·7	3·1
Cystine	0	0·9	2·5	3·2	1·6	3·3	6·0
Hydroxylysine	6·8	7·0	11	25	30	12	24
Lysine	25	24	7·5	27	27	9·0	24
Arginine	48	50	54	57	54	47	43
Histidine	4·6	4·4	2·8	5·1	1·9	3·9	3·2
Aspartic acid	48	45	62	80	83	92	97
Glutamic acid	72	80	110	94	104	95	86
(Amide groups	41	32	75	71	66	102	90)

All these collagen studies, however, suffer from the same deficiencies as mentioned earlier in the instance of silks and keratins — the collagens are not definite chemical individuals. The fibrous material in the tissues is closely associated not only with other fibrous and globular proteins but even with polysaccharides (see chapt. 11), and it is extremely difficult to liberate collagen from all extraneous material.

[32] W. GRASSMANN, K. HANNIG and M. PLOCKL, *H.-S. Zeitschr. f. physiol. Chem.* **299**, 258 (1955).

[32a] K. A. PIEZ and J. GROSS, *Biochim. Biophys. Acta* **34**, 24 (1959).

In spite of these difficulties, relatively mild methods have been elaborated which yield soluble collagen in a reasonably pure state.[33,34] For example, a paracrystalline fish collagen (ichthyocol) has been obtained by the following method.[34] The tissue (fresh carp swim bladder) was washed, minced, and

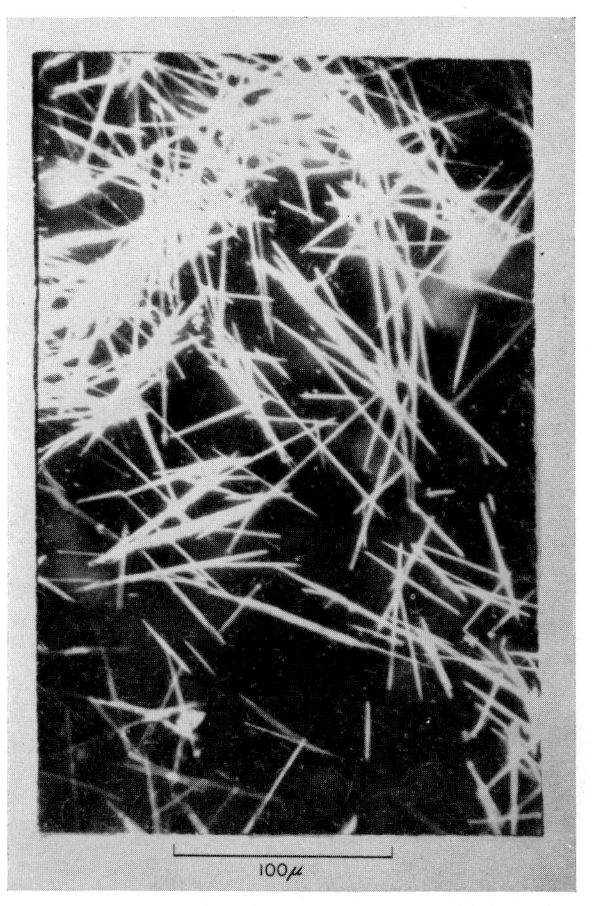

FIG. 74. Paracrystalline particles of fish collagen (by *Courtesy* of Dr. Gallop)

pre-extracted with sodium acetate thus removing some of the soluble carbohydrates and proteins. Collagen then was extracted from the remaining tissue with a cold citrate buffer of pH 4·3, the extract was filtered, centrifugated, and dialyzed against a large volume of 0·02 *M* dibasic sodium phosphate. After several hours, the fish collagen started to precipitate in the form of long needle-shaped particles (see Fig. 74). Molecular weight of 1·6 million

(33) V. N. OREKHOVITCH, A. A. TUSTANOVSKY, K. D. OREKHOVITCH and N. E. PLOTNIKOVA, *Biokhimiya* **13**, 55 (1958).

(34) P. M. GALLOP, *Arch. Biochem. Biophys.* **54**, 486 (1955); J. GROSS, J. H. HIGHBERGER and F. O. SCHMITT, *Proc. Nat. Acad. Sci.* **41**, 1 (1955).

was found for the solutions of this collagen by the method of light scattering.[34] A highly asymmetric particle shape was indicated by the high viscosity of

FIG. 75. Electron micrograph of fish collagen (ichthyocol), according to Gallop (l.c. 34)

the solutions, as well as by the light scattering and sedimentation behavior. Moreover, the solutions exhibited a high levorotation of $[\alpha]_D = -350°$.[34] Very important and interesting was also the observation that the fibrillar material which was reconstituted by dialysis showed the same long range periodicity of about 640 Å units as the native fibers. This periodicity (see Fig. 75) has been observed by many researchers earlier[35] both by electron

[35] F. O. SCHMITT, C. E. HALL and M. A. JAKUS, *J. Cellular Comp. Physiol.* **20,** 11 (1942).

microscopy and by low angle X-ray diffraction. [36] The cross-striations do not indicate a composition of oblate subunits, but are due to a more dense accumulation of the shadowing material at certain portions of the fiber.

While only small differences were found in the amino acid composition of the various collagens, the physicochemical properties of their solutions depended very much on the source, method of isolation, and method of study. Thus a soluble skin collagen had a molecular weight of only 74,000 as evaluated from osmotic pressure data and a much higher value of several million as computed from light scattering.[37] Since osmotic pressure gives a number-average molecular weight (M_n) and light scattering a weightaverage (M_w), this large difference indicates a high degree of polydispersity (see chapt. 3). It seemed likely that the very large units which so much affect the beam in light scattering measurements are aggregates of the true macromolecules.

Extensive physicochemical studies on various preparations of soluble collagens have been done recently by Helga Boedtker-Doty and Paul Doty at Harvard University. [38] First, it was demonstrated that after a meticulous clarification of the solutions, light scattering yields reproducible values in the range of 340,000–380,000 for the molecular weights of soluble collagens from various sources. Since the osmotically determined number-average molecular weight for these preparations of fish collagen (ichthyocol) also was found rather close to this value (310,000), it was concluded that the preparations were relatively homgeneous, and that the 345,000 value is the molecular weight of collagen. Such units are about 3000 Å long and only 13·6 Å thick, as estimated from light scattering, streaming birefringence, and viscosity data. The data also indicated that the fibrous macromolecule is rigid, and almost completely extended, in the sense of the earlier concept of stiff, rod-shaped units of Staudinger, as ascertained also by direct electron microscopic observations (see Fig. 76). Very important was the observation that above a certain temperature, or in the presence of thiocyanates, the rod-shaped macromolecules are denatured: the stiff rods disintegrate into three chains which assume now the configuration of random coils. It was concluded [38] that the macromolecular rods are composed of three polypeptide chains which form a compound helix, as deduced also from X-ray diffraction data. [39,40] The three chains in the strands form staggered junctions with parts of the free dangling chain ends an assumption which may help to explain the periodicities along the fiber axis.

(36) R. S. Bear, *J. Amer. chem. Soc.* **64**, 727 (1942).

(37) M. B. Mathews, E. Kulonen and A. Dorfman, *Arch. Biochem. Biophys.* **52**, 247 (1954).

(38) H. Boedtker and P. Doty, *J. Amer. chem. Soc.* **78**, 4267 (1956); see also P. Doty and T. Nishihara in *Recent Advances in Gelatin and Glue Research* p. 92 (G. Stainsby, ed.), Pergamon Press, London, 1958.

(39) G. N. Ramachandran and G. Kartha, *Nature* **176**, 593 (1955).

(40) A. Rich and F. H. C. Crick, *Nature* **176**, 915 (1955).

The researchers at Harvard have substantiated their concept on collagen structure by more recent studies on ultrasonic fragmentation of the macromolecules.[41] The exposure of soluble calf-skin collagen to 9-kilocycle ultrasonic irradiation caused fragmentation into shorter pieces that retain their

FIG. 76. The macromolecules of collagen as shown in electron microscope (magnification about 10,000×) (by *Courtesy* of C. E. Hall, Massachusetts Institute of Technology)

rigidity, as demonstrated by light scattering, sedimentation, and viscosity studies. In Table 38 are compiled some data on this collagen and its fragmentation products.

The various commercial *gelatins* and glues represent more or less denatured and degraded collagen. They are extracted from bone, connective tissues, or skin by prolonged boiling with water. The rod-shaped macromolecular strands of the collagen thereby are "melted" down into separate chains of the average molecular weight of 100,000–140,000. If the treatment is mild, a "parent gelatin" of M = 130,000–140,000 is obtained,[38] whereas the ordinary drastic industrial treatment yields highly polymolecular gelatin

(41) T. NISHIHARA and P. DOTY, *Proc. Nat. Acad. Sci.* **44**, 411 (1958).

TABLE 38

MOLECULAR CONSTANTS OF COLLAGEN AND ITS FRAGMENTATION PRODUCTS
(Nishihara and Doty, ref. 41)

Irradiation time (min)	$[\alpha]_D$	$\|\eta\|$ dl/g	Axial ratio (a/b)	Sedimentation constant $s_{20,w}$	Molecular weight
0	−415°	12·50	181	3·02	374,000
10	−410	10·75	166	2·95	336,000
40	−420	8·65	147	2·87	297,000
120	−407	4·95	108	2·68	217,000
240	−398	3·25	85	2·59	170,000

preparations of M_w = 10,000–100,000.[42,43] Hydrolytic cleavage of the long chains has occurred, and the chains are coiled up at random. It must be emphasized that the ultrasonic fragmentation and "melting" of the strands are two different processes.

Extensive studies have been made on the viscosity, gelation, and fractionation of gelatin solutions, as well as on swelling, melting, and on mechanical properties of gelatin gels, and excellent reviews are available on these subjects.[44] New light on the mechanism of gelation has been shed by optical rotation studies. The specific rotation of gelatin solutions is about −110° (sodium light), and the system becomes more levorotatory (usually to −200° or higher) when it sets on cooling. If, however, the gelation is achieved by the removal of water from the warm solution instead of cooling, the specific rotation does not change. Also it was demonstrated that the highly levorotatory cold-set-gelatin gel possessed an infrared spectrum that was more similar to the collagen spectrum than that of the warm-set-gelatin. From these facts it was concluded[45] that the macromolecules in the warm-set-gel have the same random coil configuration as in the solutions, while in the ordinary cold-set-gels the chains have assumed a collagen-like configuration. Some of the chain ends of the coils become entlangled on decreasing the temperature, and these entangled sections of the adjacent macromolecules form short paracrystalline configurations resembling native collagen. It is noteworthy that native collagen is highly levorotatory (see Table 38), and that the levorotation changes only little on the ultrasonic fragmentation of the strands but very much so on "melting", i.e. disaggregation and transformation into random coils.

(42) J. W. WILLIAMS, W. M. SAUNDERS and J. S. CICIRELLI, *J. physic. Chem.* **58**, 774 (1954); E. V. GOUINLOCK, Jr., P. J. FLORY and H. A. SCHERAGA, *J. Polymer Sci.* **16**, 383 (1955).

(43) J. POURADIER and A. M. VENET, *J. chim. physique* **47**, 391 (1950).

(44) J. D. FERRY, *Adv. Protein Chem.* **4**, 1 (1948).

(45) C. ROBINSON and M. J. BOTT, *Nature* **168**, 325 (1951); C. ROBINSON, in *Nature and Structure of Collagen* p. 96 (J. T. RANDALL, ed.), Academic Press, New York, Butterworth Publ., London, 1953.

The described optical rotatory behavior places collagen and gelatin in a special group which shows striking contrast in comparison to many other proteins and synthetic polypeptides. The transformation from a rigid and ordered linear into a disordered random coil configuration in the collagen–gelatin group is associated with a *positive shift* of the specific rotation, while in most other instances the shift in such change is *negative*. Poly-γ-benzyl-L glutamate, for example, assumes a configuration of a helical rod in m-cresol solution, and the specific rotation is positive, whereas in a dichloroacetic acid solution the macromolecules are random coils, and they are levorotatory.[46] Positive rotation has been measured also in solutions of silk fibroin in mixtures of dichloroacetic acid and ethylene dichloride, where the macromolecules probably have a helical configuration, while in pure dichloroacetic acid silk is levorotatory, and the configuration is probably more disordered than in the case of positive rotation.[46] Consequently, the ordered configuration of the chains in native collagen must be very different from the configuration in silk fiber as well as from that of the linear proteins which show the so-called α-spectrum of X-ray diffraction. As indicated before, the X-ray spectra of the collageneous fibers are poorer in reflections than those of silk fibroin or feather keratin, and the chief reason for this may be the high proline and hydroxyproline content in collagen. Since the peptide bond nitrogen in proline and hydroxyproline residues belongs to the pyrrolidine ring, the helical twisting in these chains must be strongly influenced by these bonds.

In conclusion, a note should be inserted about the chemical molecular weight and amino acid sequence. Since neither the three-strand rod-shaped unit of $M = 340{,}000$ nor the "parent gelatin" unit of $M = 140{,}000$ is chemically well characterized, the chemical molecular weight for collagen is still uncertain. Attempts to fractionate collagen have been only partially successful, since no convincing evidence has been presented that any of the preparations are chemically homogeneous. Terminal amino acid analyses on some of the best preparations have indicated the presence of alanine and aspartic acid as the N-terminal groups, and the quantities seem to indicate a chemical molecular weight of approximately 160,000.[47] A few other end groups appeared on conversion of this soluble collagen into gelatin.[47] A large number of peptides have been isolated from partial digestion products, and thus far there is no evidence of any preferential sequences in the chains. Since it has not been proven that the starting material was homogeneous, all these sequence data are of a very limited value. The great challenge for the future collagen chemist remains — to elaborate methods of preparing homogeneous collagens, and to establish the amino acid sequence in the chains. This chemical evidence then will provide also the crucial test for any of the models envisaged for the configuration.

[46] J. T. YANG and P. DOTY, *J. Amer. chem. Soc.* **79**, 761 (1957).
[47] J. H. BOWES, R. G. ELLIOTT and J. A. MOSS, *Biochem. J.* **61**, 143 (1955).

Finally, it should be mentioned that there is evidence that covalent bonds other than the ordinary peptide bonds are present in gelatin and collagen. *Ester bonds* between the free carboxyls of the dibasic amino acid residues and hydroxy proline and other hydroxyamino acids are strongly suspected. This is indicated e.g. by the fact that gelatin and collagen can be cleaved by a mild treatment with hydroxylamine without hydrolytic cleavage of the peptide bonds.[47a] Fragments of molecular weight of about 20,000 are formed in this treatment, and the idea has been considered that the large collagen macromolecules are composed of many relatively small subunits.[47a] Again, the final answers to this question can be expected from a more detailed chemical study on the kinetics of cleavage and chemical structure of the fragments.

The Fibrous Proteins of Muscle [48,49,50]

There are several types of fibrous proteins which can be extracted from minced muscle by means of salt solutions, and the most important are: *myosin*, *actomyosin*, and *tropomyosin*. Of these, actomyosin is definitely proven to consists of two components — *myosin* and *actin*. Fractionation and separation of the various components can be accomplished by working with salt solutions of various concentrations at definite pH's and temperatures. The actin component appears to exist in several forms: there are at least two forms of globular actin (G-actin) and a fibrous actin (F-actin). The molecular weight of one of the G-actins is 70,000, and the other modification of it represents a dimer ($M = 140{,}000$). Larger fibrillar units of the F-actin are formed on linear aggregation of the G-actin. The molecular (or particle) weight of actin-free myosin is in the range of 800,000–900,000, e.g. Portzehl found 840,000 by osmotic pressure measurement, and 850,000 by sedimentation-diffusion.[51] This agreement between the number- and weight-average molecular weights indicates that the preparation was homogeneous with respect to molecular weight. The macromolecules of the tropomyosin are smaller (M about 55,000), but they aggregate to long fibers which can be observed in the electron microscope. Myosin and tropomyosin show X-ray diffraction patterns which are very similar to those of the α-keratins. Oriented films of myosin are elastic, and the α-keratin type spectrum is changed to the β-spectrum on stretching. The electron micrographs exhibit cross-striations which are characteristic for the various preparations, e.g. a *paramyosin* of clam muscle has a different periodicity along the fiber, and it produces also

[47a] P. M. GALLOP, S. SEIFTER and E. MEILMAN, *Nature* **183**, 1659 (1959).

[48] K. BAILEY, in *The Proteins* Vol. II B, p. 951 (H. NEURATH and K. BAILEY, ed.), Academic Press, New York, 1954.

[49] H. H. WEBER and H. PORTZEHL, *Adv. Protein Chem.* **7**, 161 (1952); H. H. WEBER, *Ann. Rev. Biochem.* **26**, 667 (1957).

[50] A. SZENT-GYÖRGYI, *Chemistry of Muscular Contraction* 2nd ed., Academic Press, New York, 1951; *Adv. Enzymol.* **16**, 313 (1955).

[51] H. PORTZEHL, *Z. Naturforsch.* **5 b**, 75 (1950).

a somewhat different X-ray diffraction pattern. The solutions of the fibrous muscle proteins are highly viscous, and they set readily.

Workers doing research on the fibrous muscle proteins are disturbed by the fact that it is impossible to account quantitatively for all the proteins extracted from striated muscles. This "extra protein fraction" of myofibrils appears to be quite elusive, and the products obtained by various authors differ considerably. According to a recent report of Perry and Zydowo, [51a] this fraction is composed of several subfractions which were separated by diethylaminoethyl cellulose ion exchange chromatography. One of the subfractions appeared to be a complex possessing aldolase activity, another was composed chiefly of tropomyosin, and a third of a protein which resembled the so-called Y-protein described by Dubuisson. [51b]

The chemical molecular weights of the fibrous muscle proteins are uncertain, since the chemical structure has not been established. For instance, it is doubtful that the value of about 850,000 represents the true molecular weight of myosin. A lower value of 420,000 has been reported by Laki *et al.* on the basis of physicochemical measurements. [52] Also it is interesting that myosin is readily broken down by tryptic digestion into two macromolecular components named *meromyosins*. One of these has the molecular weight of 232,000, and is called H-(heavy) meromyosin, while the lighter component (L-meromyosin) has a molecular weight of 96,000. Both these meromyosins appear to be highly asymmetric macromolecules, and they show certain chemical differences, e.g. in amino acid composition. If 420,000 is the molecular weight of myosin, this unit must be composed of one H-meromyosin, and two L-meromyosin subunits. However, there is strong evidence that myosin may be composed of even smaller subunits, since fragments with a molecular weight of 14,000–16,000 could be extracted from mysin by a relatively mild treatment with urea. [53] Another type of subunit was extracted from myosin recently in an equally mild treatment with 0·1 M sodium carbonate solution. [54] The molecular weight of these units is 29,000, and they probably are dimers of the smaller units extracted by urea. Isoleucine was found as the C-terminal amino acid in these subunits, and the same amino acid is released also by carboxy peptidase treatment of myosin (2 moles per mole myosin), hence the subunits probably have been split off the one end of the long myosin unit. Since the X-ray diffraction spectra of the α-keratins and myosins are relatively similar, it is possible that the chain configuration in both classes is also similar. An identical configuration, however, is unlikely, chiefly because of the differences in amino acid composition. The cystine con-

[51a] S. V. Perry and M. Zydowo, *Biochem. J.* **71**, 220 (1959).

[51b] M. Dubuisson, *Nature* **166**, 1116 (1950); *Biochim. Biophys. Acta* **5**, 489 (1950).

[52] K. Laki and W. R. Caroll, *Nature* **175**, 389 (1955).

[53] T. C. Tsao, *Biochim. Biophys. Acta* **11**, 368 (1953).

[54] D. R. Kominz, W. R. Carroll, E. N. Smith and E. R. Mitchell, *Arch. Biochem. Biophys.* **79**, 191 (1959).

tent, for example, in the myosins is very low. The amino acid composition of the myosins and actin is presented in Table 39.

TABLE 39

AMINO ACID COMPOSITION (mole/10^5 g) OF MYOSINS AND ACTIN (Kominz *et al.*, ref. 55)

	Tropo-myosin	Actin	Myosin	L-meromyosin	H-meromyosin
Cystine/2	6·5	11·2	8·6	5·6	10·9
Methionine	16	30	22	14	19
Tyrosine	16	32	18	12	21
Tryptophan	0	10		6	3
Glycine	12·5	67	39	24	45
Alanine	110	71	78	76	73
Valine	38	42	42	39	45
Leucine	95	63	79	85	78
Isoleucine	29	57	42	35	42
Phenylalanine	3·5	29	27	9·5	40
Proline	0	44	22	8·5	29
Serine	40	56	41	37	43
Threonine	28	59	41	38	49
Histidine	5·5	19	15	19	11·5
Arginine	42	38	41	51	29
Lysine	110	52	85	83	82
Glutamic acid	211	101	155	174	138
Aspartic acid	89	82	85	77	88
Amide N	64	66			

Inspection of Table 39 shows that there are certain differences between the proteins. The amount of free basic and free carboxyl groups is high in all instances, as confirmed also by direct titration data. Also it is obvious that the composition of myosin can be obtained by adding up the composition of the meromyosins, and that the composition of the myosin is between that of the tropomyosin and actin. This has raised the question that tropomyosin and actin might be just different subunits of myosin. [55] Reversible aggregation is one of the most characteristic features of the fibrous proteins of muscle, and it might well be one of the clues in the still unsolved problem of muscular contraction (see chapt. 27). It may be mentioned that H-meromyosin reversibly combines with actin, and this reaction may be important in muscular motion. Furthermore, H-meromyosin has adenosinetriphosphatase activity. The amino acid sequences in the various myosins are very little investigated, but work is in progress in several laboratories. There is no doubt that elucidation of the chemical structure will facilitate solution of the problems on chain configuration, as well as the problem of contraction.

[55] D. R. KOMINZ, A. HOUGH, P. SYMONDS and K. LAKI, *Arch. Biochem. Biophys.* **50**, 148 (1954).

It is regretable that in spite of the great efforts of many workers, the problem of the molecular size, shape, and structure of the myosin macromolecule is far from being solved. While earlier studies [49,50,51] indicated that the particle weight is 850,000, and that the units resemble thin rods about 2,300 Å long and 25 Å thick, more recent studies have thrown doubt on these conclusions. [56,57] The physical molecular (or particle) weight appears to be somewhat larger than that found by Laki and Carroll, [52] but much lower than the earlier values. According to Holtzer and Lowey: "Light scattering, viscosity and sedimentation measurements on solutions of myosin indicate that the molecule is a rod 1620 Å long and 26 Å thick and has a molecular weight of 493,000", [57] and it was also found that these parameters are not affected by variation of temperature (from 1 to 30 °C), ionic strength (from 0·4 to 2·0 at pH 7), and pH (from 6 to 9 at ionic strength 0·6). Most interesting, however, are the conclusions of Holtzer and Lowey that the myosin rod is not uniform in thickness, and these considerations are interesting in connexion with recent findings of other authors that the molecular weight and arrangement of the meromyosins is different from that previously considered. According to Holtzer and Lowey, it is most likely that the myosin particle is built of one L-meromyosin of M = 126,000 and one H-meromyosin of M = 324,000 (plus a few smaller subunits), that the L- and H-meromyosins are of equal length, and that they are attached to each other end to end. Furthermore, calculations showed that the L-meromyosin unit must be built of two polypeptide chains, while the H-meromyosin unit would have six chains, and the whole myosin unit could be presented schematically as follows:

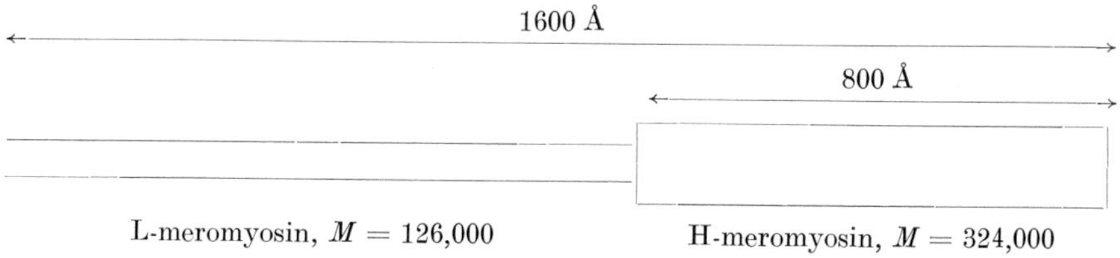

1600 Å

800 Å

L-meromyosin, M = 126,000 H-meromyosin, M = 324,000

Further studies should show whether this model has more than a tentative value of a concept that stimulates further exploration of this field.

In conclusion: it seems that the difficulties in an unequivocal interpretation of the experimental results on myosin are due chiefly to the possibility of reversible aggregation of the components. It is possible that some variation in the results is due to small differences in isolation procedures which result in different combination of the subunits in different instances. The meromyosins possibly may be associations of smaller actin and tropomyosin subunits, as indicated also by the amino acid composition (Table 39). The L- and H-

[56] E. P. Geiduschek and A. Holtzer, in *Adv. Biol. Med. Physics* **6**, 431 (1958), especially p. 511–539.

[57] A. Holtzer and S. Lowey, *J. Amer. chem. Soc.* **81**, 1370 (1959).

meromyosins themselves, however, may not be real subunits, since they are liberated only after a tryptic digestion, and this would also explain the fact that somewhat different meromyosins have been isolated by various authors. Furthermoore, this would indicate that the myosin particles may more or less differ in size and shape. What is the size of the smallest *chemical* subunit, i.e. the chemical molecular weight of any of the myosin components, is not known. As indicated before, the final answers can be expected only after the disclosure of the chemical structure of these important proteins.

CHAPTER 18

NUCLEOPROTEINS, HISTONES, PROTAMINES, AND RESIDUAL PROTEINS

Very little is known of the function of the proteins attached to deoxyribonucleic acid in different cells.

J. A. V. BUTLER and P. F. DAVISON [1]

NUCLEOPROTEINS are universal constituents of all cell nuclei, and there is no doubt that they play a decisive role in reduplication of the cell. A particle of a nucleoprotein is a complicated unit. It is simpler than any of the organelles of the cell, such as the nucleus itself, but more complex than any well defined macromolecules. In the elaborate hierarchy of an organism, the nucleoprotein stands between the nucleus and certain macromolecules, viz.:

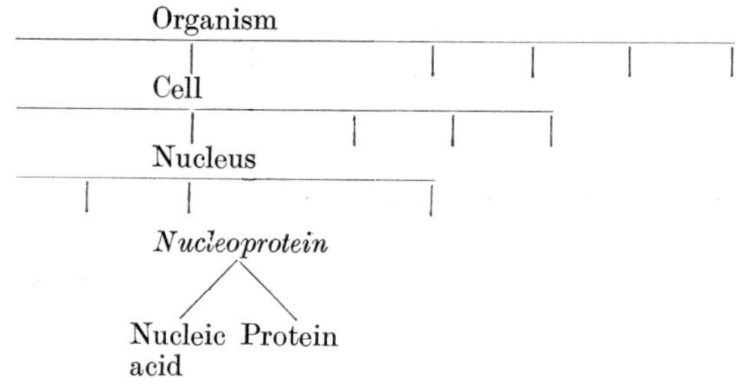

and a complete understanding of the nucleoprotein problem may provide important clues to the understanding of the unique organization in a living cell. Nucleoproteins are found also in certain particles of the cytoplasm (see chapt. 21–22).

A nucleoprotein is composed of two macromolecular components: *nucleic acid* and *protein*; in addition, there is water, and a certain amount of other micromolecular "impurities", such as inorganic ions. In order to facilitate the description of this obscure field, we may say in advance that a nucleoprotein particle can be envisaged as composed of an extended core of a nucleic acid and many protein units attached to it. The nucleic acid core is large, and more about it will be said in the next chapter; the protein molecules around it are much smaller, yet the total weight of the protein in the particle is nearly the same as the weight of the core. Since neither the number nor the structure of any of these units is known, a nucleoprotein particle hardly could be qualified as a macromolecule. Furthermore, there are reasons to believe that any

[1] J. A. V. BUTLER and P. F. DAVISON, *Adv. Enzymol.* **18**, 161 (1957); quotation from p. 184.

of the isolated preparations of the nucleoproteins differ from the nucleoprotein in a living cell. While the isolated substance is more or less "static", the nucleoprotein in a living cell, especially in the course of cell division, is "dynamic". Both the core and the protein attachments undergo various changes. Because of this uncertainty, i.e. ill defined nature of any of the isolated nucleoproteins, they will be described only briefly. Somewhat more can be said about the protein components of a nucleoprotein: the histones, protamines, and the "residual proteins". Of these, the protamines comprise a somewhat special group, as they are found in the nuclei of fish sperm, while the histones represent a very broad group of basic proteins. The "residual proteins" are the least investigated. While the protamines and histones are basic, and are attached to the nucleic acid predominantly by ionic bonds (salt bridges), the attachment of the "residual protein" to the nucleic acid core is quite obscure. It is quite possible that in the living cell the attachment is just temporary, and that alternate protein units may be bound to the nucleic acid, according to the functional requirements of the cell.

The Nucleoproteins [1,2,3,4]

As pointed out by Chargaff and others [1,2,3,4] (see also chapt. 2), the isolation of such complex constituents as nucleoproteins is associated with several uncertainties which have not been considered critically enough by some authors, especially some decades ago. The first uncertainty is that which can be summarized under the often misused term "*denaturation*". In this instance, in addition to the possibility that the protein and the nucleic acid components themselves may be denatured comes the additional possibility of affecting the *interaction* between the components. The protein units may become rearranged during the course of isolation. In addition to this, during the course of isolation, the nucleoprotein must come in contact with some substances, also macromolecular proteins, with which it was not in direct contact in the intact nucleus. Thus, during the isolation, extraneous protein or other substance may be bound. This will become clearer if we consider any of the isolation procedures. Calf thymus gland is one of the most common sources of nucleoprotein, and the isolation, according to one of the best accepted procedures is carried out as follows.[5] Fresh glands are frozen, minced in a cooled mincing machine, and the material is fractionally extracted with sodium chloride solutions containing a small amount of fluoride. (The latter prevents

[2] E. Chargaff and J. N. Davidson, *The Nucleic Acids* especially chapt. 10, Vol. I, Academic Press, New York, 1955; R. Markham and J. D. Smith, in *The Proteins* Vol. II A, p. 3 (H. Neurath and K. Bailey, ed.), Academic Press, New York, 1954.

[3] E. Chargaff, in *Fibrous Proteins and their Biological Significance* p. 32 (Symp. Soc. Exp. Biol., No. 9), Academic Press, New York, 1955.

[4] P. F. Davison, B. E. Conway and J. A. V. Butler, *Progress in Biophys.* **4**, 148 (1954) R. Stoops (ed.), *Nucleoproteins*, Interscience Subl., New York, 1960.

[5] R. Signer and H. Schwander, *Helv. chim. Acta* **32**, 853 (1949).

the enzymic degradation of the nucleic acid). The nucleoprotein is precipitated by diluting with water, and it can be purified by redissolving in salt solutions and reprecipitation. Nucleoprotein can be extracted from minced material also by means of distilled water.

Consideration of these and similar procedures makes it immediately clear where the possibility of artifact formation lies: it is the *mincing* of the tissue. This brings the original native nucleoprotein into close contact with numerous other ingredients of the tissue, and some interactions with the nucleoprotein are likely to occur, even if the temperature is kept low and various drastically acting reagents are avoided. A somewhat cleaner method involves extraction from nuclear fragments which have been first separated by fractional centrifugation at a low temperature. However, even if separate chromosomes could be picked out and the nucleoprotein extracted from them, it may not be quite the same as in the intact nucleus, especially with respect to the bound or interacting proteins.

Since a nucleoprotein particle is not a definite macromolecule, there is little sense in speaking about the molecular weight of this substance. The particles are large in comparison with ordinary proteins, and particle weights of 5–15 million, and higher, have been estimated. The solutions of the nucleoproteins are very viscous, and the viscosity increases when the protein is stripped off the nucleic acid core. Gelation occurs readily, even in very dilute solutions. Sedimentation constants of 26–31 S units have been measured, and intrinsic viscosities between thirty and several hundred have been reported,[(6)] and the solutions cannot be considered as homogeneous. It has been ascertained that the protein components in the solutions may link several nucleic acid cores thus occasionally producing very large and complex systems.

While the calf thymus nucleoprotein is soluble in dilute salt solutions, a nucleoprotein from the sperm of sea urchin is soluble in distilled water, and it is precipitated by dilute salt solutions. This nucleoprotein contained 36% of deoxyribonucleic acid, about the same amount of histones, and also another protein,[(7)] and the particles dissociated into the components in concentrated salt solutions. The intact particles appeared in the electron microscope as somewhat curved rods 4300 Å long and 250–300 Å wide. It is also known that the nucleoproteins which contain ribonucleic acid may have different shapes and nucleic acid–protein ratios. Some plant ribonucleoproteins possess nearly spherical particles,[(8)] whereas others are rod-shaped. Tobacco mosaic virus is an example of a very asymmetric ribonucleoprotein (see chapt. 20). The particle weights of these entities range between several hundred thousand [(8)] and many millions.

[(6)] D. W. Kupke, N. T. Eldredge and J. M. Luck, *J. biol. Chem.* **210**, 295 (1954).

[(7)] M. H. Bernstein and D. Mazia, *Biochim. Biophys. Acta* **10**, 600 (1953); **11**, 59 (1953).

[(8)] L. Eggman, S. J. Singer and S. G. Wildman, *J. biol. Chem.* **205**, 969 (1953).

A very important paper on nucleoproteins was published recently by Zubay and Doty.[8a] Light scattering, viscosity, and sedimentation studies indicated that the particle weight of a carefully isolated calf thymus nucleoprotein was 18·5 million, and electron-microscopic observation revealed that the particles were rod-like. About half of the mass of a particle was protein, the other half being represented by the rod-shaped deoxyribonucleic acid. The latter forms a helical central core, and the protein is packed in the grooves of the central helix.

The Protamines [9,10,11]

Protamines are strongly basic substances which may be classified either as large polypeptides or small proteins. Molecular weights of 2000–8000 have been found for various preparations of these substances. Protamines can be readily isolated from acid extracts of fish sperm or testes, since acid sets them free from the salt-like nucleic acid and protamine compound of the cell nuclei, viz.:

$$\text{Nucleic acid} - \text{Protamine} + H_2SO_4 = \text{Nucleic acid} + \text{Protamine sulfate.}$$

The sulfates and other salts of the protamines are soluble in water, and they can be purified by reprecipitation with alcohol or similar precipitants. Further purification is accomplished by precipitation with a soluble picrate, which yields a difficultly soluble protamine picrate. Traces of nucleic acid present in this precipitate can be removed by extraction with sodium hydroxide, the picrate then is decomposed by sulfuric or hydrochloric acid, and the picric acid is removed by extraction with ether.

All of the highyl purified protamines appear to be inhomogeneous mixtures of similar components which are not artifacts, since a very mild treatment of the original nucleoprotein or nuclear material yields similar inhomogeneous material. For example, the nucleoprotein (or nucleoprotamine) can be split into its components by a neutral salt solution, and carbonic acid can be used for the salt formation instead of the strong mineral acids. The best method for demonstrating this inhomogeneity is Craig's countercurrent distribution (see chapt. 2) which can be used also for preparative purposes. Even the most mildly and carefully fractionated protamine specimens appeared to be inhomogeneous in the countercurrent test. However, the various molecular species in any of these preparations are similar both chemically and also with respect to the molecular size and shape.

[8a] G. Zubay and P. Doty, *J. mol. Biol.* **1**, 1 (1959).
[9] K. Felix in *Physiologische Chemie*, Vol. I, p. 709. *Die Stoffe* (B. Flaschenträger and E. Lehnartz, ed.), Springer Publ., Berlin/Göttingen/Heidelberg, 1951. K. Felix in *A Symposium on Molecular Biology*, p. 163 (R. E. Zirkle, ed.), Univ. of Chicago Press, Chicago, 1959.
[10] K. Felix, H. Fischer and A. Krekels, *Progress in Biophysics* **6**, 1 (1956).
[11] V. G. Allfrey, A. E. Mirsky and H. Stern, *Adv. Enzymol.* **16**, 411 (1955).

The protamines from various fish species differ in amino acid composition, e.g. most of the *Salmonidae* species protamines contain arginine as the only basic amino acid, whereas sturine, a protamine from *Acipenser sturio*, contains also lysine and histidine. While arginine usually is the dominating amino acid, some protamines of carp contain more lysine than arginine. The protamines are named according to the fish species, and the clupeine of herring and salmine of salmon are the best investigated ones. Their amino acid composition is presented in Table 40.

TABLE 40

AMINO ACID COMPOSITION (in per cent amino acid nitrogen of total nitrogen, and moles amino acid per 6500 g protamine sulfate) OF CLUPEINE AND SALMINE, ACCORDING TO ANDO *et al.* (12)

	Clupeine		Salmine	
	% amino acid N	Moles per 1 mole clupeine	% amino acid N	Moles per 1 mole salmine
Threonine	1·0	1·1	0	
Serine	2·3	2·5	3·3	3·6
Proline	2·5	2·7	2·9	3·2
Glycine	0·58	0·64	2·1	2·3
Alanine	2·7	3·0	0·32	0·35
Valine	1·2	1·3	1·6	1·8
Isoleucine	0·58	0·64	0·34	0·37
Arginine	89·1	24·6	89·7	24·6
Total	99·9	36·5	100·3	36·2
N % in sulfate	24·0		23·3	

The protamines are devoid of several amino acids, such as cystine, tryptophan, and aspartic acid. All the available chemical evidence indicates that the amino acids are combined in the ordinary polypeptide chains without any cross-linking, and there is some physical evidence that the chains are randomly coiled. The high concentration of the arginine side groups confers the basic properties, and ionization of these groups makes the unit a multivalent organic cation. Because of this, the protamines react strongly with all those macromolecules which have a surplus of carboxyls or other negatively charged groups, such as the nucleic acids, or pepsin. While trypsin and papain hydrolytically cleave the chain, pepsin immediately forms an insoluble compound with it. The compounds are macromolecular salts from which both components can be recovered by decomposition with acid, and this property of the protamines is sometimes employed for precipitation and isolation of macromolecular acids.

(12) T. ANDO, K. IWAI, S. ISHII, M. YAMASAKI, T. TOBITA, F. SAWADA, Y. NAGAI, H. FUJIOKA, M. KIMURA, M. SATO, E. ABUKUMAGAWA and Y. KAWANISHI, in *Symposium on Chemical Structure of Proteins* Tokyo, 1957.

The amino acid sequence has been partially resolved in clupein and salmine. According to Felix and Ando, proline is the chief N-terminal residue and arginine is at the C-terminal.[10,12,13] In salmine, only proline was found as the N-terminal amino acid, while clupeine contained both proline and alanine.[12,14] This indicates that there are at least two molecular species in clupeine: one terminating with proline and another with alanine. It has also been established that the sequence at the N-terminal of salmine is Pro-Arg-Arg- . . ., while in the two components of clupeine it is Pro-Arg-Arg- and Ala-Arg-Arg- respectively.

According to the data of Table 40, in the main components of salmine and clupeine, there are 24 or 25 arginine residues per chain, and the number of all other residues comprises only about half of this number. The structure at the ends of the major proline-terminated chain is established as follows:

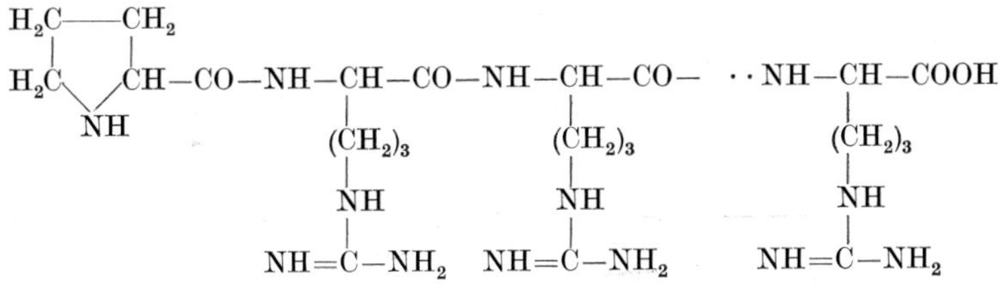

```
H2C——CH2
 |    |
H2C  CH—CO—NH—CH—CO—NH—CH—CO— ··NH—CH—COOH
  \  /          |           |             |
   NH        (CH2)3      (CH2)3        (CH2)3
                |           |             |
               NH          NH            NH
                |           |             |
           NH=C—NH2    NH=C—NH2      NH=C—NH2
```

There are two reasons why the complete sequence of these relatively small chains has not been elucidated: the difficulty in obtaining homogeneous preparations, and the oppressive predominance of the arginine as a constituent of the molecules. Moreover, the physical investigation is hampered by the semicolloidal nature of the solutions: the molecules are too large for the classical methods and too small for an accurate work with such methods as light scattering or sedimentation. The protamine molecules diffuse through the ordinary semipermeable membranes slowly, and an important study has been done recently on the dialysis of protamines and similar semicolloidal proteins through Cellophane.[15] Comparative measurements have shown that 50% of a protamine escaped through a Cellophane membrane in 40 min, while only 4 min were required for tryptophan ($M = 204$); under the same conditions (solutions in 0·01 N acetic acid), ribonuclease ($M = 13{,}600$) required 120 min, and trypsin ($M = 20{,}000$) 240 min. Another, more dense Cellophane retained 50% of the protamine in 150 min, while subtilin ($M = 3{,}300$) needed 138 min. This method can be useful for both separation and characterization of such semicolloidal materials. It must, however, be em-

(13) K. Felix, in *The Chemical Structure of Proteins* p. 151 (a CIBA Foundation symposium), Little, Brown, Boston, 1953.

(14) T. Ando, E. Abukumagawa, Y. Nagai and M. Yamasaki, *J. Biochem.* (*Tokyo*) **44**, 191 (1957); T. Ando, M. Yamasaki, E. Abukumagawa, S. Ishii and Y. Nagai, *ibid.* **45**, 429 (1958).

(15) L. C. Craig, W. Konigsberg, A. Stracher and T. P. King, in *Symposium on Protein Structure* p. 104 (A. Neuberger, ed.), Methuen, London, 1958.

phasized that there is not always a simple relation between the molecular size and dialysis time, especially when the solute is bound at the channel walls of the membrane. Since most membranes are negatively charged, binding of the positively charged protamine and clogging of the pores is likely to occur. Consequently, the molecules in this instance will appear larger than they really are.

Protamines have been isolated not only from the testicles of fish but also from other sources, such as fowl sperm.[16] The other tissues of the fish, on the other hand, do not contain protamines but histones. The question then can be raised: "To what extent does the heterogeneity of these preparations reflect the heterogeneous cell population of the gonad? For spermatogenesis involves a series of maturation stages: it begins with cells which contain histones and ends with mature sperm, which contain protamines. The whole testis may be expected to contain cells at all stages in this process, and the proportion of the total number of cells comprising mature sperm is known to vary at different times of the year. Therefore, a certain amount of protamine heterogeneity might be expected on biological grounds".[11] No differences, however, could be found between the protamine isolated from mature and immature rainbow trouts; the amino acid composition was practically identical, and proline was found as the N-terminal amino acid in both instances.[17] The absence of some essential amino acids, the heterogeneity, as well as the lack of a unique globular configuration thus seem to indicate that the protamine function does not require these properties and may involve only neutralization of the nucleic acid. This neutralized nucleic acid of the sperm cells, however, seems to be superior to the nucleic acid and protein compounds of other tissues for the specific biological function of the sperm.

The Histones [1,4,11]

The histones resemble protamines in several properties: both are basic, both are very heterogeneous, and both are devoid of cystine, cysteine, and tryptophan. The molecular weight of the histones is somewhat larger than that of the protamines. Moreover, the histones contain all ordinary amino acids, with exception of the mentioned three, whereas only 8–10 amino acids can be found in the protamines. The histones are real proteins, while protamines may be classified as polypeptides.

Histones are prepared by decomposing an extracted nucleoprotein with acid or a salt solution. In the acid treatment, the salt bridges between the phosphate groups of the nucleic acid and the amino groups of the histone are split, the liberated nucleic acid is precipitated, and the histone remains in solution. It can be precipitated with ammonia, picric acid, alcohol, or various macromolecular acids with which it forms salt-like compounds in

(16) M. M. Daly, A. E. Mirsky and H. Ris, *J. Gen. Physiol.* **34**, 439 (1951).
(17) T. Ando and C. Hashimoto, *J. Biochem.* (*Tokyo*) **45**, 453 (1958).

the same manner as the protamines. Attempts to fractionate the histones by means of fractional precipitation have never been very successful. Better results in fractionation have been achieved by zone electrophoresis and chromatography. The isoelectric point of the histones is somewhere between pH 10 and 11, and thus a neutral solution of their salts contains positively charged macromolecules. These move toward the negative pole in electrophoresis, and they are bound to acid resins.[18] Fractional elution from the column has been achieved e.g. by means of guanidinium salts, and many histone fractions thus could be prepared, most of them still of a questionable homogeneity. Of the many fractions obtained by chromatography of calf thymus histone only two appeared to be reasonably homogeneous. Molecular weight of one of them was estimated to be 10,000, and of the other 18,000–20,000. The histone of the first fraction had valine as the N-terminal amino acid and lysine as the C-terminal. In the other fraction alanine and proline were found as the N-terminals and glycine at the C-terminal of the chain. Since histones, like the protamines, are one chain macromolecules, the finding of two N-terminal amino acids in the fraction is an indication of inhomogeneity.[19] It also must be pointed out that neither mild treatment with acid nor the elution with guanidine salts can cause denaturation, because native histone can be considered as a random-chain macromolecule.

Extreme variations in amino acid composition of histones have been reported by various authors. Although some of these differences may be due to methodological reasons, striking differences were found even with the most accurate chromatographic amino acid analyses. Thus in Table 41 are compiled results obtained on two reasonably homogeneous histone fractions of calf thymus histone,[20] and also the data on electrophoretically homogeneous β-histones isolated from the erythrocytes, spleen or liver of domestic fowl.[21] While the differences between the β-histones are small, the amino acid composition of the fractions A and B of the thymus histone is very different. Also the composition of fraction A differs strongly from that of the β-histone of domestic fowl. These findings substantiate the facts that the histone of a certain tissue is very inhomogeneous, and that various tissues of the same organism contain certain identical (or almost identical) histone components.

Inspection of the data, moreover, suggests that the fraction B of calf thymus histone may be identical with the β-histone, at least in the content of the first fifteen amino acids of the Table. The small differences in serine, threonine, proline, and tyrosine content may be due to the fact that Crampton

(18) J. M. Luck, H. A. Cook, N. T. Eldredge, M. I. Haley, D. W. Kupke and P. S. Rasmussen, *Arch. Biochem. Biophys.* **65**, 449 (1956); see also N. Ui, *Biochim. Biophys. Acta* **25**, 493 (1957).

(19) J. M. Luck, P. S. Rasmussen, K. Satake and A. N. Tsvetkov, *J. biol. Chem.* **233**, 1407 (1958).

(20) C. F. Crampton, S. Moore and W. H. Stein, *J. biol. Chem.* **215**, 787 (1955).

(21) C. M. Mauritzen and E. Stedman, *Proc. Roy. Soc.* B **150**, 299 (1959).

et al. [20] corrected these values for the loss during hydrolysis, while Mauritzen *et al.* [21] did not. At least, the results indicate that certain compositional similarity prevails between certain histone components even in various species.

TABLE 41

AMINO ACID COMPOSITION OF SOME HISTONE FRACTIONS
(in per cent nitrogen from total nitrogen)

	Calf thymus fract. A [20]	Calf thymus fract. B [20]	Fowl erythroc. β-histone [21]	Fowl spleen β-histone [21]	Fowl liver β-histone [21]
Aspartic acid	1·52	3·53	3·32	3·42	3·29
Glutamic acid	2·46	5·49	5·42	5·32	5·42
Glycine	5·09	5·37	5·42	5·41	5·53
Alanine	17·73	7·57	7·22	6·43	6·39
Valine	3·79	4·32	3·42	3·62	3·61
Leucine	3·36	5·42	6·03	5·64	5·69
Isoleucine	0·77	2·95	3·01	2·96	3·14
Serine	5·05	4·65	2·96	2·59	2·86
Threonine	6·07	3·29	3·27	3·53	3·75
Cystine	0	0	0	0	0
Methionine	0	0·60	0·63	0·68	0·62
Proline	6·73	3·02	1·92	1·84	2·25
Phenylalanine	0·45	0·89	1·29	1·53	1·68
Tyrosine	0·48	2·04	1·55	1·72	1·76
Histidine	0	4·85	3·47	3·28	3·77
Lysine	37·68	16·97	11·21	9·90	11·22
Arginine	6·74	19·46	27·25	28·00	28·20
Amide N	1·68	4·40			
Total	97·78	94·82			
Total N in histone			17·9%	17·9%	17·5%

The differences between the histones A and B certainly are much greater than between B and β-histones from the two distant species. The significance of these findings is obscure. One possibility would be that the variety in the histones of the same tissue reflects the variety of the nucleoproteins, and that certain similar histones may have certain common functions in many tissues in different species. These differences and similarities may also be considered in connexion with the problem of the heterogeneity of the nucleic acids (see next chapter).

Residual Protein

Numerous observations have shown that the nucleoproteins which were isolated from nuclear material, aside from nucleic acid and histone (or protamine), contain some other protein. Thus, it appeared to be impossible to remove all protein from a nucleohistone by repeated extraction with acid. The protein which remained tightly bound to the nucleic acid moiety of the nucleohistone was named "residual protein". Since any of the nucleoprotein preparations involve tissue mincing, and since the nucleoprotein particles are fibrous colloidal units, adsorption and enmeshing of all sorts of other macromolecules which originate from the cytoplasm and other parts of the cells would not be at all surprising. The best evidence that this "residual protein" indeed originated in the nucleus, and probably can be regarded as a nucleoprotein component, has been presented by Mirsky *et al.*.[22,23] First, the nucleoprotein was isolated not directly from minced tissue but from clean isolated nuclei. Second, it was shown that the histones can be removed from calf thymus nuclei without changing the microscopic appearance of the chromosomes. "But, if the residual protein of a histone-free preparation is then disintegrated by trypsin, polymerized DNA is liberated and a viscous gel is formed in which no structure can be detected microscopically. On the other hand, if the histone-free chromosomes are treated with desoxyribonuclease, nothing remains of the chromosomal structure but a mass of minute protein threads. Thus, the morphological configuration of the chromosome, as seen under the microscope, is due to the combination of DNA with residual protein, and once these components are separated, neither the combination nor the configuration can be restored".[11] It was also demonstrated that there must be several types of these residual proteins. One fraction could be extracted before the removal of the major nucleoprotein component by neutral phosphate buffer; another fraction, which was insoluble, was separated from the nucleoprotein extract (with 1 *M* NaCl), and two other fractions were found in the NaCl-soluble nucleoprotein.[23] Metabolic studies on incorporation of ^{14}C-labeled alanine into the proteins of the intact nuclei showed that all four fractions of the residual proteins were metabolically more active (contained more ^{14}C after fractionation) than the histones. This also emphasizes their importance in the structure and functioning of the nuclear components. Chemically, the residual proteins are very little investigated. Two of the fractions seem to be associated with the small amount of ribonucleic acid (RNA) of the nucleus, while the other two seem to be additional constituents of the deoxyribo-, viz. DNA-nucleoprotein. One of the residual proteins precipitates as a gelatinous mass by saturation of the nucleoprotein solution at pH 10·9 with sodium chloride.[23] Generally, the residual proteins are less basic than the histones, and they contain tryptophan.

Histones, protamines, and residual proteins are not the only types of proteins that are found combined with nucleic acids. The nucleoproteins of viruses and phages represent other interesting examples in which the

[22] A. E. Mirsky and H. Ris, *J. Gen. Physiol.* **34**, 475 (1951).

[23] V. G. Allfrey, A. E. Mirsky and S. Osawa, *Nature* **176**, 1042 (1955); see also: I. B. Zbarsky, G. P. Georgiev and K. A. Perevoshchikova, *Abstracts*, 4th *Internat. Congr. Biochem.* p. 82, Vienna, 1958, Pergamon Press, London, 1958.

protein component is neutral or even slightly acid (see chapt. 20). For example, the protein of tobacco mosaic virus is slightly acid, i.e. it contains large amounts of aspartic and glutamic acids. The hydroxyamino acid (serine and threonine) content of these nucleoproteins also is high.

A complete removal of the residual protein from the nucleic acid moiety is important also for other reasons, viz. the preparations of nucleic acid which is completely protein-free. Several workers have shown that it is not easy to liberate deoxyribonucleic acid from the last trace of residual protein. It has been shown that the presence of a trace of the residual protein results in a high molecular weight, a higher viscosity, and in a lower solubility of the nucleic acid. In the presence of protein, a particle weight of 15 million was found for deoxyribonucleic acid by light scattering, while liberation of the protein by digestion with chymotrypsin resulted in a lower molecular weight of 6 million.[24] The latter value represents the now accepted molecular weight of deoxyribonucleic acid, as will be discussed in more detail in the next chapter.

[24] J. Hermans, Jr., *Biochim. Biophys. Acta* **32**, 504 (1959).

CHAPTER 19

THE NUCLEIC ACIDS

During the last few years deoxyribonucleic acids (DNA) have become one of the principal focal points in science. This is the result of increasingly convincing demonstrations that they are the chief carriers of genetic information and therefore hold within their structures blueprints of all the other cellular constituents.

P. Doty [1]

Apart from proteins and polysaccharides, the nucleic acids represent the third major class of natural organic macromolecules which are universally essential constituents of living organisms. Although the mass of protein in an animal body is much larger than that of the nucleic acids (and the same is true of the polysaccharide-nucleic acid ratio in plants), the nucleic acids have aroused interest because of their exceptionally important function as the carriers of genetic information.

There are two types of nucleic acids: the *ribonucleic acids* (*RNA*) and the *deoxyribonucleic acids* (*DNA*). In higher organisms, DNA's seem to be the carriers of genetic information on which depends the directive influences of the synthesis of enzymes and of the RNA's also, while the RNA's seem to participate in the protein synthesis more directly than the directing DNA. The DNA rests in the nucleus of the cell, whereas the major part of the RNA resides in the cytoplasm.

The gross chemical composition of all nucleic acids is very similar. They are built of the ordinary elements of the organic compounds (C, H, O, and N), and in addition to these they contain 8–10% of *phosphorus*. The nitrogen content is at the same level as in proteins (15–16%), but the great difference is that this nitrogen does not constitute amino acid residues — it is a part of *purine* and *pyrimidine* groups. These purine and pyrimidine residues constitute the *side groups* in the macromolecular chain, while the *backbone* of the chain is made up of *phosphate* and *pentose sugar* residues. Variation in the chain units occurs, first, by a possible change in the sugar unit. In RNA the sugar unit is α-D-*ribofuranose*, while in DNA it is α-D-2-*deoxyribofuranose*. The variability of the side groups is much smaller than in proteins, since only *six* different heterocyclic purine and pyrimidine bases have been found in the common well investigated nucleic acids: adenine, guanine, cytosine,

[1] P. Doty, *J. Cell. Comparat. Physiol.* (Symposium on Biocolloids), **49** (Suppl. 1), p. 27 (1957).

methylcytosine, thymine, and uracil. The RNA's contain adenine, guanine, cytosine, and uracil, the DNA's adenine, guanine, cytosine and methylcytosine, and thymine. The occurrence of several other sugar and heterocyclic base units is suspected in certain lower organisms.

The following general structural features are characteristic for these macromolecules: (1) the heterocyclic purine or pyrimidine groups are linked to the sugar by β-glucosidic linkages (from carbon-1 of the sugar to nitrogen of the base); (2) each phosphate links two sugar units, and the alternating phosphate–sugar units form the backbone of the chain. Since the phosphate–sugar bonds are ester linkages they can be hydrolyzed by strong acids, alkalies, or specific enzymes. The real "mer" of the macromolecule, which corresponds to the amino acid of proteins, in the nucleic acid is a *nucleotide,* composed of a heterocyclic base, a sugar, and a phosphate group. Many such nucleotides have been synthesized and found to be identical with some of the natural decomposition products of nucleic acids. Further hydrolysis can liberate the phosphate from the nucleotide, and one obtains a *nucleoside* composed only of the sugar and heterocyclic base. The literature concerning the chemistry and biochemistry of these nucleosides and nucleotides is quite voluminous, and excellent monographs and reviews are available for those who are interested in the details of this subject.[2,3] In a simplified way, the general structural features of the nucleic acid chain can be shown as follows:

$$-O-\overset{\overset{O}{\|}}{\underset{\underset{O_-}{|}}{P}}-O-\underset{\underset{\text{Base}}{|}}{\text{Sugar}}-O-\overset{\overset{O}{\|}}{\underset{\underset{O_-}{|}}{P}}-O-\underset{\underset{\text{Base}}{|}}{\text{Sugar}}-O-\overset{\overset{O}{\|}}{\underset{\underset{O_-}{|}}{P}}-O-\underset{\underset{\text{Base}}{|}}{\text{Sugar}}-O-\overset{\overset{O}{\|}}{\underset{\underset{O_-}{|}}{P}}-O-\underset{\underset{\text{Base}}{|}}{\text{Sugar}}-\cdots$$

The third acid function of the orthophosporic acid residue of the chain is free, and it confers acidic properties on the macromolecules. The protamines and histones are attached at the nucleic acids through salt bonds at these negatively charged sites of the acids. When the nucleoprotamine or nucleohistone is liberated from the basic protein component, the free nucleic acid precipitates, unless the protein cations are replaced by sodium or similar cations.

The nucleic acids are colorless substances having characteristic absorption maxima in the ultraviolet near 260 mμ. This absorption of ultraviolet light is a very important property, since the optical density of a preparation at the appropriate wavelength depends not only on concentration but also on the degree of degradation, as well as on the configuration of the macromolecular chains. Since proteins absorb much less light in this part of the spectrum, the optical density method is applied also for the detection of the nucleic acids in cells and tissues.

[2] E. Chargaff and J. N. Davidson (ed.), *The Nucleic Acids,* Vol. I, Academic Press, New York, 1955.

[3] G. R. Barker, *Adv. Carbohydr. Chem.* **11**, 285 (1956).

The Composition and Structure of Deoxyribonucleic Acids [2]

Deoxyribonucleic acids (DNA's) from various sources differ in the content of the purine and pyrimidine bases, i.e. in the *ratio* of the adenine to guanine or thymine to cytosine. Usually the sum of the adenine and thymine is divided by the sum of guanine and cytosine (+ 5-methyl-cytosine, if present), and the resulting quotient taken as the quantitative characteristic of the composition. The data on the nitrogeneous constituents are calculated per 100 g atoms of phosphorus, i.e. related to the P-content, and they usually are corrected for 100% recovery. Chromatographic analyses either on filter paper or columns are the established methods for the determination of the bases in the hydrolysates of DNA. In Table 42 are compiled some illustrative data which have been obtained by Chargaff *et al.*, Wyatt,[4] Hurst, Zamenhof, and others.[2]

TABLE 42

ADENINE (A), GUANINE (G), CYTOSINE (C) AND THYMINE (T) CONTENT IN DNA PREPARATIONS (in moles of base per 100 g atoms P, corrected for 100% recovery)

Source	Adenine	Guanine	Cytosine	Thymine	$\frac{A+T}{G+C}$
Man thymus	30·9	19·9	19·8	29·4	1·52
Man, liver	30·3	19·5	19·9	30·3	1·53
Man, sperm	30·9	19·1	18·4	31·6	1·67
Sheep, thymus	29·3	21·4	21·0	28·3	1·36
Sheep, liver	29·3	20·7	20·8	29·2	1·41
Sheep, spleen	28·0	22·3	21·1	28·6	1·30
Hen, erythrocytes	28·0	22·0	21·6	28·4	1·29
Salmon, sperm	29·7	20·8	20·4	29·1	1·43
Echinus escul., sperm	30·9	19·4	20·2 *	29·4	1·52
Echinocardium cordatum, sperm	32·9	17·0	17·9	32·2	1·86
Wheat germ	26·5	23·5	23·0 †	27·0	1·15
Yeast	31·3	18·7	17·1	32·9	1·79
E. coli (microbe)	25·4	24·1	25·7	24·8	1·01
Serratia marcescens (microbe)	20·7	27·2	31·9	20·1	0·69
Vaccinia virus	29·5	20·6	20·0	29·9	1·46

* This amount includes 1·8 moles methyl-cytosine.
† This figure includes 5·8 moles methyl-cytosine.

Inspection of Table 42 shows that there are certain differences in the DNA composition, especially in the lower species, although there is no simple relation between phylogenetic level of a species and the base ratios. Surprisingly simple general relations, however, emerge upon comparing the sum of the purine bases with that of the pyrimidine bases or the adenine/thymine and

[4] G. R. WYATT, *Biochem. J.* **48**, 584 (1951); G. R. WYATT and S. S. COHEN, *Biochem. J.* **55**, 774 (1953).

guanine/cytosine ratios. From 101 reliable entries, Chargaff comes to the following conclusions: [2]

(1) The sum of the purine nucleotides (containing adenine and guanine) equals the sum of pyrimidine nucleotides (cytosine, methylcytosine, and thymine);

(2) The molar ratio of adenine to thymine equals 1;

(3) The molar ratio of guanine to cytosine equals 1;

(4) The number of 6-amino groups equals the number of 6-keto groups. Statistical analysis has furnished the following numerical values:

Adenine/Thymine	1·009
Guanine/Cytosine (or analogs)	1·001
Purines/Pyrimidines	1·000
6-Amino/6-keto groups	1·008

This simple relation provides one of the strongest supports for the now generally accepted concept that the fibrous DNA unit is composed of two chains which are linked by hydrogen bonds between the base pairs, adenine-thymine and guanine-cytosine.[5,6] This is illustrated in the structural formula below, viz.:

```
        |
        |
        |
        O                                              CH3
        |                         H                    |
  O=P—OH                          |                    C
        |                         NH · · · · · OC/      \\CH
        O                         |                     |         |
        |                  N      C                     |         |
    5 CH2            //      \  /  \\                   |         |
        |           CH        C      N · · · HN         N—
    4 CH—O    1      |        ||     |            \CO/
        |     2 >CH—N————————C       CH          Thymine
    3 CH—CH2                   \   //
        |                        N
        O                    Adenine
        |
  O=P—OH
        |
        O
        |
       CH2
        |
       CH—O
        |     >CH—
       CH—CH2
        |
        O          Phosphate-pentose backbone
        |
        |
        |
```

[5] J. D. Watson and F. H. C. Crick, *Nature* **171**, 738 (1953).
[6] F. H. C. Crick and J. D. Watson, *Proc. Roy. Soc. A* **223**, 80 (1954).

The adenine residue which is linked to the backbone of the chain (on the left) is bound by hydrogen bonds to the thymine of an adjacent chain (not shown). The H-bonds are formed between the H of the adenine amino group and the carbonyl of the thymine, and the N of the adenine and H of the amino group of thymine. Thus each base pair is linked by a pair of hydrogen bonds. It must be emphasized that the vertically drawn phosphate-sugar chain of the macromolecule is very long, whereas the side chains form relatively short bridges between each pair of chains. The evidence that the chains are wound, i.e. are helical, will be discussed in the next section.

The chemical–structural studies on the DNA have always been hampered by the *fibrous* nature of the material, by its *inhomogeneity*, and difficulties in liberating the preparations from the last traces of protein. While the latter obstacle is more or less satisfactorily solved, e.g. by a mild treatment with proteolytic enzymes, certain salts, or detergents, the fibrous nature, large molecular size, and inhomogeneity are intrinsic properties of the DNA. The inhomogeneity has been amply demonstrated by various methods, such as fractionation by chromatography, electrophoresis, etc. For example, it was shown that the base composition of DNA's extracted by increasing salt concentrations from wheat germs depends on the salt concentration used in the extraction. The ratio of 5-methylcytosine to cytosine varies in the various fractions in a wide range.[(7)] Chargaff writes: "These findings, fully discussed in the publications cited above, suggest that the deoxypentose nucleic acid of a given cell is composed of a very large number of differently constituted individuals and that it is possible to achieve the resolution of this entire spectrum of structural gradations into several distinct 'bands', in which all the regularities characteristic of the entire nucleic acid are maintained".[(8)]

There is convincing evidence that the pentose is attached to the base at the carbon-1 of the pentose, and that the nucleotide is linked through 3',5'-phosphodiester bonds in the chain.[(9)] However, very little as yet is known about the *termination* of the chain and about the *sequence* of the nucleotides. "Strictly speaking, it cannot yet be asserted that the deoxypentose nucleic acids occur as open and not as closed chains. It is, however, probably too early to worry about the tail before we can describe the animal".[(8)] With respect to the nucleotide sequence, the first important contributions have been made within the last years.[(10)] The general approach is the same as in the instance of proteins: the macromolecules are partially degraded by either enzymes or acid, the degradation products are fractionated,

(7) R. Lipshitz and E. Chargaff, *Biochim. Biophys. Acta* **19**, 256 (1956).

(8) E. Chargaff, in *Fibrous Proteins and their Biological Significance* p. 32 (IX Symp. Soc. Exp. Biol.), Academic Press, New York, 1955; quoted from p. 47; see also: A. Bendich, J. R. Fresco, H. S. Rosenkranz and S. M. Beiser, *J. Amer. chem. Soc.* **77**, 3671 (1955).

(9) D. M. Brown and A. R. Todd, in E. Chargaff and J. N. Davidson, *The Nucleic Acids* Vol. I, p. 409, Academic Press, New York, 1955.

(10) H. S. Shapiro and E. Chargaff, *Biochim. Biophys. Acta* **26**, 608 (1957).

and their structure is determined. The first important studies which were made on the products obtained by enzymic degradation of DNA with deoxyribonuclease showed that the nucleotide sequence must be arrhythmic.[2] More recent work on the fragments obtained by degradation of various DNA preparations with acid has permitted more detailed conclusions. First, it could be shown that DNA preparations of different origin vary widely in those features of nucleotide sequence that are available for comparison. Second, at least 70% of the pyrimidine residues occur as *oligonucleotide tracts containing three or more pyrimidines in a row.* Third, the arrangement of constituents appears to be far from random. Thus, although there is not a simple perioditicty (e.g. of certain simple periodic appearance of a tetranucleotide), certain characteristic combinations, such as triplets of identical nucleotides, seem to be indicated.[10] Thus far mostly the pyrimidine nucleotides and diphosphates have been identified; because of the equality relationship, however, a triplet row of the purines must correspond to the rows of the pyrimidine bases.

The Size and Configuration of the Macromolecules of DNA [1,11]

The most straightforward evidence on the molecular size and shape of DNA has been furnished recently by electron microscopy.[12] The technique has been so much perfected that, at a magnification of over 100,000, not only the general rod-like shape but even the winding of the chains is more or less clearly discernable (see Fig. 34). There is no more doubt that the macromolecules of DNA are gently curved rods, and that the chains are helical. Their length is measured as 15,000–20,000 Å, i.e. 0·0015–0·002 mm, and their thickness (diameter of the rod) is only 15–20 Å. The rigidity of the units is in good agreement with evidence from other experimental data, such as viscosity, sedimentation, and light scattering.[12a] Also, the molecular weight which is calculated from sedimentation and viscosity, e.g. according to the equation of Mandelkern *et al.*,[13] agrees with the molecular weight obtained by the method of light scattering, and with the electron microscopic data. The molecular weights of native, undegraded DNA's lie between 4 and 8 million.[14,15]

The extreme molecular asymmetry results in such properties as extremely high viscosity in dilution as low as 0·02%, and tendency to gelation. Free DNA is insoluble in water because of the too strong interchain attraction,

[11] K. V. SHOOTER, *Progress in Biophys.* 8, 310 (1957).

[12] C. E. HALL and M. LITT, *J. Biochem. Biophys. Cytol.* 4, 1 (1958).

[12a] J. A. V. BUTLER, D. J. R. LAURENCE, A. B. ROBINS and K. V. SHOOTER, *Proc. Roy. Soc.* A **250**, 1 (1959).

[13] L. MANDELKERN, W. R. KRIGBAUM, H. A. SCHERAGA and P. J. FLORY, *J. chem. Physics* **20**, 1392 (1952).

[14] M. E. REICHMANN, S. A. RICE, C. A. THOMAS and P. DOTY, *J. Amer. chem. Soc.* **76**, 3047 (1954).

[15] P. DOTY, B. BUNCE MCGILL and S. A. RICE, *Proc. Nat. Acad. Sci.* **44**, 432 (1958).

and dissolution is possible only after neutralization of the acid groups, due to mutual repulsion of the negatively charged chains. Such a solution may contain macromolecular aggregates which are not fully dissolved, if the specimen is not stirred long enough or if the pH of the solution is not high enough. Even diluted solutions of sodium deoxyribonucleate (or any other salt of DNA) exhibit anomalies of flow, i.e. the viscosity depends on the flow gradient (see chapt. 4), and it is suggested that the viscosity be measured at various rates of flow, and extrapolated to zero gradient. The intrinsic viscosity of DNA preparations in nearly neutral solutions is found to be 40–80 dl/g, and it is not very much influenced by electrolytes. This is contrary to the usual behavior of linear polyelectrolytes which have flexible macromolecules, and it indicates that the DNA particles in solution are rigid.[16]

In a very important recent paper Doty *et al.* [15] showed that the macromolecules of DNA could be broken down to shorter fragments. Light scattering, viscosity, and sedimentation studies on a progressively degraded series of such fragments enabled correlation of the molecular weight with intrinsic viscosity or sedimentation constant by means of simple expressions. The data are compiled in Table 43.

TABLE 43
MOLECULAR CONSTANTS FOR SONIC FRAGMENTS OF DNA
(after Doty *et al.* [15])

Time of irradiation (minutes)	Molecular weight	Sedim. constant $s^0_{20,w}$ (S)	Intrinsic viscosity (dl/g)	Radius of gyration (A)
0	7,400,000	22·0	69	2500
1	3,400,000	12·2	37·3	1700
5	700,000	9·0	5·35	650
20	450,000	7·7	3·12	540
60	300,00	6·9	1·77	380

The sedimentation constant $s^0_{20,w}$ and the intrinsic viscosity $|\eta|$ can be correlated to the weight average molecular weight of the units of DNA by the following equations: [15]

$$s^0_{20,w} = 0{\cdot}063\, M_w^{0.37},$$

$$|\eta| = 1{\cdot}45 \cdot 10^{-6}\, M_w^{1.2}.$$

The last equation is especially important, since it enables computation of the weight average molecular weight of DNA by the very simple and convenient viscosimetric method (chapt. 4). In order to obtain comparable results, the DNA specimens must be free of protein, and they must be in the native state. Furthermore, the DNA must be completely dissolved, and it must be in a highly diluted solution of 0·003–0·02 g/dl. The dependence of

[16] B. E. CONWAY and J. A. BUTLER, *J. Polymer Sci.* **12**, 199 (1954).

the viscosity on the flow gradient is especially pronounced in the instance of the very long undegraded macromolecules, when extrapolation to zero gradient renders the most accurate results for the intrinsic viscosity. The intrinsic viscosity–molecular weight relation of Doty *et al.* was applied in our laboratory for the molecular weight determination of several DNA specimens. One of them yielded a molecular weight of 5·7 million, whereby the intrinsic viscosity was not extrapolated to zero gradient which would give an even higher value. A commercial DNA sample was less viscous and showed, according to this relation, a $M = 1{\cdot}2$ million.

Denaturation of DNA has been studied by many authors in various laboratories but the results are far from being consistent.[17,18,19] According to one of the most recent reports of Ehrlich and Doty,[20] in which earlier work is also summarized, denaturation by alkali or heating of an acid solution results in a considerable contraction of the macromolecules without a change in the molecular weight. For example, upon gradual addition of alkali, the viscosity remains constant up to pH 11·5, but on further increase of the alkalinity the viscosity drops sharply. Since molecular weight determinations by light scattering yielded the same molecular weight as that of the native DNA, it was concluded that the denaturation results in the *collapse* of the very extended double-stranded configuration. According to Doty, a large portion of the hydrogen bonds which are responsible for the native configuration are broken because of the very strong electrostatic interchain repulsion. Furthermore, it is assumed that the chains are not completely separated but that they become entangled forming a more symmetrical coil than the gently curved rods of the native DNA. A similar process supposedly occurs in heat denaturation when the chains are loosened by the thermal impacts, and then rearrange into the more disordered configurations of lesser asymmetry. Thus denaturation of the DNA results in effects which are opposite to those observed in denaturation of globular proteins (see chapt. 12). It must, however, be pointed out that the interpretation of the denaturation of DNA is still subject to doubt mostly because of the fact that the sedimentation constant did not change upon denaturation.[20] The same value of 22 S units was found for the native DNA ($M = 5{\cdot}1$ million, pH 7, ionic strength 0·165) and for alkali denatured DNA, while the intrinsic viscosity dropped from 56 to 6·1 dl/g. The change from a highly extended to more compact configuration certainly should be accompanied by an increase of the sedimentation constant, if the molecular weight remains the same. This discord throws doubt on the whole concept of the configuration of DNA in diluted solutions, and the subject has been treated extensively by Geiduschek and Holtzer in

(17) P. ALEXANDER and K. A. STACEY, *Biochem. J.* **60**, 194 (1955).

(18) S. A. RICE and P. DOTY, *J. Amer. chem. Soc.* **79**, 3937 (1957).

(19) E. P. GEIDUSCHEK and A. HOLTZER, in *Advances in Biological and Medical Physics* Vol. VI, p. 431ff., Academic Press, New York, 1958.

(20) P. EHRLICH and P. DOTY, *J. Amer. chem. Soc.* **80**, 4251 (1958).

a careful analysis of the light scattering data.[19] They arrive at the following conclusion: "An attempt has been made to justify the opinion that, contrary to popular belief, this body of data does not provide unambiguous evidence for the existence of a hydrogen-bonded, base-paired stabilization of the native structure of DNA. It has been pointed out that the phenomena usually interpreted in terms of hydrogen-bond breakage are in fact capable of alternative interpretations. In addition, some data have been presented which are difficult to reconcile qualitatively with a pure and simple hydrogen bond model. It is recognized nowadays that the solvent medium may radically affect the stability of hydrogen bonds and that in a molecule of the structural complexity of DNA, other stabilizing and unstabilizing factors must clearly be present" (p. 411, ref. 19). While the double stranded H-bonded configuration is quite probable in the paracrystalline preparations of DNA, and may be even in the chromosomes of living cells, the importance of the hydrogen bonds for the stabilization of the configurations in the highly diluted aqueous solutions is subject to doubt. This is the same situation as with the proteins in which *the configuration definitely is not due solely to the hydrogen bonds*, because of the competitive effects of the water (chapt. 12). It seems likely that the *cohesive forces* between the purine and pyrimidine residues along the chain may contribute considerably to the configurational stability, especially in certain spatially favorable arrangements. It is possible that new and interesting information about this could be obtained by further study of the ultraviolet absorption, infrared spectra, and optical rotation of the DNA solutions and gels. The possibility of a few covalent bonds between the two chains also should not be discarded, especially because of the fact that a complete separation of the two chains has never been achieved. If such bonds could be proved, the double-chain DNA would have earned the undisputable right to be called a real macromolecule. On the basis of the presently available evidence, however, the chemical molecular weight of DNA remains more or less uncertain. More uncertainty is introduced by the indications of some authors that the chains at certain points may be interrupted,[21] and that the unit at certain points might be more easily breakable than in others. Further interesting discussion on this topic can be found in reviews.[11,22]

Studies on the paracrystalline fibers of DNA, chiefly by means of *X*-ray diffraction, actually provided the experimental basis for the Watson–Crick double helix of DNA.[5,6] Extensive *X*-ray diffraction studies have been made not only on various specimens of DNA but also on nucleoproteins, and the interpretation has led to the conclusion that the configuration of the DNA of

[21] C. A. Dekker and H. K. Schachman, *Proc. Nat. Acad. Sci.* **40**, 894 (1954); A. R. Peacocke and H. K. Schachman, *Biochim. Biophys. Acta* **15**, 198 (1954); V. N. Schumaker, E. G. Richards and H. K. Schachman, *J. Amer. chem. Soc.* **78**, 4230 (1956).

[22] S. Zamenhof, *Progress in Biophys. and Biophys. Chem.* **6**, 85 (1956); R. L. Sinsheimer, in *A Symposium on Molecular Biology* p. 16 (R. E. Zirkle, ed.), Univ. of Chicago Press, Chicago, 1959.

the various specimens is very similar, and that a similar spectrum is observed also with the nucleoprotein specimens. Although the number and sharp-

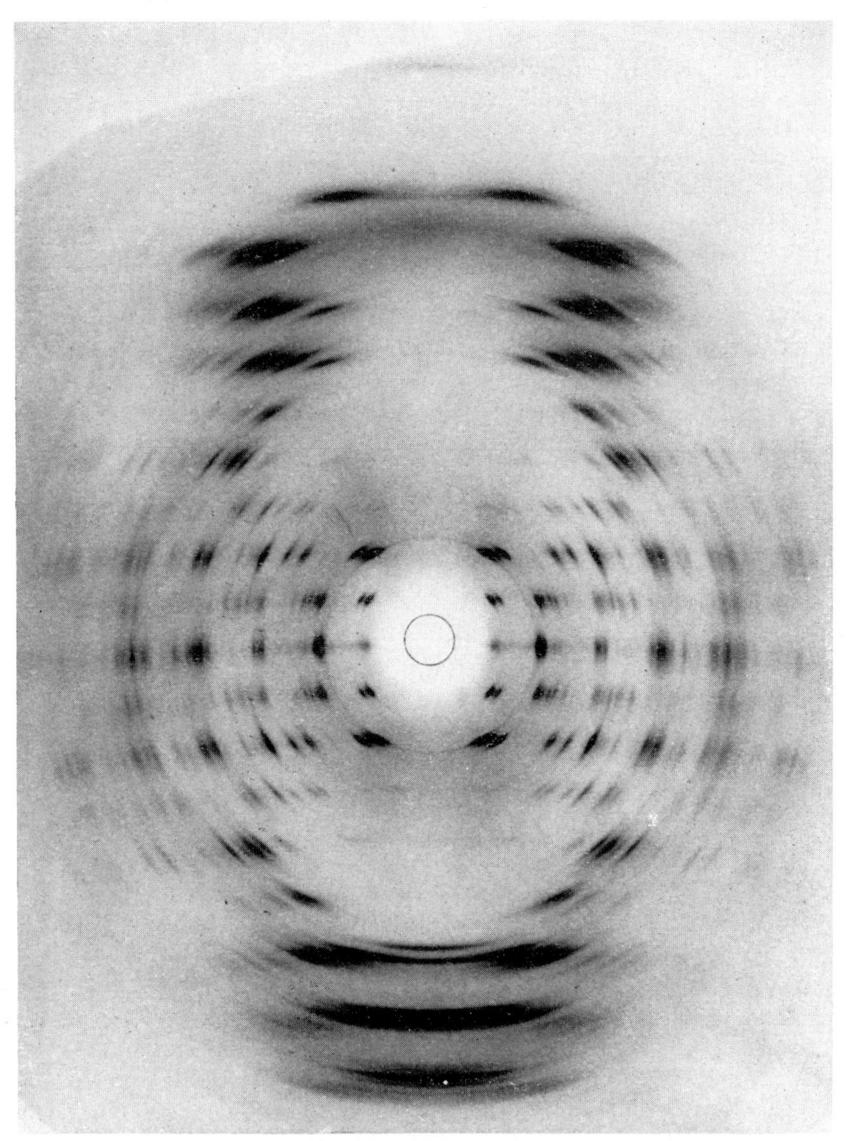

Fig. 77. *X*-ray diffraction pattern of deoxyribonucleic acid (by *Courtesy* of Dr. M. F. H. Wilkins, King's College, London)

ness of the spots and arcs depends on the condition of the preparation, e.g. the moisture content and presence of protein, the basic structural features, according to the X-ray data, are the same. The major reflections can be reasonably well accounted for from the Watson–Crick double helix. An example

FIG. 78. The double-helical model of the DNA macromolecule, according to Watson and Crick (by *Courtesy* of Dr. M. F. H. Wilkins)

of a good X-ray diffraction spectrum of DNA in shown in Fig. 77, and a photograph of the double helical model is presented in Fig. 78. Most of the X-ray diffraction work has been done by Franklin and Gosling,[23] as well as by Wilkins *et al.*.[24,25] While the *X*-ray diffraction studies thus support the concept of the double helix, they are unable to provide more detailed information, e.g. on the sequence of the nucleotides or about the attachment of the protein component to the DNA.

In conclusion it can be said that, while the general configuration, size (physical molecular weight), and shape of the DNA's are well established, the details in both the nucleotide sequence and spatial configuration of the macromolecule remain obscure. The important question — is the DNA in a living cell identical with the objects observed under the electron microscope, or measured in solutions — also has not been answered as yet. It is quite possible that at least some of the polydispersity of isolated DNA is due to the effects of treatment during isolation, while the structural inhomogeneity may be inherent to the native DNA. Also it is safe to assume that the molecular configuration of the DNA in a cell nucleus is not exactly the same as in an isolated dried DNA fiber, or in a dilute sodium deoxyribonucleate solution.

The Ribonucleic Acids (RNA's) [2,26,27]

Ribonucleic acid (RNA) differs from deoxyribonucleic acid (DNA) in chemical composition, structure, and configuration. Chemically the backbone of the RNA chain is similar to the DNA chain: in both the sugar units alternate with the phosphate residues, and in both the groups are linked by 3′,5′-phosphodiester bonds. However, the RNA chain contains *ribose* residues instead of deoxyribose of the DNA, viz. one of the hydrogen atoms at carbon-2 in the deoxyribose residue of DNA is in RNA replaced by OH. In both RNA and DNA the heterocyclic purine and pyrimidine bases are linked to the carbon-1 of the sugar; and with respect to base composition, RNA differs from DNA in that the former contains *uracil* instead of thymine. While in the DNA's the purine/pyrimidine ratio is 1·00, in many RNA's this ratio differs considerably from 1·00. The RNA's from various sources differ greatly in the base ratios, so that it is more correct to use the term in plural than in the singular. The greatest variation in the base ratios has been found in the RNA's which have been isolated from various viruses and bacteriophages.

[23] R. E. FRANKLIN and R. G. GOSLING, *Nature* **171**, 740 (1953); *Acta Cryst.* **6**, 673, 678 (1953); **8**, 1651 (1955).

[24] M. F. H. WILKINS, A. R. STOKES and H. R. WILSON, *Nature* **171**, 738 (1953). M. F. H. WILKINS, W. E. SEEDS, A. R. STOKES and H. R. WILSON, *Nature* **172**, 759 (1953).

[25] M. F. H. WILKINS, *Cold Spring Harbor Symp. Quant. Biol.* **21**, 75 (1956); L. D. HAMILTON, R. K. BARKLEY, M. H. F. WILKINS, G. L. BROWN, H. R. WILSON, D. A. MARVIN, H. EPHRUSSI-TAYLOR and N. S. SIMMONS, *J. Biophys. Biochem. Cytol.* **5**, 397 (1959).

[26] D. M. BROWN and A. R. TODD, *Ann. Rev. Biochem.* **24**, 311 (1955).

[27] W. E. COHN and E. VOLKIN, *Ann. Rev. Biochem.* **26**, 491 (1957).

A dry specimen of an ordinary RNA is a white powder, whereas an undegraded DNA is a fibrous material which is so tough that scissors are required for fragmentation. The RNA is much more readily soluble than DNA, and the solutions of RNA are much less viscous than those of the DNA salts. All this indicates that the RNA chains in solution are *coiled up*, a fact which is in accord with other physicochemical evidence that the RNA particles in solution are *single-chain* units.[27a]

Separation, isolation, and fractionation of cellular fragments has shown that most of the RNA-containing nucleoprotein resides in the cytoplasm. The separation of the RNA-nucleoprotein from the DNA-nucleoprotein is based on the fact that the particles of the former are smaller and more soluble than the latter. According to one of the most applied methods,[28] the RNA-rich microsomal fraction of the tissue is first separated by differential centrifugation, and the RNA is liberated from the protein and other contaminants by phenol. Further purification is accomplished by precipitation with 1 N sodium chloride at 4 °C, and redissolving in a 0·02 M phosphate buffer of pH 7. The macromolecular properties of microsomal RNA have been investigated recently in two laboratories: in Doty's laboratory at Harvard University and in Schramm's laboratory in Tübingen. According to Hall and Doty,[29] the RNA isolated from the microsomal particles of calf liver has two components, the one with 28 S and another with 18 S, when examined in 0·02 M phosphate buffer. The intrinsic viscosity was found to be 0·37 dl/g. From these data, the molecular weight for the heavier component would be approximately 1,300,000, and for the lighter component 600,000. According to Gierer,[30] the RNA from rat liver had a heavy component of $M = 1{,}800{,}000$ and a lighter component of $M{=}600{,}000$. Similar RNA's were isolated also from plant leaves, while the RNA from tobacco mosaic virus was found to possess a physical molecular weight of about 2,000,000.[31,32] The intrinsic viscosity of the solution of this heavy component was calculated to be 2·00 dl/g. Kinetic studies on the enzymic degradation of this RNA with ribonuclease have supported the view that the tobacco mosaic virus RNA is a single-chain macromolecule.[31] The chemical molecular weight, however, is not established; thus, it is still uncertain whether the larger units are the real native macromolecules and the smaller components degradation products or that the larger particles are aggregates of the smaller units which then could be the macromolecules. Gierer has presented evidence that in the instance of the tobacco mosaic virus the biologically active infective unit has a molecular

[27a] U. Z. Littauer and H. Eisenberg, *Biochim. Biophys. Acta* **32**, 320 (1959).

[28] J. W. Littlefield, E. B. Keller, J. Gross and P. C. Zamecnik, *J. biol. Chem.* **217**, 111 (1955).

[29] B. D. Hall and P. Doty, in *Microsomal Particles and Protein Synthesis* p. 27. (R. B. Roberts, ed.), Pergamon Press, New York, London, 1958.

[30] A. Gierer, *Z. Naturforsch.* **13 b**, 788 (1958).

[31] A. Gierer, *Z. Naturforsch.* **13 b**, 477 (1958).

[32] H. Boedtker, *Biochim. Biophys. Acta* **32**, 519 (1959).

weight of 2,000,000.[33] The smaller components in this preparation then would be degradation products. The large 2 million unit is composed of about 6000 nucleotides, and it is possible, although not yet decisively proved, that this particle is a macromolecule. In the instance of microsomal RNA's the situation is more obscure. Heating of these RNA solutions to 85° and returning to room temperature resulted in a single boundary sedimentation pattern, and a sedimentation constant of 8·2 S was estimated from these data. This, combined with the intrinsic viscosity of 0·22 dl/g of the solution, yielded a molecular weight of about 120,000.[34] Since it is doubtful that heating of a neutral solution to 85° could cause hydrolytic degradation, and since the $M = 120,000$ RNA was homogeneous, it seems probable that these smaller units of the microsomal RNA could be the real macromolecules.

The differences between DNA and RNA with respect to molecular shape and configuration are illustrated best by the difference in the intrinsic viscosity of their solutions. The intrinsic viscosity of native undegraded DNA is 40–80 dl/g, whereas that of an undegraded and undenatured RNA is only 0·3–2·0. This indicates that the RNA particles in solution must be much more compact than the DNA units. The single chain configuration of the RNA permits folding, and Doty *et al.* have arrived at the conclusion that the microsomal RNA chains are not only folded but that the folded chain configuration is stabilized by intrachain hydrogen bonds between certain base pairs of the chain. Their conclusions are supported by optical density and optical rotation measurements which can be interpreted in favor of such concept. It is also assumed that certain sections of the RNA chain have a helical configuration.[35] The drop of the specific rotation from $+300°$ to about $+20°$ on heating is interpreted as disorganization of the helical sections.[34] While the relatively compact configuration and folding of the RNA chains is undisputable, the reasons for this folding are not altogether clear. The significance of the H-bonding is disputable for the reasons mentioned in the previous section. The optical density and specific rotation changes on heating also may be interpreted differently. Gierer found that the specific rotation of tobacco mosaic virus RNA drops from $+180°$ to $+20°$ on enzymic degradation with ribonuclease, and this indicates that the configuration of the macromolecule contributes to the rotation.[31] The folding of the chain definitely is expressed in the optical rotation and optical density, but the relations are not simple. The finding of Gierer points to the possibility that the optical rotation change is due to the disruption of the folds rather than to the disorganization of the short helical sections in the folds.[35a]

[33] A. GIERER, *Z. Naturforsch.* **13 b**, 485 (1958).

[34] P. DOTY, H. BOEDTKER, J. R. FRESCO, B. D. HALL and R. HASELKORN, (a private communication).

[35] P. DOTY, H. BOEDTKER, J. R. FRESCO, R. HASELKORN and M. LITT, *Proc. Nat. Acad. Sci.* **45**, 482 (1959).

[35a] J. P. HUMMEL and G. KALNITSKY, *J. biol. Chem.* **243**, 1517 (1959).

A certain *variety* in the configuration of the RNA's from various sources must be considered.[35b] The ordinary folded configuration can be contrasted to the extended configuration of the RNA as found in the tobacco mosaic virus particles (see the next chapter). It is also obvious that the rod-shaped cores of the tobacco masaic virus particles, as observed in the electron microscope, should produce a much higher viscosity, if this extended configuration prevailed in solution. On the other hand, it is impossible to say that the RNA in the microsomes has the same folded chain configuration as is observed in the solutions of isolated RNA or — more accurately — of the salts of the isolated RNA. It is more likely that, in order to accomplish its metabolic functions most efficiently, the macromolecules should be unfolded.

Further studies on the RNA's will involve such important problems as the nucleotide sequence, and possible relations between the composition, sequence, and configuration. In this connection, it is interesting to recall the fact that the purine/pyrimidine ratio in the extended tobacco mosaic virus RNA is 1·23, whereas in the spherical turnip yellow mosaic virus the ratio is 0·66. A generalization, however, is impossible, since other globular viruses contain RNA's with base ratios closer to that of the tobacco virus than to the turnip virus. The nucleotide sequences are very little elucidated, and there is no doubt that further chemical studies on the sequence will throw light also on the unsolved problems of chain configuration.

Some Uncommon Nucleic Acids and Nucleoproteins

It is noteworthy that uncommon constituents in proteins and nucleic acids have been found only in the macromolecules of lower species, e.g. 5-hydroxymethyl cytosine can replace cytosine in certain phages; and 5-bromo- or 5-iodouracil may take the place of thymine (Chargaff, p. 370 of ref. 2).

Uncommon intermediates between the DNA's and RNA's also have been found, for example, isolation of a *single-strand DNA* from certain phages has been reported recently.[36] Chemical analysis of the constituents showed that this nucleic acid is a DNA, although the adenine/thymine and guanine/cytosine ratios differed from 1·0 significantly. Light scattering studies indicated a particle weight of 1,700,000, and the presence of flexible chains. Kinetic experiments on degradation by deoxyribonuclease also prompted the same conclusion, viz. that the degraded units are single-chain macromolecules, resembling those of the common RNA's. Thus chemically this nucleic acid resembles DNA and configurationally the RNA. Since only the base ratios differ from the strict 1·00 ratio of the ordinary DNA, it seems likely that this *base ratio* might be one important factor in influencing the configuration, However, it is also obvious that this cannot be the only factor, since the

(35b) See for instance E. Haschemeyer, B. Singer and H. Fraenkel-Conrat, *Proc. Nat. Acad. Sci.* **45**, 313 (1959).

(36) R. L. Sinsheimer, *J. Mol. Biol.* **1**, 43 (1959).

configuration must depend also on such factors as the nucleotide *sequence*, and the *interaction with the medium* in which the chains are placed.

From the biological point of view even more uncommon, i.e. unnatural, are the *polynucleotides* which can be enzymically synthesized from adenosine diphosphate and similar starting materials.(37) For example, a poly-adenylic acid of $M_w = 680{,}000$ has been prepared, and it was demonstrated that the macromolecules in solution behaved like flexible coils.(38) Particles resembling the DNA could be prepared by mixing an adenine polynucleotide with a uridine polynucleotide.(39) The viscosity thereby increased strongly, and the fibers drawn from the viscous mixture exhibited X-ray patterns which indicated the presence of a double-helical configuration.(40) These experiments show that two flexible polynucleotide chains indeed can wind around each other thus forming double-strand configurations. Detailed physico-chemical studies on these synthetic polynucleotides have been made by Doty *et al.*.(35,41) The enzymic synthesis of DNA will be discussed in chapt. 22 and 25.

A crystallized nucleotropomyosin can be mentioned as an instance of a very curious and uncommon nucleoprotein. This nucleotropomyosin was isolated by Hamoir from carp muscle,(42) and it contains a tropomyosin component and 10–20% of ribonucleic acid. It is possible that this nucleoprotein is an artifact formed by combining the cellular RNA with the protein during the course of isolation.

(37) M. Grunberg-Manago and S. Ochoa, *J. Amer. chem. Soc.* **77**, 3165 (1955); M. Grunberg-Manago, M. Ortiz and S. Ochoa, *Biochim. Biophys. Acta* **20**, 269 (1956).
(38) R. F. Steiner, *J. Polymer Sci.* **30**, 17 (1958).
(39) A. Rich and D. R. Davies, *J. Amer. chem. Soc.* **78**, 3548 (1956).
(40) R. C. Warner, *J. biol. Chem.* **229**, 711 (1957).
(41) J. R. Fresco and P. Doty, *J. Amer. chem. Soc.* **79**, 3928 (1957).
(42) G. Hamoir, *Biochem. J.* **48**, 146 (1951); *Adv. Protein Chem.* **10**, 227 (1955).

PART III

CHAPTER 20

VIRUSES AND PHAGES

At the present time, one can only conclude from all this work that the nucleic acid of each strain has the ability to provoke the synthesis, within the host cell, of new virus protein very similar to, if not identical with, its own homologous protein; and that it retains this ability even when packaged, in vitro, in the protein of another strain.

H. Fraenkel-Conrat and B. Singer [1]

In the last few decades, virus research has been so prolific and has contributed so many important results that its representatives can be justified in considering it as a special science of virology. According to Luria: "Viruses are submicrocsopic entities, capable of being introduced into specific living cells and of reproducing inside such cells only".[2] The literature on viruses is quite extensive involving their physical, chemical, and biological aspects, as well as various practical applications in such fields as agriculture and medicine, and comprehensive handbooks are available.[3] We shall be concerned in this chapter chiefly about the chemical and physicochemical aspects of the subject.

Formerly viruses were classified according to the diseases they cause in animals or plants, and thus all viruses can be classified in animal and plant viruses; a third class comprises the phages, the viruses which invade and destroy bacteria, streptomyces, and similar organisms. On the basis of the modern virus research, a more rational classification is possible with respect to size, shape, chemical composition, and internal structure of the entities. "The largest of the objects properly called viruses are about 300 mμ in diameter, while the smallest yet observed are about one-fifteenth that size. Although detailed variations in morphology are numerous, it appears likely that all viruses fit into a classification of shapes roughly described as spheres, rods, ellipsoids, and sperm-like forms. The largest viruses are nonuniform in size and appear to have a complex structure involving an outer membrane, a less dense peripheral region, and a dense core. The smaller viruses are distinguished, generally, by an electron microscopic appearance of internal homogeneity

(1) H. Fraenkel-Conrat and B. Singer, *Biochim. Biophys. Acta* **24**, 540 (1957); p. 547.

(2) S. E. Luria, *General Virology* p. 2. Wiley, New York, 1953.

(3) F. M. Burnet and W. M. Stanley (ed.), *The Viruses*, Vol. I, II, and III, Academic Press, New York, 1959.

and of complete uniformity of size and shape".[4] The plant viruses generally are simpler than the animal viruses, while the bacteriophages may be morphologically more complex than the plant viruses. From the chemical point of view, some plant viruses are *nucleoproteins*, while the animal viruses contain lipid, in addition to the nucleoprotein, and some other ingredients. Both DNA and RNA are encountered in viruses, and the protein component differs strongly from the histones and protamines of the usual nucleoproteins (chapt. 18).

According to their dimensions, the viruses are colloids, and the early studies on the nature of viruses have been done chiefly by such colloid-chemical methods as ultrafiltration, high-speed centrifugation, etc. (see chapt. 2 and 3). Most of these early findings about the size and shape of viruses were confirmed later by electron microscopy, light scattering, and other methods.[5,6,7,8]

It has been established that the nucleic acid represents the core of a virus and that this core is covered by a coat of protein. In contrast to the ordinary nucleoproteins which are composed of approximately equal portions of nucleic acid and protein, the viruses contain more protein than nucleic acid. "It is rather striking that the absolute content of RNA, for both the rod-shaped and the spherical viruses, varies over rather narrow limits compared with the highly varying amount of protein. Almost all these small viruses contain between 3000 and 7500 nucleotides and we wonder whether there may be an effective lower limit to the size of a virus corresponding to the amount necessary to make a moderately sized protein molecule".[9] It is established that the nucleic acid determines the properties of the protein coat which is synthesized upon the multiplication of the virus in a host.

Some of the most important physical and chemical characteristics of a few representative viruses are compiled in Table 44.

As mentioned before, the amount of the nucleotides in the various plant and animal viruses is surprisingly constant in comparison with the very large variation of the protein content. It is also conspicuous that the nucleic acid and protein ratio depends also on the shape of the virus: the asymmetric viruses contain more protein than the globular viruses. If one assumes that the nucleic acid core must be covered with a protein coat of certain thickness, these facts are comprehensible by purely geometric reasons, viz. an unfolded linear core has a larger surface than a globular core and thus the former needs more protein for coating than the latter.

[4] R. C. Williams, in *The Nature of Viruses* p. 19 (CIBA Found. Symp.) G. E. Wolstenholme and E. C. P. Millar, ed.), Little, Brown, Boston, 1957.

[5] E. C. Pollard, *The Physics of Viruses* Academic Press, New York, 1953.

[6] M. A. Lauffer, W. C. Prince and A. W. Petre, *Adv. Enzymol.* **9**, 171 (1949).

[7] R. W. G. Wyckoff, *Adv. Protein Chem.* **6**, 1 (1951).

[8] R. C. Williams, *Adv. Virus Res.* **2**, 183 (1954).

[9] F. H. C. Crick and J. D. Watson, in *The Nature of Viruses* p. 5, quoted from p. 12 (CIBA Found. Symp.), Little, Brown, Boston, 1957.

TABLE 44

PARTICLE SIZE * AND COMPOSITION* OF SOME VIRUSES
(data chiefly from l.c. 9)

	Dimensions (mμ)	Particle weight × 10^6	% Nucleic (RNA)	% Protein	Nucleotides per particle	Amino acids per particle
Tobacco mosaic virus	300×15 rod	40	6	94	7300	340,000
Potato virus X	300×15† filaments	30–35	6	94	5400	260,000
Bushy stunt virus	300	9	16	84	4400	69,000
Turnip yellow mosaic virus	20	5	40	60	6000	27,000
Southern bean mosaic virus	25	6	21	79	3800	43,000
Tobacco ringspot virus	19	6	40	60	7300	33,000
Tobacco necrosis virus	17	6	18	82	3300	45,000
Poliomyelitis virus	27	6–7	22	76	7000	69,000
Influenza virus **	100	100	2	75	6000	680,000
Fowl plague virus **	100	100	2	75	6000	680,000

* The figures are only approximate.
† The length of the filaments varies considerably.
** These viruses contain lipids and may contain material from host cells.

Some Simple Nucleoprotein Viruses [3,10]

Several of the simple plant viruses were isolated in pure state and crystallized in the thirties by Stanley, Bawden, Pirie, Markham, and others. *Tobacco mosaic virus* was isolated from virus infected leaves which were frozen, pulverised while still frozen, and extracted with sodium phosphate solution. The virus then was thrown down by centrifuging in a preparative ultracentrifuge at 30,000 rev/min dissolved again in a phosphate buffer of pH 7, and liberated from coarse impurities by low-speed centrifugation. The supernatant is centrifuged again in the refrigerated ultracentrifuge, and the high and low speed centrifugation is repeated several times. A pure solution is thus obtained from which the virus can be crystallized.[11] Physicochemical and chemical studies showed that the tobacco mosaic virus particles are stiff rods about 250–300 mμ long and 15 mμ in diameter, that they are composed of a RNA core and a protein coat. Let us consider first the RNA core. Detailed analyses of the nucleotide composition of the RNA, that was obtained from various strains of tobacco mosaic virus (TMV), indicated that the composition is identical. However, the nucleotide composition of several other RNA viruses

(10) R. MARKHAM and J. D. SMITH, in *The Proteins* Vol. II A, p. 1ff. (H. NEURATH and K. BAILEY, ed.), Academic Press, New York, 1954.
(11) W. M. STANLEY, *Science* **81**, 644 (1935).

was found to differ strongly from that of the TMV. The analytical data are presented in Table 45.

TABLE 45

NUCLEOTIDE COMPOSITION OF RNA'S ISOLATED FROM PLANT VIRUSES [12]

Virus	Strain	Adenylic nucleotide	Guanylic nucleotide	Cytidylic nucleotide	Uridylic nucleotide	Pu/Py
Tobacco mosaic	TMV	10	8·5	6·2	8·8	1·24
Do	M	10	8·9	6·5	8·8	1·23
Do	J 14 D 1	10	8·4	6·2	8·9	1·22
Do	GA	10	8·9	6·6	8·9	1·22
Do	YA	10	8·6	6·2	8·9	1·23
Do	HR	10	8·8	6·2	9·2	1·22
Cucumber	CV 3	10	9·9	7·1	11·9	1·05
Do	CV 4	10	10	7·5	11·5	1·05
Tomato bushy stunt	BS	10	10	7·4	8·9	1·23
Turnip yellow mosaic	TY	10	7·6	16·8	9·8	0·66
Southern bean mosaic	SBM	10	10	8·9	9·8	1·07
Potato X	PX	10	6·2	6·6	6·2	1·27

It is established that the purine/pyrimidine ratio in most cases is not 1·00, although in the cucumber virus and southern bean virus the ratio is very close to unity. Also the adenine/guanine 1 : 1 ratio in three of the mentioned twelve instances, and the guanine/uridine 1 : 1 ratio in the TMV strains seems to indicate certain regularities in the RNA chains.

The protein component has been thoroughly studied especially of the TMV and HR strains,[1] and the data are presented in Table 46. While the RNA component has been proved to determine the type of protein synthesized around it in the host, the protein determines the immunochemical properties. Quite sensational, of course, was the demonstration of Fraenkel-Conrat and Williams [13] that the TMV can be separated in the nucleic acid and protein components (by a treatment with alkali or detergent), and that biologically active particles of the virus can be *reconstituted* from the components. This then permitted the *combination* of the RNA of one virus strain with the protein of another strain, and the demonstration of the directive effect of the RNA. Table 46 not only illustrates the difference in amino acid composition between the TMV and HR strains but also delivers the decisive proof that the *protein synthesis is determined by the RNA*. This may seem somewhat surprising in view of the fact that the nucleotide composition of the RNA's of both TMV and HR (see Table 45) is similar. This leads to the conclusion

[12] B. MAGASANIK in E. CHARGAFF and J. N. DAVIDSON, *The Nucleic Acids* Vol. I, p. 373, Academic Press, 1955; the data are chiefly from the work of MARKHAM, SMITH, and KNIGHT.

[13] H. FRAENKEL-CONRAT and R. C. WILLIAMS, *Proc. Nat. Acad. Sci.* **41**, 690 (1955); H. FRAENKEL-CONRAT, *J. Amer. chem. Soc.* **78**, 882 (1956).

that the directive effects of the RNA are due not to the composition but to the *nucleotide sequence* which probably is different in the RNA's of the two strains. A direct proof of this, however, is lacking.

TABLE 46
COMPARISON OF AMINO ACID COMPOSITION OF HR AND TMV PROTEINS AND THE PROGENY OF RECONSTITUTED VIRUSES
(according to Fraenkel-Conrat and Singer, l.c. 1; all values expressed as grams of amino acid per 100 g virus)

	I HR	II Progeny of HR/TMV	III TMV	IV Progeny of TMV/HR	V Mutant strain from TMV-nucleic acid
Glycine	1·6	1·8	2·3	2·3	2·5
Alanine	8·5	8·5	6·5	6·9	5·5
Valine	5·9	6·3	9·6	9·0	9·6
Leucine + iso-leucine	12·2	12·2	14·2	14·3	13·0
Proline	5·0	5·1	5·0	5·1	4·3
Serine	8·1	8·1	9·0	8·8	7·8
Threonine	7·2	7·5	8·9	8·9	8·8
Lysine	2·4	2·3	1·9	1·8	2·1
Arginine	8·9	8·5	9·5	9·7	7·6
Histidine	0·70	0·70	0	0	0
Phenylalanine	5·3	5·4	7·2	7·1	6·8
Tyrosine	6·3	6·2	4·1	4·3	5·4
Tryptophan	2·2	2·2	2·8	2·6	2·7
Methionine	2·0	2·2	0	0	0·6
Glutamic acid	16·4	17·3	12·4	12·1	12·4
Aspartic acid	15·0	14·8	13·8	14·2	15·5

The virus recombined by joining the RNA of HR strain, even if coated with the TMV protein, produces in the host a protein which is identical with the HR strain protein, while the virus with the TMV nucleic acid (column III) produces a protein identical with the TMV protein, even if coated with the HR protein. It is noteworthy that the TMV protein differs significantly from the HR protein, since the latter contains histidine and methionine, whereas the former is devoid of these amino acids. The differences in alanine, valine, phenylalanine, and tyrosine also are conspicuous. The protein of a TMV mutant (column V) is slightly different from the parent virus. Finally, it is obvious that these virus proteins have nothing in common with the strongly basic protamines and histones, and that they resemble in the amino acid composition any of the common albumins and globulins.

The protein coat of TMV is not a giant macromolecule but it appears in fragments of various sizes which in some electron micrographs appear as doughnut-shaped particles.[14] However, these doughnuts are aggregates

[14] G. SCHRAMM, G. SCHUMACHER and W. ZILLIG, *Z. Naturforsch.* **10 b**, 481 (1955); G. SCHRAMM and W. ZILLIG, *Z. Naturforsch.* **10 b**, 493 (1955).

of even smaller subunits whose size has been estimated from amino acid analyses and terminal amino acid determinations to be of $M = 17{,}300$.[15] Each subunit of the HR strain contains one histidine residue, and each subunit in any of the TMV strains contain one threonine residue as the C-terminal

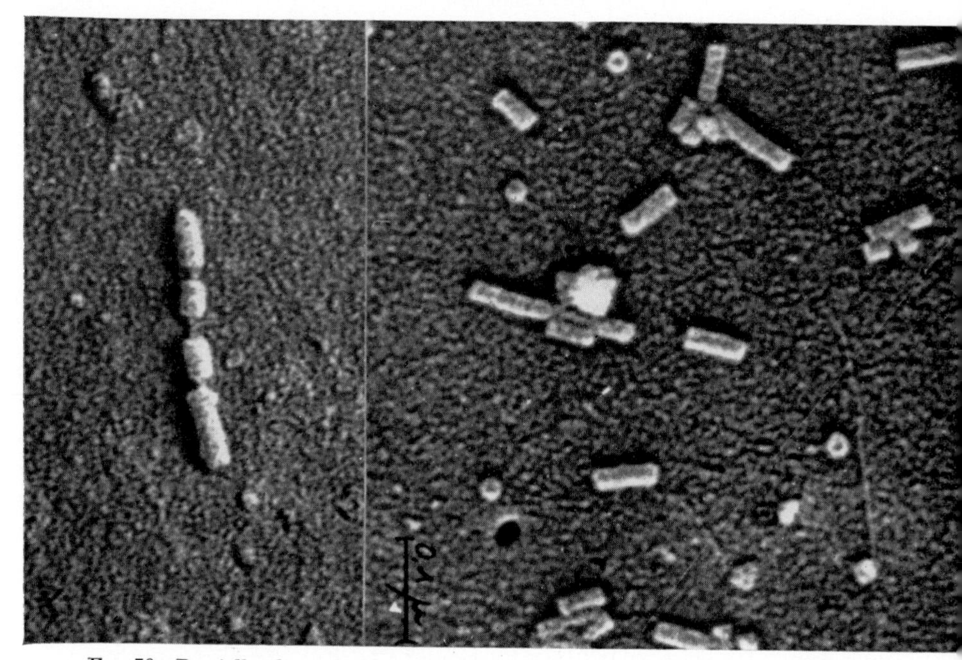

FIG. 79. Partially disintegrated particles of the tobacco mosaic virus. Some of the doughnut-shaped protein fragments are visible in the upper part of the electron micrograph (magnification 150,000×) (by *Courtesy* of Prof. Dr. G. Schramm)

group. Further sequence studies at both the N- and C-terminal have indicated that each subunit is a single chain protein which starts with the very unusual acetylated N-terminal serine followed by tyrosine, and that the sequence at the C-terminal is . . . Thr-Gly-Ser-Pro-Ala-Thr-COOH.[16] Thus far it seems that the virus protein is homogeneous, viz. that all of the approximately 2900 protein subunits combined with the RNA core are of the same (or very similar) size and composition. Work is in progress on the sequence in the middle portions of the chain, and a series of peptides of known structure have been isolated.[17]

[15] J. I. HARRIS and C. A. KNIGHT, *J. biol. Chem.* **214**, 215 (1955).

[16] H. FRAENKEL-CONRAT and K. NARITA, in *Symposium on Protein Structure* p. 249 (A. NEUBERGER, ed.), Methuen, London, New York, 1958.

[17] G. SCHRAMM, G. BRAUNITZER, F. A. ANDERER, J. W. SCHNEIDER and H. UHLIG, in *Symposium on Protein Structure* p. 262, 1958. The complete amino acid sequence of the TMV protein has been reported recently by A. TSUGITA, D. T. GISH, J. YOUNG and H. FRAENKEL-CONRAT in *Proc. Natl. Acad. Sci.* **46**, 1463 (1960).

Further structural details of the TMV virus will involve such problems as the exact configuration of the protein subunits and their arrangement in the "doughnuts", the attachment of the subunits to the RNA chain, and

FIG. 80. A model of the tobacco mosaic virus particle according to Dr. Rosalind Franklin. The loaf-shaped bodies are the protein subunits that are bound to the helical core of the RNA chain

the configuration and nucleotide sequence in the latter. A picture of the whole arrangement is revealed by the fascinating electron micrographs of Schramm *et al.* [14] (see Fig. 79). The nucleic acid core appears as a rather stiff thread inside the hole of the protein doughnuts. A more detailed picture has been deduced from the *X*-ray diffraction data by Franklin *et al.* [18] The rod-

[18] R. E. FRANKLIN, *Biochim. Biophys. Acta* **18,** 313 (1955); **19,** 203 (1956); FRANKLIN and K. C. HOLMES, *ibid.* **21,** 405 (1956); FRANKLIN, *Symposium on Protein Structure* p. 271 (A. NEUBERGER, ed.), Methuen, London, 1958.

shaped virus particle appears to have a hollow core, and the RNA chain winds around it describing a rather flat helical path. The protein subunits are packed around the core in a helical pattern, and there are 49 subunits to every three turns of the helix. The diameter of the hollow core is about 20 Å, the mean diameter of the particle 150 Å, and the protein subunit packing results in an uneven surface, so that in certain sections the diameter reaches 180 Å or 18 mμ. A model of this kind is presented in Fig. 80. The correctness of this model, of course, is still under consideration, and if it were true, it reveals only a small part of the secrets of TMV.

While the protein does not direct the biosynthetic pathways of protein and RNA synthesis in the host, it certainly affects the infectivity. Typical lesions on the tobacco leaves have been induced even with pure TMV RNA, but the infectivity of RNA is much weaker than the infectivity of the complete virus.[19] The reconstituted viruses of Fraenkel-Conrat [1] are more infective than pure RNA but less infective than a native virus. All this indicates that the protein has a certain role in starting and promoting the metabolic reactions in the host, probably by maintaining the specific configuration of the RNA. If this is so, the configurational stability of the TMV rods is not due to the central RNA helix but to the cylindrical arrangement of the protein subunits. This, however, does not fit too well into Franklin's concept.

The physical properties of the solutions of TMV and the fibrous potato X virus are those of asymmetric proteins, i.e. the solutions are viscous, and they exhibit double refraction of flow. The virus can be precipitated by the usual protein precipitants, and it is denatured on heating. If a TMV dispersion is left undisturbed, the particles slowly settle down forming an oriented bottom layer. These layers as well as TMV gels have been extensively studied by various methods including X-ray diffraction, and interesting results about these paracrystalline formations have been obtained. There are indications that the rods are arranged in hexagonal array, and that they lie rather far apart embedded in water. The virus rods seem to affect the orientation of the water itself, and this occurs not by a high degree of hydration, since only a small amount of water is bound at the surface of the virus.

Some essential properties of several other simple plant viruses are mentioned in Table 44. Bushy stunt virus, turnip yellow mosaic virus, and southern bean mosaic virus all are globular entities which have been studied by various methods, including electron microscopy (see Fig. 81 and 82). Contrary to the fibrous viruses, these globular viruses render solutions of low viscosity, and they do not show double refraction of flow. The nucleic acid chain is in the interior of the particle, and it is obvious that the chain must be folded many times. Details about this folding are unknown, as is the number of chains and their nucleotide sequence. The earlier data on amino acid composition of the protein components has been compiled by Knight.[20]

[19] A. GIERER and G. SCHRAMM, *Z. Naturforsch.* **11 b**, 138 (1956).
[20] C. A. KNIGHT, *Adv. Virus Res.* **2**, 153 (1954).

The globular plant viruses have many properties in common: they all appear spherical or polyhedric in the electron microscope, they are homogeneous with respect to particle size and shape, they all contain RNA which is the infective portion, and they all contain a slightly acid protein component. Moreover, the dimensions of the particles depend very much on the degree

FIG. 81. Molecular order in a crystal of tobacco necrosis virus (magnification 80,800×) (by *Courtesy* of Drs. L. W. Labaw and R. W. G. Wyckoff)

of drying: the wet virus appears much larger than dry virus, e.g. the diameter of the turnip yellow mosaic virus is 23 mμ in dry state and 31 mμ in a wet crystal. These data have been obtained by X-ray analysis of the crystallized viruses. The best preparations of the viruses are homogeneous in electrophoresis, while two components have been observed in an apparently homogeneous turnip yellow mosaic virus solution upon sedimentation in the ultracentrifuge. Both components look the same in the electron microscope, and both form identical crystals, yet the one sediments faster than the other. The difference in sedimentation rate is explained by the difference in particle density which is due to the presence or absence of the nucleic acid. The fast sedimenting component contains the nucleic acid, while the slower component is devoid of it, despite the fact that the particles are of the same size. Only the faster component is infective as a virus (quoted from l.c. 10). This proves that the nucleic acid must be inside the particle, and that stable protein part-

FIG. 82. Particles of the southern bean mosaic virus protein in a small portion of a crystal at a very high magnification of 170,000× (by *Courtesy* of Drs. L. W. Labaw and R. W. G. Wyckoff)

icles, resembling hollow shells, can exist without the support of nucleic acid core. This poses a series of interesting questions as to the structure and configuration of these protein shells.

The infectivity and possibility of multiplication of the plant viruses is not limited to a single species of plants, as indicated by the name of the particular virus. For example, the tobacco necrosis viruses infect not only tobacco plants but also tulips, beans, carnations, and many others. However, it is also known that any of the viruses may have different strains, and the possibility must be considered that some of these strains preferably infect certain plant species. The strains, as mentioned in the instance of tobacco mosaic virus, differ in the protein component but not in the nucleotide composition or in the particle size and shape. Since the nucleic acid probably is the sole determinant of the reproduction, the strains probably differ in nucleotide sequence and configuration of the nucleic acid chains. The differences in the protein component, on the other hand, seem to be important in accommodating the virus in a particular host tissue. An exact study of the topic is complicated by the many factors affecting the reproduction, the possibility of impurities, instability of the particles, and possibility of mutations.

The very simple possibility of infecting an unlimited number of plants with a microscopic quantity of virus elevates the latter, from a chemical point of view, to the highest rank of autocatalysts. Large amounts of virus, in comparison to the inoculated amount, can be detected in a few days after inoculation, and the maximum is reached in a few weeks. The yields in preparative isolation usually are in the range of 50–500 mg from 1 l. of sap, and represent only a fraction of the actual content. The infection is transmitted from plant in various ways, including insects.

Simple Animal Viruses

Although the animal viruses generally are more complex than the plant viruses, simple animal viruses also are known. An interesting example of the latter is the virus found in certain insects, e.g. silk worms and moths, the so called *polyhedral virus*. Bergold showed that the polyhedral particles found in diseased insects are composed of at least two components: a virus and a protein.[21] The latter comprises the bulk of the polyhedra and is not infective, while the real virus amounts to only 5%. The virus particles are rod-shaped, about 300–450 mμ long and 30 mμ wide, and they appear in the microscopic polyhedra in bunches which are covered with a membrane. Chemically the virus seems to be very simple, viz. like the plant viruses, it contains only protein and nucleic acid, and it is in this instance the DNA, not RNA.[22]

Another simple animal virus is the *poliovirus*. This was originally isolated from nervous tissue of higher animals, and since its concentration in the tissue is low, and it is there in a very complex system containing a variety of similar macromolecular compounds, the purification was extremely difficult. Of great importance was the finding of Enders *et al.*[23] that the virus can be propagated in tissue cultures. From these, the isolation can be accomplished relatively easily by the usual methods employed for separation and purification of large proteins.[24,25] It appears that the virus readily withstands such treatments as precipitation at pH 4·5, elution with alkaline buffers, precipitation with alcohols (at a low temperature), electrophoresis, etc., without

(21) G. Bergold, *Z. Naturforsch.* **2 b**, 122 (1947); *Canad. J. Research* **28**, 5 (1950).
(22) J. D. Smith and G. R. Wyatt, *Biochem. J.* **49**, 144 (1951).
(23) J. F. Enders, T. H. Weller and F. C. Robbins, *Science* **109**, 85 (1949).
(24) C. E. Schwerdt and F. L. Schaffer, *Ann. N. Y. Acad. Sci.* **61**, 740 (1955).
(25) F. L. Schaffer and C. E. Schwerdt, *Adv. Virus Res.* **6**, 159 (1959).

losing infectivity. This is due to the fact that the virus is a relatively small and simple particle composed only of nucleic acid and protein. The virus crystallizes, and the electron microscope reveals spherical or nearly spherical particles of very uniform size. Some of the most important physical properties of three strains of this virus are compiled in Table 47.

TABLE 47

PHYSICAL PROPERTIES OF THREE STRAINS OF POLIOVIRUSES [26]

	Mahoney	MEF–1	Saukett
Sedimentation constant, S	160	158	157
Density of dry virus, g/cm³	1·57	1·56	1·62
Diameter, mμ	27·3	27·0	27·2
Particle weight	6,800,000	6,800,000	6,400,000
Particle mass, grams	$1{\cdot}13 \cdot 10^{-17}$	$1{\cdot}12 \cdot 10^{-17}$	$1{\cdot}08 \cdot 10^{-17}$
Water of hydration in grams per gram dry weight	0·30	0·28	0·37

The strains are differentiated by immunochemical methods which indicate some difference in the protein. The physical properties, however, according to the data of the Table 47, are practically the same, if one considers the experimental errors involved in the methods. Some slight differences seem to be in the electrophoretic properties, which again would indicate some difference in the ionogenic groups in the protein.[25]

Chemically the poliovirus is more closely related to the simple plant viruses than to the previously mentioned insect polyhedra viruses. Only RNA and a protein component could be detected in the virus, and there are indications that the nucleic acid froms the core of the particle, and protein the outer shell. The base ratios in the RNA's of the various strains are the same.[25]

The dramatic effects of poliomyelitis, especially its acute form of infantile paralysis, have focused much attention to the polio virus, and considerable efforts have been spent in developing the popular anti-polio vaccine. The leading idea in this undertaking was to inactivate the virus so that it becomes harmless, yet still capable of antibody formation, and this was accomplished by a treatment of the virus with diluted formaldehyde solutions.[27] Although the benefits rendered by the Salk vaccine are undisputable, the problem is not completely solved. The major difficulty in the formaldehyde inactivation is the impossibility of achieving complete inactivation even after prolonged treatment. The safety of every batch of vaccine is now carefully checked by

[26] C. E. SCHWERDT, *Cellular Biology, Nucleic Acids and Viruses* Vol. 5, p. 157, spec. publ , N. Y. Acad. Sci. (1957).

[27] J. E. SALK, *Am. J. Public Health* **46**, 1 (1956); *Cellular Biology, Acids and Viruses, Nucleic* Vol. 5, p. 79, spec. publ., N. Y. Acad. Sci. (1957).

inocculating experimental animals, and infective samples are eliminated. Noneffectivity of the vaccine in some instances seems to be due to the presence of resistant strains (sometimes mutants), or to individual failure of antibody production (see chapt. 23). Inactivation by irradiating the virus with ultra-violet light, sometimes followed by heat and formaldehyde treatment, also has been investigated, and found to yield satisfactory vaccines.[25] The mechanism of inactivation is not altogether clear, and a solution of this problem certainly would be of an extreme practical importance.

Complex Organized Animal Viruses [3,10,28]

Within this section the chemically minded investigator encounters all these uncertainties which can be designated as "organization" of macromolecules. He is approaching here the ever mysterious borderline between "non-living" and "living" entities where it becomes increasingly difficult to apply the classical methods of chemistry and physics. While the simple nucleoprotein viruses can be regarded as particles formed of two types of macromolecules, some of the larger animal viruses appear to be organized in a fashion resembling the organization of microbes. One of the major difficulties in an exact study of these entities is the uncertainty as to what are the intrinsic components of the virus and what is incidentally attached from the host tissue. Moreover, these viruses are more labile than the simple nucleoprotein viruses; they are difficult to isolate, purify, and obtain in sufficiently large amounts.

The rabbit *papilloma virus* was one of the first viruses of this kind that could be isolated in reasonably pure state. The virus-containing warts were minced, extracted with salt solution, and separated by differential centrifugation. The virus forms an opalescent colloidal solution, and sedimentation and diffusion studies showed that the particle weight is about 47,000,000. The rather high frictional ratio (f/f_0) of 1·52 of the particles can be explained by a high degree of hydration,[10] since the particles appear spherical in the electron microscope. The particles are composed of protein, DNA, a carbohydrate, and lipid. The electron micrographs seem to indicate a certain internal organization, although it is not quite certain in what degree this corresponds to the actual organization of the particles when in the highly hydrated native state.

The *influenza virus* is another interesting example of the complex organized animal viruses. There are several groups and strains the dimensions being measured about 100 mμ in diameter, and the particle weights being calculated of approximately 100 million. The virus particle is composed of more than one protein, of RNA, carbohydrate and lipid. The nucleic acid

[28] F. M. Burnet, *Principles of Animal Virology* Academic Press, New York, 1955; V. A. Najjar (ed.), *Immunity and Virus Infection* Wiley, New York, 1959.

of various strains of the virus was analyzed by Ada,(29) and definite differences were established between the strains of the A and B groups. This is demonstrated in Table 48.(29)

TABLE 48
NUCLEOTIDE RATIO IN VARIOUS STRAINS OF INFLUENZA VIRUSES

	Number of experiments	Adenine + uracil / Guanine + cytosine
A Group, strain PR 8	5	1·27 ± 0·02
MEL	2	1·22 ± 0·01
WSE	2	1·26 ± 0·01
SWINE	2	1·24 ± 0·04
CAM	2	1·28 ± 0·01
B Group, strain LEE	4	1·42 ± 0·04
MIL	3	1·43 ± 0·05
ROB	2	1·38 ± 0·01

Extensive studies on the internal structure of the virus particles have been conducted in several laboratories, and attempts have been made to depict the major outlines of the organization. In a recent paper, it was concluded (30) that the particle has a multi-shell organization (see Fig. 83). The macromolecules of ribonucleoprotein are forming the nucleus of the particle; the molecular weight of each of the RNA-nucleoprotein units is 600,000, and altogether there are 70 such macromolecules in each nucleus of the virus. The nucleus is surrounded by a protein which is covered by a radiation resistant coat consisting chiefly of lipids. Finally, the outer shell is represented by several protein components which partially originate from the host, and a membrane composed chiefly of carbohydrates.

The smallpox *vaccinia virus* is one of the largest viruses resembling in size and organization the smallest microbes. The particles are brick-shaped and their dimensions extend to 200–250 mμ, so that they can be observed even in ordinary microscopes under proper illumination. The particles contain about 5% of DNA and a variety of proteins some of which are enzymes probably originating from the host. The virus contains also about 6% of lipids which can be extracted without causing any loss of infectivity; thus it is possible that, like the influenza virus, the vaccinia virus has a lipide coat. A quite well defined "nucleus" also can be observed. In spite of this complex organization, the entity is classified as a virus, since it can be propagated only in living tissues.

A variety of virus-like particles have been found in malignant tumor tissues, and there is evidence that at least some types of tumors are caused by viruses. It is assumed that the virus is necessary only for initiation of

(29) G. L. ADA, in *Symposium, The Nature of Viruses* p. 104, Little, Brown, Boston, 1957.

(30) W. FRISCH-NIGGEMEYER, *Z. Naturforsch.* **14 b**, 168 (1959).

the tumor, and that further progression of it occurs without a continuous effect of the virus. This is suspected and more or less decisively proved not only for the animal papillomas but also in certain types of human tumors.[31] The problem of infectivity, however, is very complex. First, these particles are *similar to certain cell ingredients of the host*; second, it is known that animal

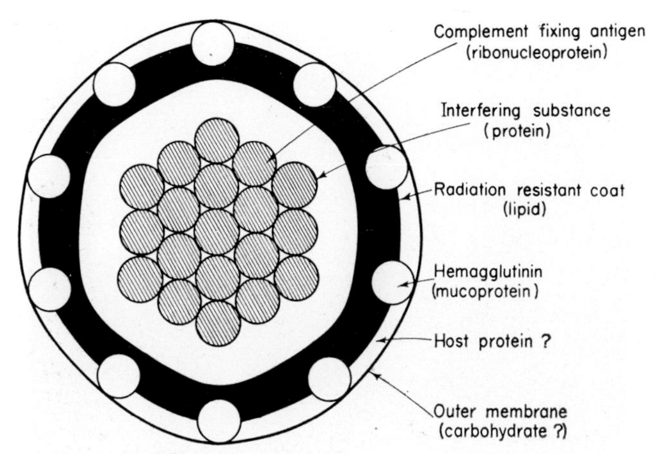

FIG. 83. Schematic presentation of the structure of an influenza virus particle after W. Frisch-Niggemeyer (*Z. Naturforsch.* **14b**, 168, 1959)

viruses often remain in the host in a *latent inactive* form, i.e. that their propagation depends on the biochemical conditions of the host. The disclosure of important relations, which also may elucidate the causation of cancer, can be expected from further research in this field (see chapt. 25).

The Phages [32]

A phage is a virus that invades and destroys bacteria, streptomyces, and similar small organisms. The phage first adheres to the surface of a microbe, and introduces its nucleic acid into the cell whose metabolism thus is greatly disturbed. The synthetic mechanisms are switched in favor of the phage, viz. more phage type nucleic acid is synthesized and more new phage particles appear in the host cell. It is noteworthy that there are certain bacteria which carry a passive or latent "prophage" transmitting it to its progeny; if set free, the phage usually does not attack the host but is active against related sensitive strains of the bacteria.

The phages are of about the same size as the medium size viruses described previously, but certain types of phages have peculiar shapes, as revealed

[31] L. DMOCHOWSKI, in *Cancer*, Vol. 1, p. 214, Butterworth, London.

[32] M. H. ADAMS, *Bacteriophages* Interscience, New York, 1959; L. M. KOZLOFF, in *A Symposium on Molecular Biology* p. 178 (R. E. ZIRKLE, ed.), Univ. of Chicago Press, 1959.

in electron micrographs (Fig. 84). A phage usually consists of a round "head" and a rod-shaped "tail". The head has a diameter of 50–100 mμ, while the tail has a length of 100–250 mμ and a diameter of 10–30 mμ. Most of the physicochemical studies have been carried out on a group of phages denoted

FIG. 84. Electron-micrograph of a frozen-dried preparation of T_4 phage, indicating the hexagonal elongated head and the thick tail. Head dimensions 95 × 65 mμ; tail 100 mμ × 25 mμ (magnification 63,000×) (by *Courtesy* of Dr. R. C. Williams)

by T_1–T_7 which attack the bacteria named *Escherichia coli*. The peculiar shape indicates complexity of structure, a fact further elaborated by electron microscopic studies on the structure of the "heads". It appears that the heads are composed of a relatively dense core and a less dense outer shell. Thus with respect to size and complexity the phages are more similar to the animal viruses than to the plant viruses. This is supported also by chemical data. Protein and DNA are the major constituents of the phages which thus far have been studied by chemical methods, but non-nucleic acid sugar, lipid, and RNA also have been found, although in small amounts; and, as in the case of animal viruses, it is difficult to decide whether these components are genuine constituents of the phage or impurities. The DNA of the phages T_2, T_4, and T_6 contains 5-hydroxymethylcytosine instead of the ordinary cytosine of DNA (see chapt. 19). Quite unusual one-chain DNA has been discovered recently in certain phages.[33] The amino acid analysis of the protein component, on the contrary, does not reveal any unusual amino acids, viz. the composition is that of a common protein similar to that found in plant viruses.

There is definite evidence that the nucleic acid component of the phage is the decisive factor that determines the course of biosynthesis in the growth and multiplication of the phage in a bacteria, while the protein seems to be important in the first phases of interaction between the phage and host.[33a] Although the details of the mechanism of the interaction are unknown, certain aspects have been clarified. For instance, it is known that a T_2 phage induced in the *E. coli* cell the formation of an enzyme which catalyzes the synthesis of 5-hydroxymethylcytosine.[34] The problems of reduplication and synthesis of the DNA and proteins will be discussed in following chapters.

The specific morphology of the phages in connexion with their function has been clarified to a certain extent. It has been shown that the tail of the phage is used as organ of attachment to the host cell and as organ of injection of the nucleic acid. In the instance of phage T_5, it could be demonstrated[35] that the tip of the tail contains an enzyme which is activated by calcium, for only in the presence of calcium ions can the injection of the nucleic acid occur. The protein shell of the phage remains outside the host, after the host cell has received the injection of the nucleic acid. It seems that upon denaturation of the phage, for example by heat, most of the damage is done to the enzyme located at the tip of the tail, since the nucleic acid then leaks out of the shell, and the empty shells or "ghosts" can be recovered in the solution. Electron microscopic studies have shown that the shells have the same shape as the original phage but they are less dense, i.e. more translucent for the beam than the phages.

Mutations and other genetic aspects of phages have been studied by Delbrueck, Hershey, Luria, and others.[36] "The details of viral inheritance suggest that bacterial viruses originated in much the same way as other organisms: that is to say, out of a dim past. They are unique only because of their structural and physiological simplicity, which corresponds to an extremity of parasitic adaptation"[36] (quoted from p. 104). An excellent

[33] R. L. Sinsheimer, *J. Mol. Biol.* **1**, 43 (1959).

[33a] A. D. Hershey and M. Chase, *J. Gen. Physiol.* **36**, 39 (1952).

[34] S. S. Cohen, *Abstracts, Amer. chem. Soc. Nat. Meeting, Chicago* p. 22 C, Sept. 1958.

[35] K. G. Lark and M. H. Adams, *Cold Spring Harbour Symp. Quant. Biol.* **18**, 171 (1953).

[36] A. D. Hershey, *Adv. in Genetics* **5**, 89 (1953); also — A. D. Hershey, in *Currents in Biochemical Research* p. 1ff. (D. E. Green, ed.), Interscience, 1956.

discussion on phage genetics and the role of nucleic acids and enzymes in it can be found in Anfinsen's new book.[37]

Some Concluding Remarks

Viruses and phages often have been called "living molecules" or "living macromolecules", i.e. regarded as living bodies, and the question is: is there some justification to such qualification? It is obvious that there we have a matter of definition, and it must be admitted that clear definitions are essential in eliminating any kind of confusion and "mystery" from these complex phenomena. The simple nucleoprotein viruses which can grow and reproduce only in a living host should not be qualified as living macromolecules because this leads to a confusing extension of the concept of life into the molecular level. If a virus is qualified as living, a nucleic acid macromolecule that determines the biosynthesis also is living; what then about the proteins, peptides, oligonucleotides? It is obvious that the concept of life thus can be reduced *ad absurdum* and loses its real meaning and usefulness.

The simple nucleoprotein viruses are neither living organisms nor molecules, they are *particles composed of at least two types of macromolecules* whose structure and chemical molecular weight is still unknown. Viruses and phages are *specific byproducts developed in the course of evolution of living organisms.* They may be either passive ingredients of a living tissue or, at suitable conditions, become active participants in the organized metabolic cycles of the living host. Like powerful autocatalysts, they effect derailment of the well-balanced metabolic cycles of the host for their benefit thus usually causing disastrous results for the host. *Virus particles redirect the biosynthetic processes of the host in such a way that the organized enzyme systems of the host synthesize predominantly the proteins and nucleic acids of the viral type.* This leads to the proliferation of the virus and gradual destruction of the host.

[37] CHR. B. ANFINSEN, *The Molecular Basis of Evolution* p. 67ff., Wiley, New York, 1959. See also S. BENZER, in *The Chemical Basis of Heredity* p. 70 (W. D. MC ELROY and B. GLASS, ed.), J. Hopkins Press, Baltimore, 1957.

CHAPTER 21

CELLULAR INGREDIENTS

> It will be the further task of modern cytology to investigate the constitution and architecture of the various integrated cell structures, at the molecular level, and to discover in what way structure conditions biological processes and insures the continuance of biochemical cycles.
>
> ALBERT CLAUDE [1]

ANY BOOK on natural organic macromolecules might as well be started with "The Cell", since "the cell" is the elementary living unit that produces all of these macromolecules. While a cell is small in comparison to our ordinary standards, it is a giant when compared with the various macromolecules. Yet it is true that in many ways science is less informed about the cell than about some of the macromolecules, just as we know less about the large molecules than about the very much smaller molecules and atoms. It is not the "small" or "large" size of the cell (depending on what one compares it with) that makes it difficult to study and understand; it is not the indescribable variety of the cells encountered in living matter either that has blocked the road; it is the *complex organization* which is not yet understood.

In spite of the variety in size and shape, and partially also in chemical composition, all cells have certain things in common: an organized system of *enzymes* and *nucleic acids* that ensure the "continuance of biochemical cycles" and even replication of the whole system. Thus, although the system or unit called cell is ever changing, it exists in a state of equilibrium which is characteristic for each type of cell. The organized system of enzymes and nucleic acids, whatever the other ingredients (there might be such macromolecules occasionally as cellulose, rubber, or glycogen) are, tends to preserve the dynamic equilibrium, and has even the potential capacity of accumulating unorganized matter, of reproduction and multiplication.

As indicated in the previous chapter, it would be confusing and incorrect to classify the nucleoproteins capable of reproduction in living cells as living. Likewise, any of the component parts of a living cell which are reproduced only within the living cell should not be designated as organisms. The *membrane*, the *nucleus*, the particles called *mitochondria*, and the smaller particles of the cytoplasm called *microsomes* are organized components or *organs* of a living cell or micro–organism. In multicellular higher organisms some cells

[1] A. CLAUDE, *Adv. Protein Chem.* **5**, 423 (1949); quotation from p. 425.

are more specialized to certain function than others, yet any living cell contains certain enzyme systems and nucleic acids. The question is not of the presence of some ten or twenty but of many hundreds of enzymes which are involved in such processes as the syntheses of the enzymes themselves, the syntheses of nucleic acids, and the production of energy needed for these synthetic and other expenditures of maintaining the life cycles to run smoothly. There is no doubt that all of the mentioned essential organs of a cell are *interdependent,* although some of the cycles, e.g. some mitochondrial enzyme systems may be run autonomously when separated from the cell.

Modern cytology, the science of cells, employs the various modern methods of biophsyics and biochemistry in a variety of ways, and an abundant literature is available on the subject.[2-6] Especially important was the introduction of electron microscopy and phase microscopy,[7] as well as the methods of fractional ultracentrifugation.[1] Even more information, however, has been revealed by systematic biochemical studies on the enzyme systems which are located in certain parts or organs of the cell.

The Cell Nucleus [1,2,3,8]

Modern microscopy has revealed that the nucleus is a complicated organ containing a variety of components. The fine structure of the nuclei, as observed in the phase microscope, depends not only on the kind of cell observed, i.e. the species, but also on the state of the cell. A nonbiologist may have the wrong idea that one always sees in a nucleus the *chromosomes,* the carriers of hereditary factors (genes). The nucleus thus is often envisaged as an assemblage of chromosomes which are identified with nucleoproteins. Although the chromosomes indeed are in every nucleus, they are not always microscopically

[2] R. MELLORS (ed.), *Analytical Cytology* McGraw-Hill, New York, 1955; E. D. P. ROBERTIS, W. W. NOWINSKI and F. A. SAEZ, *General Cytology* Saunders, Philadelphia, 1954; J. BRACHET, *Biochemical Cytology* Academic Press, New York, 1957.

[3] A. FREY-WYSSLING, *Submicroscopic Morphology of Protoplasm* 2nd. ed., Elsevier, Amsterdam. 1953.

[4] A. ENGSTRÖM and J. B. FINEAN, *Biological Ultrastructure* Academic Press, New York, 1958.

[5] G. OSTER and A. POLLISTER (ed.), *Physical Methods in Biological Research,* Vol. 1–3, Academic Press, New York, 1955–1957. See also the series: *Progress in Biophysics and Biophysical Chemistry* (Pergamon Press, London and *Advances in Biological and Medical Physics.*

[6] Symposia of the Society for Experimental Biology, a series of symposia reports published by Academic Press, New York, e.g. Vol. 6 (*Structural Aspects of Cell Physiology*) Vol. 10 (*Mitochondria and other Cytoplasmic Inclusions*) and Vol. 12 (*Biological Replication of Macromolecules*).

[7] A. H. BENNET, H. JUPNIK, H. OSTERBERG and O. W. RICHARDS, *Phase Microscopy,* Wiley, New York, 1951; F. ZERNIKE, *T. techn. Physik* **16**, 454 (1935).

[8] V. G. ALLFREY, A. E. MIRSKY and H. STERN, *Adv. Enzymol.* **16**, 411 (1955); J. H. TAYLOR, in *A Symposium on Molecular Biology* p. 304 (R. E. ZIRKLE, ed.), Univ. of Chicago Press, Chicago, 1959; H. SWIFT, *ibid.* p. 266.

visible, and they are not *simple* nucleoprotein particles. In fact, the chromosomes show up only in certain stage of cell division (mitosis), at least in great majority of animal cells. The relatively large granules observable in resting animal cell nuclei are not chromosomes but the *nucleoli* ("little nuclei"). Moreover, each nucleus is surrounded by a distinct *membrane*. In a nondividing cell the chromosomes are dispersed in the nuclear sap which may reveal certain structures under suitable optical conditions. Chemical studies on isolated nuclei, which have been separated by differential centrifugation from disrupted cells, have revealed a variety of macromolecular components, such as *proteins*, *deoxyribonucleic acid* (*DNA*), and *ribonucleic acid* (*RNA*). In addition, various lipids and other micromolecular substances have been identified. The separation of the chromosomes, nucleoli, and the other components, however, is a more difficult task.

The *nucleolus* is an organelle which in some instances can be seen as being composed of elongated granules, and a membrane. Histochemical and other investigation indicates that the nucleoli contain RNA and some lipid, in addition to protein. The size and structure of the nucleoli vary considerably, depending on the nature of the cell and its state.

The chromosomal components of the nucleus have been much better investigated than its other constituent organelles, chiefly because of their

TABLE 49

THE CONTENT OF DNA, RNA, AND PROTEIN OF NUCLEI FROM VARIOUS SOURCES [8]
The amount of RNA is expressed as RNA-phosphorus (RNA-P)

Source of nucleus	DNA-P (%)	DNA (%)	RNA-P (%)	Ratio: DNA-P / RNA-P	Protein (%)	Ratio: Protein / DNA
Calf, thymus	2·56	26·5	0·17	15	71·8	2·7
heart	1·90	19·7	0·11	17	79·2	4·0
kidney	1·71	17·7	0·16	11	80·7	4·6
liver	1·50	15·6	0·15	9·7	82·9	5·3
Beef, heart	1·65	17·1	0·22	7·6	80·7	4·8
Horse, pancreas	2·20	22·8	0·20	11	75·2	3·3
liver	1·20	12·4	0·16	7·5	86·0	7·0
Chicken, kidney	1·45	15·0	0·20	7·3	83·0	5·5
erythrocytes	2·55	26·4	0·01	255	73·5	2·9

genetic importance.[8a] DNA is established as the main component of the chromosomes, yet it has been shown by Brachet [9] that the chromosomes contain also some RNA. Some analytical data on the content of DNA, RNA, and protein of nuclei isolated from various tissues are presented in Table 49.

(8a) H. RIS, in *The Chemical Basis of Heredity* p. 23 (W. D. MCELROY and B. GLASS, ed.), J. HOPKINS, Baltimore, 1957; see also G. W. BEADLE, *ibid.*, p. 3, and S. BENZER *ibid*, p. 70; A. L. DOUNCE, *Ann. N. Y. Acad. Sci.* **81**, (3), 794 (1959).

(9) J. BRACHET, *Arch. Biol.* **53**, 207 (1941).

It is obvious that the amount of RNA per cell nucleus varies from species to species, and some variation is conspicuous also in different organs of the same species.[10] The amount of ribonucleic acid has been determined also in preparations of isolated chromosomes,[11] and it was found that this amount of RNA depends very much on the source. Thus the nucleic acid of trout sperm chromosomes contained only 0·15% RNA, while the nucleic acid of liver cell chromosomes contained 12% RNA.

The amount of DNA per cell of calf thymus is estimated to be $7 \cdot 10^{-9}$ mg. From this figure, the Avogadro number, and the molecular weight of DNA, viz. $6 \cdot 10^{6}$, the number of molecules per cell can be calculated; [12] and this computation shows that there are 1,400,000 macromolecules of DNA in each nucleus. Thus each of the 60 chromosomes in these cells contain approximately 23,300 macromolecules of DNA. This calculation shows that there are ample possibilities to accomodate the various genetic features within the molecular framework.

The metabolic activity of the various macromolecules of the nucleus has been studied by following the uptake of labeled metabolites, e.g. ^{32}P and ^{14}C in various compounds, and it is established that the DNA is the metabolically least active component, while the RNA is relatively active. Since all these reactions are promoted by enzymes, the latter must be present in the nucleus, and indeed a great variety of enzymes has been isolated from nuclear material. "One conclusion which is suggested by these enzyme distributions is that there is a selective accumulation within the nucleus of those enzymes which are likely to be concerned with the synthetic aspects of nucleic acid metabolism, but that the enzymes concerned with nucleic acid breakdown (e.g. nucleotide-specific phosphatases and desoxyribonuclease) are largely restricted to the cytoplasm".[8] The metabolic activity is greatly enhanced during the cell division (mitosis), when the DNA of the chromosomes undergoes a rather complex series of changes.[12a] At the same time more RNA and more enzymes are synthesized from smaller metabolites and precursors. Some of these probably are synthesized in the cytoplasm, while some of these syntheses occur in the nucleus. All the available evidence points to the possibility that the nuclear DNA is the most stable and species-specific substance which holds the blueprints according to which are directed the syntheses of RNA's and enzymes.

While the DNA of the chromosomes remains the same during the whole lifetime of the organism, the chromosomes themselves do not remain so. The protamine of the fertilized egg cell is gradually changed to the histone. In

(10) V. Allfrey, H. Stern, A. E. Mirsky and H. Saetren, *J. Gen. Physiol.* **35**, 529 (1952).

(11) A. E. Mirsky and H. Ris, *J. Gen. Physiol.* **34**, 475 (1951).

(12) M. E. Reichmann, S. A. Rice, C. A. Thomas and P. Doty, *J. Amer. chem. Soc.* **76**, 3047 (1954).

(12a) D. Mazia, *The Harvey Lectures* **53**, 130 (1959), Academic Press, New York.

addition, various so called residual proteins appear upon further differentiation and growths of the organism (chapt. 18). The original sperm cell, viz. its nucleus is virtually devoid of RNA, while considerable amounts of RNA are found in certain nuclei of differentiated cells.

There is new evidence that the nucleus contains at least two kinds of RNA's. It was shown recently that a portion of the RNA of calf thymus nuclei is soluble in neutral phosphate buffer, and that this part has the nucleotide composition of the cytoplasmic RNA. The other part of RNA that is more firmly bound in the nuclei has a different nucleotide composition.[12b] The same authors were able to show that the soluble nucleoprotein (RNA-protein) which was isolated from the nuclei was electrophoretically identical with the cytoplasmic ribonucleoprotein of the same cells. These experiments not only ascertain the existence of various types of RNA's in the same tissue but they also are indicating that the nucleus is the probable source of at least a part of the cytoplasmic RNA. While there are different RNA's in the same tissue, the chromosomal DNA from various human and animal sources exhibit the same *X*-ray spectra; no difference could be found also between the DNA from normal and malignant tissues.[12c] Although the *X*-ray spectra do not reveal all differences, e.g. they do not disclose the nucleotide sequence, the gross structural similarity between the various DNA's is noteworthy.

The Mitochondrion [1,13,14,15]

Mitochondria are microscopical particles of the cytoplasm which have been separated and isolated by differential centrifugation. They are about 0·5–1 μ wide, and vary in length considerably, depending on the source. In the last decade, a great deal of information has been revealed on these organelles by the various biophysical and biochemical methods now available. Interesting observations on the structure of the mitochondrion have been made recently by phase contrast and interference–microscopy, as well as by electron-microscopy. The former method allows us to observe and photograph living mitochondria, although the magnification is not as high as that obtained when using an electron microscope. It is long known that the mitochondrion has a membrane, since the particle swells when placed in water, and this swelling is a sure indication of osmotic influx through a membrane. Internal

[12b] S. Osawa, K. Takata and Y. Hotta, *Biochim. Biophys. Acta* **28**, 271 (1958).

[12c] L. D. Hamilton, R. K. Barclay, M. H. F. Wilkins, G. L. Brown, H. R. Wilson, D. A. Marvin, H. Ephrussi-Taylor and N. S. Simmons, *J. Biophys. Biochem. Cytol.* **5**, 397 (1959).

[13] *Mitochondria and Other Cytoplasmic Inclusions* (Vol. 10 of the Symposia of the Society for Experimental Biology), Academic Press, New York, 1957.

[14] D. E. Green and J. Järnefeld, *Perspectives in Biology and Medicine* Vol. II, No 2, p. 163, Univ. of Chicago, 1959.

[15] D. E. Green and F. L. Crane, *Proc. Internat. Symp. Enzyme Chem., Tokyo and Kyoto* p. 275, 1957 (1958).

membranes or channels across the rod-shaped body of the particle have been observed by electron microscopy (see Fig. 85). Although these pictures reflect

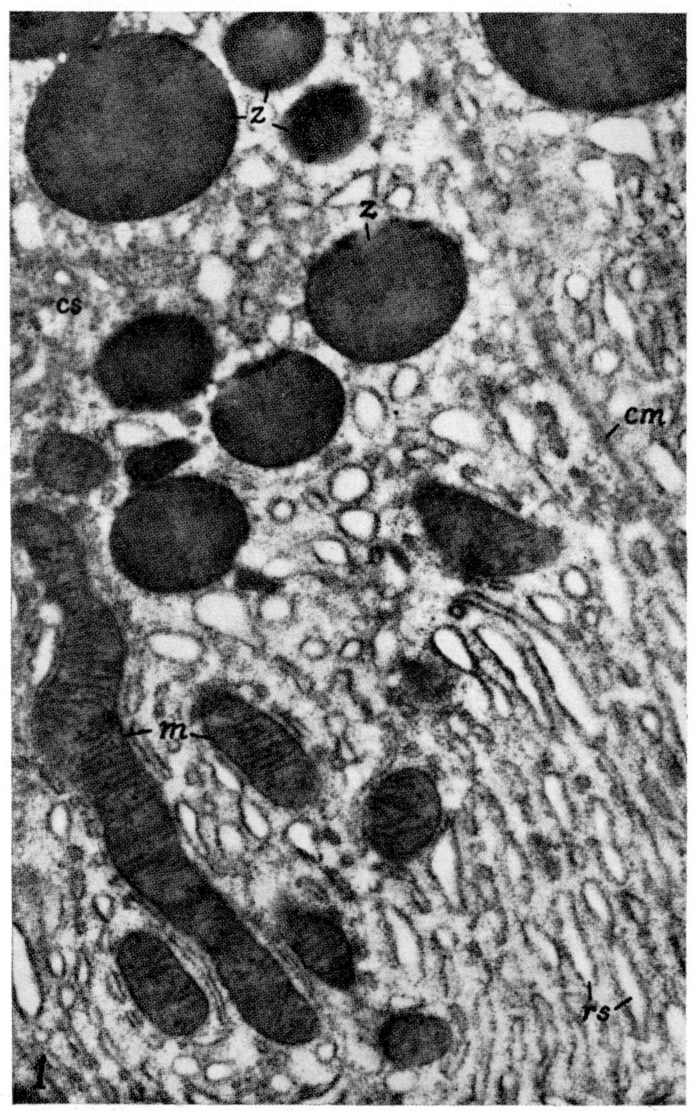

FIG. 85. Electron-micrograph (24,000×) of mitochondrial profiles (*m*) in a cell of guinea pig pancreas; *r s* — cytoplasmic reticulum; *z* — zymogen granules (from G. E. Palade, *Microsomal Particles and Protein Synthesis*, p. 51, Pergamon Press, London, 1958)

the conditions of a non-living specimen, and the living mitochondrion may look somewhat different, the presence of channels and membranes is well established.

Also it has been observed that in a dividing cell the mitochondria split into approximately equal short fragments which then grow up attaining the length of the parent particle.

Chemical analysis of isolated mitochondria has revealed that these bodies consist chiefly of proteins and lipids. Most of the proteins are enzymes, chiefly the redox enzymes, such as the cytochromes and flavoproteins. In an intricate series of enzymic reactions, involving chiefly electron transport, the chemical energy of oxygen and of the molecules supplied to the cell as nutrients is transferred to the newly synthesized adenosine triphosphate (ATP). The energy-rich ATP then is used for a great variety of reactions, including the syntheses of nucleic acids, and the activation of amino acids for protein synthesis. "Thus these cytoplasmic elements appear to constitute the power plants of the cell, where the energy of molecular oxygen is transferred and utilized and, in addition, are probably the site of active metabolic and synthetic processes".[1] As early as 1949, Claude showed by a simple calculation [1] that a single mitochondrion can accommodate an enormous number of enzyme molecules, so that many complex enzyme systems have plenty of space even in small mitochondrial fragments. According to Claude, a 2 μ long and 0·5 μ thick mitochondrion has a weight of $4{\cdot}8 \cdot 10^{-7}\,\gamma$, and it can be assumed that the mass of solid matter (dry weight) comprises about 30% of the total weight, viz. $1{\cdot}4 \cdot 10^{-7}\,\gamma$; furthermore, it can be assumed that about half of this amount or $7 \cdot 10^{-8}\,\gamma$ is protein. Since the absolute mass of an enzyme molecule of molecular weight 35,000 amounts to about $6 \cdot 10^{-14}\,\gamma$, any single mitochondrion could hold nearly one million enzyme molecules. "If we venture the further assumption that one mitochondrion has a complement of, let us say, 25 different enzymatic systems . . . each system being composed of 20 different protein molecules, it is apparent that there could exist, simultaneously in the same mitochondrial unit, as many as 2000 duplicates of each of the 25 enzyme systems postulated".[1]

Meantime, biochemists have learned lots of things about these enzyme systems, and attempts have been made even to envisage the order and spatial distribution of the components within a certain site of the mitochondrion.[13,14,15] It is interesting that some complicated sequences of enzymic reactions may occur in cell-free solution, while some other enzymic reaction cycles require a certain organization of the participating enzymes. The latter case is exemplified by the redox or electron transport system of mitochondria, as demonstrated in several laboratories. Systematic studies on beef heart mitochondria by Green, Crane, *et al.* indicate that a mitochondrion is a multiple particle composed of many similar subunits each containing spatially fixed enzyme systems. Some of these enzymes appear to be more loosely attached than others, and these are liberated into solution, e.g. on ultrasonic fragmentation of the particles, while others are bound more firmly. A whole series of enzymes have been identified, and even their arrangement has been tentatively postulated, as shown in Fig. 86. There is no doubt that the presence of the large amount of lipid is of certain functional significance, which is far from being fully understood. Several lipoproteins composed of a large phospholipid core and a protein shell around it have been isolated from the particles, and it must be assumed that the lipids have an active role in the circulation of the metabolites and electron transport. This is particulary well substantiated by the discovery of a lipid-soluble (water-insoluble) coenzyme (coenzyme Q 275 or simply Q) which has an important part in the electron transport.[16,17] This coenzyme appears to be a quinone with an isoprene side chain that makes it lipid-soluble. Quite interesting is also the finding that the mitochondria contain a relatively large amount of non-heme iron, and some copper.

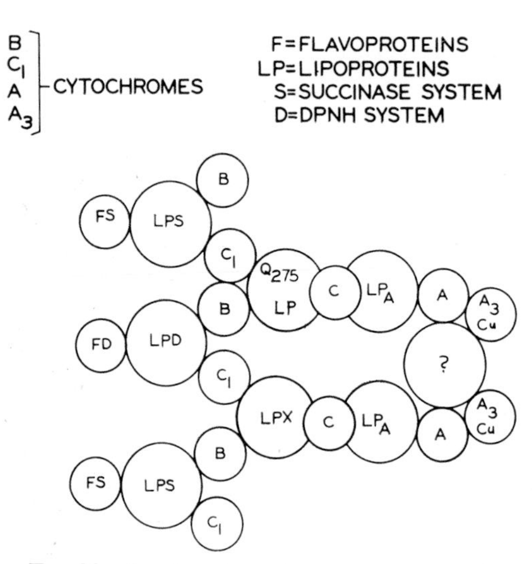

FIG. 86. Fixed order of enzymes in a mitochondrion (by *Courtesy* of Dr. F. L. Crane)

The overall picture of the mitochondrion thus has been clarified to a certain extent. It is reasonably well established that the mitochondrion contains a large number of spatially organized and more or less strongly fixed enzyme systems which are located on the surface as well as on the walls of the channels or "cristae" within the particle.[18] According to Green: ". . . the mitochondrial unit might be looked upon as a supra-macromolecule in which the components are present in strictly stoichiometric proportions and structurally arranged in a highly specific fashion".[14] The internal channeling of the particle results in an extremely large surface and possibility of efficient and fast contacting of the molecules to be metabolized. The forces which are responsible for the maintaining the structure, however, are unknown. These may involve some kind of secondary bonding between the protein or coenzyme components of the enzymes, but it would not be at all surprising if a kind of "ground substance" of fibrous macromolecules were to be found as a cementing material.

[16] F. L. CRANE, C. WIDMER, R. L. LESTER and Y. HATEFI, *Biochim. Biophys. Acta* **31**, 476 (1959).

[17] Y. HATEFI, R. L. LESTER, F. L. CRANE and C. WIDMER, *Biochim. Biophys. Acta* **31**, 490 (1959).

[18] G. E. PALADE, *Anat. Rec.* **114**, 427 (1952); *J. Histochem., Cytochem.* **1**, 188 (1953).

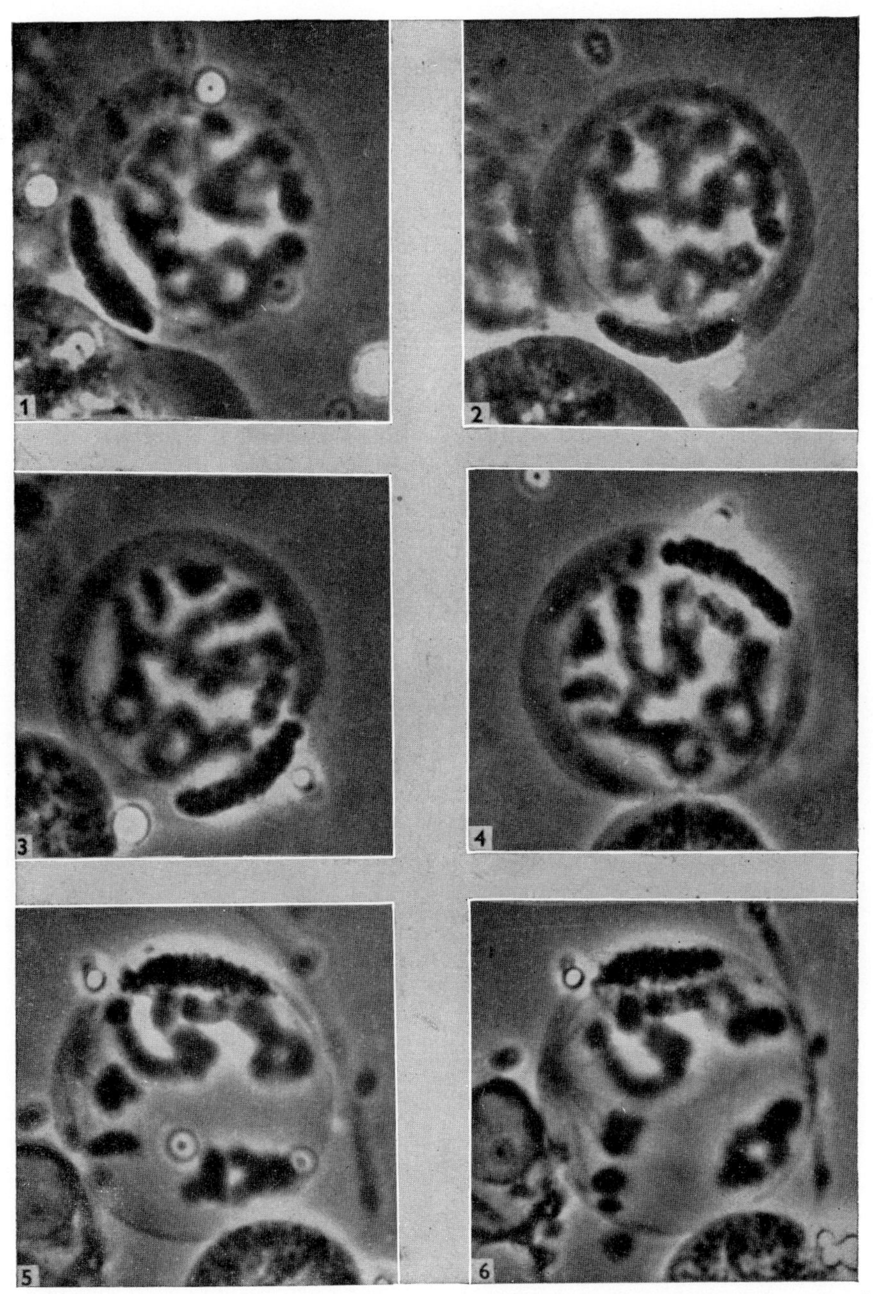

Fig. 87. Phase contrast micrograph showing the movement of a mitochondrion around the nucleus. Grasshopper primary spermatocyte. From an article of R. Barer and S. Joseph, University of Oxford (*X Symp. Soc. Experim. Biol.*, Academic Press, New York, 1957, plate I facing p. 168)

Since the mitochondria now are known to be the "power plants" of the cell, their interplay with the other organs of the cell is of considerable interest. Phase contrast microscopic observations on live cells have revealed interesting movements of the mitochondria along the nuclei, as illustrated in Fig. 87.[19] This illustrates the adherence and movement of a mitochondrion at the nucleus of grasshopper germ cell. The mitochondrion is seen adhering at the surface of the round nucleus as a dark cucumbershaped body, and the sequence of photographs shows that it is moving around the nucleus. Similar observations on other cells strongly indicate the importance of the mitochondria in providing the nuclear components with certain metabolites which the nucleus will need in the subsequent growth and replication. The energy rich adenosine triphosphate is known to be one of these substances. It is possible and quite likely that not only does the mitochondrion provide metabolites and transmit them to the nucleus, but that it also receives something from the nucleus, e.g. some ribonucleic acid which then directs protein synthesis in the cytoplasm.

The Microsome, and Protein Synthesis [20]

The microsomes or "small granules" were discovered by Claude in the late thirties in the supernatant obtained after throwing down the "large granules" or mitochondria. In the following decade these particles were studied extensively, yet their structure and function was not much clarified even at the end of forties. In his much quoted review,[1] Claude describes the microsomes as small elements ranging in size approximately from 60 to 250 mμ, rich in lipids, some enzymes, and ribonucleic acid, but is undecided about their biochemical function. The idea that these particles, especially the RNA-component, are connected with protein synthesis was advocated on the basis of cytochemical facts, first by Brachet [21] and Cassperson.[22] This idea is now developed into a quite well established concept which is supported by biochemical evidence of various kind.

The biochemical function of the microsomes has been and is studied in various ways. Labeled molecules of amino acids and other building blocks can be introduced either in living cells or added to a dispersion of isolated microsomes. The incorporation of the molecule in various macromolecular components then is determined by testing the radioactivity of these components. The study of the chemical nature of the particles, of course, involves isolation which is based chiefly on differential or fractional centrifugation.[22a]

[19] R. Barer and S. Joseph, in *Symp. Soc. Exp. Biol.* X, 160 (1957); see also ref. 13.

[20] R. B. Roberts (ed.), *Microsomal Particles and Protein Synthesis* (1st. Symp. Biophysical Soc.), Pergamon Press, London, 1958.

[21] J. Brachet, *Chemical Embriology*, Interscience, New York, 1950.

[22] T. Cassperson, *Cell Growth and Cell Function*, Norton, New York, 1950.

[22a] C. de Duve, J. Berthet and H. Beaufay, *Progress in Biophys. and Biophys. Chem.* **9**, 325 (1959).

The cells first must be disintegrated, and this can be done in a variety of ways, viz.: by grinding, ultrasonic irradiation, or by osmotic shock. The largest and heaviest particles, such as the nuclei, are thrown down first by means of low speed centrifugation of 500–1 000 g. The supernatant then is spun at a higher speed of 10,000–15,000 g, whereby the system is liberated from the mitochondria, fragments of membranes, and various other granules. Finally, the microsomes are thrown down only in an ultracentrifuge at 20,000–100,000 G.

The term "microsome" now is known to cover a wide variety of particles which differ both in size and composition, depending chiefly on the source. The microsomes of such tissues as liver or pancreas are relatively large objects which can be detected even in phase contrast microscope or dark field ultramicroscope. The electron microscope shows these units as closed vesicles, egg-shaped particles with a membrane at the outside of which are adhering very dense, round granules (see Fig. 88). The latter have a diameter of only 10–20 mμ, and probably are macromolecules of ribonucleoprotein.[23] These composite microsomes of liver, pancreas or tumor cells all contain large amounts of lipid, a variety of proteins, including enzymes, and RNA. It has been indicated that the term should be restricted to these smaller ribonucleoprotein units, since these are the actual sites of protein synthesis. (The complex vesicles might even be artifacts produced after disintegration of the fibrous and lamellar macromolecular aggregates of the cytoplasm). It is also noteworthy that the microsome fraction isolated from microbes of pea seedlings is composed of these relatively simple and small ribonucleoprotein particles (or macromolecules). According to Roberts *et al.*,[24] a single cell of the bacterium *Escherichia coli* contains about 10,000 microsomal particles (which Roberts proposes to call "ribosomes"). The larger of these particles have a sedimentation constant of about 80 S and a diameter of 20 mμ, and they appear to be aggregates of smaller ribonucleoprotein subunits which are held together by linkages through magnesium ions. The protein of these microsomes or ribosomes does not contain cystine and cysteine, and it is not a precursor of the other proteins of the cell. Especially interesting are the results of Dintzis *et al.* [25] on the rabbit reticulocyte (immature red cell) microsomes. According to these authors, the microsomal particles of these cells have a diameter of 34 mμ, and the particle weight of the globular sponge-like units is about 4,000,000. "One-half of the mass is represented by ribonucleic acid which appears to be present as four strands of molecular weight 500,000. The half of the microsomal particle which is protein appears to be almost entirely (99·9 per cent) structural in nature; i.e. it is not transient protein precursor. Woven into this sponge-

(23) G. E. Palade, in *Microsomal Particles and Protein Synthesis* p. 36 (ref. 20).

(24) R. R. Roberts, R. J. Britten and E. T. Bolton, in *Microsomal Particles and Protein Synthesis* p. 84 (ref. 20); I. D. Raacke, *Biochim. Biophys. Acta* **34**, 1 (1959).

(25) H. W. Dintzis, H. Borsook and J. Vinograd, in *Microsomal Particles and Protein Synthesis*, p. 95.

like structure in some way is a very small amount (0·05 per cent by weight) of transient protein precursor. Taken together with the observed rate of hemoglobin production, this amount of precursor is compatible with the

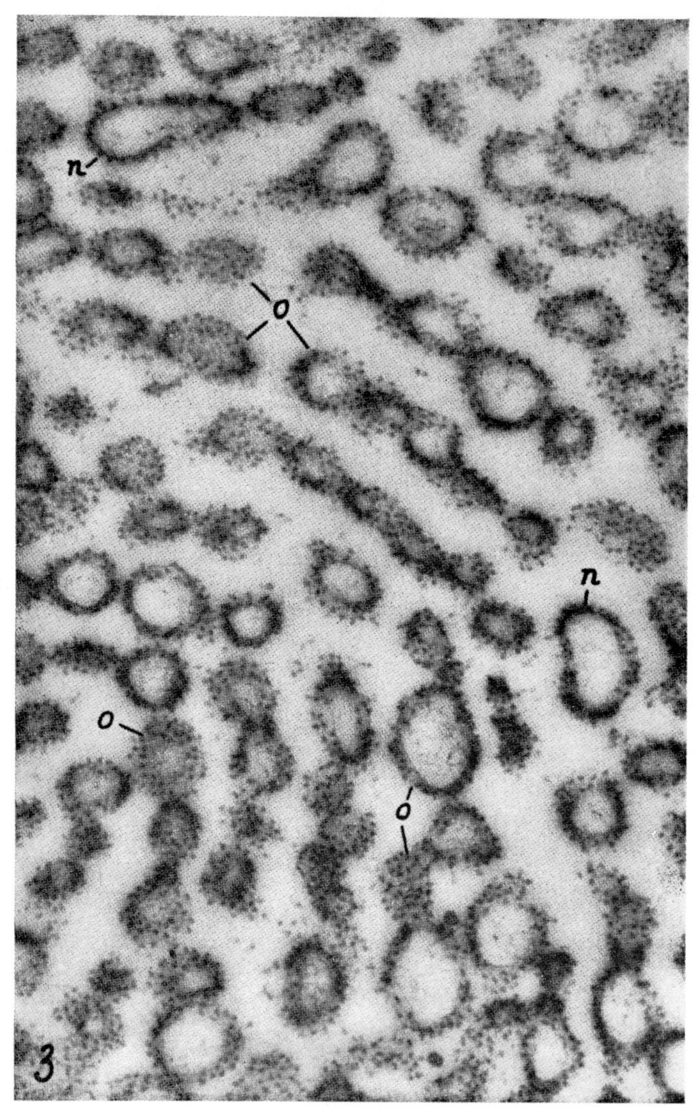

FIG. 88. Electron micrograph of microsomes in a pancreas cell. The microsomes are shown as closed vesicles limited by a thin membrane in normal (n) and oblique (o) section. Dense particles of 150 A in diameter are attached to the surface of the microsomes (magnification 50,000×) (from G. E. Palade, *Microsomal Particles and Protein Synthesis*, p. 55. Pergamon Press, London, 1958)

conclusion that one microsomal particle makes one polypeptide chain of hemoglobin in approximately 1 min".[25]

Several more steps in the mechanism of protein synthesis have been elucidated recently. It appears that the amino acids first are activated by the energy-rich adenosine triphosphate (ATP) which is produced by the mitochondria. The reaction between the ATP and a particular amino acid is catalyzed by an enzyme, and there seem to be as many activating enzymes as amino acids. Furthermore, magnesium ions are required in these activation reactions which are reversible and proceed as follows:

$$\text{ATP} + \text{Amino acid} \xrightleftharpoons{Mg^{++}} \text{Amino-acyl-adenosine monophosphate} + \text{Pyrophosphate.}$$

The same enzymes catalyze a second reaction, viz.:

$$\text{Amino-acyl-adenosine monophosphate} + \text{RNA} \rightleftharpoons \text{Amino acyl-RNA} + \text{Adenosine monophosphate.}$$

Thus the first phase in the synthesis involves incorporation of the activated amino acids onto the RNA according to the following over-all reaction:

$$\text{ATP} + \text{Amino acid} + \text{RNA} \rightleftharpoons \text{Amino-acyl-RNA} + \text{Pyrophosphate} + \text{Adenosine monophosphate.}$$[25a]

It also has been ascertained that the amino acid acceptor represents about 5–15% of the total RNA of growing cells, and that this RNA is of a relatively low molecular weight. "The chemical nature of the acceptor sites has been found to be the 2 - or 3′-hydroxyl group of the ribose of the terminal nucleotide in the polynucleotide chain." This has been verified by several facts, such as treatment of the RNA with periodate, digestion of leucyl-RNA, etc., and it is concluded that "there are specific acceptor polynucleotide chains for each different amino acid and that only a single amino acid is attached per chain" (Berg, l.c.).

The next step involves the transfer of the relatively short Amino-acyl-RNA chains to the microsomal ribonucleoprotein, and this step is less investigated than the firstly described phase. It is known that energy is needed for this transfer, and that this energy is supplied by the guanosine triphosphate (GTP).[26] The intriguing question — what causes the various amino-acyl-RNA chains to arrange themselves in the specific order of an amino acid sequence of a particular protein remains unanswered. Since a large variety of proteins is synthesized, it seems probable that there must be a large variety

[25a] P. Berg, *Abstracts, Amer. chem. Soc. Nat. Meeting, Boston*, p. 37 C, April, 1959; M. B. Hoagland, P. C. Zamecnik and M. L. Stephenson, in *A Symposium on Molecular Biology* p. 105 (R. E. Zirkle, ed.), Univ. of Chicago Press, Chicago, 1959; F. H. C. Crick, in *Biological Replication of Macromolecules* p. 138 (12. *Symp. Soc. Exp. Biol.*), Academic Press, New York, 1958; L. I. Hecht, M. L. Stephenson and P. C. Zamecnik, *Proc. Nat. Acad. Sci.* **45**, 505 (1959).

[26] M. B. Hoagland, M. L. Stephenson, J. F. Scott, L. I. Hecht and P. Zamecnik, *J. biol. Chem.* **231**, 241 (1958); H. Chantrenne, *Ann. Rev. Biochem.* **27**, 35 (1958).

of microsomal structures. It is unlikely that one and the same ribonucleoprotein of a microsome could at the same time direct a portion of the various Amino-acyl-RNA compounds so that the amino acids form a sequence of, say, histone, trypsin, and aldolase. The microsomes of some cells, such as the immature red cells, are known to synthesize only one protein (in this instance hemoglobin), while the microsomes of bacteria, pea seedlings, or liver cells probably have different types of microsomal macromolecules which determine the particular amino acid sequences assembled through the aid of ATP, GTP, and the small RNA fragments.

Finally, it must be admitted that it is not altogether certain that microsomes are the only organelles that are able to synthesize protein. Recent studies on isolated mitochondria have indicated that protein synthesis, to some extent, occurs also in the mitochondria.[26a] At least the synthesis of the essential enzyme cytochrome-*c* seems to be ascertained in the mitochondria of calf liver[26b] and calf heart.[26c] Since there is very little of RNA in the mitochondria, and since cytochrome-*c* is one of the important enzymes in the organized enzyme system in the organelle, these findings point to two possibilities: (1) that other enzymes of the redox system may be likewise synthesized in the mitochondria, and (2) that an enzyme template is needed for this synthesis. It seems that the biosynthesis of an organized enzyme system *in situ* is more comprehensible than its assemblage taking the macromolecules from a distant site. Thus, while the microsomes may be the major organelles which make proteins, the biosynthesis of these macromolecules to a limited extent probably takes place in other parts of the cell, including mitochondria, and possibly even the nucleus.

The Fibrous Framework and Organization of the Cell

Apart from the already mentioned organelles, and other granular matter originating from secretory activities of certain cells, a fibrous framework can be discerned in many types of cells. The fibrous matrix is responsible for the consistency, i.e. high viscosity of the cytoplasm, and it is known that the consistency changes in the various cytoplasmic movements, especially on such occasion as the formation of asters and spindles on cell division. There is no doubt that the various micro- and macromolecular components are moving around in the cytoplasm, e.g. the mitochondria must receive starting material for the synthesis of ATP and other energy rich molecules, and these must be transported to the microsomes or near them in order to build the activated amino acid–RNA compounds, and finally proteins in or onto the surface of the microsomes. The molecules and particles are moving, and it is

[26a] P. J. Reis, J. L. Coote and T. S. Work Nature **184**, 165 (1959).
[26b] H. M. Bates, V. M. Craddock and M. V. Simpson, *J. Amer. chem. Soc.* **80**, 1000 (1958); *J. biol. Chem.* **235**, 140 (1960).
[26c] H. M. Bates and M. V. Simpson, *Biochim. Biophys. Acta* **32**, 597 (1959).

obvious and comprehensible that accumulation of certain electrically charged units at certain spots must cause either a decrease or increase of the consistency. There is no doubt that fibrous and lamellar structures are present in cells, but these structures are not so definite and stable as those of the mitochondria and other organelles. Even the very existence of certain cytoplasmic structures, such as the so called "Golgi apparatus", is questioned. The fibrous framework in general is composed of proteins, nucleic acids, lipids, etc., and the structural features of it depend very much on the cell type, i.e. the tissue from which they are derived. Since the structures are labile, they are difficult to study, e.g. it is quite certain that the dried preparations placed in the electron microscope do not represent the actual conditions of the living cell. It is easily possible that some of the fibrous structures discerned in stained preparations under the phase microscope represent some permanent channels or membranes, while some others my be temporary linear aggregates of globular particles or macromolecules. Any such linear aggregation is known to be associated with an increases of viscosity, and vice versa.

What makes the cell function as an organized unit? This is one of the greatest unsolved problems of natural science, and we shall be confronted with it in the following chapters on several occasions. The vitalists believe that the organization cannot be derived from the macro- and micromolecular components of the cell, and that the organisation is due to some non-material principle of higher order. Others are convinced that the organization could be conceivable on the physical–chemical basis as an interplay between the various components, if the systems were more fully understood. Several attempts have been made to explain the cellular organization by an interplay of some long-range forces, such as electromagnetic oscillations, as the one recently of Marshak.[(27)] According to this author; "A source of power for driving these oscillating systems might be derived from energy input at nucleotide turnover . . . The shapes of components of the cytoplasm would also have meaning in the light of this consideration. For example, the vesicular character of the endoplasmic reticulum with its regularly spaced microsomes, suggests a role as a transducer of electromagnetic radiation from the nucleus. The mitochondrion with its chambers and cristae suggests a resonant cavity with wave channels". It is interesting to note that Oparin refutes such attempts and stresses the necessity to invoke *specific biological laws*. "This form of the motion of matter, in addition to obeying the general physical and chemical laws, also has its own specific laws. If one is to understand life it is therefore important to take into account these qualitative differences from other forms of motion" . . . "Not only are the many tens and hundreds of thousands of chemical reactions which occur in protoplasm, and which together constitute its metabolism, strictly co-ordinated with one another in

(27) A. Marshak, in *The Biological Replication of Macromolecules* p. 205 (No 12 *Symp. Soc. Experim. Biol.*), Academic Press, New York, 1958.

time, harmoniously composed into a single series of processes which constantly repeat themselves, but the whole series is directed towards a single goal, towards the uninterrupted self-preservation and self-reproduction of the living system as a whole in accordance with the conditions of the surrounding medium".[28] According to Oparin, any explanation of cellular co-ordination and organization must be based on the phylogenesis of the cell, viz. the species down to its very origin. Thus the major difficulty in the understanding of the cellular organization lies in the unaccessibility and difficulty of grasping the course of phylogenesis through the uncountable eons of the past. "The origin of the organization of protoplasm which characterizes living organisms, biological metabolism, is understandable only on the basis of the same principles which govern the origin of the 'purposefulness' of the structure of higher organisms, that is to say, on the basis of the interaction between the organism and the environment and on the basis of the Darwinian principle of natural selection. This new biological law arose during the actual process of the establishment of life and later took a leading part in the development of living matter" (ref. 28, p. 350–351). If one accepts these relevant statements, the outlook for a full understanding of the cellular organization is not very bright, since the evolution of even the simplest organisms is hidden for us in the immeasurable past. One certainly would need at least some kind of "time machine" which could show the events in the early stages of the development of our planet some billion years ago . . .

[28] A. I. OPARIN, *The Origin of Life on the Earth* p. 348 and 350, 3rd, ed. (transl. by A. SYNGE), Oliver and Boyd, Edinburgh, 1957.

CHAPTER 22

RECENT IDEAS ON BIOLOGICAL REPLICATION

> It is pleasant to speculate that modifications of the DNA molecular helix might lead to parallel changes in the chromosomal helix. It is to be admitted, however, that there is a complete gap between what we know at the cytological and at the molecular level.
>
> J. BRACHET [1]

THE PERTINENCE of the above statement of Brachet should be evident to everybody who compares the simple macromolecular models of nucleic acids with the bewildering variety of morphological details observed in cells. Yet it is encouraging that the gap between the cytological and molecular level seems to be narrowing down, at least at a few points. It is the purpose of this chapter to report the most important recent attempts to bridge this gap. While much of the experimental material presented by various authors is often controversial, some generalization is already possible without too much speculation. Some of the most important discoveries have already been mentioned in the previous chapters, and it seems to be worthwhile to recapitulate some of them here.

Macromolecules and their Functional Relationships in the Cell

It is established that the macromolecules of proteins and nucleic acids are essential consituents of cells, and the following more detailed information relates them to the functions of the living cell. Any cell contains a great variety of proteins, many millions of different macromolecules which act as enzymes, i.e. catalyze the many reaction chains which are essential for maintaining the life of the cell and its reproduction. The other functions of proteins involve such important assignments as participation in fibrillar and lamellar structures of the cell wall, and the various organelles. Furthermore, the basic histones (and the basic protamines) are used to neutralize the acid groups of the nucleic acids. It has also been established that in the mitochondria the proteins constitute spatially organized enzyme systems. The exact arrangement of these enzymes in the mitochondrial membranes and channels is unknown, yet this is one of the most successful attemps to bridge the gap between the microscopic and macromolecular levels. The nucleic acids are found in both the nucleus and cytoplasm. The major portion, if not all, of the DNA is found in the nuclear

[1] J. BRACHET, *Biochemical Cytology* p. 209, Academic Press, New York, 1957.

chromatin substance which carries the genetic blueprints, while the RNA is found in many parts of the cell: in the nucleolus, microsomes, and possibly also in the nuclear sap, and other regions. There is also a difference between the molecular size and configuration. The DNA macromolecules all are very large (M = 4–8 million), and they represent gently curved rods, whereas the RNA units may be either large (M = 0·5–2 million) or relatively much smaller (M = 5000–50,000), and have a tightly coiled globular configuration. There is not much doubt that the large and relatively stable DNA units of the chromosomes are connected with the transmission of genetic information, and very directly these DNA effects can be studied in the multiplication of phages and the effects of isolated DNA on bacterial transformations. It has been found that the DNA which was isolated from a strain of certain bacteria (e.g. *Pneumococcus*) can transform another strain into the one from which the DNA originates.[2,3] The mechanism of the transformation is not fully understood, although it is known that it is not the bacterium which absorbs the DNA that is transformed; the new features become obvious only in the progeny. The role and importance of the RNA and residual protein which still may be present even in "highly purified" DNA also should not be disregarded. This phenomenon is similar to the imprinting of the species specificity by the RNA of tobacco mosaic virus described in chapt. 20. Thus the very large macromolecules of RNA, like those of DNA, are able to transmit genetic information. But it seems that RNA displays some directive effects not only in some viruses. The hemoglobin synthesis, as mentioned in the previous chapter, is directed by the RNA of the microsomes of immature red cells. Now, it is known that the hemoglobin synthesis is genetically controlled, and that abnormal hemoglobins can be synthesized as a result of inherited mutations (chapt. 14). This brings the RNA in a direct connection with the effectuation of inherited features. However, it also must be admitted that there is scarcely any RNA in a spermatozoid cell, and thus the synthesis may still be indirectly dependent on a chromosomal gene of DNA, and that in the course of differentiation the defect is transmitted to the RNA.

It seems that *the triad DNA-RNA-protein is the pivot around which the processes of the cell are revolving and are being kept in a well-balanced equilibrium.* Although the nuclear DNA probably holds the "blueprints" for the complex series of processes, the RNA and some of the so-called residual protein tightly bound to DNA may also be important. Some of the RNA is very probably synthesized in the nucleus, and is migrating to the cytoplasm, where its synthesis continues in a variety of ways. These various macromole-

[2] R. D. HOTCHKISS, in *The Nucleic Acids* Vol. 2, p. 435 (E. CHARGAFF and J. N. DAVIDSON, ed.), Academic Press, New York, 1955.

[3] S. ZAMENHOF, *Progress in Biophys. and Biophys. Chem.* **6**, 85 (1956); J. LEDERBERG, *Harvey Lectures* **53**, 69 (1959); see also the articles of H. EPHRUSSI-TAYLOR, R. D. HOTCHKISS, S. ZAMENHOF, R. M. HERRIOTT, and others in *The Chemical Basis of Heredity* (W. D. MCELROY and B. GLASS, ed.), Hopkins Press, Baltimore, 1957.

cules then are used as templates for assembling the amino acids, viz. protein synthesis. However, these directive effects of the nucleic acids are not one-sided, that is — *protein synthesis depends on the nucleic acids as much as the nucleic acid synthesis depends on the enzyme proteins*!

These are some of the shaky bridges between the abyss of the unknown separating the domains of cytology and macromolecular chemistry of the cellular ingredients. It is not the purpose of this treatise to describe the very interesting morphological details which have been observed in various cells by means of the modern optical and other methods, but it may be relevant to mention some facts. First, the nuclear chromosome is not a simple assemblage of DNA fibers but it is a rather complex organ. The chromatin threads in the cells of various plant and animal cells may assume an indescribable variety of shapes and constellations. Moreover, a chromosome is not always a thread, it may be also granular, or filamentous. A variety of structures have been observed not only in chromosomes but also in the nucleolus.[4] The mitotic asters and spindles are very interesting and diverse, and little is known what exactly are the macromolecules that are forming these structures. The same is true about the fibrous matrix of the cell, and about the various membranes. In the instance of the small microbial cells, which do not contain any mitochondria, some of the "power generating" enzyme systems are probably located at the inside of the membrane.

The distribution of the major macromolecular components in a cell is illustrated in the following scheme:

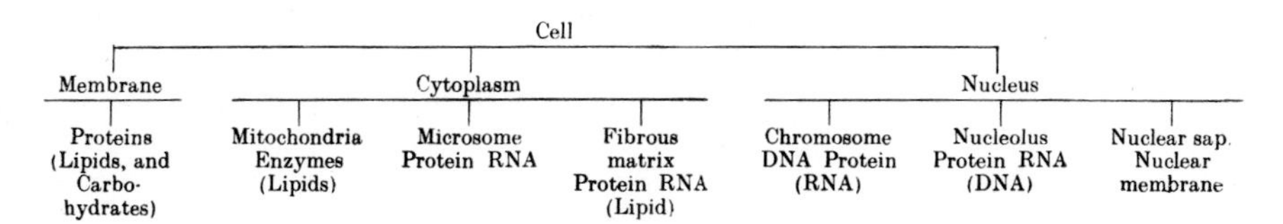

Several other terms used for the description of the various cellular structures by the cytologists have been avoided, partially because these structures are not permanent and partially because they are very little investigated from a biochemical point of view.

The Replication of Cellular Macromolecules

A cell functions as an organized unit, and Claude suggests that the mechanisms of cellular processes would be better understood if the concept of reduplication would be extended to all components of the cell. "In recent years, attention has been centered almost exclusively on the problem of redu-

(4) C. Estable and J. R. Sotelo, in *Fine Structure of Cells* p. 170, Interscience, New York, 1955.

plication of gene substance, although it is obvious that all the other essential cell structures are likewise reduplicated during cell growth, or at the time of cell division".[5] At the time when these words were written, and it is only about ten years ago, several variations of the *template* concept were much in fashion. According to this view, the gene substance plays the role of a mold that imprints the structural features on the assembled molecular material. Such simple template idea, according to Claude, is unacceptable, since the template would produce a "negative" which would be unusable; hence, it would be necessary to assume the building of an intermediate replica; this then would assemble the material in the right order, and could be later discarded. There was no evidence of such intermediate replicas and their discarding, and so it happened that the whole concept itself was discarded. "In the light of biochemical processes already known, it is conceivable that the duplication of essential and characteristic cell substances is the end result of a series of rigidly ordered chains of reactions, the final product in turn taking part at some point, and thereby directing the specificity, of the same or other, interlocked, biochemical cycles".[5]

In 1953, Watson and Crick proposed the now so popular *double-helix* for DNA which permitted a somewhat more realistic interpretation of replication than the old template hypothesis.[6] Since the double helix has already been discussed in chapt. 19, the basic features will be only briefly recapitulated. In the model of Watson and Crick, the two DNA chains are spiralling in opposite directions around each other, and they are bound together by hydrogen bond pairs between the base pairs adenine–thymine and guanine–cytosine. There are three groups of factual evidence that support this kind of model: (1) analytical data about the base ratio, (2) X-ray diffraction data, and (3) physicochemical data on the molecular dimensions, asymmetry, and stiffness in solutions (see chapt. 19). The replication of this double-helical DNA can be thought to occur as follows: due to some as yet unknown reason, the double helix *unwinds*, and each of the chains serves as a template for its counterpart, viz. the polynucleotide sequence as it was in the original double helix; upon completion of this process, there are two identical double helices which are also identical with the original unit. The energy needed could be provided by the nucleotides themselves which are synthesized in the mitochondrial enzyme systems. While the model certainly is attractive, and was accepted by most biochemists with enthusiasm, the gap between the macromolecular level and cellular level is still very considerable. First, there are difficulties in understanding of the mechanism of unwinding. Crick suggests that this difficulty may be overcome by the assumption that the assemblage of the nucleotides and the formation of the complementary chains does not require complete unwinding, i.e. that the complementary chains are formed

[5] A. Claude, *Adv. Protein Chem.* **5**, 423 (1949); quoted from p. 433 and 434.

[6] J. D. Watson and F. H. C. Crick, *Nature* **171**, 737, 964 (1953); Crick, *Proc. Nat. Acad. Sci.* **0**·, 756 (1954).

at the end as soon as a little unwinding has occurred (Fig. 89). The energy needed for further breakage of the hydrogen bonds of the parent chains then would be provided from the excessive energy liberated at the growing new chains. However, there are several other difficulties, for example, to explain

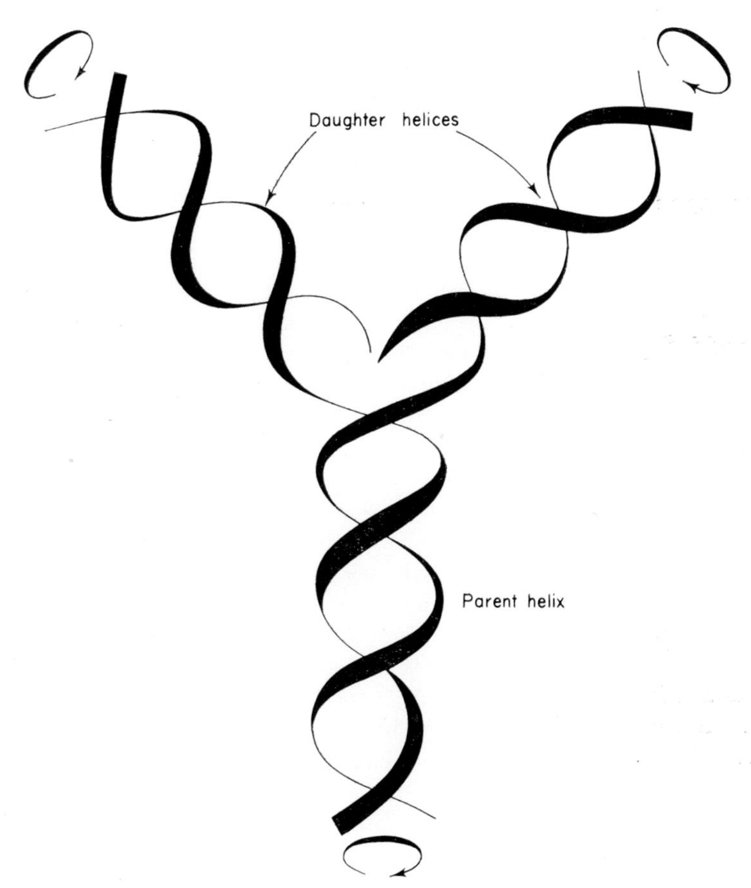

FIG. 89. Unwinding of the DNA double helix according to Watson and Crick

the DNA interaction in crossing over, i.e. the interaction of the DNA strands from two cells (mating). Further difficulties would involve such matters as the role of protein components associated with the DNA in the chromosomes. It seems likely that the newly formed DNA might need a protein coat, since DNA is known to be existing in a nucleoprotein complex, and thus the replication of DNA should be associated with protein synthesis.[7] Also it has

[7] CH. B. ANFINSEN, *The Molecular Basis of Evolution* chapt. 8–11, Wiley, New York, 1959.

been concluded that "the increase in mutation frequency promoted by preirradiation incubation with purines and pyrimidines is dependent on postirradiation protein synthesis".[8] Since any mutation involves changes in the DNA, the close association between the DNA and protein components is obvious. The Watson–Crick model, however, ignores the protein entirely.

"Much thought and effort has been spent in attempting to understand the molecular nature of isolated DNA, and this has culminated in the two-stranded model of Watson and Crick, which seems to be compatible with all of the physicochemical and physical investigations of DNA to date. However, it appears that no really satisfactory way has yet been proposed to make the Watson–Crick model account for the dynamics of the cellular duplication of DNA molecules. It seems possible that it will be necessary to take into account the mode of binding of DNA to protein in the chromosomes in order to understand this process completely, as well as to understand the replication of chromosomal structure" . . . "In regard to the role of histone, I propose what I believe to be a new idea, namely that histone may serve to block one of the two strands of the DNA double helix. One of the strands is redundant as far as information storage is concerned and, therefore, it may be necessary to block possible template function of one strand of DNA in whatever process may exist for the expression of gene action in RNA or protein synthesis. The mode of attachment of DNA to the residual protein could determine which chain of the DNA was to be blocked by the histone".[8a]

The theory of Watson and Crick has initiated a series of experiments which were designed in order to check the one or other consequence of the concept. For example, the incorporation of labeled nucleotides into the DNA macromolecules of phages has been investigated. In accord with the Watson–Crick model, it was found that there were DNA macromolecules which had half of the radioactivity of the original molecule.[9] The involvment of a more complicated mechanism in the phage DNA multiplication than the original scheme of Watson and Crick, however, has been indicated by Stent.[10] The study of other biological systems has led to rather conflicting results. The incorporation of tritium-labeled thymidine into the DNA of bean chromosomes proceeded according to the Watson–Crick model,[11] while the incorporation of ^{14}C-labeled thymidine into the seedlings of some other plants took a different course.[12] The problems are being studied intensively in

(8) F. L. Haas and C. O. Doudney, *Proc. Nat. Acad. Sci.* **43**, 871 (1957).

(8a) A. L. Dounce, *Ann. N. Y. Acad. Sci.* **81**, (3), 794 (1959).

(9) C. Levinthal, *Proc. Nat. Acad. Sci.* **42**, 394 (1956); M. Meselson and F. W. Stahl, *Proc. Nat. Acad. Sci.* **44**, 671 (1958).

(10) G. S. Stent, *Adv. Virus Res.* **5**, 95 (1958).

(11) J. H. Taylor, P. S. Woods and W. L. Hughes, *Proc. Nat. Acad. Sci.* **43**, 122 (1957).

(12) D. Mazia and W. S. Plaut, *Biol. Bull.* **100**, 335 (1955); D. Mazia, in *Enzymes, Units of Biological Structure and Function* p. 261 (O. H. Gaebler, ed.), Academic Press, New York, 1956.

various laboratories, and the results thus far obtained have been presented in reviews and discussed in conferences.[13,14] In addition, some geneticists are attempting to correlate their genetic maps with the structure of DNA. Although at present there is nothing much more than an analogy between the linear arrangement of the genes in a chromosome and the linearity of the DNA macromolecule, the basic idea is sound. There is hope that a time will come when it will be possible to identify the genes with quite definite *nucleotide sequences* in the macromolecules of DNA. This, however, is a distant goal, since very little is known about the nucleotide sequences. One of the greatest difficulties, from the chemical side, is the difficulty to obtain pure and homogeneous DNA preparations (see chapt. 19). Not only is it difficult to liberate a DNA preparation from traces of protein and RNA, but any of the DNA's which can be considered "pure" are composed of macromolecules of somewhat different size, configuration, and nucleotide sequence. According to Chargaff: "Conceivably, no two nucleic acid molecules, within the same nucleus, are entirely identical",[15] and chemistry has not yet devised methods for separating macromolecules which differ but slightly.

While the general idea of Watson and Crick about the double helix, unwinding, and complementation of the chains is clear and acceptable, the assemblage of the nucleotides in the *exact complementary sequence* is not fully explained. It must be borne in mind that, although the DNA double helix is relatively stiff, it still possesses some flexibility. It is obvious that this flexibility must be enhanced in the state of replication when the strands unwind and react with the nucleotides. Thus, even if the sequence of the nucleotides be spatially conditioned, "mistakes" could readily occur due to the Brownian movement and flexibility of the chain segments.

The replication of a single-chain nucleic acid, such as the RNA, is even more difficult to understand. Since the protein synthesis is genetically determined (see chapt. 14 about the abnormal hemoglobins), and since the RNA participates in protein synthesis, the synthesis of RNA must be determined by the DNA. But how? Lockingen and DeBusk have tried to explain this as follows.[16] There are indications that the DNA chains in the double helix have breaks,[17] and that these breaks may be staggered relative to one another; thus a piece of a DNA chain can be split off, and it can be assumed that a new RNA chain is assembled in the segment of the distorted double helix. When the synthesis is completed, the newly formed RNA leaves the

(13) *The Biological Replication of Macromolecules* (XII *Symp. Soc. Exp. Biol.*), Academic Press, New York, 1958.

(14) W. D. McElroy and B. Glass (ed.), *The Chemical Basis of Heredity*, Hopkins Press, Baltimore, 1957.

(15) E. Chargaff, in *Fibrous Proteins and their Biological Significance* p. 32 (IX *Symp. Soc. Experim. Biol.*), Academic Press, New York, 1955; quotation from p. 47.

(16) L. S. Lockingen and A. G. DeBusk, *Proc. Nat. Acad. Sci.* **41**, 925 (1955).

(17) C. A. Dekker and H. K. Schachman, *Proc. Nat. Acad. Sci.* **40**, 894 (1954).

groove of the double helix, and another RNA unit can be assembled in the same place. This hypothesis, however, has several weak points. First, the existence of subunits and breaks in the double-chain DNA unit is not well proved. Second, it is not clear why some segment of the one chain should split off. Third, it is difficult to comprehend why a RNA rather than a DNA chain should be assembled in the groove. But if it really could be proved that a RNA chain is somehow assembled onto a DNA chain, this would be comprehensible only assuming certain variability and flexibility of the DNA. At least the intervention of certain enzymes which modify the DNA would be necessary.

There is experimental evidence that RNA is synthesized in the nucleus, a fact best proved by tracer studies. "The RNA of the nucleus was labeled with radioactive tracer, and the nucleus was grafted into a cell whose RNA was unlabeled. Transmission of labeled material from nucleus to cytoplasm was then traced directly by autoradiography. The evidence presented shows that RNA is synthesized in the nucleus and that RNA, or at least a nucleus-modified precursor of RNA, is transmitted to the cytoplasm".[18] This was ascertained by using amoebae as test organisms. While these and other observations establish the role of the nucleus in the synthesis of RNA, the mechanism of this synthesis is unknown. It is possible that the production of these important macromolecules occurs in the nucleoli upon the unwinding of specific double helical RNA, which then would represent a specific type of nucleic acids occurring in such small amounts that it has thus far escaped preparative methods and identification. Some fraction of the double-helical nucleic acid units, either in the chromosomes or nucleolus, due to specific nucleotide composition and sequence, may unwind, be fragmented, and carried away into the cytoplasm. Thus it is possible that the *replication of the RNA occurs principally in the same way as the replication of DNA*. The appearance of the RNA in the form of single chain macromolecules, as observed in the preparations of native RNA (chapt. 19), then would be due to its *composition* and also *enviromental effects*, viz. that the double helix can persist only in the specific nuclear mileu. (The cytoplasmic RNA, as well as the macromolecules of isolated RNA, are globular, due to extensive coiling of the linear single chain macromolecules.) Of course, the configuration of the hypothetical double chain RNA of the nucleus cannot be the same as that of DNA, because of the extra oxygen in the sugar residues and differences in base composition.

While the above mentioned mechanism is not too unreasonable for cells, the multiplication of RNA of plant viruses poses new problems. The species specificity-determining-RNA of the tobacco mosaic virus is a single chain macromolecule which seems simply to grow longer when introduced into the host. It not only grows according to a fixed pattern, but even determines the

[18] L. GOLDSTEIN and W. PLAUT, *Proc. Nat. Acad. Sci.* **41**, 874 (1955); L. GOLDSTEIN and J. MICON, *J. Biophys. Biochem. Cytol.* **6**, 301 (1959); D. M. PRESCOTT, *ibid.* **6**, 203 (1959).

protein synthesis (see chapt. 20). It is, however, very difficult to imagine how the various nucleotides could line up in the exact order, if the multiplication is thought to be linear growths without a template. It seems more likely that in this instance too the chains are used as patterns for building complementary chains.

Another fact to take into account in these considerations is the possibility of enzymatic *in vitro* synthesis of RNA from nucleotides.[18a] According to Ochoa, this reaction proceeds in the presence of the enzyme polynucleotide phosphorylase and magnesium ions as follows:

$$n\,X\text{-}R\text{-}PP \rightleftarrows (X\text{-}R\text{-}P)_n + n\,P,$$

where X stands for any of the bases, R for ribose, and P for phosphate. The formula $(X-R-P)_n$ represents the macromolecules of the polynucleotides that may vary in size between molecular weights of 30,000 and 2,000,000. Although these polynucleotides are not identical with any of the native RNA's, the similarity, especially with respect to composition, structure, and *X*-ray diffraction spectra is very remarkable. This work indicates that the biosynthesis of certain types of RNA may be possible without the participation of a DNA template.

One can see from this brief survey that in spite of the progress of the last five years the replication of the nucleic acids is still an unsolved problem. "There exists suggestive experimental evidence that protein synthesis may be an essential part of DNA replication, that information transfer occurs to some unknown molecular structure, that mating may be an integral part of replication" ... "It appears to us that no definite conclusions regarding replication can be drawn at the present moment".[19] The same scepticism appears in Chargaffs' remarks about the determining role of DNA: "The ease with which transforming principles can be inactivated makes it improbable that nucleotide sequence in itself can be the only determinant; and a similar conclusion would apply to the amino acid sequence in many proteins".[20]

It must be admitted that the assemblage of identical protein molecules from activated amino acids at a RNA template is an even much more difficult unsolved problem than the replication of the nucleic acids. First, it must be pointed out that there are two principal possibilities: first, that the polypeptide chain is assembled from activated amino acids directly on a RNA template, or, second, that the major role of the RNA is to unfold a parent molecule of a protein which then serves as a template together with the RNA.

(18a) M. Grunberg-Manago, P. J. Ortiz and S. Ochoa, *Biochim. Biophys. Acta* **20**, 269 (1956); S. Ochoa, *Arch. Biochem. Biophys.* **69**, 119 (1957); S. Ochoa, *Ann. N. Y. Acad. Sci.* **81** (3), 690 (1959); L. A. Heppel, M. F. Singer and R. J. Hilmoe, *ibid.* p. 635; R. J. Hilmoe, *ibid.* p. 660; E. S. Canellakis, *ibid.* p. 675.

(19) M. Delbruck and G. Stent, in *The Chemical Basis of Heredity* p. 699 (W. D. McElroy and B. Glass, ed.), Hopkins Press, Baltimore, 1957, quotation from p. 735.

(20) E. Chargaff, *ibid.* p. 521; quotation from p. 526.

The first possibility admits that a protein chain could be assembled *de novo*, i.e. without a parent protein, while the other requires a parent molecule as part of the template.

Biosynthesis of DNA

The enzymic synthesis of deoxyribonucleic acid is one of the greatest achievements in modern biochemistry, and the credit is due to Kornberg, and his associates.[21,22] It has been demonstrated that DNA can be synthesized in vitro from the deoxynucleoside triphosphates of adenine, guanine, cytosine, and thymine, in the presence of an enzyme from *Escherichia coli*, magnesium ions, and a DNA primer. The reaction is reversible, and it proceeds as follows:

$$n\,\text{ATP} + n\,\text{GTP} + n\,\text{CTP} + n\,\text{TTP} + \text{DNA} \xrightleftharpoons{\text{Enz., Mg}^{++}} \text{DNA}-(\text{AP, GP, CP, TP})_n + 4\,n\ \text{Pyrophosphate},$$

where ATP, GTP, CTP, and TTP are the triphosphates of the nucleosides, and AP, GP, CP, and TP, the respective nucleotide residues in the macromolecule. Evidence has been presented that the deoxynucleoside triphosphates reacted only with the *ends* of the primer, and that the new mers were linked through the 3′,5′-phosphodiester linkages, as in the native DNA.[23]

"Analysis of the purine and pyrimidine composition of DNA, enzymatically synthesized in the presence of a variety of DNA primers, reveals that the content of adenine residues is equal to that of thymine and that the number of guanine residues equals the cytosine residues. These results agree with the composition data for DNA samples isolated from nature and with the requirements of the DNA structure proposed by Watson and Crick. The ratio of the number of adenine–thymine pairs to the number of guanine–cytosine pairs in an enzymatically synthesized sample reflects the ratio present in the primer used in its synthesis; the ratios in the primers tested varied from 0·5 to 40. Distortion of the relative concentrations of the deoxynucleotide substrates in the reaction mixture or variation of the extent of enzymatic

(21) M. J. Bessman, I. R. Lehman, J. Adler, S. B. Zimmerman, E. S. Simms and A. Kornberg, *Proc. Nat. Acad. Sci.* **44**, 633 (1958).

(22) I. R. Lehman, S. B. Zimmerman, J. Adler, M. J. Bessman, E. S. Simms and A. Kornberg, *ibid.* **44**, 1191 (1958); A. Kornberg, *The Harvey Lectures* p. 83. **53** (1957–1958), Academic Press, New York, 1959. A. Kornberg, in *A Symposium on Molecular Biology* p. 31. (R. E. Zirkle, ed.), Univ. of Chicago Press, Chicago, 1959. The Nobel Prize was awarded to Kornberg and Ochoa in 1959.

(23) J. Adler, I. R. Lehman, M. J. Bessman, E. S. Simms and A. Kornberg, *Proc. Nat. Acad. Sci.* **44**, 641 (1958); see also M. J. Bessman, I. R. Lehman, E. S. Simms and A. Kornberg, *J. biol. Chem.* **233**, 171 (1958), and A. Kornberg, in *The Chemical Basis of Heredity* p. 579 (W. D. McElroy and B. Glass, ed.), Hopkins Press, Baltimore, 1957.

synthesis from 2 to more than 1000 per cent had no effect on the composition of the DNA product. These results suggest that the enzymatic synthesis of DNA by the *'polymerase'* of *E. coli* represents the replication of a DNA template" (ref. 22, quotation from Proc. Natl. Acad. Sci. **44,** p. 1196, 1958.)

While the four triphosphates were found to be essential in the synthesis of a DNA which has the same composition as the native DNA, synthetic deoxyribonucleoside triphosphates of analogues of pyrimidine and purine bases also could be incorporated. Thus uracil and 5-bromouracil could be incorporated in place of thymine, 5-methyl- and 5-bromocytosine in place of cytosine, and hypoxanthine in place of guanine, while xanthine was not incorporated. These data also are in agreement with the Watson–Crick hydrogen bond linked double-helix.[21]

Whether the DNA synthesis in a living cell occurs according to exactly the same mechanism, is not known. It is conceivable that the nucleotide units, in the form of the energy-rich triphosphates, are supplied by the mitochondria, and that the polymerase resides in the nucleus. There is no doubt that the synthetic DNA resembles the native DNA very closely, especially in the base ratio. However, a full identity between the native and enzymically synthesized nucleic acid is not yet established. One of the tests in which the synthetic DNA has failed was its efficiency as a bacterial transforming factor. What is the reason for this failure, is not known. One of the reasons might be contamination of the preparations with deoxyribonuclease. It might be also more than that, viz. that the cellular DNA has a different nucleotide sequence from the synthetic product. Moreover, it is possible that the residual protein of the native DNA has some important function as yet not explained.

Finally, the recent attempts of step-by-step chemical syntheses of oligonucleotides should be mentioned.[23a] Thus far only relatively small molecules of predetermined sequence and known end groups have been obtained, but further progress is ascertained. This work is of great importance. First, it provides relatively simple oligonucleotides which can serve as standards of known structure for the identification of partial degradation products of DNA, and these identifications are essential in the sequence studies of the macromolecular DNA (see chapt. 19). Second, these oligonucleotides may serve as building blocks for either a chemical step-by-step synthesis or polymerization in order to make macromolecules of definite structure. Of course, it is obvious that a chemical synthesis of DNA of a definite structure is an extremely distant goal, but the first steps towards it have been made. This approach somewhat resembles the early work of the great Emil Fischer on step-by-step syntheses of large polypeptides. The difficulties involved in these attempts are fully realized only now, as we know so much more about the protein structure. Will the nucleic acids be easier to manage ? Although they are structurally

(23a) H. G. Khorana, *J. Cellular Comp. Physiol.* **54,** *Suppl.*, 5 (1959); P. T. Gilham and H. G. Khorana, *J. Amer. chem. Soc.* **81,** 4647 (1959); A. F. Turner and H. G. Khorana, *ibid.* **81,** 4651 (1959).

simpler than proteins, the linear configuration of the DNA's renders these macromolecules extremely unwieldy for handling (isolation and identification as chemical individuals). The ultimate success in this challenging field will depend not only on the development of convenient and efficient syntheses of the oligo- and polynucleotides but also on the development of new sensitive methods of fractionation and analytical determination.

Concluding Remarks

In conclusion, it can be said that considerable progress has been made in the understanding of the replication of the deoxyribonucleic acids (DNA's). The replication is comprehensible as complementation of the partially unwound double-helix of Watson and Crick. While the phenomena on the cellular level are much more complex than the model, the basic idea is sound, and it is supported by experimental evidence from chemical-analytical, physico-chemical, and biochemical sources. The enzymic synthesis of DNA, accomplished by Kornberg *et al.*, supports the paired double-helical model. It can be hoped that some of the still existing controversies will be explained by taking into account some thus far disregarded factors in the process of replication, such as the presence of the protein moiety.

The replication of the ribonucleic acid (RNA's) cannot be explained as satisfactorily as the replication of DNA. It is possible that the nuclear synthesis of RNA is somehow conditioned (directed) by the DNA, and that the replication may involve a somewhat similar mechanism as the replication of the DNA. The replication certainly requires a definite *medium*, i.e. the presence of enzymes. Compositional correlations between the DNA's and RNA's have been established recently on a wide experimental basis, in 19 species. A part of RNA, however, seems to be independent of DNA.[24]

Definite progress has been achieved also in elucidating the protein synthesis. The first definitive proof of the involvment of RNA was presented at about 1955,[25] and during the last few years it was demonstrated by several groups of biochemists, that a whole series of enzymes are involved in these reactions. It is now known that the activated amino acids are first attached to the ends of relatively small RNA-chains (the soluble RNA or SRNA). These pieces then are assembled at the larger microsomal RNA's where they combine, forming the macromolecules of proteins. Speculations on the possible mechanisms of this assemblage and directing effects of the nucleic acid, however, are not convincing,[26] and any thorough experimental study reveals

[24] A. N. BELOZERSKY and A. S. SPIRIN, *Nature* **182**, 111 (1958); A. SPIRIN, *Abstracts, 4th Internat. Congr. Biochem., Vienna* p. 35, 1958, Pergamon Press, London, 1958; see also: M. YCAS, in *A Symposium on Molecular Biology* p. 115 (R. E. ZIRKLE, ed.), Univ. of Chicago Press, Chicago, 1959; A. RICH, *Ann. N. Y. Acad. Sci.* **81**, (3), 709 (1959).

[25] E. F. GALE and J. P. FOLKES, *Biochem. J.* **59**, 661 (1955).

[26] F. H. C. CRICK in *The Biological Replication of Macromolecules* p. 138 (XII *Symp. Soc. Exp. Biol.*), Academic Press, New York, 1958.

more and more facts which show the inadequacy of any of these speculations.[27] The crucial problem is the *sequence* of the amino acids in the polypeptide chains. There has been speculation about the possibility that the sequence is coded by certain sequence of three or four nucleotides in the RNA templates. Thus far these speculations have not explained anything.[27a]

No protein is replicated by a simple growth and division, or by simple autocatalytic modification. (The enzymes formed in autocatalytic activation of precursors are not synthesized *de novo* but they are produced by splitting off a piece of the macromolecule of the precursor; see chapt. 15). *Thus we come to the conclusion that any enzyme is synthesized by the aid of many other enzymes, and with the intervention of RNA.* The mechanism of this intervention, however, is obscure.

The organized cellular processes involve *mutual interdependence between the major macromolecular components, such as the nucleic acids and proteins.* The proteins cannot be synthesized without the nucleic acids, and the nucleic acid synthesis and replication requires enzymes. In addition, a whole series of inorganic ions, lipids, and other small molecules are participating in these highly developed, organized cycles. These interrelationships are visualized in the following scheme:

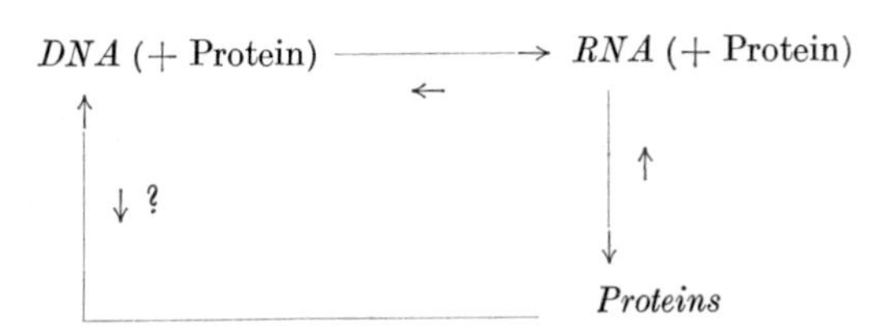

Finally, a model illustrating the possible alignment of the amino acids on the surface of a microsomal RNA will be presented. Although the model is about as primitive as that of hooking atoms by small hooks and loops, as was envisaged by some chemists a couple of hundred years ago, it gives some idea what actually happens. According to this model, the alignment in a specific sequence is determined by the interaction of the amino acid side chains (pictured black) with the RNA. In addition, the positively charged amino groups of the amino acid are bound electrostatically to the phosphate groups of the RNA. The template functions of the RNA thus are determined chiefly by the specific configuration and structure of the RNA and the side groups of the amino acids[28]. The aminoacyl anhydrides, which are attached at the ends of polynucleotide chains (N), are thus arranged in a certain order.

(27) N. Sueoka, J. Marmur and P. Doty, *Nature* **183**, 1429 (1959).

(27a) See e. g. *Symposium on Information Theory in Biology*, H. P. Yockey, R. L. Platzman and H. Quastler (ed.), Pergamon Press, London, 1958.

(28) R. B. Loftfield, *Progress in Biophys. and Biophys. Chem.* **8**, 347 (1957).

(Although the presented illustration does not show it, the nucleotide portion of the activated amino acid also may interact with the template). The peptide bonds then are formed by the interaction of the energy-rich carbonyl–phosphate anhydride group and the amino group of a vicinal amino acid (see Fig. 90). The polynucleotide thereby is split off, while the newly formed peptide remains still at the surface of the RNA template. However, since

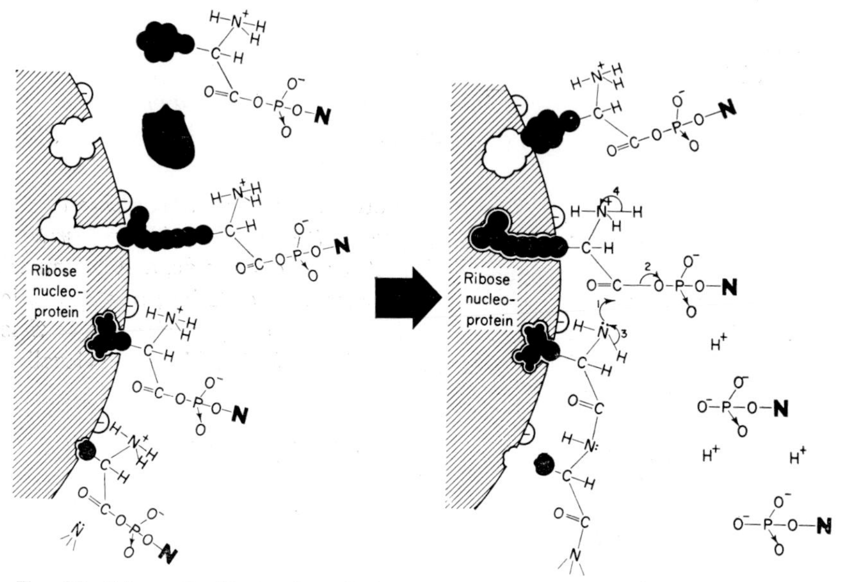

FIG. 90. Schematic illustration of the biosynthesis of protein at the surface of a ribonucleoprotein particle according to Loftfield (from Loftfield, *Progress in Biophysics*, vol. 8, p. 380, Pergamon Press, London, 1957)

there are no more amino groups (they were changed into imino groups of the peptide bonds), the peptide chains remain bound by the relatively weak interaction between the side chains and template, and its liberation should not require too much energy.

Similar ideas about the role of microsomal RNA in directing the amino acids in the proper order have been developed by Hoagland *et al.*,[29] who have done most of the experimental work in this field (see also p. 347). However, these authors suggest that the sequences are determined solely by the complementary nucleotide sequences in the microsomal RNA and the soluble RNA which carries the activated amino acids.

[29] M. B. HOAGLAND, P. C. ZAMECNIK and M. L. STEPHENSON, in *A Symposium on Molecular Biology* p. 105 (R. E. ZIRKLE, ed.), Univ. of Chicago Press, Chicago, 1959. See also: F. LIPMANN *et al.*, *J. Cell. Comparat. Physiol.* **54,** (Suppl. I), 75 (1959).

CHAPTER 23

MACROMOLECULES IN BLOOD

> More recent electrophoretic studies have all yielded evidence which clearly demonstrates that the plasma protein patterns as determined in this manner are distinctive for each individual.
>
> ROGER J. WILLIAMS [1]

BLOOD is a very complex component of the circulatory system of a higher organism. Microbes and similar simple organisms do not have a special circulatory systems and blood. All the essential functions of life, such as obtaining nutrients, excretion of waste, defence, internal transport and communication, are accomplished in a microbe by direct transport through the cell wall and protoplasmic movements. A special circulatory system is developed only in the larger, more specialized and differentiated organisms, and a variety of intermediate stages of organization can be observed in the various species, starting with simple channels and ending with the elaborate circulatory system of higher mammals. The anatomic complexity is paralleled by the compositional complexity of the liquid contents of the system.

As an integral component of the circulatory system, blood is involved in a series of important functions, such as transport of nutrients and waste products, regulatory function of contact and communication between various tissue systems and organs, sometimes in distant parts of the body, and of protective function. A subfunction in the general nutritional assignments is the respiratory function, viz. transport of oxygen and the carbon dioxide waste. The regulatory functions include maintenance of water content, body temperature, acidity–alkalinity, ionic strength, and circulation of hormones. The protective function is exerted by various means, such as the activity of leukocytes, and of a whole series of proteins.

The circulatory system and blood is studied from various points of view. The practically most important approaches include physiological studies on circulation, activity of heart, blood pressure, etc.; clinical and medical studies involve chiefly determination of the various cellular and chemical constituents in connexion with the health status of the body, and a whole discipline — hematology — has been developed. Biologists and biochemists are investigating blood from various more or less theoretical, viz. fundamental views. The literature on blood, due to the importance of the subject, is so extensive

(1) ROGER J. WILLIAMS, *Biochemical Inividuality* p. 50, Wiley, New York, 1956.

that only a few general sources can be mentioned,[2,3,4,5] particularly those concerned with the macromolecules found in blood. As already indicated in previous chapters, certain proteins are of paramount importance in the respiratory function (hemoglobin), transport (albumin), as well as regulatory (hormones), and protective (γ-globulins) functions.

When blood is drawn from a vein it tends to clot. The framework of the clot is composed of the formed elements, and the yellowish serum includes the various serum proteins and other ingredients. The framework is cemented together by fibrin, a modified macromolecular derivative of the soluble fibrinogen. Clotting can be prevented by drawing the blood into a container with a solution of oxalate or another anticlotting agent. In this instance the blood separates in to two layers: a dark red layer containing the corpuscles or formed elements, and a yellowish layer, called plasma. The chief difference between plasma and serum is that the former contains fibrinogen which is absent in the latter. Sometimes the plasma or serum are colored red; this indicates that part of the red cells have burst (hemolyzed) and have released their contents into the solution. There are three major classes of corpuscles (formed elements) in the blood: the red cells or erythrocytes, the white cells or leukocytes, and the platelets of thrombocytes.

A very important subject concerned with the properties of whole blood is that of blood groups.[6,7] Blood transfusion cannot be done indiscriminately, since mixing of blood taken from two individuals may result in disastrous agglutination effects. This agglutination or agglomeration of red cells is due to the interaction of certain blood-group-specific macromolecules (see chapt. 11). The group-specific macromolecules are bound at the surfaces of the red cells, and they interact with specific proteins of the plasma (agglutinins or isoagglutinins). Four general blood types are known: A, B, AB, and O, and they are determined by mixing the red cells of the one blood with the serum from another blood. The group specific mucopolysaccharides of the red cells can be regarded as antigens, and they react with the corresponding antibodies of the serum. Thus the blood of a person of the A-type contains the anti-B antibodies or agglutinins and is incompatible with the B-type blood which contains the anti-A proteins. If the red cells of an unknown blood are not clumped by either the A or B type sera, the corresponding blood is one of the O-type, while clumping by both A and B type indicates the AB-type. Although a careful testing of the types has largely eliminated incompatibility,

[2] M. M. WINTROBE, *Clinical Hematology* 4th ed., Kimpton, London, 1956.

[3] J. L. TULLIS (ed.), *Blood Cells and Plasma Proteins* Academic Press, New York, 1953.

[4] H. A. KREBS, *Ann. Rev. Biochem.* **19**, 409 (1950).

[5] A. WHITE, P. HANDLER, E. L. SMITH and D. STETTEN, Jr., *Principles of Biochemistry* chapt. 23–27, McGraw-Hill, New York, 1954.

[6] R. R. RACE and R. SANGER, *Blood Groups in Man* Blackwell, Oxford, 3rd. ed., 1958.

[7] E. A. KABAT, *Blood Group Substances* Academic Press, New York, 1956.

there are indications of "subtypes", as demonstrated by a weak agglomeration. If then a person of such subtype receives the "right" blood of the ordinary type (A or B), more or less serious complications may take place. For example, in the group A there are at least two subgroups: A_1 and A_2. The strongly agglutinated variety of A cells are the A_1, and the weakly agglutinated A_2. A series of quite specific but unfrequently encountered individual substances have been described. "Extensive investigation of blood groupings has established that the number of immunological types is legion and that, from this standpoint, the bloods from different individuals are not the same". [1]

Individual variations are found not only in the immunologically specific mucopolysaccharides and agglutinins but also in the number of formed elements, and in the concentration of the macromolecular components. Thus the number of red cells of normal human male blood varies between 4·6–6·2 million per milliliter. Similar variations are found by counting the white cells and platelets.

Surgenor has presented a very interesting compilation on the numerical occurrence of the various corpuscles and macromolecules in an unit volume of blood, [8] as shown in Table 50.

This compilation demonstrates the dominating role of the red cells among the mass of formed elements, and the preponderance of hemoglobin, as compared e.g. with the albumin of the same molecular size. This indicates that the respiratory function of the blood is the dominating one, or that it requires most of the material transported for this purpose in the circulatory system. It seems relevant to recapitulate at this point the important recent discoveries that hemoglobin is synthesized in the microsomes of the red cells [9] (chapt. 21), and that *this*

TABLE 50

ESTIMATED NUMERICAL OCCURRENCE OF CERTAIN COMPONENTS IN A 10^{-10} l. VOLUME OF HUMAN BLOOD [8]

Component	Number of corpuscles of macromolecules
White cells	1
Platelets	25
Red cells	500
Properdin	500,000
Cholinesterase	670,000
Caeruloplasmin	66,700,000
β-Lipoproteins	89,700,000
α_2-Glycoproteins	93,300,000
Prothrombin	120,000,000
Fibrinogen	206,000,000
α-Lipoprotein	350,000,000
Acid glycoprotein	500,000,000
β_1-Metal-combining protein	770,000,000
γ-Globulins	1,630,000,000
Albumins	17,300,000,000
Hemoglobin (inside red cells)	133,000,000,000

(8) D. M. Surgenor, in *Currents in Biochemical Research* p. 653 (D. E. GREEN, ed.), Interscience, New York, 1956.

(9) H. W. DINTZIS, H. BORSOOK and J. VINOGRAD, in *Microsomal Particles and Protein Synthesis* p. 84, Pergamon Press, London, 1958.

synthesis is genetically controlled. Sickle-cell anemia is a disease inherited in a strictly Mendelian manner, and the mutation in the gene results in the replacement of only one amino acid residue (valine for glutamic acid) in each macromolecule of hemoglobin [10] (see chapt. 14).

Plasma Proteins [3,4,11,12]

Blood plasma is a viscous solution composed of about 90% water and 10% of various solutes, chiefly proteins. According to Table 50, albumins and γ-globulins comprise the bulk of these proteins, at least in respect to the number of units per unit volume. Since the size of the other macromolecules is in average about the same as the size of albumin and γ-globulin, this approximately corresponds also to the mass distribution of the proteins. The number of proteins found in plasma or serum, however, is much larger than indicated in Table 50, since some enzymes and hormones found in very small amounts have not been mentioned. Moreover, some of the proteins mentioned actually are known to be inhomogeneous mixtures of several components. Also it must be stressed that the numbers are average values, and that large individual variations have been ascertained in specimens of normal blood. Species differences also are considerable. Data on some of the most important protein components of serum are compiled in Table 51.

TABLE 51

AMOUNT OF PROTEINS (IN PER CENT OF TOTAL PROTEIN) IN NORMAL HUMAN SERUM [13] AND IN SERA OF OTHER MAMMALIAN SPECIES [14]

The data are averages of many determinations (60 human sera)

	Albumins	α-Globulins	β-Globulins	γ-Globulins
Human	56·8 ± 3	15·9 ± 2	12·8 ± 2·3	14·4 ± 2·4
Cow	41	13	8	38
Guinea pig	56	14·5	8	21·5
Horse	32	14	24	30
Pig	42	16	16	25
Rabbit	60	7	12	21
Sheep	57	11	7	25

The variations are conspicuous, especially in the β- and γ-globulin groups, e.g. the relatively high content of the γ-globulins in the equine and bovine sera. It has been reported that the serum of turtle contains very little albumin,

[10] J. A. HUNT and V. M. INGRAM, *Nature* **181**, 1062 (1958); V. M. INGRAM, *Abstracts, Amer. chem. Soc. Natl. Meeting, Boston* p. 38 C, April, 1959. A general treatise: D. Y. HSIA, *Inborn Errors of Metabolism* The Year Book Publ., Chicago, 1959.

[11] W. L. HUGHES, in *The Proteins* Vol. II B (H. NEURATH and K. BAILEY, ed.), Academic Press, New York, 1954.

[12] F. WUHRMANN and C. WUNDERLY, *Die Bluteiweißkörper des Menschen* 3rd ed., B. Schwabe, Basel, 1957.

[13] M. REINER, R. L. FENICHEL and K. G. STERN, *Acta Hematol.* **3**, 202 (1950).

[14] H. SVENSSON, *Arkiv Kemi* **22** A, No 10, 1946.

but a relatively large amount of α-globulins instead.[15] The literature on the amounts of the various serum or plasma proteins as determined by various methods is very voluminous. The most reliable method seems to be the free boundary electrophoresis, although it does not reveal as many components as the gel electrophoresis (see chapt. 2). Most of the determinations, however, have been made by means of the paper electrophoresis, and the variations found by various authors by this method are disturbing.[16] For example, Wunderly examined by this method 261 normal sera, and found the following variations: albumin 55·4–72·9%, α_1-globulin 1·4–4·4%, α_2-globulin 3·5–9·5%, β-globulin 8·6–12·6%, and γ-globulin 13·6–22·2% (l.c. 12, p. 37). These facts should warn everybody who hopes to detect small differences in plasma proteins by means of paper electrophoresis, e.g. for diagnostic purposes. At any rate first the *reproducibility* of the method should be tested repeatedly on many specimens of normal serum or plasma.

Only a few of the many plasma proteins have been isolated in pure state and crystallized. These include the whole albumin fraction and the mercaptalbumin component (chapt. 13), an acid α_1-glycoprotein,[17] and the metal binding β_1-globulin.[18] Many of these proteins contain a nonprotein component, thus the glycoproteins or mucoproteins contain some carbohydrate, which appears chiefly in the form of hexoses, hexosamines, or sialic (neuraminic) acid; in addition, a variety of lipoproteins is found in the plasma. For example, the lipoprotein which has the α_1-globulin mobility is composed of about 57% of protein, and of a large amount of phospholipid and cholesterol, while the β_1-lipoprotein contains only 23% of protein and the major part of the particle is fat, phospholipid, cholesterol, and other lipophilic substances.[19] Since the lipoproteins are water-soluble, it can be assumed that the protein moiety is largely at the surface of the particle and that the hydrophobic lipids are hidden in the interior of them.

Data on the most important plasma proteins are compiled in Table 52.

It must be admitted that the data on the composition as well as the physicochemical parameters of the various plasma proteins are very incomplete. This is partially due to the fact that some of the components are found in very small amounts, and that the macromolecules are easily denatured on fractionation and attempted purification. For example, properdin disaggregates readily into smaller fragments which are physiologically inactive.[22]

[15] C. V. Tondo, *Rev. brasil. biol.* **18**, 105 (1958); *Chem. Abstr.* **52**, 14727 (1958).

[16] See for example: J. A. Owen, *Adv. Clin. Chem.* **1**, 237 (1958).

[17] K. Schmid, *J. Amer. chem. Soc.* **75**, 60 (1953).

[18] B. A. Koechlin, *J. Amer. chem. Soc.* **74**, 2649 (1952).

[19] J. L. Oncley and F. N. Gurd, in *Blood Cells and Plasma Proteins* p. 337 (J. L. Tullis, ed.), Academic Press, New York, 1953.

[22] H. Isliker, *Abstracts, 4th Internat. Congress of Biochem., Vienna,* p. 192, 1958, Pergamon Press, London, 1958; D. S. Spicer, L. I. Priester, E. V. C. Smith and B. E. Sanders, *J. biol. Chem.* **234**, 838 (1959).

TABLE 52

HUMAN PLASMA PROTEINS
(data from ref. 11, 12, 20, 21, and other sources)

	Per cent of total protein	Sedimentation constant, S	Molecular weight	Isoelectric point, pH	Function
Albumin	52–59	4·4–4·6	65,000	4·9	Osmotic regulation, transport
Acid α_1-glycoprotein (17% hexose)	0·5	3·1–3·5	44,000	2·7–3·0	Unknown
α_1-Lipoprotein	3	5·0	(200,000)	5·0	Lipid transport
α_2-Macroglobulin	2	20·1	900,000	5·4	Unknown
α_2-Mucoprotein (4·4% hexose)	0·5	6–9	(190,000)	4·9	Unknown
α-Ceruloplasmin	0·5	7·1	(150,000)	4·4	Unknown
β_1-Lipoprotein	5	7	(1,300,000)	5·5	Lipid and carotinoid transport
β_1-Metal-binding glob.	3	5·0	90,000	5·8	Iron transport
β_2-Globulins	3	7	(150,000)	6·3	Unknown
Properdin [22]	0·03	6–27			Defense
Fibrinogen	4	7·7–7·9	270,000	5	Clot formation
Prothrombin	0·1	4·8	63,000		Thrombin precursor
γ-Globulins	11–15	6–7	(150,000)	6–7·3	Antibodies

The highly purified preparation appeared to be homogeneous in electrophoresis but showed several components in sedimentation. There are indications that the very large properdin unit is composed of subunits which have a sedimentation constant of 6 S, and it seems that the subunits are linked by a few disulfide bridges.[22] It is, however, surprising that these assumed disulfide bridges are so weak that the macromolecule disaggregates so readily.

Many of the proteins mentioned in Table 52 are known to be strongly inhomogeneous, hence the molecular weights were placed in parentheses. The homogeneity of even the crystallized proteins, such as the ordinary crystallized albumin, and some of the globulins, is subject to doubt. In addition to the proteins mentioned in Table 52, small amounts of other proteins with the α- and β-mobility, and a whole series of enzymes and hormones can be

(20) H. E. SCHULTZE, I. GÖLLNER, K. HEIDE, M. SCHÖNENBERGER and G. SCHWICK, *Z. Naturforsch.* **10 b**, 463 (1955).

(21) M. SCHÖNBERGER, *Z. Naturforsch.* **10 b**, 474 (1955).

detected. While the functions of the enzymes, such as the phosphatases and esterases, and hormones, is well known, the roles of some of the glycoproteins and mucoproteins are obscure. Finally, there are a few proteins which have been found in normal plasma but which probably are not universal constituents, like albumin or the γ-globulins. An example of this kind is the "cold insoluble globulin" which appears in the fractionation procedure after Cohn [23] in the fraction I, together with fibrinogen.[24] This protein is characteristic with its low solubility at 0 °C. Its sedimentation constant was found to be between 14 and 15 *S* which is much higher than that of fibrinogen (see Table 52). The intrinsic viscosity of the globulin was 0·15 which is lower than the viscosity of fibrinogen solutions. Moreover, contrary to fibrinogen, the cold-insoluble-globulin solutions do not clot. The mentioned physicochemical data indicate that the globulin particles in solution are larger and less asymmetric than those of the asymmetric fibrinogen. It is noteworthy that similar cold-insoluble "cryoglobulins" have been found occasionally in certain diseases when they usually are found in the plasma in high concentrations (see next chapter). Although the cold-insoluble-globulin of Edsall *et al.* [24] was isolated from large pooled blood specimens from healthy subjects, the "normality" of the cold-insoluble-globulin is not fully established. In this connection, it would be interesting to find out whether some of the apparently normal and healthy donors do not contain substantial amounts of this protein, and thus might have the malignant disease in an early stage. Since the presence of this globulin has not been ascertained in all specimens of normal individual plasmas, the specimens which were pooled from a large number of individual bloods may include some abnormal cases. In addition, it is not fully established if this globulin, as well as several others, which have not been sufficiently well characterized by chemical methods, could not be artifacts, i.e. aggregation products of several normal components.

The discrepancies between the results obtained by various authors on certain plasma fractions are due to several reasons. One of such reasons is the impossibility of reproducing a fractionation exactly in the same manner as it was done in another laboratory, or even by the same worker in the same laboratory. Other reasons include individual compositional differences between blood from various individuals, the age of the specimen and method of drawing the blood.

Some recent advances in characterization of the plasma or serum fractions include combined study by preparative zone electrophoresis and sedimentation.[25] The first step is to remove the light lipoprotein fractions by means

[23] E. J. Cohn, L. E. Strong, W. L. Hughes, D. J. Mulford, J. N. Ashworth and H. L. Taylor, *J. Amer. chem. Soc.* **68**, 459 (1946).

[24] J. T. Edsall, G. A. Gilbert and H. A. Scheraga, *J. Amer. chem. Soc.* **77**, 157 (1955).

[25] G. Wallenius, R. Trautman, H. Kunkel and E. C. Franklin, *J. biol. Chem.* **225**, 253 (1957).

of preparative ultracentrifugation of plasma or serum whose density is increased by adding salt. From such dense medium the light lipoproteins float out on the top of the serum. This delipidified serum is then subjected to zone electrophoresis, and the electrophoretic fractions are investigated by means of the analytical ultracentrifuge. The distribution of the various components is illustrated in Fig. 91. This distribution may be regarded as typical for "normal" serum of human origin, although it also must be admitted that it is not altogether certain how "normal" these values are.[1] A study on a large number of individual sera could give more definitive answers. Also some

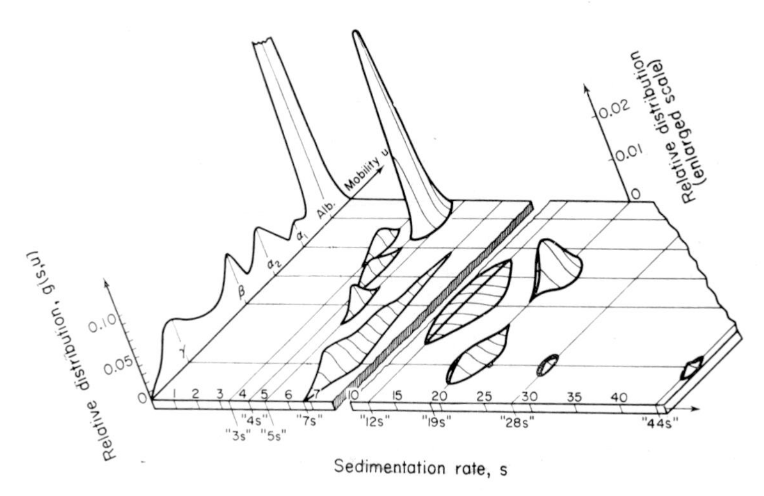

FIG. 91. Electrophoretic and ultracentrifugal distribution of plasma proteins after G. Wallenius, R. Trautman, H. Kunkel, and E. C. Franklin (*J. biol. Chem.* **225**, 253, 1957)

artifact formation is not excluded, especially in the heavy range of 28 and 44 *S*.[25] The 19 *S* components are very interesting. While the 19 *S* component with the electrophoretic mobility of the γ-globulin may be a polymerized γ-globulin, the 19 *S* protein which has the α_2-globulin mobility seems to be a specific component. According to recent studies of Schönenberger *et al.*,[26] the $s^0_{20,w}$ value for this protein is 20·0 *S*, which is an average of 20·0, 20·5, and 19·6 found on three different preparations. The molecular weight was found to be 820,000–950,000 from sedimentation and diffusion data, and 920,000–970,000 from light scattering. The intrinsic viscosity of the solutions was very low — 0·068 dl/g, indicating a globular shape of these large units, which probably are not macromolecules since they dissociated in 5 *M*

[26] M. SCHÖNENBERGER, R. SCHMIDTBERGER and H. E. Schultze, *Z. Naturforsch.* **13 b**, 761 (1958).

urea into two components, a heavier of 15·7 S and a lighter of 11·0 S. This dissociation was reversible. The protein contained approximately 8% of carbohydrate which included galactose, mannose, N-acetyl hexosamine, sialic acid, and even some fucose.[26] Extensive studies on the carbohydrate components of the other plasma proteins also have been conducted in the same laboratory, and it is noteworthy that relatively large amounts of fucose were detected in the carbohydrate of the γ-globulins.[27] The latter contain about 2·5–3% carbohydrate, and it was found that γ-globulin contains 3–4 moles galactose, 6–8 moles mannose, 2 moles fucose, 8–10 moles N-acetyl-hexosamine, 1–2 moles sialic acid, and 1–2 moles hexuronic acid per mole γ-globulin. No fucose was found in fibrinogen which contained 2·5% carbohydrate.[27] As mentioned before, the function of the carbohydrate is unknown.[27a]

Plasma proteins that sediment in the ultracentrifuge more slowly than albumin, or that migrate in electrophoresis faster than albumin, have been reported by several authors (e.g.[28,29,30]). The chemical identity of this component, however, could not be well established. According to Chargaff *et al.*,[28] the electrophoretically faster moving component was a complex of albumin and heparin (see chapt. 11), but this could not be confirmed by some other investigators. Isolation of a definite "*prealbumin*" has been reported recently by Schultze *et al.*[31] According to these workers, the prealbumin has a 50% higher electrophoretic mobility than albumin; also this protein absorbs more light than albumin (at $\lambda = 280$ mμ), a fact that is explained by the high tyrosine and tryptophan content of this protein. It was found that the prealbumin contained twice as much tyrosine as albumin, and ten times as much tryptophan as albumin. Moreover, the prealbumin contained 1·1% of hexoses, while only a trace of carbohydrate can be found in pure albumin. The molecular weight of the prealbumin was found to be 61,000 by light scattering. The prealbumin, however, could not be found in all specimens of individual normal plasmas or sera, and the appearance of this component in certein individual plasmas is one of the best examples of individuality. However, extreme caution must be observed in any generalizations, since the possibility of artifact formation may involve serious complications. While the Schultze's high-tryptophan-content prealbumin definitely is not the same substance as the heparin-albumin complex, the mobility changes observed upon purification of the prealbumin are suspicious. "Mit zunehmender Reinigung nahm aus unbekannten Gründen die absolute Wanderungsgeschwindigkeit des Präalbumins zu" (31, p. 269). Thus, although these prealbumins very prob-

(27) H. E. Schultze, R. Schmidtberger and H. Haupt, *Biochem. Z.* **329**, 490 (1958).

(27a) F. R. Bettelheim-Jevons, *Adv. Protein Chem.* **13**, 36 (1958).

(28) E. Chargaff, M. Ziff and D. H. Moore, *J. biol. Chem.* **139**, 383 (1941).

(29) P. Grabar and C. A. Williams, *Biochim. Biophys. Acta* **10**, 193 (1953).

(30) O. Smithies, *Biochem. J.* **61**, 629 (1955).

(31) H. E. Schultze, M. Schönenberger and G. Schwick, *Biochem. Z.* **328**, 267 (1956).

ably are distinct macromolecules, they seem to be either unstable, reactive, or not well enough purified.

All these examples show that, in spite of the extensive studies, the plasma proteins still are concealing a wealth of unsolved problems.

Antibodies and their Reactions [32,33,34]

The defense functions of blood are exercised by several devices, such as the white cells, the antibodies, and several other protein systems. The distensible white cell is constantly changing its shape, sticks to a foreign body, e.g. a microbe, engulfs it, and slowly digests the invader. The process, called phagocytosis, can be observed, for instance, by means of the phase contrast microscopy, photographed on microfilms and demonstrated in the most impressive fashion. These observations have revealed a wealth of information on the effects of various agents on the phagocytosis, and they have indicated also the co-operative effects of the antibodies and other proteins in this defence effort. There are indications that the antibodies and other protein systems involved in the defense facilitate the engulfing and disarming of the foreigner. Before going into the discussion of the antibody problem, let us mention briefly the other proteins. These include, first, the *properdin* which has already been mentioned in the previous section. Properdin has some lytic effect on the so-called gram-negative bacteria [35], and the reactions involve the participation of other proteins and inorganic ions. The mechanism, however, is unknown. Somewhat similar functions are ascribed to several lytic enzymes, e.g. the lysozyme. Moreover, the fact is noteworthy that the white cells carry a considerable amount of antibodies and proteolytic enzymes.

An *antibody* is a protein interacting *specifically* with a definite substance which has elicited its formation in the body. This specific counterpart of the antibody which enters the body and causes antibody formation is called *antigen*. Any toxin, microbe, virus, etc. elicits the formation of specific antibodies, and these antibodies protect the host against the invasion of the corresponding antigens and its harmful toxic effects. In other words: the body becomes *immune* against a certain invader. In contrast to the indiscriminate activities of the white cells and lytic proteins, the antibodies display an

[32] W. C. Boyd, *Fundamentals of Immunology* Interscience, New York, 1956; E. A. Kabat and M. M. Mayer, *Experimental Immunochemistry*, Thomas, Springfield, Illinois, 1948; K. Landsteiner, *The Specificity of Serological Reactions* 2nd. ed., Harvard Univ. Press, Cambridge, Mass., 1945; A. M. Pappenheimer, *The Nature and Significance of Antibody Response* Columbia Univ. Press, New York, 1953.

[33] H. C. Isliker, *Adv. Protein Chem.* **13**, 387 (1957).

[34] P. Grabar, *Adv. Protein Chem.* **13**, 1 (1958); H. E. Schultze, *Clin. Chim. Acta* **4**, 610 (1959).

[35] L. Pillemer, L. Blum, I. H. Lepow, O. A. Ross, E. W. Todd and A. C. Wardlaw, *Science* **120**, 279 (1954); Pillemer *et al.*, *ibid.* **122**, 545 (1955).

extreme specificity. Antibodies which have been mobilized against one strain of polio viruses may be helpless against a mutant strain of the same virus. This specificity has been studied to a considerable extent by using pure proteins as antigens, and by modifying them through substitution of various atomic groups [32], and it has been found that the specificity of the antibody can be modified even by minor modifications in these groups. This has been ascertained by means of the very sensitive antigen–antibody interaction tests, i.e. flocculation, which appears to be highly dependent on the surface and configuration of the interacting macromolecules.

The antibodies are globulins, and most antibodies have the mobilities and other physiochemical properties of the *γ-globulins.* Since the most important properties of these macromolecules have been mentioned in chapt. 13, it will suffice to recapitulate the fact that the γ-globulins are medium size macromolecules of about $M = 160{,}000$, and that they are heterogeneous. Fractionation of the γ-globulins has been attempted by various methods, and subfractions rich in certain specific antibodies have been obtained, yet none of these subfractions represent a definite homogeneous protein. [35a] Since no significant differences could be found between definite antibodies and ordinary γ-globulins, the antibody properties have been associated with *structural differences.* What these differences are, is not known, and since the molecules are so large there is plenty of space for speculation. Two possibilities have been considered: differences in *configuration,* and differences in *amino acid sequence.* Since a small structural difference of an antigen, e.g. introduction of a few diazo groups at the surface of an antigenic protein, causes production of a specific antibody, it seemed likely that an antibody might be a γ-globulin with a specifically adapted configuration. According to Pauling, [36] the antigen elicits partial unfolding of the γ-globulin chain, which is then refolded in a somewhat different configuration from before, viz. assuming a configuration complementary to that of the antigen. This explanation is in accord with the facts that only large and relatively rigid macromolecules or particles act as antigens. However, this hypothesis has its weaknesses. Metabolic studies with labeled antigens have shown that the antigen, as well as the corresponding antibody, have a relatively short lifetime of days and weeks, while the immunity persists for a much longer time [37]. The idea about the remolding of the γ-globulins under the influence of an antigen is inconsistent with the now established data on biosynthesis of proteins, and the genetic control exerted on it. There is experimental evidence suggesting that the antibodies are not formed by a slight modification of globulin precursors but

[35a] See a revent review of J. R. Cann in *Immunity and Virus Infection* p. 100 (V. A. Najjar, ed.), Wiley, New York, 1959.

[36] L. Pauling, *J. Amer. chem. Soc.* **62,** 2643 (1940).

[37] M. Heidelberger, *Lectures in Immunochemistry* especially chapter 8, Academic Press, New York, 1956.

that they are synthesized *de novo* from amino acids.[37a] This could be shown even in *in vitro* systems, such as rabbit spleen cells,[37b] or lymph nodes from rabbits immunized with diphtheria toxin.[37c] "On the basis of isotope experiments it was concluded that cellular proteins were not converted to antibody *in vitro* and antibody was derived largely, if not exclusively, from free amino acids"[37c] (quoted from p. 11).

Thus the antigen is not a mold that imprints a specific configuration onto the macromolecules of γ-globulins but it only *electively stimulates certain cellular systems* involved in the synthesis of the antibodies.[38] This view has been recently further developed especially by Lederberg.[39] The principles were formulated in nine paragraphs which were supported in part by experimental evidence. According to Lederberg: "The stereospecific segment of each antibody globulin is determined by a unique sequence of amino acids", and "The cell making a given antibody has a correspondingly unique sequence of nucleotides in a segment of chromosomal DNA: its 'gene for globulin synthesis'". Furthermore: "The genic diversity of the precursors of antibody-forming cells arises from a high rate of spontaneous mutation during their lifelong proliferation", and "This hypermutability consists of the random assembly of the DNA of the globulin gene during certain stages of cellular proliferation".[39] These fundamental statements are followed by a more elaborate outline of the possible mechanism, and some supporting evidence is presented in favor of these views. The latter, although not explaining everything, seem to be in better agreement with the facts about immune response and present concepts on genetic control of protein synthesis than the older hypotheses.

While the first stage of the immunochemical reaction, namely the antibody formation, is more the subject of speculation than direct experimental approach, the following stage — the reaction of the antigen with antibody — has been studied directly to a great extent.[32,37] However, here again, much is understood about the in vitro reactions, i.e. precipitation and its mechanism of antigen–antibody combination, but it is uncertain whether the same mechanism is working in the living body. It has been found, for example, that egg albumin (as antigen) reacts with its rabbit antibodies (used as the γ-globulin fraction of rabbit serum) according to the equation:[40]

$$\text{Antib.} + \text{Antigen} \rightleftharpoons \text{Antib.-Antigen, and}$$
$$\text{Antib.-Antigen} + \text{Antigen} \rightleftarrows \text{Antigen-Antib.-Antigen.}$$

(37a) R. Schoenheimer, S. Ratner, S. Rittenberg and M. Heidelberger, *J. biol. Chem.* **144**, 545 (1942); P. Gros, J. Coursaget and M. Macheboeuf, *Bull. Soc. Chim. biol.* **34**, 1070 (1952); H. Green and H. S. Anker, *Biochim. Biophys. Acta* **13**, 365 (1954).

(37b) D. F. Steiner and H. S. Anker, *Proc. Nat. Acad. Sci.* **42**, 580 (1956).

(37c) A. B. Stavitsky and B. Wolf, *Biochim. Biophys. Acta* **27**, 4 (1958).

(38) F. M. Burnet and F. Fenner, in *The Production of Antibodies* Macmillan, Melbourne, Australia, 1949.

(39) J. Lederberg, *Science* **129**, 1649 (1959).

(40) S. J. Singer and D. H. Campbell, *J. Amer. chem. Soc.* **77**, 4851 (1955).

Both reactions were found to be reversible under certain specific conditions; thus the first reaction is reversible in acid solution of pH 3·0–4·5, and the second between the antigen-antibody complex and one more molecule of antigen is reversible in alkaline solution of pH 8·5 (at 0 °C and ionic strength of 0·3). Equilibrium constants and thermochemical data were calculated, and it was concluded that only one carboxyl group is involved in each bond between one molecule of antigen and one molecule of antibody.[41] However, the conditions are very different from those *in vivo*, and nothing definite is known how really the antibodies take care of the antigenic substances in the body. These and other aspects are discussed in more detail in recent reviews and conference reports.[42]

Macromolecules in Blood Clotting [43,44,45]

Development of the circulatory system in the course of evolution of animal species was associated with a simultaneous development of protective mechanisms which could be used to maintain the system. In primitive species this protection is exerted by plugging the damaged vessel with agglomerated cells. In mammals, a very complex system involving the platelets and a whole series of proteins is used for this purpose. Whenever a blood vessel is damaged and the blood comes in contact with a surface other than the vessel wall, a series of fast reactions occur leading to the formation of a clot. The main event in this process is the conversion of the soluble fibrinogen into a fibrin clot, a reaction which can be performed easily *in vitro* by taking a solution of fibrinogen and introducing the clot formation by thrombin. A solution of fibrinogen does not clot by pouring it from one container into another, or by similar disturbance. This indicates that *in vivo* the reactions are regulated with a much higher degree of subtlety than happens with pure fibrinogen in a test tube. Extensive studies on blood clotting have shown that there are some 15–20 different micro- and macromolecular substances which participate in the clotting process. Some of these factors have been well identified, while the role of a quite large number of others is controversial. It is also somewhat regretable that some investigators like to introduce strange new names for "factors" they only suspect.

(41) S. J. Singer, L. Eggman and D. H. Campbell, *J. Amer. chem. Soc.* **77**, 4855 (1955).

(42) D. W. Talmage, in *A Symposium on Molecular Biology* p. 91 (R. E. Zirkle, ed.), Univ. of Chicago Press, Chicago, 1959; *Serological and Biochemical Comparison of Proteins* (W. H. Cole, ed.), Rutgers Univ. Press, New Brunswick, N. J., 1958; V. A. Najjar (ed.), *Immunity and Virus Infection* Wiley, New York, 1959.

(43) H. A. Scheraga and M. Laskowski, Jr., *Adv. Protein Chem.* **12**, 1 (1957); H. Endf, G. Meyerhoff and G. V. Schulz, *Z. Naturforsch.* **13 b**, 713 (1958).

(44) W. H. Seegers, *Adv. Enzymol.* **16**, 23 (1955).

(45) D. M. Surgenor, in *Blood Cells and Plasma Proteins* p. 61 (J. L. Tullis, ed.), Academic Press, New York, 1953; B. Alexander, *ibid.* p. 75, and J. H. Ferguson, p. 93; R. G. Macfarlane, *Physiol. Rev.* **36**, 479 (1956).

The most remarkable event in the clot formation on injury is the act of *initiation*. Blood apparently is such an extremely labile system that the slightest disturbance may lead to far reaching changes, and one may ask the question: what prevents the blood clotting in the vein? According to Surgenor,[46] the series of the reactions proceed at such a rate, and they are so efficient, that the many factors participating in these reactions must be present in an organized system: "... we must ask ourselves whether the blood we started with ... was a suspension of formed elements in a random solution of plasma proteins, or might there perhaps have been a chemical morphology which was unintentionally disrupted when the blood was removed" ... [46] (p. 672). It is quite possible that the enzymes and other essential macromolecules are oriented around the surfaces of the platelets, thus forming large complex units of loosely associated chains extending into the medium.

The major enzyme catalyzing the clotting of fibrinogen is *thrombin*. It is not found in the blood in its active form but as its precursor — *prothrombin*. This protein has been isolated in pure state.[47] The protein contains carbohydrate, and its specific rotation is −31° (sodium light). The activation of prothrombin involves several components, and the resulting thrombin is polymolecular, one of the active components having the molecular weight of 45,000. Thrombin activates fibrinogen upon splitting off some peptides, and the activated fibrinogen polymerizes and aggregates into a fibrous meshwork encompassing the liquid. The whole process can be illustrated briefly by the following scheme:

Platelets + Plasma factors + Foreign surface → Thromboplastin.

Thromboplastin + Prothrombin + Ca^{++} + Various activators and inhibitors → → Thrombin.

Fibrinogen $\xrightarrow{\text{Thrombin}}$ Act. Fibrinogen + Peptides

Act. Fibrinogen → Fibrin.

Fibrinogen is the material which is activated and used to build the long fibrous strands of fibrin thus enabling the production of a clot or gel. Fibrinogen is one of the largest and least soluble plasma proteins, and thus it appears in the first fraction when plasma is treated with either ammonium sulfate or dilute alcohol. The molecular weight of fibrinogen has been determined by various methods, and the values found range between 270,000 and 700,000. A critical comparison of recently obtained values prefers the lower value as the most correct.[43] However, it is not quite certain whether this physical molecular weight is also the chemical molecular weight, since smaller frag-

[46] D. M. Surgenor, in *Currents in Biochemical Research*. p. 653 (D. E. Green, ed.), Interscience Publ., New York, 1956.

[47] F. Lamy and D. F. Waugh, *J. biol. Chem.* **203**, 491 (1953); K. Laki, D. R. Kominz, P. Symonds, L. Lorand and W. H. Seegers, *Arch. Biochem. Biophys.* **49**, 276 (1954).

ments are split off in alkaline solutions.[48] While the fibrinogen particle thus is much larger than that of γ-globulin, the sedimentation constant of fibrinogen is found to be 7·7–8 S, i.e. only a little higher than that of the γ-globulins. The relatively slow sedimentation of fibrinogen could be explained by three possible reasons: (1) high asymmetry, (2) high degree of hydration, or (3) low particle density, viz. a high partial specific volume. The latter was found to be 0·71, and cannot account for the low sedimentation rate. Formerly it was believed that the fibrinogen particle in solution is a long rod or ellipsoid

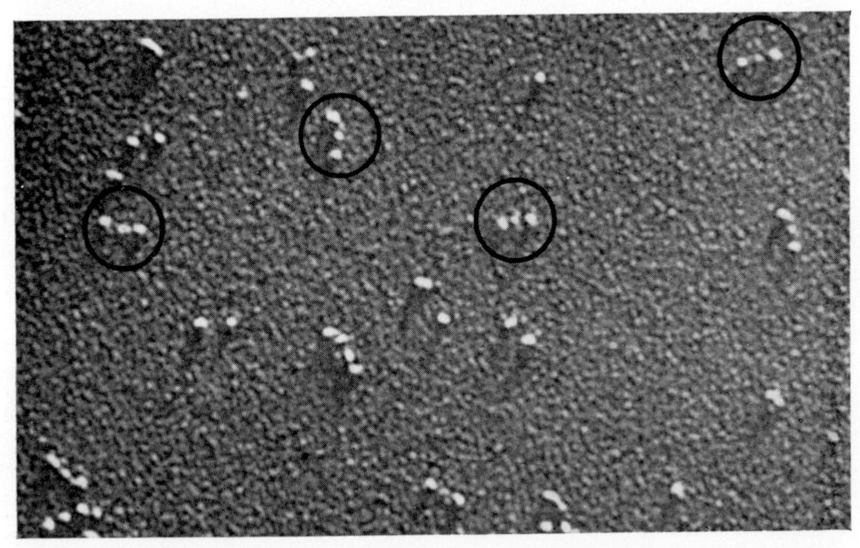

FIG. 92. Electron-micrograph of fibrinogen. Typical macromolecules consisting of three nodules connected by a thin thread are circled. Magnification 160,000 (see C. E. Hall, and H. S. Slayter, *J. Biophys. Biochem. Cytol.* **5**, 11, 1959) (by *Courtesy* of Dr. C. E. Hall)

of a considerable length, an idea which would be compatible also with the intrinsic viscosity of the solutions, which is 0·25 dl/g. Recent electron microscopic studies on carefully prepared samples show the particles as consisting of three nodules connected by a thin thread,[49] as illustrated in Fig. 92. Thus the resistance to displacement of the particle in solution is explained by an unusual irregular shape. The role of hydration is uncertain, although the high content of dissociable groups indicates the possibility of a high degree of hydration. Fibrinogen appears practically homogeneous in electrophoresis, and in spite of its high charge density, it moves only a little faster than γ-

(48) J. E. FITZGERALD, N. S. SCHNEIDER and D. F. WAUGH, *J. Amer. chem. Soc.* **79,** 601 (1957); E. SCHAUENSTEIN and M. HOCHENEGGER, *J. Polymer. Sci.* **10,** 63 (1953); *Z. Naturforsch.* **8 b,** 473 (1953).

(49) C. E. HALL and H. S. SLAYTER, *J. Biophys. Biochem. Cytol.* **5,** 11 (1959).

globulin (at pH 8·6), a fact which can be explained by the resistance to displacement due to the irregular particle shape.

Chemically, fibrinogen is distinguished by its high nitrogen content of 16·9%, which is due to the high content of basic amino acids (9·2% lysine and 7·8% arginine). In spite of this, the isoelectric point of the protein is near pH 5, because the basic groups are outnumbered by the carboxyl groups of the glutamic and aspartic acid residues. Thus the macromolecule has a high charge density, a property which probably has some importance for the clotting. Also fibrinogen contains about 1·8% hexose and 0·6% hexosamine. Tyrosine and glutamic acid were found as the N-terminal groups of fibrinogen, whereas tyrosine and glycine were found in the N-terminal positions of the fibrin.[50] Phenylalanine was found as the C-terminal group in both fibrinogen and fibrin.[51] These facts indicated that activation of fibrinogen by thrombin involves a specific proteolysis somewhere near the N-terminal. At about the same time it was found that two peptides each of a molecular weight about 3000 were split off in the process of activation. The activated fibrinogen, which thus is only a little smaller than the original particle then undergoes polymerization. This process has been extensively studied with isolated fibrinogen–thrombin systems, and intermediate polymers having highly asymmetric particles could be found, if the reaction rate was checked by means of certain additives.[52] The mechanism of this polymerization, however, is not fully understood. There is no doubt that it will be better known when the chemical structure of fibrinogen will be elucidated.

In the actual clotting of blood *in vivo*, there are certain types of macromolecules which either promote or prevent clotting. The participation of an "*accelerator globulin*" has been indicated. Another principle which also is essential in securing clotting is the "*antihemophilic globulin*". The lack of this globulin causes hemophilia, a dramatic hereditary disease characterized by the inability of the blood to clot. Although the anomaly has been extensively investigated, a satisfactory practical solution has not been found. It seems that the antihemophilic globulin is a large and rather unstable protein which remains with fibrinogen in the course of plasma fractionation. Also there are indications that more than one antihemophilic factor may be involved.

While it is essential to secure clotting, it is equally important to prevent unnecessary clot formation. Occasional clot formation, especially after surgery is even more common than the inability of the blood to set. Such "thrombosis" is very dangerous, and a great deal of effort has been spent in order to elucidate the phenomenon and control it. There is no doubt that the body has control mechanisms which prevent the blood from spontaneous gelation in the veins.

[50] K. Bailey, *Biochem. J.* **49**, 23 (1951).

[51] K. Bailey and F. R. Bettelheim, *Biochim. Biophys. Acta* **18**, 495 (1955).

[52] S. Shulman and J. D. Ferry, *J. physic. Chem.* **55**, 135 (1951); I. Tinoco and J. D. Ferry, *Arch. Biochem. Biophys.* **48**, 7 (1954); J. D. Ferry, S. Katz and I. Tinoco, *J. Polymer Sci.* **12**, 509 (1954).

One of such substances is a polysaccharide *heparin* which was mentioned in chapt. 11. There are indications that heparin needs a cofactor. Moreover, the interference of an "*antithrombin*" and of an "*antithromboplastin*" seems to be ascertained. Finally, blood contains small amounts of special proteins that are able to digest freshly formed small fibrin clots: a *plasminogen* or *protofibrinolysin* which is readily activated to a *plasmin* or *fibrinolysin*. The activation itself, like many other physiological conversions, is quite complex, as an activator is required, and there are indications that this is formed from a "proactivator" which in its turn must be activated by an enzyme — streptokinase. Thus the whole series of reactions can be illustrated as follows:

Streptokinase + "Proactivator" → Activator

Activator + Plasminogen → Plasmin

Plasmin + Fibrin → Products of fibrinolysis.

Shulman *et al.* [53] were able to isolate plasminogen and plasmin in a reasonably pure state, and the proteins were characterized by chemical and physico-chemical methods. The molecular weight of plasminogen was estimated to be 143,000, whereas plasmin had a molecular weight of 108,000. Thus the activation, like that of the activation of fibrinogen and many proenzymes, consists in splitting off a part of the macromolecule. The resulting plasmin appeared inhomogeneous on sedimentation, and the molecular weight of it was estimated for the major component. The protein, however, was homogeneous in electrophoresis. Also it was found that plasmin contained 1·5% hexose, and plasminogens 1%, and that the nitrogen content was 14·1% and 15·8% respectively.[53] Moreover, it has been found that plasminogen can be activated not only by the specific activator but e.g. also by trypsin, and that the fibrinolytic activity of plasmin can be inhibited by certain inhibitors. One of such especially potent inhibitors is ε-aminocaproic acid which has been investigated recently in several laboratories.[54]

[53] S. Shulman, N. Alkjaersig and S. Sherry, *J. biol. Chem.* **233**, 91 (1958).

[54] Brit. Pat. 770,693; Her Majesty's Stationery Office, London, 1957; N. Alkjaersig, A. P. Fletcher and S. Sherry, *J. biol. Chem.* **234**, 832 (1959); F. B. Ablondi, J. J. Hagan, M. Philips and E. C. De Renzo, *Arch. Biochem. Biophys.* **82**, 153 (1959); S. Sherry, A. P. Fletcher and N. Alkjaersig, *Physiol. Rev.* **39**, 343 (1959).

CHAPTER 24

ABNORMAL PROTEINS IN DISEASES

Despite their manifold relationships to normal γ-globulin, macroglobulins appear to be abnormal proteins resulting from individually specific aberrations in serum protein synthesis.

F. W. PUTNAM [1]

ATTEMPTS to correlate certain protein characteristics with diseases are not new. Biochemists and clinicians have paid special attention to the plasma proteins, and many qualitative precipitation and color tests have been proposed and used for centuries. The scientific basis of all these procedures, however, was, and still is, so poor that nobody ever could tell what the observed phenomena mean; in addition to this, these fully empirical tests often failed to give the expected answer or were contradicting the results of other tests of the same empirical kind. The obscurity and limited value of such approach is obvious when one compares some of the most modern outlines treating the subject [2]. A new phase in these developments began with the introduction of the modern methods of protein chemistry. One of the most spectacular achievements in this respect is the elucidation of the correlation between certain blood diseases and the chemical structure and physicochemical properties of the abnormal hemoglobins (see chapt. 14).

In this chapter we shall discuss some of the modern advances in the study of pathalogical plasma and urinary proteins. The most important method, which appears to be at the same time the simplest and most efficient, is paper *electrophoresis* (chapt. 3). The method has been compared with the more accurate free boundary electrophoresis (which is somewhat impractical for routine clinical tests), and found satisfactory. Even more can be expected from the electrophoresis in gels, especially the immunoelectrophoresis,[3] but these methods have not been developed yet so far as to be able to replace paper electrophoresis. The most common approach in these electrophoretic methods is to determine the relative *amounts* of the various proteins, and then to correlate these data with the particular disease. The purpose of all this is diagnosis, and also study of the course of the disease, as well as the effects of various treatments as reflected in the protein pattern. Although this approach

[1] FRANK W. PUTNAM, *Arch. Biochem. Biophys.* **79**, 67 (1959); quot. from p. 84.

[2] F. WUHRMANN and CH. WUNDERLY, *Die Bluteiweißkörper des Menschen* 3rd. ed., Schwabe, Basel/Stuttgart, 1957.

[3] P. GRABAR, *Adv. Protein Chem.* **13**, 1 (1958); P. GRABAR and C. A. WILLIAMS, *Biochim. Biophys. Acta* **10**, 193 (1953); **17**, 67 (1955).

considers only the *ratio of the normal components*, the appearance of abnormally high concentration of some apparently normal protein may be indicative of some abnormality in native protein. Thus the *quantitative* comparison often leads to a consideration of *possible qualitative differences*, i.e. the discovery of *truly abnormal proteins*.

In Table 53 are presented the ranges of variations as computed from many determinations of many authors for serum proteins.[4] The normal range variations reflect individual differences caused by variety of reasons, while "slight change" must be considered as indicative of some definite disease.

TABLE 53
ELECTROPHORETIC DISTRIBUTION OF PROTEINS IN NORMAL SERUM AND IN DISEASE [4]

	Albumin	α_1-globulin	α_2-globulin	β-globulin	γ-globulin
Normal range	53–68	2–6	5–11	8–16	10–22
Slight change	44–52	6–8	11–14	16–20	22–28
Moderate change	28–44	8–12	14–20	20–28	28–40
Severe change	below 28	above 12	above 20	above 28	above 40

Thus it is obvious that generally a decrease of the albumin concentration and the increase of the globulin concentration is indicative of disease. Somewhat exceptional in this respect is γ-globulin which may diminish below normal in certain diseases, the so-called hypogammaglobulinemias. Definite changes in the serum protein patterns have been observed in diseases affecting liver, kidney, collagen disease, in various infections, in neoplastic diseases, anemias, as well as disorders of endocrine glands. For example in such collagen diseases as rheumatic fever or rheumatoid arthritis the albumin tends to decrease and the α_2- and γ-globulins to increase. In tuberculosis most characteristic is the decreases of albumin and increae of α_2-globulin. In some neoplastic diseases of blood and bone marrow the β- or γ-globulins may be moderately or even strongly increased, and in some instances these globulins appeared to be qualitatively different from the normal protein components (see next sections). Since we are interested chiefly in these abnormal proteins, the quantitative abnormalities and their correlation with various diseases was only very briefly mentioned. It also should be borne in mind that an electrophoretic pattern alone is not a reliable enough criterion for any diagnosis, since many diseases exhibit the same kind of abnormalities. For instance, many infectious diseases, such as tuberculosis, may show the same abnormal increase of the α_2-globulins as some cases of cancer. Even in such conditions as pregnancy the albumin concentration is slightly decreasing and the concentrations of the α_1-, α_2- and β-globulins are on the high side. In spite of these weaknesses, the electrophoretic characterization of the plasma proteins is one of the most significant innovations in clinical chemistry.

[4] J. A. OWEN, *Adv. Clin. Chem.* **1**, 237 (1958).

The Cryoglobulin Problem

The term "cryoglobulin" covers a variety of strange proteins which have the common property of precipitating upon cooling to about 1–5 °C. They have most often been observed in certain disorders but it has been impossible to associate their appearance with a particular disease. Generally, they are uncommon, in fact very rare, and thus quite interesting. Abrams *et al.*,[5] for instance, have studied a cryoglobulin which appeared in the blood and lymph nodes of a patient suffering from lymphosarcoma; this globulin had a sedimentation constant of 16 *S*. The same authors presented a compilation of older data on other specimens of such cryoglobulins, and this shows that the sedimentation constant can vary as much as between 7 and 23 *S*. The problem was even more exciting after the communication of Edsall *et al.*[6] that normal pooled plasma contains small amounts of cryoglobulins. The sedimentation constant of this "normal" material was 14–15 *S*. Putnam and Miyake compared the properties of eight cryoglobulins from different individuals and they concluded that "cryoglobulins are truly unnatural proteins formed only in disease".[7] It is noteworthy that the eight cryoglobulins differed from each other in several properties, such as sedimentation constants, electrophoretic mobility, isoelectric point, and N-terminal amino acids. The electrophoretic mobilities of all of them were in the γ-globulin range, but in some instances they differed significantly. The lowest isoelectric point value of one of the specimens was pH 5·5, while two others showed higher values of 7·2 and 7·5. The sedimentation constants and amounts of N-terminal amino acids (moles per 160,000 g) are compiled in Table 54. Immunochemi-

TABLE 54
SEDIMENTATION CONSTANTS AND N-TERMINAL AMINO ACIDS OF CRYOGLOBULINS[7]

Protein	Sedimentation constant (S)	N-terminal amino acids (moles/160,000 g)
Normal γ-globulin	6·6	1·1 Asp., 1·7 Glu., 0·1 Ser
Cryoglobulin Th	6·6	1·8 Asp., 0·16 Glu.
Cryoglobulin Ag	6·6	2·0 Asp.
Cryoglobulin Mi, cryst.	6·7	2·0 Asp., 0·16 Glu.
Cryoglobulin R, cryst.	7·6; 11 *	2·0 Asp., 2·6 Glu.
Cryoglobulin Gu	6·0	2·3 Asp., 2·2 Glu.
Cryoglobulin Se	6·4	2·6 Glu.
Cryoglobulin I	7·6; 11 *	0·15 Asp., 2·7 Glu.
Cryoglobulin WK	7·2; 18; 28 *	0·12 Asp., 3·1 Glu.

* A minor component; all sedimentation constants presented in the Table are corrected $s_{20,w}$ values.

[5] A. ABRAMS, P. P. COHEN and O. O. MEYER, *J. biol. Chem.* **181**, 237 (1949).
[6] J. T. EDSALL, G. A. GILBERT and H. A. SCHERAGA, *J. Amer. chem. Soc.* **77**, 157 (1955).
[7] F. W. PUTNAM and A. MIYAKE, *Arch. Biochem. Biophys.* **65**, 39 (1956).

cally some of the cryoglobulins appeared to be similar to normal γ-globulins, although some antigenic determinants present in normal γ-globulins were lacking in the abnormal globulins. In general, the cryoglobulins appeared more homogeneous than the normal γ-globulins. In a few instances it was even possible to obtain these proteins in a crystalline form.

A comparison of these data with the data of other authors [5,6] leads to the conclusion that the cryoglobulin group is a very diverse one, and it is questionable whether the insolubility in cold might not be a fortuitous property caused by different reasons in different cases. The cryoglobulins examined by Putnam and Miyake strongly resemble normal γ-globulins, whereas some others are quite different. The cryoglobulins which appear in serious illnesses might be regarded as "imperfect antibodies" synthesized by some defective cell mechanisms.

The Macroglobulins

Macroglobulins are very large proteins having a sedimentation constant of at least 15 S or much higher, and they appear in the blood in some ill defined hemorrhagic syndromes.[8] The abnormal globulin usually appears in a high concentration, and it shows up in electrophoresis as a homogeneous component with the mobility of the β- or γ-globulins. Sedimentation in the analytical ultracentrifuge, however, always reveals several components which probably represent aggregation and disaggregation products of the main component. On plasma fractionation, the macroglobulin appears either in fraction I together with fibrinogen and other large proteins, or in fraction II together with γ-globulin. This indicates variety in solubility properties, and this pertains also to the effect of temperature on solubility, so that some macroglobulins are difficult to differentiate from cryoglobulins. Since the macroglobulins appear rarely, not very much is known about their chemical and physicochemical properties. Deutsch and Morton reported recently the interesting fact that the large macroglobulins of 15–38 S are split into the much smaller 7 S units upon reduction with sulfhydryl reagents (mercapto-ethanol, and others).[9] If the freshly formed SH groups of the smaller units are not blocked, they react, and the 7 S units reunite forming the original macromolecule. If, however, the SH groups of the split products are blocked by means of iodoacetate, the high-polymeric macroglobulin is not restored. These findings indicate that the macroglobulin is composed of several subunits cemented together by means of disulfide bonds. It is, however, not certain that the 7 S subunits ($M = 160{,}000$) would be the normal γ-globulin macro-molecules, since the macroglobulins contain much more carbohydrate than the γ-globulins. The macroglobulins contain 6–8% of carbohydrate, whereas normal γ-globulin contains only about 2·5–3% of it. However, it has been

(8) J. Waldenström, *et al.*, *Adv. Internal Med.* **5**, 398 (1952).
(9) H. F. Deutsch and J. I. Morton, *Science* **125**, 600 (1957).

found that the heavy 19 *S* component, present in small amount in normal serum and having the γ-globulin mobility, contains as much carbohydrate as the abnormal macroglobulins.[10]

Like cryoglobulins, the macroglobulins are less definite proteins than any of the normal plasma constituents. Thus a macroglobulin has been described recently which dissociated into subunits (the 7 *S* units) in weakly acid medium at pH 4·2, and the heavy components reappeared when the pH was raised to 8·6.[11] Putnam reported recently his results obtained with eight purified macroglobulins,[1,12] and he comes to the conclusion that they are truly abnormal. Moreover, they display an individuality, if several properties are compared. None of these disaggregated by diminishing the pH even to 3·5, but the monomeric units (of about 6·6 S) were found under the influence of sulfhydryl reagents.[9] The individuality was displayed chiefly in the N-terminal amino acids, as shown in Table 55. Differences were found also in

TABLE 55

N-TERMINAL AMINO ACIDS AND SOME PHYSICAL CONSTANTS OF MACROGLOBULINS [1,12]

Specimen	N-terminal groups (mole/160,000 g)	Sedimentation const. (*S*)	Mobility at pH 8·6 (units of 10^{-5} cm^2/V sec)
KLI	0·1 Asp.; 0·1 Glu.	17 (22)	− 0·5
SM	none	15 (21, 26)	− 2·3
KE	1·2 Asp.; 0·2 Glu.; 0·1 Ser.	17 (6, 24)	− 0·7
HE	1·2 Asp.; 0·2 Glu.; 0·2 Ser.	17 (6·3, 21)	
CA (cryst.)	1·5 Asp.	18 (21, 26)	− 1·6
MO	1·8 Asp.; 0·4 Glu.; 0·3 Ser.	16 (6·2, 24)	−1·8 (heterogeneous)

the sedimentation constants, but since these were not corrected for infinite dilution, these may not be so significant as the differences in the terminal amino acids. In two cases Putnam is uncertain whether to classify the abnormal proteins as cryoglobulins or macroglobulins; according to the sedimentation patterns, these proteins were macroglobulins, while their low solubility in cold characterized them as cryoglobulins (e.g. sample WK, Table 54). The diagnosis in these two cases was uncertain.

Putnam points out the fact that the crystallized macroglobulin CA [13] was electrophoretically more homogeneous than the others, and that it contained only aspartic acid as the terminal group, while MO, the most heterogeneous in electrophoresis, contained significant amounts of other amino

[10] H. J. MÜLLER-EBERHARD and H. G. KUNKEL, *Clin. Chim. Acta* **4**, 252 (1959).
[11] E. D. REES and R. RESNER, *Clin. Chim. Acta* **4**, 272 (1959).
[12] F. W. PUTNAM, *J. biol. Chem.* **233**, 1448 (1958).
[13] C. H. KRATOCHVIL and H. F. DEUTSCH, *J. biol. Chem.* **222**, 31 (1956).

acids.[1] It is also noteworthy that the N-terminal amino acids are the same as found in the cryoglobulins as well as normal γ-globulins, an indication that the proteins are synthesized by similar mechanisms.

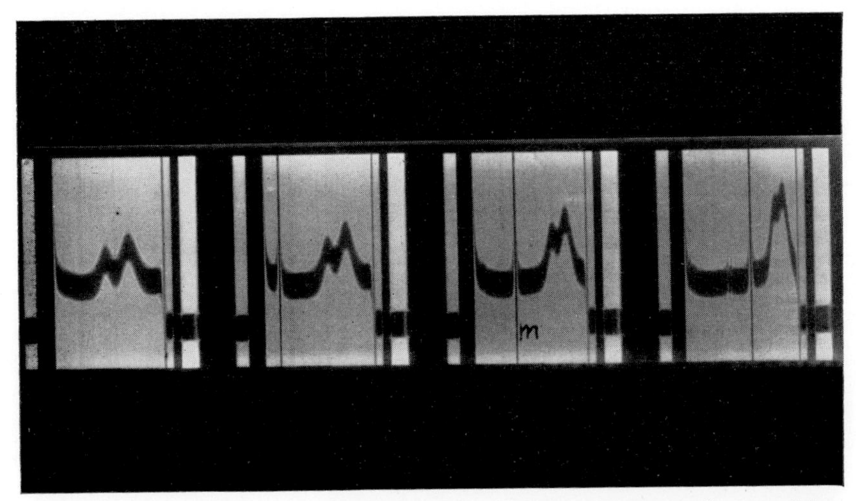

FIG. 93a. Sedimentation of a diluted serum containing an abnormal macroglobulin (m). Sedimentation proceeds to the left. Speed 56,100 rev/min. The photos taken in 8 minute intervals

FIG. 93b. Sedimentation of the isolated macroglobulin at similar conditions

A typical macroglobulin was isolated recently in this laboratory by either dialyzing fraction I, which was dissolved in 0·2 M citrate of pH 6·0, or by slow dilution of serum with water. The sedimentation diagrams of the serum and the isolated macroglublin are presented in Fig. 93, and the electrophoretic pattern is shown in Fig. 94. The sedimentation constant of the major component was 17 S (uncorrected), when measured in 0·2 M citrate buffer of pH 6·0, and it depended strongly on concentration of the macroglobulin. (The sedimentation constant of 17 S was measured at a protein concentration of 0·4%, whereas in a 1·6% solution of the same pH and ionic strength it was 13 S). The intrinsic viscosity of the macroglobulin in 0·2 M citrate buffer of pH 6·0 was found to be 0·20 dl/g. The specific rotation of the macroglobulin was −39° when determined with green light of $\lambda = 546$ mμ, and the dispersion constant was 205 (± 2) mμ,[14] i.e. the same as the constant of normal γ-globulins.[15] The identity of the macroglobulin with γ-globulin with respect to the rotatory dispersion is one more indication of the similarity of configuration of these proteins.

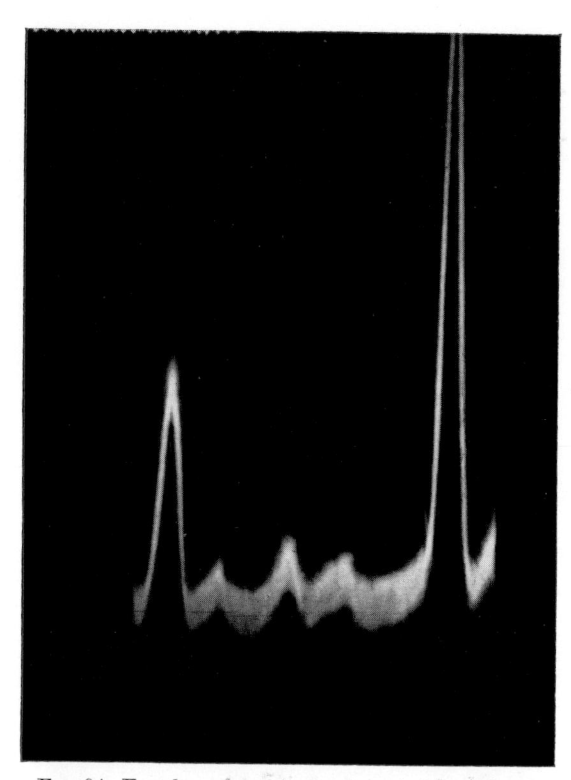

FIG. 94. Free boundary electrophoresis of a diluted serum containing a macroglobulin in a high concentration. Parkin-Elmer instrument used. Ascending boundaries after 105 min at 180 V and 10 mA current. The high peak at the right represents the slowly moving macroglobulin. The run was made by Dr. T. Ikenaka.

Denaturation and cleavage upon reduction with thioglycollic acid of the macroglobulin also was studied. The specific rotation changed from −39° (with $\lambda = 546$) to −74° on denaturation with alkali (at pH 11·9) at room temperature, whereby slow sedimenting components appeared in the sedimentation pattern. Denaturation with 2 M guanidine thiocyanate and heating at 50 °C for 1 hr resulted in even a higher increase of levorotation, i.e. up to −99°, while the dispersion constant of this denatured macroglobulin attained the usual value of 217 mμ. Reduction of the disulfide bonds, and protection of the free —SH groups with iodoacetate produced an unusually high increase of levorotation (−144° as measured with the green light), and sedimentation in the ultracentrifuge revealed the presence of slowly sedimenting components. The S-values of the latter, as well as their concentrations, depended on the conditions of denaturation with the guanidine salt as well as on the conditions of the reduction and carboxymethylation.

(14) B. JIRGENSONS, *Arch. Biochem. Biophys.* **89**, 48 (1960).
(15) B. JIRGENSONS, *Arch. Biochem. Biophys.* **74**, 57 (1958); **78**, 235 (1958).

Abnormal Serum Globulins in Multiple Myeloma [16,17]

Multiple myeloma is a relatively rare malignant disease of bone marrow, and its symptoms may include the appearance of abnormal proteins either in blood plasma or urine, sometimes in both. On electrophoresis of serum,

TABLE 56

PHYSICAL CONSTANTS AND N-TERMINAL AMINO ACIDS OF MYELOMA GLOBULINS [17,18]

Specimen	E.-phor. mobility at pH 8·6	Isoelectric point, pH	Sedimentation constant (S)	N-terminal amino acids (Moles per 160,000 g)
La	− 0·7	> 6·6	6·4	2·0 Leu.; 0·2 Asp.; 0·2 Glu.
Li	− 0·8	6·7	6·2	2·0 Leu.; 0·1 Glu.; 0·2 Ala.; 0·1 Ser.
Ag	− 1·1	6·4	6·6	2·0 Asp.
Wi	− 1·1	6·6	7·0	1·8 Asp.; 0·1 Glu.
Th	− 1·1	7·5	6·2	1·8 Asp.; 0·2 Glu.
Mi	− 1·3		6·7	2·1 Asp.; 0·2 Glu.
Mn	− 2·1		6·3	2·3 Asp.; 0·2 Ser.
D	− 3·6	4·7	6·6	1·0 Asp.
A	− 0·5	7·2	6·6	2·1 Glu.
Se	− 0·8		6·4	2·7 Glu.
B	− 1·0	7·1	9·7	2·0 Glu.
I	Insoluble		7·6; 11	2·8 Glu.; 0·2 Asp.
Wn	− 1·6		6·1	3·9 Glu.; 0·2 Asp.; 0·3 Ala.; 0·3 Ser.; 0·2 Phe.
Kl	− 1·5	7·4	6·1; 9·5	5·3 Glu.; 0·1 Asp.
C	− 2·1	6·4	6·5	2·9 Glu.
R	Insoluble		7·6; 11	2·0 Asp.; 2·6 Glu.
MS	− 1·4			1·5 Asp.; 1·5 Glu.
Jo	− 2·4	< 6·7	6·1; 9	2·1 Asp.; 2·7 Glu.; 0·1 Ser.
GM	− 2·4	< 6·7	6·2; 9; 12	1·3 Asp.; 1·7 Glu.; 0·1 Ser.
We	− 1·0		6·2	1·5 Glu.; 0·2 Ala.; 0·3 Ser.; 0·3 Val.
Du	− 1·2	6·7	6·2	0·5 Asp.; 0·5 Glu.; 0·7 Ala.
Wa	− 0·7		6·5	0·4 Asp.; 0·4 Glu.; 0·2 Ser.
IA	− 1·3		6·0	1·6 Glu.; 1·4 Phe.

moderate or large amounts of protein are seen with the β- or γ-globulins, while the sedimentation pattern may appear normal. Upon fractionation, these proteins usually precipitate together with the γ-globulins, and thus are difficult to purify and obtain free of γ-globulins. Immunochemically they are similar but not identical with the γ-globulins. While the amino acid composition of the multiple myeloma globulins is very similar to that of the γ-globulins, the latter contain less carbohydrate than the former. Moreover, the myeloma globulins show striking *individuality* in both physicochemical constants and chemical properties.(16,17) While most of these abnormal globulins, like the cryo- and macroglobulins, have aspartic and glutamic acid as the N-terminal groups, other specimens with terminal leucine and with phenylalanine also have been found (see Table 56). The amino acid composition of four specimens of the myeloma proteins is presented in Table 57. The proteins for these analyses were isolated by combining the method of electrophoresis convection (see chapt. 2) with precipitation methods, and the amino acids were determined by the modern chromatographic methods.(18)

TABLE 57

AMINO ACID COMPOSITION OF FOUR MYELOMA GLOBULINS

(As grams of residue per 100 g of anhydrous protein (18))

	Globulin A	Globulin B	Globulin C	Globulin D
Aspartic acid	8·48 ± 0·14	7·65 ± 0·22	8·19 ± 0·17	7·28 ± 0·18
Threonine	6·41 ± 0·07	8·49 ± 0·19	6·40 ± 0·14	7·92 ± 0·04
Serine	10·16 ± 0·04	9·10 ± 0·14	10·54 ± 0·33	7·81 ± 0·02
Glutamic acid	10·58 ± 0·17	11·30 ± 0·45	10·69 ± 0·35	10·09 ± 0·12
Proline	5·94 ± 0·05	7·14 ± 0·32	6·64 ± 0·27	6·61 ± 0·25
Glycine	3·78 ± 0·14	3·84 ± 0·03	3·61 ± 0·06	3·24 ± 0·10
Alanine	3·88 ± 0·10	4·93 ± 0·26	4·69 ± 0·17	4·36 ± 0·05
Valine	8·44 ± 0·33	6·96 ± 0·04	8·60 ± 0·09	6·18 ± 0·12
Methionine	0·97 ± 0·06	0·98 ± 0·06	1·38 ± 0·02	0·80 ± 0·04
Isoleucine	2·30 ± 0·06	2·56 ± 0·05	2·94 ± 0·01	2·27 ± 0·01
Leucine	8·24 ± 0·18	9·14 ± 0·28	5·80 ± 0·08	8·38 ± 0·08
Tyrosine	6·66 ± 0·22	4·96 ± 0·10	6·05 ± 0·06	4·38 ± 0·13
Phenylalanine	4·78 ± 0·15	4·92 ± 0·16	4·37 ± 0·10	4·62 ± 0·10
Histidine	2·12 ± 0·03	2·01 ± 0·01	2·22 ± 0·06	2·10 ± 0·06
Lysine	7·42 ± 0·12	5·33 ± 0·03	7·44 ± 0·26	5·44 ± 0·21
Arginine	4·91 ± 0·21	5·07 ± 0·22	2·72 ± 0·05	4·96 ± 0·08
Ammonia	1·26 ± 0·02	1·31 ± 0·02	1·20 ± 0·02	1·51 ± 0·04
Tryptophan	1·48 ± 0·19	1·51 ± 0·09	2·84 ± 0·02	2·45 ± 0·03
Half cystine	1·83 ± 0·03	2·48 ± 0·07	1·77 ± 0·04	2·27 ± 0·06
(Hexose	1·59 ± 0·03	0·83 ± 0·05	1·11 ± 0·02	3·99 ± 0·05)
(Hexosamine	0·03 ± 0·01	0·81 ± 0·01	1·32 ± 0·02	3·10 ± 0·10)
Total weight recovery	100·27	100·01	99·32	98·25
Total N recovery in grams	16·48	16·52	16·01	15·90

Smith *et al.* concluded from their findings that: "The proteins differ from one another in composition but resemble normal γ-globulins" . . . and "The proteins are immunologically related, but are not identical with one another"

(16) F. W. PUTNAM, *Physiol. Rev.* **37,** 512 (1957).

(17) F. W. PUTNAM, *J. biol. Chem.* **233,** 1448 (1958); F. W. PUTNAM and A. MIYAKE, *Arch. Biochem. Biophys.* **65,** 39 (1956).

(18) E. L. SMITH, D. M. BROWN, M. L. MCFADDEN, V. BUETTNER-JANUSCH and B. V. JAGER, *J. biol. Chem.* **216,** 601 (1955).

(18, quoted from p. 618). Lohss and Wollensak have arrived recently at the same conclusion.[19] Putnam concludes: "A remarkable biochemical individuality in patients with multiple myeloma, macroglobulinemia, and cryoglobulinemia has been revealed by comparison of the electrophoretic data, ultracentrifugal properties, and the amino acid end groups of the purified pathological globulins from 31 cases" [*J. biol. Chem.* **233**, 1453 (1958)]. All these abnormal globulins seem to be truly abnormal proteins produced by some kind of derailment of the mechanism that is responsible for the formation of antibodies. This would explain the similarity between them and the normal γ-globulins, as well as the individual differences which are due to the complexity of the bio-genetic background of each individual case (see previous chapter). On the basis of all that we know now about protein synthesis in cells, it is unlikely that the abnormal serum globulins are formed by some modification of normal γ-globulins. It is more likely that the abnormal cryo-, macro-, and myeloma globulins are synthesized in each case *de novo*, and that the abnormality is caused by defects in the nucleic acid and enzyme systems which are responsible for these syntheses (see chapt. 21, 22, and 23).

The Urinary Bence–Jones Proteins[16,20]

In about a half of all cases of multiple myeloma the patients produce a strange protein which appears in urine. This protein has the peculiar property in that, after being precipitated by heating to about 55–60 °C, it redissolves on boiling. Upon cooling it reprecipitates again. These interesting proteins have been studied in various laboratories to a great extent, and the findings can be summarized briefly as follows.[16,20] The Bence–Jones proteins have electrophoretic mobilities in the β- and γ-globulin range, and their sedimentation constants are between 2 and 4 S units. Thus they are much smaller than any of the previously mentioned abnormal globulins of serum. Since the solutions of these proteins are of low viscosity, the low sedimentation constant definitely must be attributed to a relatively much lower molecular weight than that e.g. of γ-globulins. The molecular weights of Bence–Jones proteins have been found in the range 20,000–40,000, and this explains the ease with which they pass the kidney glomeruli and get into urine. With respect to all physicochemical parameters as well as chemical properties the Bence–Jones proteins display the same individuality as the above mentioned abnormal serum globulins. Even the characteristic redissolving on boiling is not exhibited by all samples in the same manner. Some specimens can redissolve only in a very narrow pH range, while others dissolve but partially.

Since the Bence–Jones proteins are relatively small, there is hope that their complete chemical structure might be unraveled much more easily than the structure of any of the other abnormal globulins. Thus far, however, there

(19) F. Lohss and J. Wollensak, *Z. Naturforsch.* **14 b**, 328 (1959).
(20) H. Vis and R. Crokaert, *Acta Clinica* **11**, 455 (1956).

are data only on amino acid composition and terminal amino acids. The amino acid composition varies, depending on the individual specimen, but some general features common to all of these urinary proteins also are obvious. These abnormal urinary proteins are similar in amino acid composition to the γ-globulins and to all the other abnormal serum globulins. They all are distinguished with a high content of *hydroxyamino acids*, and with a low methionine content. The carbohydrate content of the Bence–Jones proteins usually is very low, much lower than that of the abnormal serum globulins, and lower than the carbohydrate content of the γ-globulins, but exceptions also are known. We were able to show in this laboratory that a specimen could be subfractionated by chromatographic methods, and that the subfractions differed in terminal amino acids. In most instances, aspartic acid has been found as the N-terminal group, and leucine as the C-terminal residue.[(21)] However, in one of our subfractions we found also half-cystine as another N-terminal group in addition to aspartic acid.[(22)]

The peculiar solubility properties of the Bence–Jones proteins of course are especially interesting. In one instance we were able to isolate and compare the abnormal proteins from both urine and serum. The urinary and also the serum protein displayed the characteristic redissolving on boiling, and the amino acid composition of both proteins was similar.[(23)] Furthermore, the fact is noteworthy that Bence–Jones protein is more soluble in 50% alcohol than in 15–30% alcohol, a property which probably can be explained by the high hydroxyamino acid content of this protein and its relatively small molecular size. On the basis of this property, a new clinical test for this protein was proposed.[(24)] When varying amounts of propanol are added to equal amounts of urine in a series of test tubes, flocculation is observed at 15–30 vol% propyl alcohol but not with 50–70% of the alcohol. Albumin flocculation is proportional to the alcohol concentration. If some of the serum globulins happen to be in the urine, they may exhibit flat flocculation peaks at 20–40 vol% propyl alcohol.

The origin of Bence–Jones protein, and its relation to normal γ-globulin, has been a subject of a considerable debate. Since the amino acid composition is very similar to the composition of γ-globulin, it seemed likely that the abnormal urinary protein might simply be a split product of the serum globulins. This view seemed to be supported also by immunochemical tests which show some similarity between the γ-globulins and Bence–Jones proteins. Moreover, the Bence–Jones proteins display a similar optical rotatory dispersion be-

(21) A. Drèze, *Clin. Chim. Acta* **3**, 89 (1958).

(22) B. Jirgensons, T. Ikenaka and V. Gorguraki, *Clin. Chim. Acta* **4**, 876 (1959).

(23) B. Jirgensons, A. J. Landua and J. Awapara, *Biochim. Biophys. Acta* **9**, 625 (1952).

(24) B. Jirgensons, *Makromol. Chem.* **10**, 78 (1953); *Arch. Biochem. Biophys.* **48**, 154 (1954).

havior as the γ-globulins.[15,25] In spite of these similarities, there are also differences. Moreover, metabolic studies have indicated that the synthesis of Bence–Jones proteins involves a somewhat different mechanism from the synthesis of serum globulins. In agreement with Putnam, it seems likely that the abnormal urinary proteins are similar "misprints" in protein synthesis as the abnormal plasma proteins.

(25) B. Jirgensons, *Arch. Biochem. Biophys.* **85**, 89 (1959).

CHAPTER 25

THE PROBLEM OF MALIGNANT GROWTH

> There is one phenomenon which appears to be universally common to all tumors, and that is the property of increased autonomy, or the capacity for unlimited and uncontrolled growth. The ultimate control of cancer necessitates an understanding of the chemical factors involved in this capacity, factors presumably absent or present to different degrees in normal tissues.
>
> JESSE P. GREENSTEIN [1]

THE PROBLEM of malignant growth is one of the most important of biology and medicine. Despite the tremendous efforts of armies of investigators which have attacked this problem by various methods and approaches, the main questions remain unanswered. The mechanism involved in the transformation of a normal cell into a malignant one is not yet understood. Is there then any justification of the relevance of these questions in a treatise on macromolecules? It is hoped that, in spite of the many reviews and discussions by authorities in medicine, biology, biochemistry, and related fields, a "macromolecular" point of view may elucidate some aspects not sufficiently exposed before. The implications are obvious from all that has already been said in the previous chapters, especially chapt. 11–24, on the chemistry of macromolecular nucleic acids, proteins, and polysaccharides. Any processes of cellular growth and multiplication involve the synthesis of macromolecular nucleic acids and proteins, and all these reactions are catalyzed by enzymes which are macromolecular entities. There is no doubt that considerable progress has been achieved in solving the problems of configuration, structure, and even biosynthesis of these macromolecules. Some aspects of malignant growth will be discussed based on these new achievements in the chemistry of organic macromolecules.

Facts and Ideas Relative to the Origin of Malignancy [1,2,3]

No attempt will be made to survey the whole field of oncology, the science of tumors. Some of the most important facts as to the characteristic properties and origin of tumors will be mentioned briefly. As indicated, charac-

[1] J. P. GREENSTEIN, *Biochemistry of Cancer* 2nd ed., p. 591, Academic Press, New York, 1954.

[2] A. C. GRIFFIN, in *Cancer* Vol. I, p. 123, Butterworth, London, (1957).

[3] H. P. RUSCH, in *Currents in Biochemical Research* p. 675 (D. E. GREEN, ed.), Interscience, New York, 1956.

teristic features of malignant growth are uncontrolled growth and loss of specialized functions of certain cells. While benign tumors are strictly localized, a malignant tumor (cancer) may release cell clusters which disseminate via the blood and lymph throughout the body and invade vital organs and other tissues. Malignant tumors appear not only in humans and other mammals but also in other animal species, and even in plants. In the first stages of development, the tumor cells may closely resemble the normal tissue cells, and also retain many of the special functions. The further development is characterized with a gradual loss of all special functions and increasing autonomy and growth rate. Cells of practically every tissue and organ may become cancerous or neoplastic, and the tumors display a considerable variety not only with respect to their morphology but also with respect to metabolism.[4] While these differences may be striking in the early stages of development of the tumor, they diminish with the degree of development, so that the originally very different tumors in the course of development become more and more similar with their common feature — uncontrolled growth. This loss of specialized function and increased *autonomy* is especially pronounced in transplanted tumors. An autonomous tumor, e.g. in the stomach, does not contribute to the special assignment of the organ which is beneficial for the organism, e.g. the stomach tumor does not produce pepsin, but the cells multiply at a rapid rate receiving the essential nutrients from the blood stream. In a tumor cell, all of the organelles and the component macromolecules are mobilized for the single purpose of growth and replication, and any of the specialized functions of the particular cell system are neglected. Otherwise, both morphologically and metabolically, the tumor cells do not differ qualitatively from the normal cells: both types of cells have the same organelles, both have the same enzymes and nucleic acids, although some slight differences in the concentrations of some enzymes and nucleic acids have been reported. It must, however, be emphasized that the *qualitative identity* of either the proteins or nucleic acids has not been proved, and the facts now available on the variability of proteins and nucleic acids in general are indicative of possible differences. In fact, such differences have been reported, e.g. between the histones of normal and neoplastic tissues.[5] It has been found that the histones from malignant tissues were less soluble at pH 5–7 and had a lower electrophoretic mobility than the histones from normal cells. Although other authors have criticized these experiments,[6] the significance of the findings has not been disproved. Another characteristic property of tumors is the heterogeneity of the neoplastic cell population, and some quantitative differences in metabolism.[7] Neoplastic cells may

[4] J. Furth, *Cancer Res.* **19**, 241 (1959).

[5] H. J. Cruft, C. M. Mauritzen and E. Stedman, *Nature* **174**, 580 (1954).

[6] J. A. V. Butler and P. F. Davison, *Adv. Enzymol.* **18**, 161 (1957).

[7] Review: S. Kit and A. C. Griffin, *Cancer Res.* **18**, 621 (1958); S. Kit, ibid. **20**, 1121 (1960).

differ in chromosome number and in content of deoxyribonucleic acid (DNA) and ribonucleic acid (RNA). Worthy of mention is the distribution of the nuclear RNA, as shown in Table 58. Here the distribution of RNA and protein in the various organelles of tumor cells is compared with the distribution of these components in various normal tissue cells.[8] Differences between the various normal tissues are conspicuous, and the high nuclear RNA of the tumors provides the only basis for the differentiation of neoplastic cells from all normal cells that were studied. The concentration of DNA and the corresponding nucleotides in tumors is often higher than in normal tissues. The mitochondria of some tumor cells are found to be deficient in certain of the enzymes participating in the electron transport, and this has been reported to be one of the causative factors responsible for the imbalance between respiration and glycolysis in the tumors. "The apparent controversy in recent years has not been as to the reality of this imbalance but rather as to the causal factors whereby it *originates* and the *mechanisms* by which it *persists*".[7]

With respect to the origin of malignant growth, there is a wide gap between the *facts* of carcinogenesis and the proposed explanations of the mechanisms of cellular transformations. While the facts are well established, the explanations usually have a character of general speculations. Cells may become neoplastic by some unknown internal reason or a tumor can be induced artificially by a variety of agents, such as azo dyes, irradiation with ultraviolet light, by means of certain carcinogenic hydrocarbons, etc. Generally, the effects can be reduced to some kind of persistent *irritation*, and it is possible, although not proven, that the apparently spontaneous tumors of lung, stomach, brain, or any other organ or tissue, have been caused by *persistent* stress. There are obvious difficulties in studying the various stages of development of tumor in man and consequently a great deal more is known about the experimental tumors of animals, such as those induced by carcinogenic hydrocarbons in skin or muscle or by azo dyes in liver.[2] For example, it has been demonstrated that the carcinogenic 3,4-benzpyrene combines with the proteins of the skin,[9,10] and that the carcinogenic azo dyes combine with certain proteins of the liver.[11] The strongly carcinogenic nitrogen mustards also react with proteins.[12] These results suggest that the carcinogens may effect a gradual deletion of certain enzymes and other proteins which are necessary for the specialized function of the cell but not for its growth and reproduction.

(8) A. K. Laird and A. D. Barton, *Science* **124**, 32 (1956).

(9) E. C. Miller, *Cancer Res.* **11**, 100 (1951).

(10) W. G. Wiest and C. Heidelberger, *Cancer Res.* **13**, 246, 250, 255 (1953).

(11) E. C. Miller and J. A. Miller, *Cancer Res.* **12**, 547 (1952); *Adv. Cancer Res.* **1**, 339 (1953). J. C. Arcos and M. Arcos, *Biochim. Biophys. Acta* **28**, 9 (1958).

(12) A. C. Griffin, E. L. Brandt and E. L. Tatum, *J. Amer. Med. Assoc.* **144**, 571 (1950); P. Alexander, *Adv. Cancer Res.* **2**, 1 (1954).

It is tempting to speculate on the possible mechanisms of action of carcinogens in the cells. The cytoplasmic components may suffer certain permanent damage. Since the cytoplasmic organelles are in contact with the nucleus, this alteration may also affect the nuclear components. When a cell loses its *specificity* of function this change is irreversible; and since the total course of these events is due to the control of the nuclear DNA, the latter must be somehow affected by the carcinogen. Another important fact

TABLE 58

DISTRIBUTION OF PROTEIN (as percentage of total protein nitrogen) AND RNA AMONG CELL FRACTIONS OF VARIOUS NORMAL AND MALIGNANT TISSUES [7]

	Protein nitrogen				Ribonucleic acid			
	Nucleus	Mito-chondria	Micro-some	Soluble fraction	Nucleus	Mito-chondria	Micro-some	Soluble fraction
Animal tumors	38	8	13	40	32	10	29	30
Normal thymus, rat	58	3	8	32	15	3	37	61
Adrenal, human, normal	20	13	17	51	16	9	37	37
Liver, mouse, normal	21	32	11	37	11	39	29	21
Kidney, rat, normal	16	26	17	40	14	13	32	40
Pancreas, rat, normal	14	8	32	46	4	2	51	42
Salivary gland, rat	11	8	29	52	9	3	54	35

should not be overlooked, viz. the differences in *individual response* to the various agents, such as carcinogenic azo dyes, tobacco smoke, or radiation effects. Since the genetic background of each individual organism is inscribed in its *chromosomal DNA*, the latter must be as important a factor in the final outcome of the carcinogenic effect as the elimination of certain enzymes. Extensive experiments of the mutation of microbes have shown that the metabolic pathways are genetically determined.[13] Also the studies on the development of drug-resistant cells provide beautiful examples of the interplay between cytoplasmic effects and nuclear DNA, demonstrating the work of natural selection.[14] While chemical carcinogens can reach the nuclear chromosomes only through the cytoplasm, radiation can affect the nuclear DNA more directly. It is established that radiation can affect macromolecules in two ways: by direct hit, or through the chemical action of free radicals

(13) G. W. BEADLE, *Chemical Genetics in Genetics in the 20th Century* p. 221 (L. C. DUNN, ed.), MacMillan, New York, 1951; G. W. BEADLE and E. L. TATUM, *Amer. J. Botany* **32**, 678 (1945).

(14) L. W. LAW, *Cancer Res.* **14**, 695 (1954).

formed upon the action of the radiation on water. Both of these effects may take place in the nucleus, and it is noteworthy that the most effective wave lengths are those which are maximally adsorbed by the nuclear DNA.[15] Furthermore, it is of interest that induction of mutations by irradiation with ultraviolet light are initiated most effectively during cellular division.[16] While the very energetic radiations, such as the γ-rays or X-rays, penetrate deep into the tissues, the ultraviolet light affects only the surface of the body. It is known that irradiation of micro-organisms with ultraviolet (U.V.) light can cause mutations, an indication that the light quanta have affected the macromolecules of the nucleic acids. The reactions induced by irradiation of a mouse with U.V. light, however, seem to be very complex, and the mechanism of tumor induction by ultraviolet light is not understood. Prolonged irradiation with high intensity U.V. light produces burns, e.g. profound denaturation and decomposition of proteins. It seems likely that the essential enzymes and nucleic acids of the skin also are affected by the irradiation. The wave lengths in the 230–280 mμ range are known to be the most damaging and carcinogenic, while the somewhat longer wave length U. V. light of 320–390 mμ is known to be relatively harmless. Significant contributions on the U.V. light carcinogenesis have been rendered from the Biochemistry Department of the University of Texas M. D. Anderson Hospital and Tumor Institute. For example, it has been established that injection of certain substances, such as oxypsoralen, sensitizes mice against the radiation effects of the longer U.V. of the wave length of 320–400 mμ. Also it has been found that orally given oxypsoralen protects albino mice against the carcinogenic effects of ultraviolet light.[17] The mechanism of these phenomena is under study.

Rusch has summarized the major events of neoplastic transformation in the following four points. (1) "Carcinogens induce a change in one or more of the special functions of the cell. The resulting change is heritable. (2) An untimely alteration of function disrupts the normal sequence of differentiation and the resulting metabolic patterns. In such cells, the pattern for reduplication is retained and predominates to varying degrees. (3) Cells which have suffered from such heritable change may require additional loss of accessory factors before becoming completely autonomous neoplasms. (4) The formation and growth of cancer cells are affected by conditions within the host, the genetic constitution, the hormone balance, the diet, the presence of irritation, chemotherapeutic agents — any factor that affects the internal environment of the host" (3, quoted from p. 692).

[15] A. HOLLAENDER and C. W. EMMONS, *Cold Spring Harbor Symp. Quant. Biol.* **9**, 179 (1941).

[16] F. L. HAAS and C. O. DOUDNEY, *Proc. Nat. Acad. Sci.* **43**, 871 (1957).

[17] M. A. O'NEAL and R. HAKIM, *in Radiation Biology and Cancer* p. 276, 12 *Ann. Symp. on Fundam. Cancer Res.*, Univ. of Texas Press, Austin, 1958. A. C. GRIFFIN, R. E. HAKIM and J. KNOX, *J. of Investig. Dermatology*, **31**, 289 (1958).

In spite of the efforts to find some specific differences in the metabolic pathways of proteins (or of nucleic acids) synthesized in tumors, the results thus far are not glamorous, and one recent review on this subject is concluded with the statement: "It is not known, at present, whether the mechanism of protein synthesis in tumor cells differs from that in normal cells".[18] Although the loss of certain specialized functions in malignant tissue is plausible, it is impossible to tell with which of the known mechanisms of macromolecular biosyntheses these losses are associated. But it is also true that the biosyntheses of macromolecules in normal cells still are not completely understood.

One important aspect in the problem has thus far been omitted: the part possibly played by *viruses* in carcinogenesis. Since excellent recent reviews are available on this topic, it will be mentioned but very briefly [19]. There is experimental proof that certain types of tumors in birds and some other animals can be transmitted from one organism to another by cell-free filtrates of the tumor. Electron microscopic studies have revealed in these filtrates small virus-like particles which have the size of microsomes. The problem then is: are viruses involved in all types of malignant growth or only in certain special animal tumors? Human cancer in general is considered to be non-contageous, and the possible role of viruses in human cancer is questionable. High incidence of leukemia in mice was observed by treating the animals with cell-free extracts of leukemic organs.[20] Also it is known that the incidence of breast cancer in mice depends at least on three factors: (1) hereditary factors, (2) hormonal effects, and (3) on the presence of virus-like particles in the mouse milk.[21] Similar particles were found also in the tumor tissue. According to fractional centrifugation data, the virus-like bodies sediment with the microsomal fraction, a fact which is partially in agreement with electron microscopic observations. It is also noteworthy that the fraction is not immunologically active in mice, viz. it behaves as a normal, not foreign, constituent of the organism. All this leads to the idea that the virus might be a somewhat degenerated microsome. Since the latter are concerned with the synthesis of enzymes, and since some of the enzymes control the synthesis of the nucleic acids (see chapt. 21 and 22), such degenerated microsomes certainly may upset the balance of the cell functions. These degenerated microsomes, moreover, may differ from normal microsomes so little that the difference will not show up even in immunochemical tests.

[18] P. N. Campbell, *Adv. Cancer Res.* **5**, 97 (1958); quoted from p. 148.

[19] H. B. Andervont, in *The Viruses* Vol. 3, p. 307 (F. M. Burnet and W. M. Stanley, ed.), Academic Press, New York, 1959.

[20] L. Gross, *Ann. N. Y. Acad. Sci.* **68**, 501 (1957); L. Dmochowski, C. E. Grey and I. Gross, in *Radiation Biology and Cancer* p. 382, Univ. of Texas Press, Austin, Texas, 1959.

[21] L. Dmochowski, *Adv. Cancer Res.* **1**, 104 (1953).

Most effective results on the tumor induction by viruslike agents have been obtained by means on the *polyoma viruses* which can be propogated in tissue cultures.[22] When the cell-free extracts of these filterable agents are injected into mice, rats, or hamsters, a variety of tumors develop in the animals, and the filterable extracts of these tumors can be used for further propagation of the agent. Electron-microscopic studies have revealed virus-like particles in the infected tissues and tumor cells. The size of the particles has been found about 27 mμ in diameter, and a higher magnification has revealed in some of the particles a dense center of about 5 mμ in diameter, surrounded by an electron-translucent zone and a poorly visible membrane.[23] There are indications that the variety of the tumors induced by these agents may be due to a corresponding multiplicity of the agents. However, since the susceptibility of the host tissue in carcinogenesis is *at least* as important as the agent, the multiple nature of the polyoma virus induced tumors do not necessarily imply a multiple nature of the virus. It is not excluded that the same agent causes different types of tumors in different tissues. It must be remembered that the subtle constitutional differences which render a tissue of an individual organism susceptible to a carcinogenic agent and make another resistant to the same agent are unknown. Further studies on the isolated and purified agent may solve some of these problems.

Serum Proteins in Cancer [24,25,26]

The abnormal globulins mentioned in chapt. 24 do not appear in all cases of neoplastic growth. In fact, they appear so rarely that their appearance is of little value for the general diagnostic purposes of malignancy. Even in such specific malignancies as e.g. multiple myeloma only the common components of the serum often can be found. However, some abnormalities are usually observed in the protein pattern, i.e. the *ratio* of the various components. In Table 59 are presented data obtained by Mider *et al.* [25] on selected plasma specimens of cancer patients.

According to these data, the albumin concentration in cancer decreases and the concentration of all the other proteins increases. If these changes were specific for malignant growth, cancer diagnosis would be relatively simple and the researcher would have a solid factual basis for the study of the effects and causes of the malignant growth. Unfortunately, the elevated globulin pattern is not specifically indicative for malignancy but it occurs

[22] S. E. Stewart, *J. Nat. Cancer Inst.* **15**, 1319 (1955); **16**, 41 (1956); S. E. Stewart, B. E. Eddy *et al. Virology*, **3**, 380 (1957); B. E. Eddy, S. E. Stewart, R. Young and G. B. Mider, *J. Nat. Cancer Inst.* **20**, 1223 (1958).

[23] L. Dmochowski, C. E. Grey and L. A. Magee (a private communication).

[24] A. B. Gutman, *Adv. Protein Chem.* **4**, 155 (1948); R. W. Begg, *Adv. Cancer Res.* **5**, 1 (1958).

[25] G. B. Mider, E. L. Alling and J. J. Morton, *Cancer* **3**, 56 (1950).

[26] R. J. Winzler, *Adv. Cancer Res.* **1**, 503 (1953).

in several other diseases. Some delicate differences between the globulin ratios in cancer and other diseases have been found, but these differences are inconsistent. This is due partially to the individuality in general, and also to the type of malignant disease and its stage. Especially difficult is the

TABLE 59

ELECTROPHORETIC COMPONENTS IN PLASMA OF CANCER PATIENTS AND NORMAL INDIVIDUALS
(The variation of each figure, calculated as standard deviation was between $\pm$ 0·01 and $\pm$ 0·05)

	Albumin (g %)	α_1-globulin (g %)	α_2-globulin (g %)	β-globulin (g %)	fibrinogen (g %)	γ-globulin (g %)
Normal adults	4·04	0·38	0·66	0·76	0·31	0·66
Cancer	2·94	0·53	0·90	0·89	0·58	0·75
Advanced cancer	2·38	0·65	1·05	0·99	0·82	0·82

situation in finding some differences in protein patterns in early cancer, and no formula has been found which would express the globulin ratios specifically for malignant growth. The same is true for such approaches as determination of glycoproteins and mucoproteins in the blood plasma of cancer patients. Although the carbohydrate content in blood is often elevated in cancer, the same is found in some other diseases. Further tests include determination of enzymes, such as the acid and alkaline phosphatases, aldolase, and others. Although these tests are of some value in the diagnosis of a few types of cancer, the meaning of these variations is obscure. The same applies for the suspected qualitative differences between plasma proteins in cancer and normal proteins.[26] A large number of diagnostic tests based on some suspected differences in colloid stability, dye binding, and other possibly specific reactions of the proteins have been proposed, and all of them have been discarded as inconsistent. "From the work that has thus far been carried out, it would appear that a large number of pathological conditions lead to very similar abnormalities in the plasma protein picture. This suggests that most of the abnormalities considered in previous pages are *associated with systemic changes in the host elicited by the neoplasm*, rather than a direct effect of the tumor" (26, quoted from p. 538).

In spite of these facts, the search for a *specific* effect of a tumor continues. According to Greenstein,[1] this specificity may be expressed in the presence of a *toxin* released by the tumor, a specific substance produced *only by a malignant tumor*. Several authors had observed before that in the instance of malignant growth the blood plasma contains a toxin that specifically inhibits the liver catalase activity. Also it was found that a malignant tumor produces a greater depression of catalase activity than a benign tumor of similar size.[27] Attempts to isolate the toxin have been made.[28] The toxin probably represents a polypeptide, since the active principle was found to be dialyzable, and yielded amino acids on hydrolysis. Sato and Yunoki[29] separated an active substance from an extract of human carcinoma by adsorbing on kaolin at pH 5·4, eluting at pH 9·0, and finally precipitating the eluate with acetone. This fraction was active in 10 mg doses when injected in a mouse subcutaneously. Since this is a relatively large dose, the preparation apparently was not pure. Significant new results in the purification of the toxin have been achieved recently by Dr. GRIFFIN in the University of Texas M. D. Anderson Hospital and Tumor Institute. As there were indications that the substance is a basic protein or polypeptide, extraction from human tumors was attempted by means of glacial acetic acid. An acetone dried powder of tumors was treated with sixteen-fold weight of glacial acetic acid, and from this extract the toxin was precipitated with acetone and ether. The precipitate was purified further by ion exchange chromatography. Elution from an Amberlite XE-64 column with alkaline glycine buffers yielded three major components: TH_1, TH_2, and TH_3. The active principle was found chiefly in TH_2 which emerged by elution at pH 9·5. The minimum effective doses of this substance were 5–1 μg per mouse. The finding also is noteworthy that a comparative treatment of a similar normal tissue did not yield the fraction TH_2. Another form of the toxohormone was obtained by batch operation by adsorbing on carboxymethyl cellulose. This purified toxin, however, was less active than TH_2 of the Amberlite procedure, and it was nondialyzable. The toxin appears either as a free polypeptide or a compound of it with a protein.[30]

In the same connection, the possibility of truly abnormal components in some of the normally appearing plasma protein fraction still remains under consideration. It is not excluded that the waste materials released by the tumor in the blood stream affect in some way the cells involved in plasma protein synthesis. In the liver, the catalase activity of these toxins certainly is affected. On the other hand, the appearance of abnormal macroglobulins and other abnormal components in a few cases of neoplastic disease ascertains the fact that a truly abnormal protein can be synthesized in certain cases. According to Bernfeld and Homburger,[31] immunologically specific α-globulins can be detected in the serum of tumor bearing mice. Other authors have reported other abnormal components among the known normal serum proteins (see Begg's review, l.c. 27.)

[27] R. W. BEGG, T. E. DICKINSON and J. MILLAR, *Canad. J. Med. Sci.* **31**, 319 (1953); R. W. BEGG, *Adv. Cancer Res.* **5**, 1 (1958).

[28] W. NAKAHARA and F. FUKUOKA, *Adv. Cancer Res.* **5**, 157 (1958).

[29] H. SATO and K. YUNOKI, *Acta Med. Univ. Kagoshima* **1**, 50 (1958).

[30] K. YUNOKI, a private communication; K. YUNOKI and A. C. GRIFFIN, *Cancer Res.* **20**, 533 (1960).

[31] P. BERNFELD and F. HOMBURGER, *Cancer Res.* **15**, 359 (1955).

If the transformations of normal cells into neoplastic depends on genetic factors (predisposition), the presence of abnormal protein components in serum may be due not only to the direct effect of tumor toxins but also to *genetically determined derailment of protein synthesis.* If this assumption is correct, the abnormal protein components should possibly be detectable in

TABLE 60

OPTICAL ROTATION AND CARBOHYDRATE CONTENT OF SERUM ALBUMIN FRACTIONS [32,33]

	$-[\alpha]_D$ at pH 5	Hexose (%)	Hexosamine (%)
Normal albumins			
A 144	62·5 ± 0·5°	1·35 ± 0·1	0·51 ± 0·1
A 145	60·0	0·56	0·52
A 153	62·1	1·15	0·42
A 155	62·2	1·30	0·77
A 156	63·0	1·12	0·75
A 157	62·5	1·40	0·89
A 172	63·1	0·94	0·84
A 173	61·2	1·85	0·80
A 207	62·4	0·90	0·32
A 272	61·8	0·36	
Albumins, nonmalignant source			
A 62	58·8	1·35	0·80
A 68	59·6	0·82	0·45
A 70	58·4	1·12	0·59
A 71	58·4	2·10	1·06
A 73	60·0	1·10	0·49
A 74	59·7	1·00	0·53
A 75	59·8	1·00	
Albumins from cancer patients			
AC 31	45·5	1·11	0·32
AC 32	54·4	0·92	0·84
AC 33	54·2	1·72	0·76
AC 43	57·9	1·29	0·58
AC 44	59·5	0·89	0·78
AC 52	47·4	1·16	1·20
AC 61	56·9	0·98	0·50
AC 63	55·8	1·22	0·77
AC 107	61·5	0·60	0·40
AC 119	57·4	0·72	0·58
AC 148	58·0	1·30	0·82
AC 149	60·2	1·68	1·00

(32) B. JIRGENSONS, *J. Amer. chem. Soc.* **77,** 2289 (1955); *Arch. Biochem. Biophys.* **59,** 420 (1955).

(33) B. JIRGENSONS, *Makromol. Chem.* **21,** 179 (1956).

the earliest stages of the disease, or even before the neoplastic transformation. Only very slight differences in the composition and constitution of the protein components, however, can be expected; and it is questionable if such differences would be detectable by the present methods.

About four years were spent in this laboratory in trying to find some differences between the albumin fractions of cancer patients and healthy

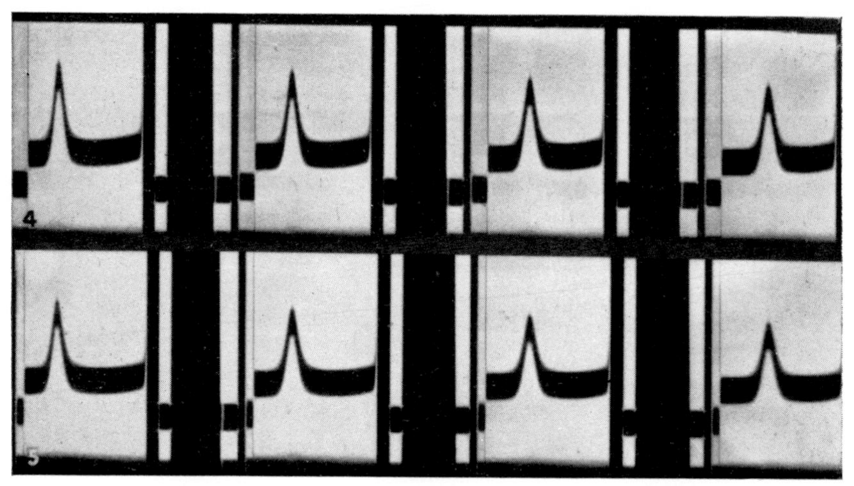

FIG. 95. Sedimentation of two albumins isolated from the plasma of two cancer patients. Speed 59,780 rev/min. Both albumins showed abnormally low specific rotation

persons. The chief method of characterization was an optical rotation function, viz. the dependence of the specific rotation on pH, because of the fact that the optical rotatory properties are known to be sensitive to variations in structure and configuration (see chapt. 5 and 12). The albumin specimens were characterized also by means of electrophoresis, viscosity, and sedimentation, and the purity was tested by carbohydrate analyses. Altogether more than 300 albumin fractions were investigated. About 200 of them were isolated from the plasmas of cancer patients, and the rest from either healthy individuals or patients with nonmalignant diseases. A part of the data is presented in Table 60.[32,33] Since the albumin fractions were 90–95% pure, the variation in the specific rotation is partially due to the impurities, such as the carbohydrate-containing α- and β-globulins, lipids and fatty acids, and other extraneous material firmly bound to the albumin. It is, however, interesting that the "cancerous" albumins in general were less levorotatory than those from individuals with nonmalignant diseases, in spite of the fact that in some instances the latter contained even more hexose and hexosamine than the former. Also it is noteworthy that a few of the "cancerous" albumins exhibited extremely low levorotation, while some others appeared practically "normal". Some of these "cancerous" albumins, although abnormal in rotatory properties, possessed quite symmetrical sedimentation peaks, as shown in Fig. 95.[34]

The rotation curves that express the dependence of the specific rotation on the acidity of the solutions of the cancerous albumins showed a considerable variety,[32] as shown in Fig. 95a. Here A 54 represents a normal albumin, while AC 52 and AC 57 are examples of albumins from cancer patients. The interpretation of these phenomena, however, was difficult

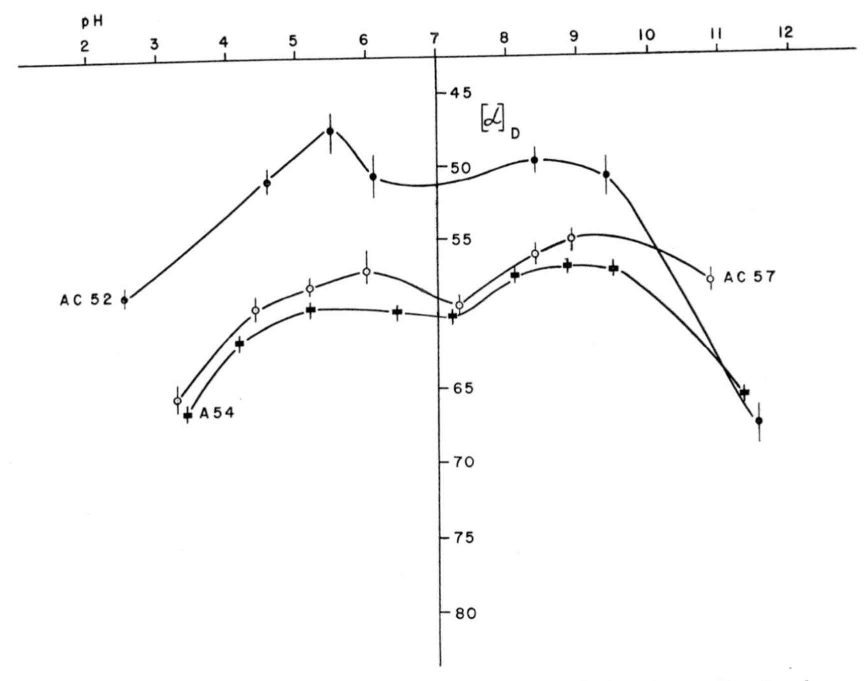

Fig. 95a. Dependence of the specific rotation on pH for three albumins from various sources. AC 52 and AC 57 were albumins from the blood plasma of cancer patients. A 54, an albumin from a more normal source

because of the uncontrollable effects of the impurities. The highly purified albumins yielded more uniform curves[33] than the less pure fractions, although all of the rotational differences could not be explained by the effects of the impurities. Recently, we succeeded in preparing albumin specimens free from any globulin and other impurities by means of diethylaminoethyl cellulose ion exchange chromatography at 5 °C, using albumin fractions as starting material. Individual specimens of the pure albumins were slightly different in their optical rotatory properties. The presently available methods seem to be still too crude to ascertain any qualitative (compositional,

(34) B. Jirgensons, *Cancer* 8, 809 (1955).

structural, or configurational) differences between individual specimens of albumins. Since genetically controlled structural differences have been found in hemoglobins, in the instances of certain types of anemias (chapt. 14), it is quite possible that some kind of differences may exist also between normal and "cancerous" albumins, γ-globulins, and any other proteins.

Antimetabolites in the Biosynthesis of Macromolecules [35,36,37]

Recent trends in the chemotherapy of malignant diseases are based on the idea of finding nontoxic antimetabolites which would interfere with the biosynthesis of such macromolecules as the nucleic acids and proteins. Since the protein synthesis depends to a great extent on the nucleic acids, the latter have become the main objects of interest. It is known that the biosynthesis of both ribonucleic and deoxyribonucleic acids is a very complicated chain of reactions which are catalyzed by a series of enzymes. The total biosynthesis of a macromolecule of RNA or DNA can be envisaged as occurring in several series of reactions, viz.: biosynthesis of the pyrimidines, biosynthesis of purines, biosynthesis of ribose and deoxyribose; the assemblage of the units into the nucleosides; formation of the nucleotides, and polycondensation of the latter thus forming the chains of RNA or DNA. The reactions in each of these series or levels have been studied in great detail, chiefly by introducing molecules labeled with either radioactive tracers or stable isotopes. The antimetabolites which are employed are "fraudulent" intermediates in these chains of reactions, i.e. they are molecules which resemble natural intermediates, and thus are able to participate in the event, but at the same time interfere with the normal course of transformation. Although many thousands of substances have been screened in biological tests as potential antitumor agents without having this in mind, most of the recent efforts are directed towards a more rational investigation of the effects of substances that are structurally related to definite metabolites.[35] It is impossible to mention in this survey all of these compounds, but purine, pyridine, and amino acid derivatives deserve mention. Extensive experiments have been carried out on micro-organisms and small mammals, chiefly certain strains of mice, and some of the most promising antimetabolites have been applied clinically, e.g. in leukemias. Although these antimetabolites have not produced any definite cures, improvements have been recorded in many instances, and these are considered to be encouraging.[36,37] The reason that any of the potent antimetabolites have not revolutionized the therapy of malignant diseases (surgery and radiation therapy are still the major treatments) is the *toxicity* of the antimetabolites. The more effective an agent in suppressing

[35] J. A. Montgomery, *Cancer Res.* **19**, 447 (1959), a review.
[36] S. Farber, R. Toch, E. M. Sears and D. Pinkel, *Adv. Cancer Res.* **4**, 1 (1956).
[37] C. P. Rhoads (ed.), *Antimetabolites and Cancer* Amer. Assoc. Adv. Sci., Washington, D. C., 1955.

the growth of a tumor the more toxic it usually is. This is perfectly clear when one considers the mechanism of nucleic acid synthesis and its affection by various means. If an antimetabolite stops the synthesis of nucleic acids and proteins in a tumor cell it will do the same in a normal cell. And, since these syntheses belong to the normal course of life of the organism, any interference must cause some disturbances (toxicity). This is illustrated in Table 61 in which the tumor inhibiting effects of various purine derivatives are compared with their toxicity [35]. The antimetabolites were tested on their effectiveness to prevent the growth of adenocarcinomas in mice.

TABLE 61

INHIBITION OF ADENOCARCINOMA BY PURINE DERIVATIVES
(after Skipper, Montgomery *et al.*, see ref. 35)

R_1	R_2	R_3	Degree of inhibition *	Therapeutic index **	Toxic dose (mg/kg day)
SH	H	H	++	30	40
$S—CH_3$	H	H	++	80	150
$S—CH_2CH_2CH_3$	H	H	++	25	250
$S—C_{10}H_{21}$ *n*	H	H	+	4	250
$S—CH_2C_6H_5$	H	H	++	120	200
SH	NH_2	H	++	8	3
SH	OH	H	++	1	500
SH	C_2H_5	H	—		500
SH	H	C_2H_5	++	25	100
Cl	H	H	++	15	200
Cl	C_2H_5	H	—		500
NH_2	SH	H	±	1	15

* Based on ratio of average tumor weights, treated/control: ++ 6 per cent, + 6–25%, ± 26–42%, — 42%.
** The ratio of maximum tolerated dose to minimum effective dose.

The ultimate success in cancer chemotherapy may depend chiefly on the eventual existence of *specific pathways* of biosynthesis of the essential macromolecules in the tumor cells. If such specific pathways do exist in cancer cells, viz. if pathways differ from those in normal cells, there would be the hope to find ways of blocking these specific reactions by some means which would not interfere with the normal metabolism. If, however, it would be established that there are only *quantitative* differences between normal and cancer cells, the only hope for a successful chemotherapy would be in exploiting the *higher metabolic rate* of the malignant cells. "Selective concentration of agents in tumor cells is the crux of cancer chemotherapy. Rapidly metabolizing cells in general take up nutrients from the body pool, depleting the supply for normal cells . . . In this greediness lies a vulnerable spot of tumors; they also grab avidly the antihormones and antimetabolites, and in so doing limit their own growth" (l.c. 4, quoted from p. 225).

Although the antimetabolites which are most active as antitumor agents are generally also the most toxic ones, some have a higher therapeutic index than some others. Thus of the agents mentioned in Table 61, 6-benzylthiopurine is one of the most effective and least toxic agents. These findings are encouraging in further efforts to find even less toxic yet active antimetabolites, as well as in the attempts to understand in detail the mechanism of inhibition.

One more aspect is worthy of mention in this connection: the *adaptation* of neoplastic cells to an antimetabolite, i.e. development of resistance to it. In the heterogeneous population of malignant cells, some cells respond to the antimetabolite somewhat differently from others. While the growth and division of most of the cells is stopped or strongly inhibited, a certain number of the cells are only slightly affected. Upon further treatment with the same agent, a certain fraction of these cells do not submit, and even recover, and they gradually *become resistant* even to higher doses of the antimetabolite. This adaptation to extraneous effects is a very general phenomenon, and it has far reaching implications in the understanding of life processes in general. For the chemotherapy of malignant diseases, however, it means serious difficulties. In clinical treatment attempts to overcome these difficulties have been made by using several antitumor agents periodically one after another. The adaptation to certain antimetabolites is explained by the development of alternative metabolic pathways, or by the more extensive use of already existing alternate pathways of biosynthesis.

The *individuality* of the host as well as in the characteristics of the tumors involve further difficulties in the chemotherapy. When five patients suffering from a similar malignant disease are treated with the same antitumor agent in exactly the same fashion, they do not respond equally well. Certain improvements are usually observed only in one or two cases, while the others remain unaffected or even show some new complications. This is due to constitutional differences of the host as well as to some differences in their tumors.

Regional therapy, i.e. local application of the antitumor agents has also been considered. Exploratory studies are carried out for example in The University of Texas M. D. Anderson Hospital and Tumor Institute, and the results can be qualified as promising.

Only a few highlights could be mentioned in this brief survey on antimetabolites. Extensive studies are continued in various laboratories, and it may be expected that these will throw new light on the biosynthesis of macromolecules in both normal growth and in neoplastic growth. At present, little is known of the differences, especially at the macromolecular level. The crucial point in the action of antimetabolites seems to be on the *micro*molecular level, e.g. in the formation of nucleotides. The "fraudulent" building blocks affect not only the biosynthesis of the macromolecular RNA and DNA, but also the synthesis of the many enzymes which contain nucleotides as coenzymes. Moreover, the protein synthesis is affected indirectly, i.e. by failing to build the microsomal and soluble RNA's involved in protein synthesis (see chapt. 21). Other sources ([35,36,37] and the literature mentioned therein) should be consulted for more detailed information, for example on the hormone effects, nutritional problems, radiation effects, etc. in combination with antimetabolites, as well as on the interesting facts that many carcinogens under certain conditions may act as antimetabolites.

In conclusion, it can be said that very little is known about the mechanism of neoplastic growth. However, recent advances in biology and biochemistry at least have exposed the major problems rather clearly. There is little doubt that extremely important parts in these events are played by such macromolecular substances as the DNA's, RNA's, and the enzymes that are essential in the biosynthesis of proteins and the DNA's and RNA's. The ultimate solution of the cancer problem will depend to a large extent on further advances in the understanding of the structure, configuration, and metabolism of the mentioned macromolecular substances.

CHAPTER 26

MACROMOLECULES IN CONNECTIVE TISSUE

> We may, on the basis of the facts at present available, consider the extracellular phase as a functional extension of plasma which acquires its specific character and gel-like consistency by the deposition of collagen and elastin fibers and the presence of hyaluronic acid and other polysaccharides.
>
> A. NEUBERGER [1]

CONNECTIVE tissue, as the name indicates, *connects* the multitude of cells and cellular systems into an organic entity — the organism. Thus connective tissue is the unifying tissue and as such it is found throughout the body: in skin, bone, cartilage, tendons, the walls of blood vessels, etc. Connective tissue binds and embeds muscle and nerve fibers and the cells in every organ, and there is no better way of expressing its functional role and meaning as in the above quotation of Neuberger. Connective tissue is in a way the *functional extension of the blood.* It is closely dependent on the circulation, and it is structurally and functionally associated with the muscle and nerve tissues. Like blood plasma, connective tissue is an *inter*cellular tissue, yet, unlike plasma, it is highly consistent and metabolically rather inactive tissue.

Three principal components are distinguished in the connective tissue: the white *collagen fibers*, the yellow *elastic fibers*, and the *ground substance.* In addition, connective tissue contains cells — the so called fibroblasts — which represent the metabolically active loci in the tissue. The various levels of submicroscopic structure of the connective tissue are illustrated in Fig. 96.

Collagen Fibers and their Functions [1,2,3,4]

Collagen is the major component of the connective tissue of vertebrates, and even in many invertebrates; it is not found in protozoa, microbes, and plants. The richest sources of this fibrous protein are tendons and skin which contain about 65–90% collagen. The aortas contain 25–35% collagen, bone 15–25%, stomach and intestines 10–20%. The collagen content of muscle, lung, liver, and spleen is lower, e.g. the liver of pig contains 2·5% collagen.

[1] A. NEUBERGER, in *Fibrous Proteins and their Biological Significance* p. 72, quoted from p. 77 (IX *Symp. Soc. Exp. Biol.*), Academic Press, New York, 1955.

[2] R. H. SMITH, *Progress in Biophys. and Biophys. Chem.* 8, 218 (1957).

[3] K. H. GUSTAVSON, *The Chemistry and Reactivity of Collagen,* Academic Press, New York, 1956.

[4] J. C. KENDREW, in *The Proteins* Vol. II B, p. 845 (H. NEURATH and K. BAILEY, ed.), Academic Press, New York, 1954.

Since the chemical aspects of the protein were discussed in chapt. 17, we shall be concerned here chiefly with its functional and metabolic aspects.

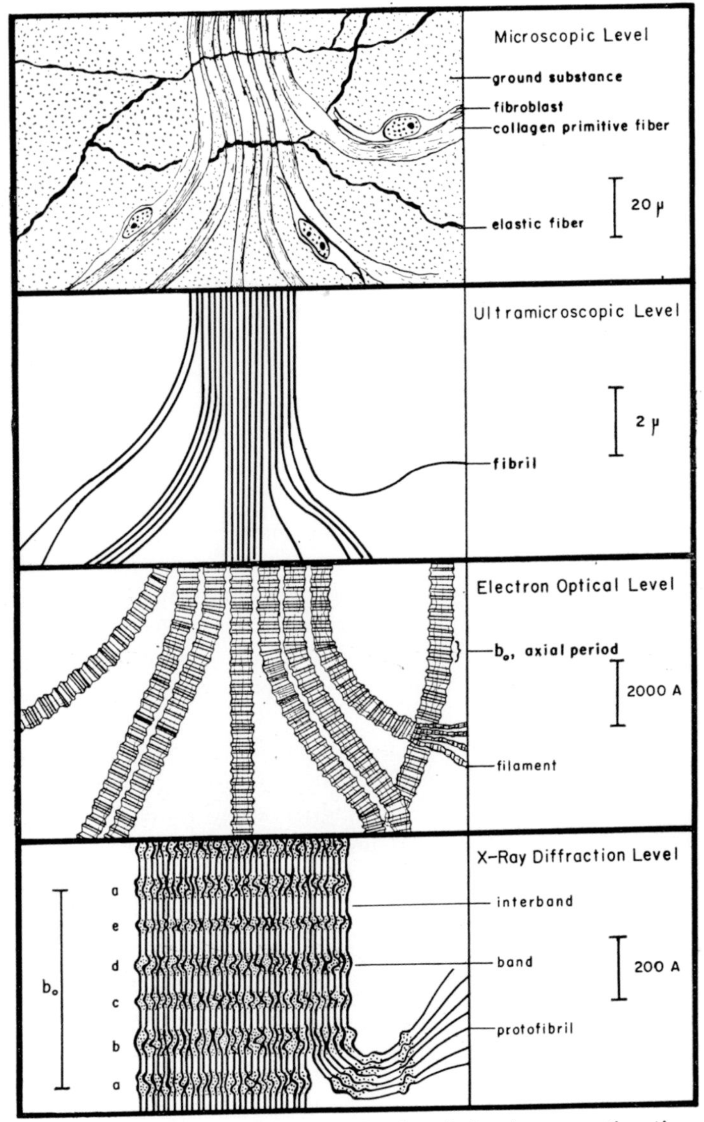

FIG. 96. Fibers, fibrils, and macromolecular chains in connective tissue. *Courtesy* Dr. R. S. Bear

Some twenty years ago, Schoenheimer *et. al.* showed in their classical work with isotopically labeled amino acids that the turnover rate of proteins is different in various tissues.(1) While the isotopes were readily incorporated in the plasma and liver proteins, the tissue of skin and muscle appeared to be metabolically rather inactive. The incorporation of isotopes specifically in collagen was studied more recently by Neuberger *et al.*,[1,6,7] and Robertson,[8] and it was found that collagen was metabolically passive. "It can be concluded that collagen, quantitatively the most important protein of the mammal, has a very slow rate of turnover and makes only a small contribution to the 'dynamic pool' of body proteins" (1, quoted from p. 80). There was only a slight difference in the turnover rate in young and old animals. Larger differences, however, were found between the incorporation of the isotope in the collagen of various tissues. The average values of radio-activity measured in the collagen of tendon were 32; skin, 83; bone, 169; liver, 180. While the passivity of the structural collagen fibers in tendon is not surprising, the high turnover rate in the collagen of bone is noteworthy.

The collagen of a certain connective tissue, e.g. tendon, is not a homogeneous protein but it is composed of several components which have different solubility properties. A part of the collagen of the connective tissue can be dissolved in dilute acid of pH 3–5; this is the "procollagen" of Orekhovitch.[9] Beside the insoluble (or not easily soluble) fraction, there is a small fraction which can be extracted from the tissue by means of neutral or weakly alkaline buffer. This fraction, which on further purification was readily converted into the acid-soluble form, seems to be the real procollagen or precollagen, since isotopically labeled glycine was rapidly incorporated in this fraction.[10] According to Neuberger,[1] the cells of the connective tissue (fibroblasts) excrete this protein into the extracellular space where it is converted into the less soluble forms of collagen which are metabolically inactive.

The mechanism of the collagen fiber formation has been studied by means of phase contrast microscopy and electron microscopy observing specimens grown in tissue cultures.[11,12,13] These observations indicated that the fibroblasts did not have a definite membrane, and that fine fibers were formed at the diffuse surface sections of the cells. Time-lapse films showed that the

(5) R. SCHOENHEIMER, S. RATNER and D. RITTENBERG, *J. biol. Chem.* **130**, 703 (1939); D. SHEMIN and D. RITTENBERG, *ibid.* **153**, 511 (1944).

(6) A. NEUBERGER, I. C. PERONNE and H. G. B. SLACK, *Biochem. J.* **49**, 199 (1951).

(7) A. NEUBERGER and SLACK, *ibid.* **53**, 47 (1953).

(8) W. VAN B. ROBERTSON, *J. biol. Chem.* **197**, 495 (1952).

(9) V. N. OREKHOVITCH, A. A. TUSTANOVSKY, K. D. OREKHOVITCH and N. E. PLOTNIKOVA, *Biokhimyia* **13**, 55 (1948).

(10) R. D. HARKNESS, A. M. MARKO, H. M. MUIR and A. NEUBERGER, *Biochem. J.* **56**, 558 (1954).

(11) S. FITTON JACKSON, in *Nature and Structure of Collagen* p. 146 (J. T. RANDALL, ed.), BUTTERWORTH, London, 1953; *Proc. Roy. Soc.* **142 B**, 536 (1954).

(12) K. R. PORTER, in *Repair Processes in Connective Tissue* Second Congress on Connective Tissue, New York, J. Macy Jr. Foundation, 1952.

(13) S. FITTON JACKSON and R. H. SMITH, in *Fibrous Proteins and their Biological Significance* p. 89, IX. *Symp. Soc. Exp. Biol.*, Academic Press, New York, 1955.

surface of the fibroblasts is not only diffuse but also that it is dynamic, changing rapidly, somewhat like the white cells in plasma. Since protein synthesis is known to be carried out in the microsomes (small granules) of the cells, the various granular components of the fibroblasts were isolated by differential centrifugation and studied. It was found that the granules contain nucleic acids, protein, phospholipids and polysaccharides. The protein component contained hydroxyproline, the typical amino acid of collagen, and this ascertains the fact that the synthesis is carried out in the granules. This was confirmed also by immunological studies.[14] Somewhat surprising, however, was the observation [2] that the large granules (mitochondrial fraction) incorporated ^{14}C-L-proline at about the same rate as the small granules. However, one need not necessarily agree with Smith's conclusion [2] that these experiments prove that protein is synthesized in the mitochondria. Since the large granules contain the redox enzyme systems, it is quite possible that the administered proline is oxidized in these organelles. The assembly of the activated amino acids, including the proline and the unique hydroxyproline, most probably occurs in the microsomes which contain the required RNA templates, whereby the hydroxyproline comes from the mitochondria. This conclusion is supported by the results of Smith himself [15] who showed that the collagen-forming chick osteoblasts readily converted proline into hydroxyproline *in vitro*. It is, however, difficult to assess how large the macromolecules are which are synthesized in the microsomes. The high reactivity of the pre-collagen, as found by Neuberger [10] indicates that the primary units are small, and that the microfibrils are formed in several successive stages. The chemical molecular weight of collagen is not known, yet the ease with which the large collagen particles are disaggregated into smaller units indicates that the true chemical molecular weight may be somewhere in the range of 20,000–80,000 (see chapt. 17). Assuming the smaller single-chain unit as the one which is originally formed in the microsome, one can envisage the biosynthesis as occurring in the following stages:

Amino acids → Single-chain unit $M = 20{,}000$ → Three-strand aggregate →

Rod-shaped aggregate $M = 380{,}000$ → Protofibrils → Submicroscopic and microscopic fibers.

From a chemical point of view, the problem about the compositional and sequential uniformity of the collagen chains is very interesting. Are the collagen chains as synthesized in various tissues in various species the same? Since protein synthesis is under genetic control, species differences can be expected. Only small differences in the amino acid composition of collagens of various species could be detected (see chapt. 17). The amino acid com-

[14] W. C. Robbins, F. R. Watson, G. D. Pappas and K. R. Porter, *J. Biophys. Biochem. Cytol.* **1**, 381 (1955).

[15] R. H. Smith and S. Fitton Jackson, *Biochem. J.* **64**, 8 P (1956).

position of the various collagens from the same source (rabbit skin) also has been determined,[16] and it was found that the differences between the neutral salt-soluble, insoluble, and citrate (acid) soluble collagens are very small. These results thus indicate that there are not three chemically different collagens, and that the solubility differences are due to different degrees of aggregation (or polymerization) of the same fundamental unit synthesized in the microsomes. Such conclusion, however, is by no means final, since none of the collagen preparations are well enough defined as chemical individuals.

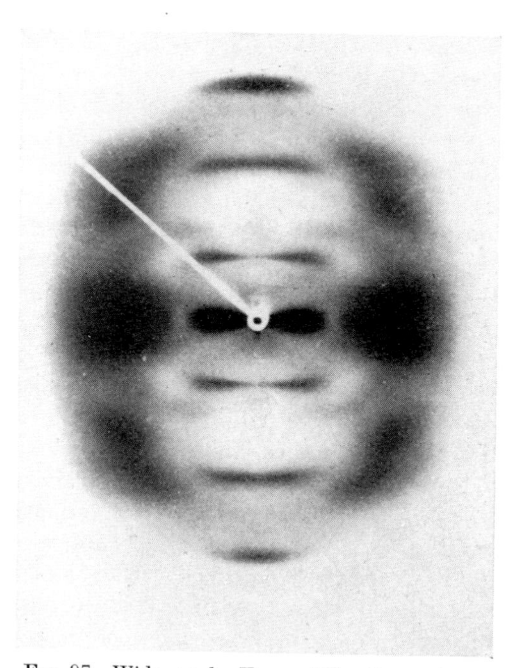

FIG. 97. Wide angle *X*-ray diffraction pattern of kangaroo-tail tendon (by *Courtesy* of Dr. R. S. Bear)

The periodic band patterns observed under the electron microscope also have been an object of considerable discussion.[17] Variations in the banding in various collagen specimens are explained by differences in the arrangement of the subunits in the fiber, not by chemical differences. The band patterns are exhibited also by collagen which was dissolved and then reprecipitated at a certain pH and ionic strength, and the pattern can be altered to some extent by alteration of the conditions of precipitation.

The *X*-ray diffraction of various collagen tissues has been studied extensively by using both the large and small angle technique,[17a] and these studies have permitted certain conclusions about the degree of orientation and arrangement of the macromolecular chains in the tissues. An example of a wide angle diffraction pattern of kangaroo-tail tendon (under tension) is shown in Fig. 97. An example of the low angle diffraction and its change upon swelling is shown in Fig. 98, and these changes in the diffraction reveal some facts about the mechanism of hydration and configurational changes of the

[16] D. S. JACKSON, A. A. LEACH and S. JACOBS, *Biochim. Biophys. Acta* **27**, 418 (1958).

[17] R. S. BEAR, *Adv. Protein Chem.* **7**, 69 (1952); J. H. HIGHBERGER, J. GROSS and F. O. SCHMITT, *J. Amer. chem. Soc.* **72**, 3321 (1950); F. O. SCHMITT, *J. Cell. Comparat. Physiol.* **49**, suppl. 1, p. 85 (1957).

[17a] R. S. BEAR, in *IX Symp. Soc. Exp. Biol.* 98 (1955); M. A. ROUGVIE and R. S. BEAR, *J. Amer. Leather Chem. Assoc.* **48**, 735 (1953).

swelling chains. All parts of the fibrils were found to be susceptible to invasion by water, which enters first the band regions and then the interband sections. The changes of the spacings have been measured, e.g. it has been found that the macroperiod of the dry tendon was 603 Å, and that it increased to 670 Å on swelling.[17a] Although these studies have provided important

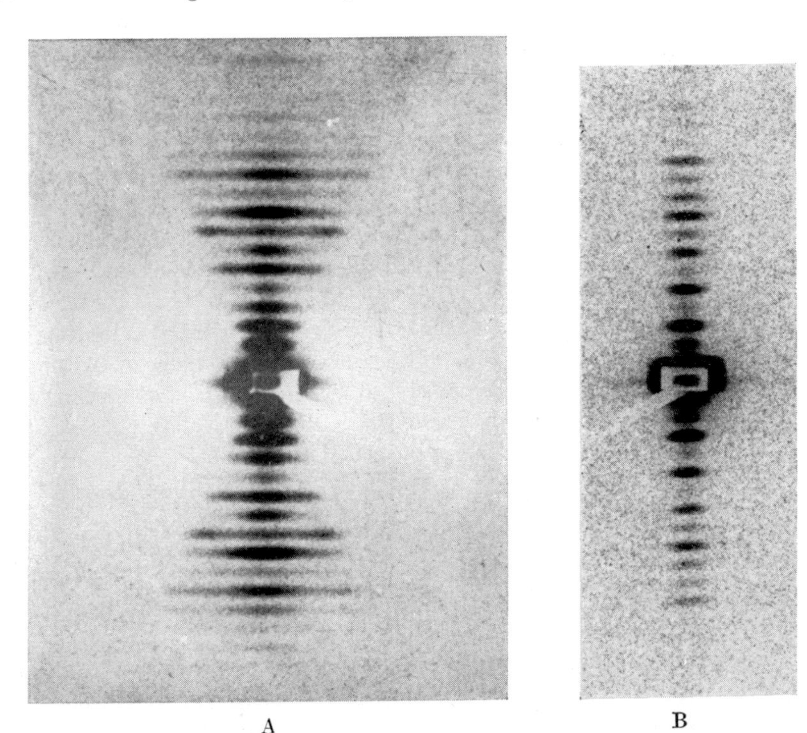

FIG. 98. Small angle *X*-ray diffraction spectra of kangaroo-tail tendon. *A* — dry tendon; *B* — swollen tendon (by *Courtesy* of Dr. R. S. Bear)

information on the macromolecular structure of the tissue, they have not contributed much to the understanding of the biochemical phenomena of biogenesis and function, in which the physiologists and biologists are interested most of all.

What forces the primary chain units of cellular collagen to assemble into the higher order structures? Two fundamentally different causes can be envisaged: (1) environmental conditions, and (2) the chemical properties of the chain itself. Could the fiber formation be due to a cellular mechanism comparable to a spinnerette extruding a nylon fiber? Although it is true that the ionic environment must have some effect on the fiber formation, it is unlikely that the noncollagenous components "... provide the necessary viscous, even thixotropic, medium required to keep the precipitated fibrils localized to specific areas and arranged in a particular pattern".[18] Since the ground substance itself is an amorphous mass of entangled linear macromolecules, it is inconceivable how it would orient the collagen chains or fibrils. It seems more likely that the orientation is due chiefly to the properties of the polypeptide chain itself, i.e. its peculiar *amino acid composition*. This is characteristic with the high content of proline (13–15%) and hydroxyproline (12–14%), and the absence of cystine. The nitrogen of the peptide bond in the proline and hydroxyproline residues belongs to a ring, and at these points the chain is stereochemically conditioned in a different way than at the other peptide bonds. Furthermore, the proline and hydroxyproline nitrogens are devoid of hydrogen. These may be the decisive factors which determine the peculiar configuration, i.e. the twisting of the chains together into the now accepted three-stranded helix. While the formation of the higher order fibrillar structures may be somewhat conditioned by the acidity and salt concentration, the geometric and chemical properties of the rod-shaped macromolecular units ("tropocollagen") certainly play the dominating role. The linear and lateral association of the units probably occurs within the fibroblast. Any orientation of the newly grown fiber outside of the fibroblast may be exerted by the already pre-existing fibers of collagen rather than by the amorphous matrix of the ground substance.

The biosynthesis of collagen is affected by a number of substances, such as ascorbic acid.[19] The mechanism of action of ascorbic acid, however, is only partially understood. There is some evidence that ascorbic acid participates in the electron transport system of the mitochondria.[20]

It seems that the interesting and important problems on biosynthesis of collagen and of the various collagen diseases will be solved when the reactions occurring within the fibroblast are better understood. It is noteworthy that in embryonic connective tissue the cells are numerous and very active, and that there is little of intercellular collagen. In a fully developed organism the cells are few and rather inactive, and an elaborate and stable fibrous system of the connective tissue supports the body. Upon *aging*, the amount of the amorphous highly dispersed portions of the tissue decreases and the amount of the fibrous collagen increases. At the same time the fibers tend to become coarser and less elastic, and the amount of water in the connective tissue decreases. On what factors this natural aging depends is unknown, but, inasmuch as there is little metabolic activity, this probably is a process of slow aggregation of the units due to Brownian movement. This process could be described also as a slow recrystallization or coagulation of the macromolecules in the microfibrils. It is probably the same process which causes

(18) J. GROSS, *J. Biophys. Biochem. Cytol.* Suppl. **2**, 261 (1956).

(19) W. VAN B. ROBERTSON and B. SCHWARTZ, *J. biol. Chem.* **201**, 689 (1953); B. S. GOULD, *J. biol. Chem.* **232**, 637 (1958).

(20) H. KERSTEN, W. KERSTEN and HJ. STAUDINGER, *Biochem. Z.* **328**, 24 (1956).

a gel to synerize,[21] viz. the tendency to decrease the free surface energy.* The slow natural aging, however, often is affected by external factors resulting in various *diseases of the connective tissue.* Apart from the conditions caused by the deficiency of ascorbic acid, rheumatic fever, rheumatoid arthritis, scleroderma, and lupus erythematosus are the names of some of the maladies of connective tissue.[22] In rheumatoid arthritis, the normal fibrous collagen tissue has been found to be replaced by a more amorphous material together with broken and disintegrated collagen fibers. In rheumatic fever, a large amount of protein with a low hydroxyproline and high tyrosine and hexosamine content was found in the affected tissue.[23] What causes such disintegration of collagen, and deposition of amorphous material, is not known. Again, the answer scarcely could be expected from the study of collagen but rather from a better understanding of the biosynthesis of proteins. The fact that some of the collagen diseases respond to a treatment with cortisone indicates that the lipid components of the fibroblasts, e.g. those of the mitochondria, may be involved in these anomalies. Another interesting question is the *regeneration* of collagen in wound healing. Any injury of the tissue results in activation of the cells which start to produce large amounts of collagen, as if reacquiring the capacity of the cells of embryonic stage. The amount of collagen thus produced is usually excessive resulting in the formation of scar tissue. Activation of the cells upon injury probably involves a series of enzymic reactions, something like that as in blood clotting.

The importance of collagen is not restricted to the briefly mentioned fields of biochemistry and pathology but reaches into such quite different and distant branches as food technology and manufacture of glue and leather. Gelatin is a purified degradation product of collagen (see chapt. 17), while glue represents an impure and highly heterogeneous mixture obtained in a drastic degradation of the macromolecules of sinews, tendons, and bone. The tanning process results in the diffusion of the tanning agent into the swollen hide, and combination with the collagen thus interlinking the fibers into a tighter network.[24] Tannic acid and various polyphenolic compounds, formaldehyde, and the three-valent chromium salts are the important tanning

(21) B. Jirgensons, *Organic Colloids* chapt. 15, Elsevier, Amsterdam, 1958.

(22) J. H. Kellgren, in *Fibrous Proteins and their Biological Significance* p. 163 (IX *Symp. Soc. Exp. Biol.*), Academic Press, New York, 1955.

(23) R. Consden, L. E. Glynn and W. M. Stanier, *Biochem. J.* **55**, 248 (1953).

(24) K. H. Gustavson, *The Chemistry of Tanning Processes* Academic Press, New York, 1956.

* It must be pointed out that increased order (crystallinity) of the fibrous macromolecules upon aging does not indicate a decrease of entropy of the system. The decrease of entropy occurring in the gradual orientation of the macromolecules is overweighed by the large entropy increase due to dehydration. The water bound to the highly dispersed (disordered) chains of a young tissue is in a higher state of order than the free water. When the highly hydrated single macromolecules aggregate into oriented bundles, a large part of the bound water is liberated, and the entropy increases.

agents. The cationic chromium complexes react initially with the carboxyl groups of the collagen, and the complex is chemically bound to the fiber. Stable cross-links between the fibers are formed when some of the polynuclear chromium complexes interlink two adjacent chains. Thus cross-linked and stabilized meshwork of the collagen fibers withstands boiling, and resists the attack of micro-organisms. Formaldehyde reacts with collagen in a different way: it reacts with the amino groups of the collagen chains, and cross-links them by forming methylene bridges. Vegetable tannins are bound in between the polypeptide chains by multipoint attachment, most probably by hydrogen bonding between the hydroxy groups of the tannin and the oxygen of the =CO groups of the collagen. These studies on tanning have lead Gustavson to important conclusions about the structure of collagen, viz. that the configuration and stability of the collagen helix are due partially to the hydrogen bonding between the =CO groups of the peptide bonds and the OH groups of the hydroxyproline residues. This apparently results in configurations which differ to a great extent from the chain configurations of other fibrous proteins, such as the keratins, myosin, and others.

Elastic Fibers of Connective Tissue

Elastin of the yellow elastic fibers of connective tissue differs from collagen in both physical and chemical properties. Elastin is amorphous and much more elastic than collagen, and it is found mostly in those tissues in which the elasticity is very important, such as the arteries. Chemically elastin is characteristic with its high content of nonpolar amino acids, and its low content of aspartic acid, glutamic acid, lysine, histidine, and arginine. Elastin differs from collagen also with its extremely low hydroxyproline content.[25] The biosynthesis of elastin is little investigated, but the chemical differences do not support the contention of some authors that elastin might be a transformation of collagen. It is more likely that elastin is synthesized by a different microsome fraction than collagen in the cells of the connective tissue.

Several possible relations between elastin and aging, as well as elastin and arteriosclerosis have been considered. Lansing *et al.* found [26] that elastin of old aortas had a lower nitrogen content and a somewhat higher content of polar amino acids (arginine, lysine, glutamic acid, etc.) than elastin from young aortas. Even more significant seems to be the finding of Balo and Banga[27] that the walls of arterosclerotic vessels contain fragments of elastin. These Hungarian researchers extensively studied an enzyme, elastase, which was known to be able to hydrolyze elastin, and they found that the elastase

[25] S. M. Partridge and H. F. Davies, *Biochem. J.* **61**, 21 (1955).

[26] A. I. Lansing, E. Roberts, G. B. Ramasarma, T. B. Rosenthal and N. Alex, *Proc. Soc. Exp. Biol. Med.* **76**, 714 (1951).

[27] J. Balo and I. Banga, *Acta Physiol. Acad. Sc. Hung.* **4**, 187 (1953); *Biochem. J.* **46**, 384 (1950); I. Banga, *Acta Physiol. Acad. Sc. Hung.* **3**, 317 (1952).

levels in individuals suffering from arteriosclerosis were different from those of healthy subjects. Lewis *et al.* [28] isolated elastase in crystalline from, and found that its molecular weight is 25,000. It appeared that the enzyme did not digest elastin only but also various other proteins, and thus its role is not altogether clear. Although the degradation of elastin and collagen may have some connexion with arteriosclerosis and similar ailments, other factors, such as deposition of lipids from the blood, have received more attention.[29]

Elastin as a macromolecular substance is still very incompletely characterized. Nothing is known about its homogeneity and structure, as well as identity of preparations from various sources. Structural proteins with functions similar to those of collagen and elastin but of different chemical and physical properties have been isolated from lower animal species, such as fishes and worms. For example, the elastoidins of the fins of certain fishes are composed of two fibrous proteins: a collagen and a tyrosine-rich protein.[30]

The Role of Polysaccharides [2,31]

The various types of macromolecular polysaccharides which are found in animal tissues were described briefly in chapt. 11. The connective tissue contains chiefly the nitrogen-containing mucopolysaccharides. These are linear polymers forming highly viscous solutions, and they are more or less firmly bound to the proteins of the tissue. Various chondroitin sulfates, a keratosulfate, and hyaluronic acid are the major polysaccharides found in connective tissue. Together with certain protein components, these linear polysaccharides form the ground substance or cementing matrix of the connective tissue. The polysaccharide content in most connective tissues is rather low (about 1%) yet the importance of these macromolecules should not be overlooked.

The biosynthesis and functionation of the nitrogen-containing polysaccharides is little investigated. According to Whistler and Olson,[32] "biosynthetic investigations show that the hyaluronate chain is assembled by the alternate incorporation of preformed N-acetyl-D-glucosamine and D-glucuronate units". There is some evidence that uridine nucleotides are participating in the synthesis of mucopolysaccharides, since uridine nucleotides containing hexose sugar components of mucopolysaccharides have been isolated from sources where such syntheses may occur.[33,34]

Metabolic studies with labeled sulfates, acetates and glucose have shown that the hyaluronic acid of rabbit and rat skin is rapidly metabolized, while

[28] U. J. Lewis, D. E. Williams and N. G. Brink, *J. biol. Chem.* **222,** 705 (1956).
[29] L. Rosenfeld, *Amer. J. Clin. Nutr.* **5,** 286 (1957) (a review); see also: I. H. Page (ed.), *Connective Tissue, Thrombosis, and Artherosclerosis* Academic Press, New York, 1959.
[30] J. Gross and B. Dumsha, *Biochim. Biophys. Acta* **28,** 268 (1958).
[31] F. R. Bettelheim-Jevons, *Adv. Protein Chem.* **13,** 35 (1958).
[32] R. L. Whistler and E. J. Olson, *Adv. Carbohydr. Chem.* **12,** 299 (1957).
[33] R. B. Hurlbert and V. R. Potter, *J. biol. Chem.* **209,** 1 (1954).
[34] J. L. Strominger, *Biochim. Biophys. Acta* **17,** 283 (1955).

the chondroitin sulfates are relatively passive.[35] This may be due to the fact that the chondroitin sulfates form the more stable and permanent fibrous structures, whereas hyaluronates are dispersed, in the amorphous gel. There are indications that the chondroitin sulfates may be participating not only in the formation of the network of the ground substance but also in interlinking the collagen fibers. The hard and stable structures, such as those of cartilage and bone, are relatively rich in chondroitin sulfates, while the soft tissues, such as the walls of veins and umbilical cord, are rich in hyaluronates. It is also noteworthy that the skin of embryonic pig contains predominantly hyaluronic acid, whereas the skin of the grown-up animal contains more chondroitin sulfates than hyaluronates.[36] Keratosulfate, which is composed of equimolar amounts of N-acetyl glucosamine, galactose, and sulfate, has been found in relatively large amounts in bovine cornea, and more recently also in hyaline cartilage.[37] Some of the chondroitin sulfates are closely related to the heparin of blood.

Hyaluronic acid is hydrolytically degraded by an enzyme — hyaluronidase, and it is noteworthy that this enzyme is found in snake and bee venoms, as well as in spermatozoids. It is obvious that the biological role of this enzyme is to facilitate permeability and spreading of substances in tissues. Mammalian egg is surrounded by a layer of fibrous macromolecules, partially resembling those of the ground substance, and it is obvious that the lack of hyaluronidase and similar enzymes may be the cause of infertility. Clinical applications of hyaluronidase preparations include enhancement of the effects of local anesthetics, as well as dispersion of fluid collections (edema). Good reviews on hyaluronic acid and hyaluronidase are available.[38,39]

The changes observed in the polysaccharide components of connective tissue in certain diseases are of considerable interest. It has already been mentioned that scorbutic animals deprived of ascorbic acid are unable to replace the worn-out collagen. Instead, an increased amount of hyaluronic acid is synthesized and deposited in the tissues.[40] Another interesting observation pertains to the synovial fluid of arthritic patients: the hyaluronate of their synovial fluid is much less viscous than one from a normal source.[41] Although the significance of such scattered observations is not clear, they should stimulate further research. Especially important would be the elucidation of the factors which affect the biosynthesis of these macromolecules in health and in disease.

(35) S. Schiller, M. B. Mathews, J. A. Cifonelli and A. Dorfman, *J. biol. Chem.* **218**, 139 (1955).
(36) G. Loewi and K. Meyer, *Biochim. Biophys. Acta* **27**, 453 (1958).
(37) K. Meyer, P. Hoffman and A. Linker, *Science* **128**, 896 (1958).
(38) K. Meyer and M. M. Rapport, *Adv. Enzymol.* **13**, 199 (1952).
(39) B. L. Baker and G. D. Abrams, *Ann. Rev. Physiol.* **17**, 61 (1955).
(40) W. van B. Robertson and H. Hinds, *J. biol. Chem.* **221**, 791 (1956).
(41) C. Ragan and K. Meyer, *J. Clin. Investig.* **28**, 56 (1949).

CHAPTER 27

MACROMOLECULAR REACTIONS IN MUSCLE AND NERVE TISSUES

> I would like to sum up my remarks on proteins by saying that we should not be content to ask questions about the structure of proteins but should inquire also into the deeper meaning of the structures found. Owing to its specific function, generation of motion, nature has endowed myosin with specific qualities that open new ways for its analysis and that may possibly lead to new basic concepts about protein structure and function.
>
> ALBERT SZENT-GYÖRGYI [1]

IN ANY higher organism, the macromolecular structures of connective tissue, muscle, and nerve tissues are all interlinked in a unified system. From an evolutionary point of view, the system of muscles and nerves represents the highest level in the hierarchy of Life. Evolution of muscle and nerve tissues provided the animal with specific capacity of *voluntary motility* thus opening new unprecedented possibilities of further evolution.

There are but a few other areas of inquiry that have involved as much controversy as the problem of muscular motion and motility in general. The literature on muscular motion is so extensive that there seems to be no genius who could keep in mind all the diverse facts and build on the basis of those data a sensible theory. What usually happens is that the man who creates a "theory" disregards some of the facts and as a result has formed an hypothesis that conforms with the facts he picked as support. In addition, some authors have a tendency to overgeneralization, viz. extending the notion of motility to such events as cellular motions, e.g. the change of cellular shape of the white blood cells, mitotic motions, or even the flow of protoplasm. It seems reasonable to consider, from the same point of view, systems which are composed of similar macromolecules taking into account both chemical and configurational aspects. In this chapter only the motility of myosin systems and the very similar fibers of lower animals will be considered, and no claim of a complete coverage of the subject matter can be made. One of the greatest difficulties which has thus far prevented a more complete elucidation of the problem is the extreme intricacy of the systems. What seems relatively simple when observed under a microscope is in fact a complex system of large and small molecules. The biologist who studies the anatomy

[1] A. SZENT-GYÖRGYI, in Symposium on Biocolloids *J. Cell. Comparat. Physiol.* **49**, Supplement 1, p. 316 (1957).

and physiology of muscle and nerve usually forgets about these submicroscopic structures. Similarly the chemist who isolates some of the macromolecular components forgets about the complicated macrostructures. Only very recently have attempts been made to integrate the various data, such as those pertaining to histology, physiology, biochemistry, energetics, and macromolecular chemistry of muscle and nerve tissues.

Macromolecules and Their Motions in Muscle [2,3,4,5,6,7]

Development of the various muscles starts in embryonic tissue from somewhat differentiated cells, the so-called myoblasts. These myoblasts at first multiply by mitotic division. Later they elongate considerably and the number of nuclear granules increases in them due to simple amitotic division. The strongly elongated cells become more and more filled with the myosin fibers, and the granular components are gradually pushed closer to the membrane, the so called sarcolemma. At about the same time each of the developing muscles is contacted by a growing nerve fiber, and also becomes attached to a tendon or other type of connective tissue. Anatomists report that there are no less than 434 skeletal muscles in the human body, and that the total muscle tissue makes up 25 per cent of body weight at birth, and even 40–45% of the body weight of grown-up man. The various muscles, depending on their function, are structurally different, although the fibrous myosin is found in all of them. The microscopic and submicroscopic differences are even more pronounced when the muscle tissues of crustaceans or insects are compared with the tissues of mammals. Yet the presence of membranes, of fibrous proteins resembling myosin, as well as of the granular elements and a similar cytoplasm is common to all muscle tissues independent of source.

While the diameter of muscle fibrils ranges between about 10–120 μ, their length often extends through the whole muscle and is measured in centimeters. Each fibril, however, is composed of bundles of finer microfibrils embedded in the cytoplasm that contains the usual components, such as the mitochondria. Early microscopic observations revealed that the fibers of ordinary skeletal muscles show very characteristic cross striations. These interesting features have been extensively studied by the modern methods of phase contrast microscopy and electron microscopy, and these observations

[2] A. Szent-Györgyi, *Chemistry of Muscular Contraction* 2nd ed., Academic Press, New York, 1951. G. H. Bourne (ed.), *Structure and Function of Muscle*, vol. 1—3, Academic Press, New York, 1960.

[3] H. H. Weber and H. Portzehl, *Adv. Protein Chem.* **7**, 161 (1952).

[4] K. Bailey, in *The Proteins* Vol. II B, p. 951 (H. Neurath and K. Bailey, ed.), Academic Press, New York, 1954.

[5] A. F. Huxley, *Progress in Biophys.* **7**, 255 (1957).

[6] H. H. Weber, in *Fibrous Proteins and their Biological Significance* p. 271, IX *Symp. Soc. Exp. Biol.*, Academic Press, New York, 1955.

[7] A. Engström and J. B. Finean, *Biological Ultrastructure* p. 125ff., Academic Press, New York, 1958.

can be summarized in the following statements.[5] The cross striations are due to material of high and low refractive index. The high refractive index bands (A bands) are birefringent, and their middle portion is usually somewhat lighter than the edges. This less dense middle part of the A band is called H band. The zones of low refractive index (I bands) are optically nearly isotropic, and each of these zones is bisected by a highly refractive narrow line, called Z band (Fig. 99). Other important facts pertaining to the optical properties of the fibers have been furnished by low and wide angle *X*-ray spectroscopy. These ascertain the fact that the macromolecular structure of the fibers is

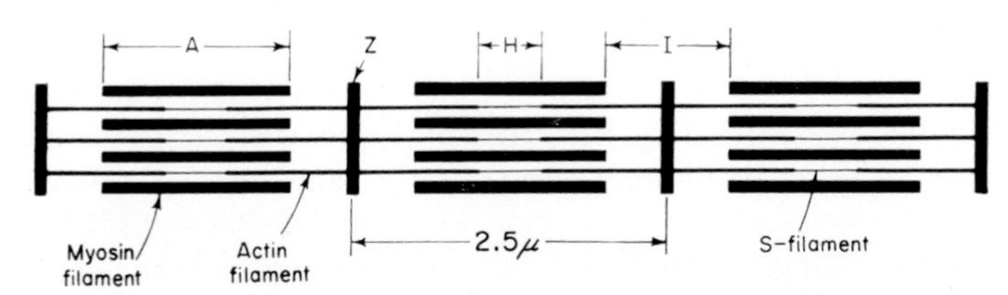

FIG. 99. Schematic diagram showing the possible arrangement of filaments within a myofibril, according to A. F. Huxley (from *Progress in Biophysics*, Vol. 7, p. 261, Pergamon Press, London 1957)

relatively ordered, i.e. paracrystalline, and that the macromolecules probably are like twisted ropes.

This set of optical data, however, is not sufficient for the understanding of the macromolecular structure and function of the muscle. Important additional data are provided by the study of energetics of muscular motion, by the study of the isolated macromolecular components, and by the investigation of the metabolism of muscle. It is, for instance, interesting that extraction of myosin without affecting much the actin component produces a reduction of density of the A band, whereas the I band is practically not affected. When both actin and myosin are removed, most of the banding disappears, leaving only the somewhat distorted Z lines. These experiments indicate that myosin is located chiefly in the A bands, while the actin filaments probably extend through the A and I bands. The Z bands seem to represent transversal membranes (probably perforated), and they seem to be connected with the outer sarcolemma membrane of the cell. The presence of two sets of filaments is indicated also by interference microscopic and electron microscopic observations.[8,9]

A wealth of important information has been provided by studies on isolated myosin fibers, as well as from experiments on other contractile macromolecules. It is important to realize that isolation of myosin or actomyosin

[8] J. HANSON and H. E. HUXLEY, in *Fibrous Proteins and their Biological Significance* p. 228, IX *Symp. Soc. Exp. Biol.*, 1955; also: A. F. HUXLEY and R. NIEDERGERKE, *Nature* **173**, 971 (1954).

[9] H. E. HUXLEY, *J. Biophys. Biochem. Cytol.* **3**, 631 (1957).

(see chapt. 17) results in complete destruction of the muscle cells: the membranes are disintegrated, the granular components, enzymes, and all other components of the cytoplasm are removed. Yet, the isolated myosin fiber contracts under suitable conditions like the muscle does.[6] These conditions include: a neutral reaction, the same ionic strength as in living tissue, the presence of magnesium ions, and the presence of the energy-rich adenosine triphosphate (ATP). It has been shown [10] that myosin plays the role of the ATP-ase, i.e. it acts as an enzyme that promotes the conversion of adenosine triphosphate into adenosine diphosphate and free orthophosphate [10]. The energy liberated in this reaction somehow produces the contraction of the isolated myosin fiber. This contraction is slower than the contraction of skeletal muscles but as fast or even faster than the reaction in some smooth muscles. It is also interesting that the tension developed by contraction of a fiber spun from myosin is approximately the same as the tension developed by the muscles from which the myosin was isolated. Since ATP is known to be present and being metabolized in the living muscle, these results support the general idea that contraction of myosin fibers causes a muscle to contract. The chemistry of the living muscle, however, is much more complicated than the reactions of the isolated myosin. Living muscle is endowed with an anaerobic mechanism that takes care of a rapid regeneration of the ATP, viz. the phosphocreatine–creatine system. An enzyme, creatin kinase catalyzes the reversible transfer of the phosphate from phosphocreatine and adenosine diphosphate thus restoring the ATP. However, the mentioned di- and triphosphates are only small intermediate links in the long chain of energy transfer in the muscle, since the major sources of chemical energy are the macromolecular glycogen and oxygen of the air. Anaerobic glycolysis and oxidative phosphorylation are long chains of enzymic reactions that have been elucidated to a certain extent. However, many things are still obscure, e.g. the fact that only ATP can cause the muscle fiber to contract and that phosphocreatine is unable to do it directly. The role of ATP in muscle seems to be a double one: it makes the final energy transfer, and also affects the electrical charge of the fibrous macromolecules and hence their configuration. Since magnesium ions also are involved, there is plenty of material for speculation on the interactions between the charged components [11]. The impulse delivered to the muscle by the nerve also is electrical, although it is not at all clear how these electrical impulses produce contraction and relaxation.

There are other facts that are relevant in this discussion on muscular motions, viz. the linear aggregation of the globular actin and its combination with myosin (see chapt. 17). Since these interactions are affected by ATP, ionic strength, and acidity, some authors have advocated the concept that linear and lateral aggregation and disaggregation of the various protein com-

[10] W. A. Engelhardt and M. N. Ljubimova, *Nature* **144**, 669 (1939).

[11] M. F. Morales and J. Botts, in *Currents in Biochemical Research*. p. 609 (D. E. Green, ed.), Interscience, New York, 1956.

ponents of the muscle might explain the motility. There is, however, no good evidence that these aggregations and disaggregations, as observed on isolated preparations of the muscle proteins, actually occur in a living tissue.

Although the mechanism of muscular contraction is far from being fully understood, the submicroscopic structures and their significance are now elucidated to a considerable extent. Two important facts deserve a special mention: (1) the discovery of two sets of filaments in various muscle fibrils by means of electron microscopy,[5,12] and (2) the discovery that the A band does not change in width on moderate contraction.[5,8] According to A. F. Huxley and H. E. Huxley,[5,8] the myosin fibers are located within the dense A bands, while the actin filaments run continuously through the A and I bands "as far as the boundary of the less dense H regions, which represents the gap between adjacent sets of actin filaments" (see Fig. 99). "Except in extreme shortening, changes of muscle length take place not by stretching or shortening of either of these sets of filaments, but by their sliding past one another in each zone where they overlap. The dense Z line which bisects the I band is concerned with conveying the influence of the electrical changes in the fibre membrane which accompany excitation to activate the contractile myofibrils" (l.c. 5, quoted from p. 311). A comparison of these results with the earlier mentioned facts on the contraction of fibers drawn from extracted myosin results in a curious discrepancy. According to the results of Huxley and Huxley, the myosin rodlets in the muscle are rather passive, while the work of Weber indicates that myosin is the active contractile principle. A solution of the problem perhaps will have to wait upon the solution of the chemical structure of the muscle proteins, since the present methods of their characterization are insufficient. It is not known whether the myosin rodlets observed in the electron microscope are the same things which are in the contractile threads drawn from isolated myosin. The discoveries about the subunits of myosin are quite disturbing, since they are indicative of instability of the macromolecule. A great variety of relatively mild treatments are known which yield various disaggregation products,[13] and the smallest which were obtained in the treatment of the light meromyosin with urea (4·7–5·5 *M* urea at pH 7–8) were found to have molecular weights as low as 4600.[14] Although these "subunits" were found upon treatment of a myosin component which was obtained by an enzymic pretreatment of myosin, the composite character of myosin is strongly suspected. Very curious are the findings of Laki [15] that myosin and the meromyosins might be looked upon as compounds of tropomyosin and actin. This is strongly indicated by the amino acid composition of these proteins, and Laki has even expressed the idea that: "...it points out the possibility that myosin may be formed

(12) H. E. Huxley, *Biochim. Biophys. Acta* **12**, 387 (1953).
(13) See for example: A. G. Szent-Györgyi, *Adv. Enzymol.* **16**, 313 (1955).
(14) A. Szent-Györgyi and M. Borbiro, *Arch. Biochem. Biophys.* **60**, 180 (1956).
(15) K. Laki, *J. Cell. Comparat. Physiol.* **49**, Suppl. 1, p. 249 (1957).

outside the primary protein-manufacturing centers from the meromyosins or actin and tropomyosin as its ingredients. Whether this assemblage of myosin occurs on the moment of excitation or at some other instant, a mechanism should exist to accomplish this combination of ingredients" (l.c. 15, quoted from p. 261). The isolation of these asymmetric macro-

FIG. 100. Electron micrograph of tropomyosin fibrils deposited from aqueous solution and shadowed with gold (by *Courtesy* of Prof. W. T. Astbury)

molecules from muscle tissue, at the same time preserving their native state, is a formidable task, and it is not yet proven that any of these tropo-,para-, and meromyosins and actins exist in the living muscle in the same state as they appear in the test tubes. The relatively recently discovered tropomyosin (see Fig. 100) may well be more important than was previously assumed. The contraction of myosin fibers spun from extracted myosin is interesting; it has been found that the *in vitro* contracted fiber relaxes if muscle extracts containing certain enzymes, creatine, phosphate and some other components, are added to the system. Yet, the significance of these results is not so obvious, since synthetic polyphosphates and several other polyelectrolytes also shrink or expand depending on acidity, the presence of various ions, etc. Thus it is possible that the isolated myosin system does not represent the genuine muscular phenomena, i.e. the contractile components of muscle cell. Indeed, all of the investigators who have expressed some ideas on the mechanism of muscular movement have admitted that the solution of the problem is still a distant goal.

While the detailed mechanism of muscular movement is still obscure, many facts have been established and they permit us to envisage the general features of the process. A very important fact, which is sometimes disregarded in building hypotheses is the *speed* of muscular motions. This is especially spectacular in the instance of the small muscles of insects and the striated muscles of vertebrates, while the smooth muscles show a slower response. The extreme *rapidity* of muscular motions excludes any mechanisms based on series of chemical reactions involving covalent bonds. Thus it is doubtful if reactions of the sulfhydryl groups of the muscle proteins could be important in the actual process of movement. Electrostatic interactions between the small inorganic ions and the large ionized proteins probably play the dominating role, but what actually happens with the fibrous macromolecules during the contraction and expansion cycle is not known. This may involve change of configuration (folding–unfolding) or aggregation–disaggregation, as well as gliding, and there is no doubt that ATP and other organic and inorganic ions (especially Mg^{++}, Ca^{++}, Na^{+}, and K^{+}) are participating in this interplay of components. The problem of the energy release during the performance of work by a muscle is very difficult [15a]. The energy sources are known, and much is known also about the biochemical changes associated with the supply of the energy, but the transmission of the chemical energy to the working fiber is quite a mystery. One of the sources of the chemical energy is glycogen, another is oxygen transmitted from hemoglobin to myoglobin, and then to the mitochondria of the muscle cells. There the chemical energy is introduced into the ATP which transmits it somehow to the contracting and expanding fibers. Since the synthesis of ATP can be accomplished in a series of reactions involving covalent bounds, and since the working muscle requires a constant supply of energy by the aid of ATP, the tissue must have an admirably efficient organization for fast resynthesis and recycling of the nucleotide. Although the roles of the phosphocreatine and glycolysis are known, the efficiency of the system suggests a purposeful spatial arrangement of the enzymes, that possibly is something similar to the organization in the mitochondria (chapt. 21).

The rapidity of muscular motion, as well as efficiency in energy transfer, is different in different muscles. The more elementary and slow smooth

(15a) A. V. Hill, *Proc. Roy. Soc. B.* **126**, 136 (1938); **136**, 195 (1949); **137**, 268 (1950); **141**, 503 (1953).

muscles are found in the walls of blood vessels, digestive and urinary tract, and similar organs; the heart muscle tissue represents an intermediate type between the smooth and striated skeletal muscles. Striated muscles are found not only in vertebrates but also in the more developed species of invertebrates, such as insects and crustaceae. Worms, snails, mollusks and similar lower animals move by the aid of smooth muscles of various types. If the lowest

FIG. 101. Electron micrographs of bacterial flagellae at two different magnifications: 41,700× (left) and 73,400× (right) (by *Courtesy* of Dr. L. W. Labaw)

species are considered, the application of the term "muscle" becomes a matter of agreement. Even some bacteria have whip-like appendages that serve as swimming organs. The similarity of these flagella with myosin appears in several ways, such as in X-ray spectra, amino acid composition, was well as exploitation of ATP as the source of energy. Electron microscopic observations have revealed the interesting fact that these flagellae resemble twisted ropes (Fig. 101). The diameter of the helical strands is about 150 Å. Some animal flagella and cilia have a composite structure in that nine filaments are twisted around two central filaments.[16] In mammalian sperm tails these eleven filaments are covered by another layer of nine filaments.

Finally, some muscular anomalies in human beings will be mentioned. Apart from infectious and malignant diseases of muscle, there are known

[16] J. R. G. BRADFIELD, in *Fibrous Proteins and their Biological Significance* p. 306 IX *Symp. Soc. Exp. Biol.*, Academic Press, New York, 1955.

anomalies in embryogenesis resulting in the absence of some muscles. "As judged by their strong familial incidence many of these are determined by hereditary factors which interfere with the differentiation of individual muscles from the myotomes. Associated faults in other organs may occur and indicate that the maldevelopment must occur early. Some anomalies such as the congenital absence of certain muscles may be linked to inherited dystrophic disease whereas others appear as isolated defects. While it is certain that a congenital deficiency of skeletal muscle may be conditioned by a defect in the nervous system so that the trophic or maturation factors provided by innervation are lacking, all deformities due to an imbalance of muscle action cannot be explained in this way".[17] Similar conclusions seem to hold for the various types of muscular dystrophies. In this disease the muscle in question is present but it does not function properly and histological examination reveals various anomalies in the structure of the tissue. The fibers are disordered, some are greatly swollen, others are disintegrated into single fibrils which are intermeshed with connective tissue. Also a large proportion of nuclear particles is obvious. Since the innervation of the affected muscles usually is normal, the disease cannot be attributed to some malfunction of the nervous system. Also the congenital dystrophies are known to be independent of nutritional deficiencies or hormonal factors. Statistical data support the contention that muscular dystrophies may be inherited, and this points to the possibility that the cause of the disorder may be found in the structures of the deoxyribonucleic acids (DNA) of the embryonic cells at a certain stage of differentiation. In malignancy, the cells of the fully developed tissue lose some of their specialized functions acquiring at the same time an exaggerated tendency of proliferation. In muscular dystrophy the specialized function of the muscular cells of producing the fibrous proteins is lost at an early stage of embryonic development. When fibers are ruptured in a dystrophic muscle, the fragments do not regenerate. "The genetic aspects of muscular dystrophy points to the existence of some essential defect in the function of the muscle nucleus that interferes with postnatal production of myofibrils, rather than an inadequacy in the contractile properties of such myofibrils as are produced.[18] For this reason it appears more promising to search for a primary fault in the chemistry of the reparative process than in the mechanism of contraction" (l.c. 17, quoted from p. 279). It may be added that the inability of the cells to synthesize the fibrous muscle proteins is caused by the lack of certain microsomal ribonucleic acid components and enzymes; and the reason for their absence then could be traced back to some defects in the synthesis of the nuclear DNA that determines the production of these ribonucleic acids and enzymes. These defects apparently have materialized in an early stage of embryonic deve-

(17) R. D. ADAMS, D. DENNY-BROWN and C. M. PEARSON, *Diseases of Muscle* p. 235, P. B. HOEBER Publ., New York, 1953.

(18) D. DENNY-BROWN, *Canad. Med. Assoc. J.* **67**, 1 (1952).

lopment and are dependent on the structure of the chromosomal DNA of the germ cells. Apart from these speculations, an important biochemical feature in muscular dystrophy is an increased output of creatinine in the urine. Creatinine is the anhydride of creatine, the important link in the energy transfer in a working muscle (see p. 424). The increased output of creatinine in the urine is significant for the diagnosis of the disease.

Macromolecular Structures of Nervous Tissue

Investigation of nerve and brain tissues is carried out from several points of view, such as: (1) study of the electrical and other physical phenomena of activity and impulse transmission, (2) study of the biochemical events of the activity, (3). research on the submicroscopic structures of the tissues, and (4) investigation of the chemical components of which these structures are built. The physical and physiological approaches thus far have been the dominating ones,[19,20,21,22] while the study from the other points of view has rendered significant results but recently. Thus biochemical research has elucidated to a certain extent the chemical changes taking place in transmission of nerve impulse.[23,24] According to these studies, acetylcholine plays an exceptionally important part in these events. In resting condition acetylcholine probably is bound to a protein; on excitation of the nerve, it is released from the protein and combines with another protein thus changing its configuration; this is the trigger action resulting in permeability change, influx of ions, and generation of the action current. The acetylcholine–protein complex is in dynamic equilibrium with the free acetylcholine, and the latter is subject to the attack of cholinesterase. This enzymic reaction upsets the equilibrium, the receptor protein returns to its original configuration, resulting in a decrease of permeability.[24] Moreover, biochemists have found that the enzymic hydrolysis of acetylcholine by the acetylcholine esterase is a very rapid reaction, and that it is irreversible. Acetylcholine is resynthesized from choline by the aid of another enzyme system that needs the chemical energy provided by ATP. In the nerve, as in muscle, there is a difference in the concentrations of sodium and potassium ions across the cell membrane, and it is assumed that these ions are involved in the generation of the electromotive force. In this section, however, we are concerned chiefly with the

[19] J. C. Eccles, *Physiology of Nerve Cells* Hopkins Press, Baltimore, Md., 1957.

[20] K. S. Cole, in *Electro-chemistry in Biology and Medicine* p. 121 (T. Shedlovsky, ed.), New York, 1955.

[21] J. M. Tobias, *Ann. Rev. Physiol.* **21**, 299 (1959).

[22] G. Hoyle, *Comparative Physiology of the Nervous Control of Muscular Contraction* Cambridge Univ. Press, Cambridge, 1957.

[23] D. Richter (ed.), *The Metabolism of the Nervous System* Pergamon Press London, 1957.

[24] D. Nachmansohn and I. B. Wilson, in *Currents in Biochemical Research* (D. E. Green, ed.), Interscience, New York, 1956; H. McIlvain, *Biochemistry and the Central Nervous System*, Little, Brown, Boston, 1955.

submicroscopic structures and the macromolecular components of the tissue. Considerable progress has been recorded in the study of the ultrastructures,[25,26,27] while the macromolecular components as chemical individuals have been very little investigated.

The fine submicroscopic structures of nervous tissue have been studied chiefly by means of electron microscopy, and the findings can be summarized briefly as follows. A nerve fiber is composed of three major parts: an outer membrane, a myelin sheath, and a central core or axon (Fig. 102). The outer

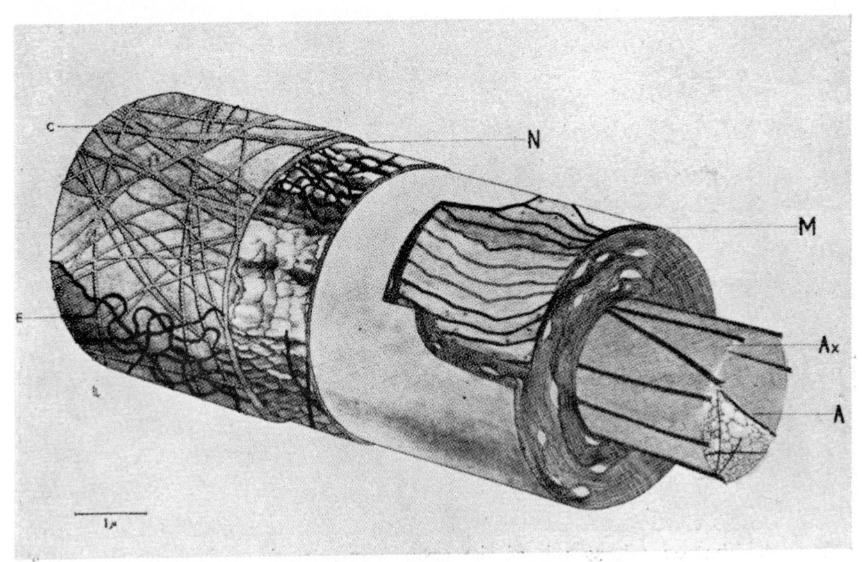

FIG. 102. Schematic diagram of the structure of nerve fiber according to Fernandez-Moran. *N* — neurilemma membrane; *M* — envelopes of the myelin sheath; *A x* — axolemma membrane; *A* — axon (from *Progress in Biophys.* Vol. 4, opposite to p. 140, 1954)

membrane is not concerned with the transmission of impulse but serves as a support of the active components; collagen and elastic fibers can be discerned in such membranes. The myelin sheath represents a series of thin-walled tubes fitted tightly into each other, while the central axon core is built of long filaments that are oriented predominantly in the longitudinal direction of the nerve fiber. Comparison of the fibers from various sources has shown large differences in the degree of intricacy of these structures, e.g. the finer fibers may contain only one tubular myelin membrane around

(25) H. WAELCH (ed.), *Ultrastructure and Cellular Chemistry of Neural Tissue*, Hoeber, New York, 1957.
(26) H. FERNANDEZ-MORAN, *Progress in Biophys.* **4**, 112 (1954).
(27) F. O. SCHMITT and N. GESCHWIND, *Progress in Biophys.* **8**, 166 (1957).

the single axon filament. In Fig. 103 a medium size fiber from frog spinal cord nerve is shown. This fiber contains about 20 axon filaments enveloped into one tubular sheath. The width of a single axon filament is about 100 Å, and the filaments are proteins. The myelin sheath is composed of layers of proteins and lipids, the hydrocarbon chains of the latter being arranged radially. An excellent outline on the orientation and grouping of the various

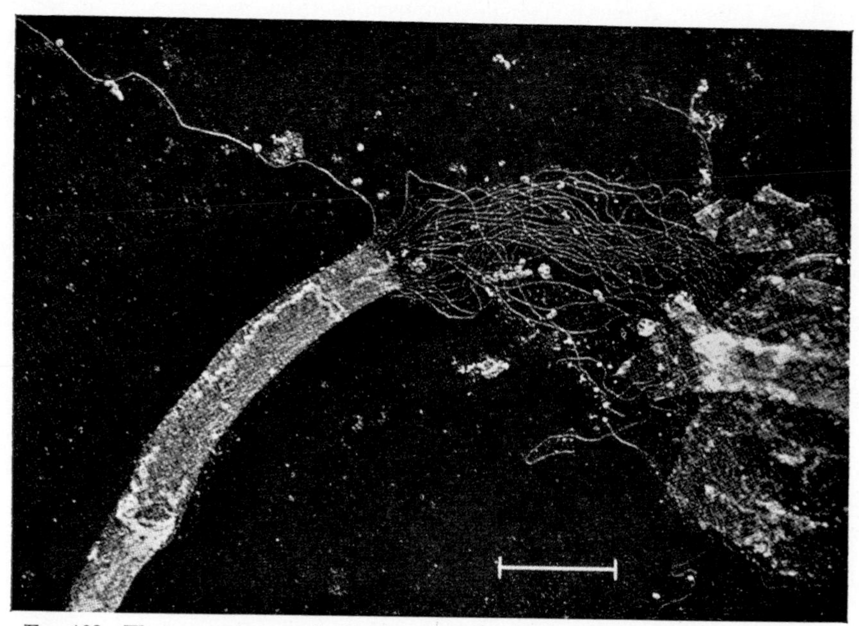

Fig. 103. Electron micrograph of the axon filaments of a submicroscopic nerve fiber of frog spinal cord, according to H. Fernandez-Moran (Fig. 18 from *Progress in Biophysics* Vol. 4, Facing p. 140, Pergamon Press, Oxford 1954).

micromolecular lipid components in these structures can be found in the book of Engstrom and Finean.[28] The roles of the various structural components in the physiological functioning of the fibers, however, are not quite well established. The multilayer structures of the myelin sheath, as well as of any single membranes of this sheath, in which the highly conducting polar protein layers are between the non-conducting layers of the hydrophobic chain ends of the lipids, suggests a highly elaborate system developed for transmission of impulses. There are also various degrees in the intricacy of these microstructures, and in the simplest nerve fibers a separate myelin sheath is not discernible. The nerve cells and the muscle cells have in common the extremely high degree of asymmetry, i.e. they are very long. Granular bodies discerned in the nerve fibers seem to have the functions of mitochondria.

[28] l.c. 7, especially chapt. 5.

The macromolecular components of the myelin sheath and axon fibrils have been very little studied. The protein of the myelin sheath has some similarity with the keratins (see chapt. 17), while the filaments of the axon are known to have a very labile structure.(29) These fibrous protein particles disaggregate even on raising the pH from 6 to 7·7. This dissociation is reversible in the region of physiological pH variations,(29) and it suggests that this reversible disaggregation of the filaments may have something to do with the special functions of the nerve. Reversible changes in the nerve proteins upon stimulation also have been described.(30,31) Furthermore, young nerve fibers has been found to contain almost exclusively deoxyribonucleic acid, whereas adult nerve fibers contain predominantly ribonucleic acid. The concentration of the nerve tissue protein increases with this increase of the RNA. Also, stimulation has been shown to affect the metabolism of RNA and protein in the cells, while DNA is not affected. This is in good agreement with the modern concepts on the roles of DNA and RNA in the synthesis of proteins (see chapt. 21 and 22).

(29) M. Maxfield and R. W. Hartley, Jr., *Biochim. Biophys. Acta* **24**, 83 (1957).

(30) G. Ungar, E. Aschheim, S. Psychoyos and D. V. Romano, *J. Gen. Physiol.* **40**, 635 (1957).

(31) H. Hyden, in *Neurochemistry* p. 204 (K. A. C. Elliott, I. H. Page and J. H. Quastel, ed.), Thomas, Springfield, Illinois, 1955; F. N. LeBaron, *Ann. Rev. Biochem.* **28**, 579 (1959).

CHAPTER 28

CONCLUDING REMARKS ABOUT THE SYNTHESIS OF MACROMOLECULES AND ORIGIN OF LIFE

> In the area of the present discussion it is easy to over-emphasize the ignorance and the problems. On the positive side, it is at least possible to discern the dim outlines of how our complex protein-centered life of today could have arisen from very simple beginnings, and how the multitudes on multitudes of living cells may be in their own ways re-enacting a smaller or larger part of the biochemical history which they have inherited.
>
> SIDNEY W. FOX [1]

THESE concluding remarks may be started with a reminder of three rather trivial yet important facts: (1) the indescribable *variety* of living forms, (2) the enormous span of *time* spent for the development of this variety, and (3) *the small number of structural types of macromolecules* as found in organisms of today. As indicated in the first chapter, there are only *four* major structural types of natural organic macromolecules. One of these four types, the polyprenes, appear but occasionally in cells, hence there remain only *three* chemically distinct classes of macromolecules: the polysaccharides, proteins, and nucleic acids. Even these three are not of equal importance. While the proteins and nucleic acids are present in all animals, plants, and micro-organisms, the presence of polysaccharides may be doubted in many instances. Thus only *two* structural types of large molecules, the *proteins and nucleic acids* remain as universal constituents without which life is impossible.

It is true that there are many proteins and many nucleic acids, yet the diversity in the composition and structure of the proteins, and even more so of the nucleic acids, is relatively very limited. There are only two fundamental types of nucleic acids: the ribonucleic acids (RNA's) and the deoxyribonucleic acids (DNA's). The RNA's are of different molecular sizes, configurations, and sequences of the attached purine and pyrimidine heterocycles, but the *phosphate–sugar backbone is always the same*. Even more uniform seem to be the DNA's. Although the nucleotide sequence may vary in uncountable billions of ways, the structural pattern remains the same. Recent *X*-ray

[1] SIDNEY W. FOX in FOX and FOSTER's *Introduction to Protein Chemistry* p. 439, Wiley, New York, 1957; see also: S. W. FOX, *J. chem. Educat.* **34**, 472 (1957).

diffraction studies on DNA's from a large variety of sources have shown that the X-ray spectra of all preparations were the same.[2] A similar uniformity is found in proteins. Although there are more building units (amino acids) in proteins than such units in the nucleic acids (nucleotides), all proteins are built of peptide chains, and the diversity is limited. Calculations have shown that the 18 or 19 amino acids of the ordinary proteins could be combined in astronomical numbers of isomers, yet Nature has built only a very limited number of sequences. Study of the simpler proteins, such as insulin, lysozyme, or ribonuclease have shown that there are slight species differences in that one or two amino acid residues are replaced by some others, but these differences practically do not affect the properties of the large molecule. "The strikingly limited diversity of protein, as indicated by some data, does not pose a special problem of explaining the tremendous diversity in organisms. Organisms can be thought of as representing a kind of molecular ecology, in which they express not so much the component molecules as the interactions of the component molecules. The interactions of a limited number of protein types with a limited number of protein types or of nucleic acid types, or with other macromolecular types, exponentializes the diversities possible" (1, quoted from p. 435).

What is the reason for this uniformity of structural patterns? Why Nature has chosen only a few types of macromolecules instead of the unlimited possibilities of arranging the C, O, N, S, P, Si, and other atoms? Synthetic polymer chemistry has created many of these possibilities, and some of such polymers are formed even spontaneously, yet they are not found in nature. The answers to these questions may be found from the study of *evolution* of living forms. The long history of Life, the uncountable eons, the millions and millions of years of evolution hold the clues. Unfortunately, most of the clues are not directly accessible for study, and the investigator must be content with vague extrapolations into the past. Some important facts in this search are provided by geology and paleontology. The age of rocks and formations, and the imprints of the primitive organisms found in these formations, can be determined by means of analysis of the radioactive elements and their decomposition products found in these formations.

All sensible concepts regarding the origin of life are based on the assumption that this occurred in an early stage of the development of our planet.[3] The presence of an atmosphere rich in volatile carbon, nitrogen, and other compounds, and poor in oxygen, can be assumed. The temperature was generally higher than at present, but low enough for preserving water in the liquid state. Also it is generally agreed that life did not arise in these

(2) L. D. Hamilton, R. K. Barclay, M. H. F. Wilkins, G. L. Brown, H. R. Wilson, D. A. Marvin, H. Ephrussi-Taylor and N. S. Simmons, *J. Biophys. Biochem. Cytol.* **5**, 397 (1959).

(3) A. I. Oparin, *The Origin of Life on the Earth*, 3rd ed. (translated by Ann Synge), Oliver and Boyd, Edinburgh and London, 1957.

conditions suddenly but that it was preceded by the formation of a multitude of micro- and macromolecular organic compounds. A variety of physical factors, such as high temperature, pressure, radiations, and electrical discharges probably affected the formation of molecular forms of various stability. Some types of these compounds were activated further by metals, inorganic, as well as other organic compounds acting as catalysts. Adsorption onto the surfaces of minerals and rocks may be one way in which the organic compounds were collected in higher concentrations, and even oriented spatially.[4] If the surface of the mineral acted as a catalyst, it provided ample chances for further interactions in an oriented fashion, including polymerization. This is also the most probable way in which the optical isomers of organic compounds could have been formed.[4]

According to Urey,[5] the primeval earth atmosphere was composed chiefly of methane, ammonia, water vapor, and hydrogen, and Miller was able to show that amino acids and even some polymerized compounds are formed when the mixture of the mentioned gases is subjected to prolonged electrical discharges.[6] Hydrocyanic acid and various aldehydes appear as intermediates, while carbon monoxide, carbon dioxide, and nitrogen were found as byproducts. Nitrils are other possible intermediates. Akabori demonstrated that poly-glycine $(-NH-CH_2-CO-)_n$ is formed by heating amino-acetonitrile NH_2-CH_2-CN in the presence of clay. According to this author, the synthesis of polyaminoacids and primitive proteins ("fore-protein") has occurred in the following three steps:[7]

(1) Formation of amino-acetonitrile from formaldehyde, ammonia, and hydrogen cyanide, viz.:

$$H-CHO + NH_3 + HCN = H_2N-CH_2-CN + H_2O;$$

(2) Polymerization of the amino-acetonitrile on a surface of a mineral, followed by hydrolysis to polyglycine and ammonia:

$$n\,H_2N-CH_2-CN = (-NH-CH_2-\underset{\underset{NH}{\|}}{C}-)_n;\ (-NH-CH_2-\underset{\underset{NH}{\|}}{C}-)_n + n\,H_2O =$$

$$(-NH-CH_2-CO-)_n + n\,NH_3;$$

(3) Introduction of side chains into the polyglycine by the reaction with aldehydes, unsaturated hydrocarbons, and other compounds. Not only the formation of polyglycine from amino-acetonitrile was shown but it also was demonstrated that polyglycine spread on kaolinite reacted and could be partially converted to serine, threonine, and some other residues. A survey of this and other evidence regarding the formation of organic substances

[4] J. D. Bernal, *The Physical Basis of Life*, Routledge & Kegan Paul, London, 1951; *New Biol.* **16**, 28 (1953); *Science and Culture* **19**, 228 (1953).

[5] H. C. Urey, *The Planets* Yale Univ. Press, New Haven, 1952. See also: S. L. Miller and H. C. Urey, *Science* **13o**, 245 (1959).

[6] S. L. Miller, *J. Amer. chem. Soc.* **77**, 2351 (1955).

[7] S. Akabori, *Science (Japan)* **25**, 54 (1955); *Bull. chem. Soc. Japan* **29**, 609 (1956); *Chem. Abstr.* **50**, 16893 (1956).

indicates that the conditions for the formation of such compounds in the primeval stage of earth were favorable. Not only the small molecules of such compounds as hydrocarbons, nitriles, aldehydes, and amino acids could be formed readily, but polymerization into a variety of large molecules occurred as well.

One important point, however, should be borne in mind: the primordial macromolecules were not the polysaccharides, proteins, or nucleic acids as we know them existing on the earth now. Our present albumins, hemoglobins, hormones, enzymes, and nucleic acids are formed in *long series of metabolic pathways* as occurring in organized cellular systems. Many enzymes and nucleic acids are needed for the biosynthesis of any of these proteins or nucleic acids (see chapt. 21 and 22), and the probability that any of these enzymes were formed by chance is infinitesimally small. This becomes even clearer if one considers the unique amino acid sequences and configurations of the particular enzymes and nucleic acids. Even if some of these macromolecules were to appear in the primordial mixtures of organic substances, their prevalence would be by no means ensured. Neither a protein nor nucleic acid macromolecule can reproduce itself by simple gathering the building blocks from the environment and assembling these blocks into a replica. On the contrary, they are synthesized in the elaborate cellular organization as evidenced even in the very simplest monocellular organisms. "In the same way, both proteins and nucleic acids appeared as the result of the evolution of whole protoplasmic systems which developed from simpler and less well adapted systems, that is to say, from whole systems and not from isolated molecules. It would be quite wrong to imagine the isolated primary origin either of proteins or of nucleic acids" (l.c. 3, quoted from p. 287).

What were these simpler systems? With this question we enter the realm of speculation, since there is no direct way to know what actually happened on our planet several hundred million years ago. There is no evidence that organisms are formed from organic compounds at present, and there is no evidence of any "semi-living" systems of macromolecules in the nature. Yet, since a spontaneous formation of organisms from a molecular mixture is incomprehensible, the existence of intermediate systems must be assumed. It can be assumed these simpler systems were at first composed of some kind of "fore-proteins" and "fore-nucleic acids". It is even possible that at the primeval high temperatures and other factors which favor activation of molecules an unwieldy variety of macromolecules was formed, and that structural types quite unknown to us have appeared and vanished forever. The same can be said about the hypothetic simpler systems of the primitive macromolecules which can be thought of having been something like the multiple coacervate drops of Bungenberg de Jong.[8] Nature had plenty of time to experiment by producing macromolecules and systems of small and

[8] H. G. Bungenberg de Jong, in H. R. Kruyt, *Colloid Science* Vol. II, chapt. 8–11, Elsevier, Amsterdam, 1949.

large molecules. Billions of different sequences of amino acids probably were formed in the protein-like polymers, depending on the concentrations of the available starting materials in any particular case.

All this is acceptable in the light of present knowledge. A great variety of macromolecular organic substances could be formed in the early age of our planet, and it is also conceivable that these macromolecules in some places assembled into drops and layers. Furthermore, it is conceivable that these systems differed from each other, and that some contained catalytically active molecules. Yet, the gap between such macromolecular systems and living cells of today is still tremendous. The leap from inorganic elements to organic "fore-proteins" and "fore-nucleic acids" is very small in comparison to the next step from these systems to an organized cell with all its enzymes and other macromolecules and their organizations. The eminent Russian scientist Oparin [3] probably is the one who has been most successful in trying to present a synthetic picture about the origin of life. Yet most convincing in his publications are those passages in which he oulines the difficulties and describes the specific highly developed organization of living systems. "Indeed, although we are now very rapidly approaching a full understanding of the chemical nature of enzymes, and even the solution of the problem of their synthesis by artificial means, these catalysts still bear all the marks of their biological origin. In nature they are only to be found in organisms and can only be formed naturally there. Such a 'fortunate' combination of atomic groups as we find in enzymes, such an intimate association between their structure and their biological function, could not have arisen by chance or simply as a result of the action of the laws of physics and chemistry. The formation of enzymes required a definite orientation of the process of the evolution of matter, it required selection, the destruction of all 'unsuccessful' combinations and the retention for further evolution of only those systems in which the catalytic apparatus fulfilled its biological function most rationally" (l.c. 3, quotation from p. 373). It is obvious that all hopes are then resting on the idea of *natural selection*, an idea that even in explaining the evolution of species is more a creed than self-evident axiom or fact. The chief objection raised by some biologists against the importance of this factor in evolution is the unimportance of undeveloped new features (organs) in the fight for existence. For example, it is obvious that specimens with better vision or better hearing have advantages over specimens with a poor vision or hearing, but it is not clear what advantages have the specimens which have an undeveloped eye to those that have none. Vision did not appear suddenly, the respective organ must have had a course of long evolution, and it is difficult to comprehend what advantage had the organisms who had a "primitive cellular basis for eye formation" without being endowed with sight. Likewise, it is even more difficult to envisage how any selection in the coacervate drops of "fore-proteins" and "fore-nucleic acids" could lead to organization, and how any selection could have occurred at all. According to Oparin, one of the first bases of selection in a multitude of coacervate drops was their slightly different stability. This "selection" of the most stable drops is self-evident. Also nobody would much argue about the statement that in a later stage those cells will be eliminated by selection which have defective enzyme systems. The greatest difficulty seems to be in the inability of presently available concepts and facts to explain the first stages of macromolecular organization leading to the purposeful, self-preserving and replicating systems. In this respect, not too much can be expected from experiments with the coacervate drops containing proteins and nucleic acids, since our present-day proteins and nucleic acids are products of live cells and *could not have arisen before the cells themselves have formed.* More promising perhaps could be experiments with the various synthetic "fore-proteins" and "fore-nucleic-acids" (these latter should be first synthesized by purely chemical methods) with added catalysts etc. Reactions of these macromolecules either in coacervate drops or surfaces of minerals probably might give some leads toward the solution of these mysteries of the origin of life.

Is there any chance that a living cell capable of replication could be artificially made in some of these ways? On the basis of all we learned about the unique structures of proteins and nucleic acid (2nd part), as well as the elaborate cellular organelles (mitochondria, nucleus, etc.), such chance is infinitesimally small. There are, however, unlimited open areas for the study of macromolecular systems in which some of the components are organized by adsorption on mineral surfaces or interphase boundaries. Perhaps the time is not ripe yet for a successful attack on these problems, since too little is known about the mechanism of enzyme action and intracellular metabolism, but there is no doubt that a time will come when the origin of life will be better understood than it is possible at present. One of the first general tasks of chemistry will be to synthesize macromolecules which resemble enzymes more closely than the presently available polyamino acids.

Exploration in the field of chemical nonenzymic syntheses of nucleic acids, and macromolecules resembling them, are as important as the endeavors in chemical synthesis of enzymes and other proteins. Yet practically nothing is done in the field of synthesis of such "fore-nucleic-acids". Also little has been done in exploring the possible evolutionary changes and adaptations of the nucleic acids. "Nothing is known about the survival of the nucleic acids in the evolutionary process. However, because we see these two closely related molecules with different functions, we are, of course, tempted to ask whether they may have originated historically from a common molecule that then specialized in the course of evolution into the two different classes of molecules we see today. To pursue this argument further, we note the fact that the RNA molecule is also able to carry genetic information, as mentioned above in the case of the tobacco mosaic virus infection. Hence it may be reasonable to speculate that the first polynucleotide molecule that Nature used was an RNA-like molecule that is able both to convey genetic information and to organize the amino acid molecules to produce specific types of proteins. DNA might then be regarded as a specialized derivative molecule that evolved in a form that only carried out the molecular replicating cycle that is an inherent part of the transmission of genetic information. DNA is less reactive metabolically, perhaps because of the absence of the hydroxy group, and this may have a selective advantage in an evolving biochemical system".[8a]

Although the principle of selection may not be the only factor in the development of macromolecular systems, many facts point out its dominating role. Perhaps most impressive are the facts mentioned in the beginning – the existence of only a few macromolecular types in the living forms of today. The uncountable billions of other potential macromolecular forms were eliminated; since it is unlikely that the present types (proteins, nucleic acids, polysaccharides) were the only ones in the early age of our planet, such elimination must be assumed. What were the factors which brought about this elimination, is not known. Chemical stability might be one of such factors, though not the decisive one, since an evolution towards most stable forms, according to the second law of thermodynamics, should have brought any further development to a standstill long ago. In the development of living forms, however, can occur processes leading to a decrease of entropy in the macromolecular systems (such as the coacervate drops), this decrease being compensated by corresponding increase of the entropy in the external medium. Interesting discussion about the energetics of the open systems in general can be found in the book of Oparin (l.c. 3, especially pp. 323–335). One should also always consider the fact that the living forms and macromolecules found in them are by no means "perfect". The course of evolution seems to be not straight towards an unmistakable higher perfection but runs through "ups" and "downs", and so it continues. The appearance of the human mind is a very recent product of this evolution, and the insatiable curiosity of it to search and explain is beginning to throw light into the immense past.

Anfinsen[9] has pointed out the interesting fact that some proteins are found in the lower as well as in the higher species, while some other proteins appear only in the higher species. Cytochrome-*c*, for example, is one of the indispensable enzymes found throughout *all* species; this is one of the proteins which once developed did not change much in the whole course of evolution. Serum albumin, on the other hand, is an example of a relatively new protein that is found only in the higher species, and more detailed studies on the albumins from various higher species may disclose important phylogenetic relationships. Other relatively "new" macromolecules are those of the protein hormones. The chemical structure of some of them is already known, although the biosynthesis and mechanism of action is still obscure.

[8a] A. Rich, *Ann. N. Y. Acad. Sci.* **81**, (3), 709 (1959); quoted from p. 721.
[9] Chr. B. Anfinsen, *The Molecular Basis of Evolution*, Wiley, New York, 1959.

While a reasonable theory on the origin of life is still a quite distant goal, recent advances in the understanding of the structure, configuration, and biosynthesis of proteins, as well as nucleic acids and polysaccharides, is greatly encouraging. The submicroscopic structures of the cells and the interplay of the various types of the large and small molecules in these structures is now better understood than a few decades ago. There are ample reasons to hope that further advances will lead not only to a better understanding of metabolism, replication, regeneration, and similar phenomena, but that these advances also will provide means for conquering the still undefeated diseases and for the amendment of natural imperfections. Indeed, this expansion of the potentialities of human mind and scientific method is even more admirable than the origin of life. And in this unprecedented adventure of Mind on our planet we are still at the very beginning . . .

AUTHOR-INDEX

Ablondi, F. B., 381
Abrams, G. D., 420
Abrams, M. E., 48
Abramson, H. A., 26
Abukumagawa, E., 292, 293
Ada, G. L., 330
Adair, G. S., 10
Adams, E. C., 82, 217
Adams, M. H., 331, 333
Adams, R. D., 429
Adler, J., 360
Afanaseva, E. M., 145
Affonso, O. R., 34
Akabori, S., 187, 193, 436
Alex, N., 418
Alexander, A. E., 6, 64
Alexander, B., 377
Alexander, L. E., 96
Alexander, P., 203, 274, 306, 396
Alkjaersig, N., 381
Allfrey, V. G., 291, 297, 336, 338
Allgen, L. G., 72
Alling, E. L., 400
Altermatt, H., 158
Altgelt, K., 122
Ambrose, E. J., 105
Anderegg, J. W., 69
Anderer, F. A., 322
Andervont, H. B., 399
Ando, T., 292, 293, 294
Anfinsen, C. B., 95, 185, 191, 194, 221, 240, 249, 250, 334, 355, 440
Anker, H. S., 376
Anson, M. L., 51
Antonini, E., 232, 233
Aoki, K., 212
Appel, P., 56
Aquist, S., 174
Arcos, J. C., 396
Arcos, M., 396
Armstrong, S. H., 205
Arond, L. H., 170
Arreguin, B., 117
Aschheim, E., 433
Ashworth, J. N., 205, 371
Astbury, W. T., 168, 266, 426
Aubel-Lesure, G., 216
Awapara, J., 392

Babcock, G. E., 170
Bailey, E. D., 17
Bailey, K., 19, 107, 185, 197, 204, 215, 226, 238, 245, 251, 266, 272, 283, 289, 319, 368, 380, 410, 422
Bain, J. A., 221
Baker, B. L., 420
Baldwin, E., 251
Baldwin, R. R., 144
Ballou, G. A., 214
Balls, A. K., 243, 245
Balo, J., 418
Bamford, C. H., 100, 105, 185, 267
Banga, I., 418
Barbu, E., 195
Barclay, R. K., 339, 435
Barer, R., 343, 344
Barker, G. R., 300
Barkley, R. K., 310
Barnes, B. A., 205
Barrett, F. C., 21
Barry, A. J., 161
Bartl, H., 149
Bartlett, M. F., 40, 255
Barton, A. D., 396
Batchelder, A. C., 48
Bates, H. M., 348
Bath, J., 130
Batzer, H., 7
Bawn, C. E. H., 82
Beach, D. C., 164
Beadle, G. W., 337, 397
Bean, R. S., 243
Bear, R. S., 98, 153, 275, 279, 411, 414
Beaufay, H., 344
Beauquesne, L., 164
Beaven, G. H., 231
Bebbington, A. E., 153
Becker, R. R., 94
Beeman, W. W., 69

Begg, R. W., 400, 402
Behrens, O. K., 260
Beilands, J. B., 237
Beiser, S. M., 303
Bell, P. H., 260
Bellamy, L. J., 105
Belozersky, A. N., 362
Bemiller, J. N., 162
Benard, H., 233
Bendich, A., 303
Bennet, A.-H., 336
Benoit, H., 136
Benzer, S., 334, 337
Berck, I. E., 120
Berenson, G. S., 181
Berg, P., 347
Bergman, M., 238
Bergold, G., 327
Bernal, J. D., 436
Bernfeld, P., 35, 142, 145, 402
Bernstein, M. H., 290
Berthet, J., 344
Bessman, M. J., 360
Bettelheim, F. A., 157, 380
Bettelheim-Jevons, F. R., 373, 419
Bier, M., 26, 59
Bikerman, J. J., 23
Bishop, F. W., 178
Block, R. J., 34, 203, 273
Blout, E. R., 105
Bluhm, M. M., 102
Blum, L., 374
Blumberg, B. S., 178
Blumenfeld, O. O., 239
Boardman, N. K., 25
Bodo, G., 102
Boedtker, H., 279, 311, 312
Boissonas, R. W., 261
Bolton, E. T., 345
Bonnar, R. U., 43
Bonner, J., 116, 117, 143, 225
Booth, F., 87
Boppel, H., 133
Borbiro, M., 425
Borsook, H., 345, 367
Bott, M. J., 281
Bottle, R. T., 200
Botts, J., 424
Bourne, E. J., 153
Bourne, G. H., 422
Bovey, F. A., 170
Bowes, J. H., 282
Boyd, W. C., 215, 374
Boyer, P. D., 214, 237
Brachet, J., 69, 336, 337, 344, 351
Bradbury, J. H., 110, 202
Bradfield, J. R. G., 428
Bragg, Sir L., 96
Brand, E., 206
Brandt, E. L., 396
Branson, H. H., 268
Braunitzer, G., 187, 271, 322
Brauns, F. E., 140
Bray, H., G. 174
Brice, B. A., 58, 62
Briggs, D. R., 163
Brimley, R. C., 21
Brink, N. G., 419
Britten, R. J., 345
Brohult, S., 223
Bromer, W. W., 260
Brosteaux, J., 58
Brown, A., 48, 137, 216
Brown, D. M., 303, 310, 390
Brown, F., 165
Brown, G. L., 310, 339, 435
Brown, R. A., 26, 216
Brown, R. K., 205
Brown, S. A., 126
Brunish, R., 178
Buchanan, T. J., 72
Budka, M. J. E., 205
Buettner-Janusch, V., 390
Bull, H. B., 78, 199
Bunce, B. H., 61
Bunce McGill, B., 304
Bungenberg de Jong, H.-G., 437
Bunn, C. W., 118
Bunzl, M., 81, 86
Burk, N. F., 10
Burnet, F. M., 317, 329, 376, 399
Burnett, G. M., 94
Butler, J. A. V., 288, 289, 304, 305, 395
Buzzell, J. G., 78, 87, 211, 246

Cacciola, A. R., 260
Caines, G. W., 168
Calmon, C., 21, 25, 37
Cameron, M. P., 187
Campbell, D. H., 376, 377
Campbell, P. N., 399
Canellakis, E. S., 359
Cann, J. R., 26, 212, 216, 375
Cannon, M. R., 78
Cantow, H. J., 122
Caroll, W. R., 284
Carothers, H., 10

CARPENTER, D. K., 137
CARTER, W. C., 121
CASSIDY, H. G., 23
CASSPERSON, T., 344
CAVALLINI, D., 228
CERF, R., 66
CHANCE, B., 252
CHANDA, S. K., 168
CHANTRENNE, H., 347
CHARGAFF, E., 12, 145, 289, 300, 303, 320, 352, 357, 359, 373
CHARLES, A. F., 180
CHARLESBY, A., 124
CHARLWOOD, P. A., 211
CHASE, M., 333
CHEESMAN, D. F., 199
CHIBNALL, A. C., 225
CHILD, R. G., 260
CHRISTIAN, W., 252
CHRISTIANSEN, J. A., 178
CICERELLI, J. S., 281
CIFONELLI, J. A., 420
CLARK, C., 105
CLARK, G. L., 173
CLAUDE, A., 335, 341, 354
COHEN, C., 201
COHEN, S. S., 301, 333
COHN, E. J., 205, 371
COHN, W. E., 310
COLE, K. S., 430
COLE, R. D., 261
COLE, W. H., 377
COLOWICK, S. P., 52, 59, 86, 105, 155, 237
COLVIN, J. R., 30
CONRAD, C. M., 136
CONSDEN, R., 417
CONWAY, B. E., 289, 305
COOK, H. A., 295
COOK, W. H., 30, 169
COOPER, J. A., 217
COOTE, J. L., 348
COREY, R. B., 192, 266, 268, 271
CORI, C. F., 153, 252
CORI, G. T., 153, 252
COURSAGET, J., 376
CRADDOCK, V. M., 348
CRAGG, L. H., 20, 76
CRAIG, D., 21
CRAIG, L. C., 18, 21, 41, 256, 293
CRAMER, G., 154
CRAMPTON, C. F., 295
CRANE, F. L., 339, 341, 342
CREETH, J. M., 210
CRICK, F. H. C., 102, 189, 192, 231, 246, 279, 302, 309, 318, 347, 354, 356, 362
CROKAERT, R., 391
CRON, M. J., 174
CRUFT, H. J., 395
CULLIS, A. F., 227
CUMMINS, A. B., 17
CURL, A. L., 243
CUTTER, F. J., 205
CZERNIAK, R. S., 87

DALY, M. M., 294
DANDLIKER, W. B., 252
DAVIDSON, E. A., 174, 175, 177
DAVIDSON, J. N., 289, 300, 303, 320, 352
DAVIES, D. R., 103, 314
DAVIES, H. F., 418
DAVIES, M. C., 260
DAVIES, J. T., 199
DAVISON, P. F., 288, 289, 395
DE BUSK, A. G., 357
DEBYE, P., 58
DE DUVE, C., 344
DEISS, W. P., 175
DEKKER, C. A., 307, 357
DELBRUCK, M., 359
DE MARCO, 228
DENNY-BROWN, D., 429
DE RENZO, E. C., 381
DEROUAUX, C., 205
DERVICHIAN, D. C., 69
DE STEVENS, G., 140
DEUEL, H., 25, 158, 160, 166
DEUTSCH, H. F., 221, 385, 386
DE WITT STETTEN JR., 144
DICKERSON, R. E., 103
DICKINSON, T. E., 402
DIMBAT, M., 43
DINTZIS, H. M., 26, 102, 205, 206, 227, 345, 367
DIXON, J. S., 260, 261
DIXON, M., 237
DJERASSI, C., 107
DMOCHOWSKI, L., 331, 399, 400
DODDS, E. C., 163
DONNAN, F. G., 48
DORFMAN, A., 279, 420
DOTY, P., 15, 59, 60, 61, 86, 87, 107, 110, 111, 136, 199, 202, 279, 280, 282, 291, 299, 304, 305, 306, 311, 312, 314, 338, 363
DOUDNEY, C. O., 356, 398
DOUNCE, A. L., 337, 356
DREYER, W. J., 242

Dréze, A., 392
Dubuisson, M., 284
Dumsha, B., 419
Dunn, L. C., 397
Durrum, E. L., 34
Dus, K., 253
du Vigneaud, V., 40, 255

Eakin, R. E., 220
Earland, C., 274
Eccles, J. C., 430
Eddy, B. E., 400
Eddy, C. R., 157
Edelhoch, H., 240
Edelman, G. M., 220
Edman, P., 187
Edsall, J. T., 20, 59, 371, 384
Eggenberger, D. N., 163
Eggman, L., 290, 377
Ehrlich, P., 306
Eicher, T., 135
Einbinder, J., 174
Eirich, F., 81, 86
Eisenberg, H., 78, 311
Eisenschitz, R., 86
Eldredge, N. T., 290, 295
Elford, W. F., 18
Elias, H. G., 170
Elliott, A., 105, 185, 203, 267
Elliott, K. A. C., 433
Elliott, R. G., 282
Ellis, J. W., 130
Emmons, C. W., 398
Ende, H., 377
Enders, J. F., 327
Engelhardt, W. A., 424
English, J. P., 260
Engström, A., 336, 422, 432
Ens, A., 211
Ephrussi-Taylor, H., 310, 339, 352, 435
Epstein, J. A., 137, 257
Erickson, J. O., 195
Ericksson-Quensel, I. B., 227, 234
Erlander, S. R., 148
Estable, C., 353
Ewart, R. H., 117

Farber, S., 406
Farmer, E. H., 122
Farr, A. L., 36
Felix, K., 291, 293
Fenichel, R. L., 368
Fenner, F., 376
Ferguson, J. H., 377
Fernandez-Moran, H., 431, 432
Ferry, J. D., 18, 281, 380
Fevold, H. L., 220
Filitti,-Wurmster, S., 216
Finean, J. B., 336, 422, 432
Finn, B. M., 260
Firfarova, K., 195
Fischer, H., 291
Fisher, H. L., 120
Fitton Jackson, S., 412, 413
Fitts, D., 112, 203
Fitzgerald, J, E., 379
Flaschenträger, B., 291
Fletcher, A. P., 381
Flodin, P., 28
Flory, P. J., 3, 46, 73, 85, 94, 115, 137, 281, 304
Folkes, J. P., 362
Folt, V. L., 120
Ford, T. F., 57
Foster, A. B., 28, 179
Foster, J. F., 65 144, 195, 197, 211, 212
Fournet, G., 69
Fox Jr., J. B., 252
Fox, S. W., 65, 197, 434
Fraenkel-Conrat, H., 40, 187 188, 243, 313, 317, 320, 322
Frank, H., P. 170
Franklin, E. C., 371
Franklin, R. E., 310, 323
Fraser, R. D. B., 105, 106
Fredericq, E., 41, 256
Freeman, M. P., 110
Frei, E. H., 78
French, D., 144, 148, 154
Fresco, J. R., 303, 312, 314
Freudenberg, K., 112, 125, 133, 140, 154
Frey-Wyssling, A., 336
Frilette, V. J., 131
Frisch-Niggemeyer, W., 330, 331
Frisman, E., 66
Fritschi, J., 9
Fromageot, C., 185, 187
Fujioka, H., 292
Fujiwara, S., 193
Fukuoka, F., 402
Furth, J., 395

Gaebler, O. H., 356
Gage, J. C., 51
Gale, E. F., 362
Gallop, P. M., 194, 277, 283
Galston, A. W., 116
Gardell, S., 174

Gaylord, N. G., 94
Geddes, A. L., 50
Gee, G., 73, 121
Geiduschek, E. P., 107, 286, 306
Georgiev, G. P., 297
Gergely, J., 178
Geschwind, I. I., 260, 261
Geschwind, N., 431
Gibbs, C. F., 120
Gierer, A., 112, 311, 312, 324
Gilbert, G. A., 371
Gilham, P. T., 361
Gillespie, J. M., 205
Ginsburg, A., 56
Gladner, J. A., 244
Glass, B., 193, 232, 334, 337, 352, 357, 359, 360
Glass, C. A., 170
Glasstone, S., 101
Glick, D., 188
Glynn, L. E., 417
Golding, H. B., 15
Goldstein, A. M., 164
Goldstein, L., 358
Göllner, I., 370
Golova, O. P., 131
Goodman, M., 185
Gordon, A. H., 174
Gorguraki, V., 25, 243, 392
Gorin, M. H., 26
Goring, D. A. I., 168
Gosling, R. G., 310
Gosting, L. J., 50
Gouinlock, Jr. E. V., 281
Gould, B. S., 416
Grabar, P., 373, 374, 382
Grafflin, M. W., 129
Gralèn, N., 131, 164
Grassmann, W., 28, 276
Greathouse, G. A., 126
Green, D. E., 11, 162, 185, 236, 254, 333, 339, 341, 367, 378, 395, 424, 430
Green, D. W., 102
Green, H., 376
Green, N. M., 238
Greenberg, D. M., 10, 50, 52
Greenstein, J. P., 195, 394, 401
Greenwood, C. T., 148, 157
Gregory, J. E., 174
Grey, C. E., 399, 400
Griffin, A. C., 263, 394, 395, 396, 398, 402
Griswold, P., 105
Gronwall, A., 169
Gros, P., 376
Gross, I., 399
Gross, J., 276, 277, 311, 414, 416, 419
Gross, L., 399
Grotjan, H., 134
Gruen, D. M., 105
Grunberg, Manago, M., 314, 359
Guinier, A., 69, 96
Gurd, F. R. N., 205, 369
Gurter, F. J., 25
Gustavson, K. H., 275, 410, 417
Gutfreund, H., 256
Gutman, A. B., 400
Guttman, S., 261

Haas, F. L., 356, 398
Hadidian, Z., 178
Hagan, J. J., 381
Haggis, G., H. 72
Hagglund, E., 140
Haines, R. T. M., 163
Hakim, R., 398
Haley, M. I., 295
Hall, B. D., 311, 312
Hall, C. E., 66, 67, 68, 253, 278, 304, 379
Halsall, T. G., 145
Halwer, M., 58, 62
Hamilton, L. D., 339, 435
Hammerschlag, H., 20
Hamoir, G., 314
Hanafusa, H., 187
Hanby, W. E., 105, 185, 203, 267
Handler, P., 366
Hanes, G., 153
Hanle, J., 131
Hannig, K., 28, 276
Hanson, J., 423
Hardin, R. L., 226
Harfenist, E. J., 41, 256
Harker, D., 101, 246
Harkness, R. D., 412
Harrington, W. F., 56, 193, 251, 258
Harris, J. I., 244, 256, 260, 261, 322
Hart, R. G., 103
Harting, J., 252
Hartley, G. S., 51
Hartley, R. W., 433
Hartzog, M. B., 157
Haruna, I., 187
Haschemeyer, E., 313
Haselkorn, R., 312
Hashimoto, C., 294
Hassid, W. Z., 145, 153
Hasted, J. B., 72

HATEFI, Y., 342
HAUENSTEIN, J. D., 246
HAUPT, H., 373
HAUROWITZ, F., 200, 226
HAVES JR., J. E., 252
HAWORTH, W. N., 153
HECHT, L. I., 347
HEHRE, E. J., 154, 170
HEIDE, K., 370
HEIDELBERGER, M., 375, 376
HEILBRUNN, L. V., 75, 80
HELLER, W., 76, 107
HELLFRITZ, H., 48
HELLMAN, N. N., 170
HENGLEIN, F. A., 159
HEPPEL, L. A., 359
HERBERT, D., 69
HERMANS JR., J., 298
HERRIOTT, R. M., 238, 352
HERSH, R., 56
HERSHEY, A. D., 333
HESS, K., 134
HEYNE, E., 165
HIGHBERGER, J. H., 277, 414
HILBERT, G. E., 144
HILL, A. V., 427
HILL, R., 118, 245
HILMOE, R. J., 359
HINDERT, M., 133
HINDS, H., 420
HIRS, C. H. W., 185, 190, 246, 247
HIRST, E. L., 145, 163, 164, 165, 168
HOAGLAND, M. B., 347, 364
HOCH, H., 231
HOCHENEGGER, M., 379
HODGE, J. E., 144
HOEBER, P. B., 429
HOFFMAN, P., 175, 178, 420
HOLIDAY, E. R., 231
HOLLAENDER, A., 398
HOLMES, K. C., 323
HOLTZER, A. M., 110, 136, 202, 286, 306
HOMBURGER, F., 402
HOPKINS, J., 337
HORNE JR, S. E., 120
HOTCHKISS, R. D., 352
HOTTA, Y., 339
HOUCK, J. C., 177
HOUGH, A., 285
HOUGH, L., 165
HOUWINK, R., 124
HOWARD, K. S., 260
HOYLE, G., 430
HSIA, D. Y., 368
HUGGARD, A. J., 179
HUGGINS, C., 210
HUGGINS, M. L., 82, 192, 266, 275
HUGHES, W. L., 204, 205, 209, 356, 368, 371
HUISMAN, T. H. J., 228
HUMMEL, J. P., 312
HUNT, J. A., 368
HURLBERT, R. B., 419
HUSEMANN, E., 10, 20, 67, 81, 92, 139, 148, 149, 153
HUTSCHNEKER, K., 25
HUXLEY, A. F., 422, 423
HUXLEY, H. E., 423, 425
HVIDT, A., 258
HYDEN, H., 433

IKENAKA, T., 25, 187, 196, 207, 210, 219, 243, 244, 392
IMMERGUT, E. H., 48, 136
INGERSOLL, H. G., 130
INGRAM, V. M., 102, 226, 229, 230, 368
ISHII, S., 292, 293
ISLIKER, H., 369, 374
ITANO, H. A., 226
IVANOV, V. I., 131
IWAI, K., 292

JACKSON, D. S., 414
JACOBS, S., 414
JAGER, B. V., 390
JAHN, E. C., 140, 161
JAKUS, M. A., 278
JAMES, T. W., 112
JANSEN, E. F., 160, 243
JAQUENOUD, P. A., 261
JÄRNEFELD, J., 339
JENSEN, C. E., 178
JENSEN, E. V., 210
JENSEN, R., 181
JIRGENSONS, B., 6, 17, 20, 25, 82, 110, 193, 195, 196, 199, 203, 207, 212, 214, 217, 220, 223, 240, 243, 244, 258, 388, 392, 393, 403, 405, 417
JÖHL, A., 40, 255
JOHNSON, P., 6, 64, 224
JOLLES, P., 185
JOLLES, THAUREAUX, J., 185
JOLY, M., 195
JONES, D. W., 130
JONES, J. K. N., 145, 164, 165
JORPES, E., 179
JOSEPH, S., 343, 344
JUPNIK, H., 336

Jurisch, J., 15
Jutisz, M., 187

Kabat, E. A., 181, 366, 374
Kaesberg, P., 69
Kahnt, F. M., 205
Kalnitsky, G., 312
Kaplan, N. O., 52, 59, 86, 105, 155, 237
Karabinos, J. V., 133, 180
Kargin, V. A., 127
Karjala, S. A., 35, 144
Karrholm, M., 164
Kartha, G., 279
Karush, F., 200, 212, 213, 219
Katsoyannis, P. G., 40
Katz, S., 380
Katzen, H. M., 144
Kauzmann, W., 92, 112, 193, 195, 199, 232
Kawanishi, Y., 292
Kay, L. M., 271
Kearney, E. B., 251
Kegeles, G., 56
Keil, B., 206
Keller, E. B., 311
Kellgren, J. H., 417
Kendrew, J. C., 99, 102, 103, 104, 192, 231, 246, 266, 410
Kenner, G. W., 185
Kersten, H., 416
Kersten, W., 416
Kertesz, Z. I., 155
Khorana, H. G., 361
Kiel, J. P., 120
Kimmel, J. R., 239, 245
Kimura, M., 292
King, T. P., 18, 293
Kirkwood, J. G., 26, 112, 203, 216
Kit, S., 395
Kitai, R., 41, 185
Klainer, S. M., 56
Klipp, L. W., 57
Klotz, I. M., 73, 105, 198, 215
Klug, H. P., 96
Knight, C. A., 322, 324
Knox, J., 398
Koechlin, B. A., 369
Koenig, V. L., 210
Kominz, D. R., 284, 285, 378
Konigsburg, W., 18, 293
Kornberg, A., 360
Kozloff, L. M., 331
Kramer, H., 48
Kratky, O., 69, 216
Kratochvil, C. H., 386
Krebs, H. A., 366
Krekels, A., 291
Kressman, T., 21, 25, 37
Krigbaum, W. R., 85, 304
Krotkov, G., 116
Kruyt, H. R., 437
Kubal, J. V., 165
Kuhn, R., 23
Kulonen, E., 279
Kunitz, M., 238
Kunkel, H., 34, 371, 372, 386
Kupke, D. W., 41, 256, 290, 295
Kuratomi, K., 193

Laird, A. K., 396
Laki, K., 284, 285, 333, 378, 425
Lamberts, E. L., 170
Lamy, F., 378
Landmann, W. A., 261
Landsteiner, K., 374
Landua, A. J., 392
Lansing, A. I., 418
Lardy, H., 237
Laskowski, M., 243
Laskowski Jr., M., 243, 377
Lauffer, M. A., 86, 318
Laurence, D. J. R., 304
Laurent, T. C., 178
Law, L. W., 397
Lawler, H. C., 255
Lay, W.-P., 219
Leach, A. A., 414
Leach, S. J., 203
Le Baron, F. N., 433
Le Bras, J., 120
Lederberg, J., 352, 376
Lederer, E., 21, 23
Lederer, M., 21, 34
Lehman, I. R., 360
Lehnartz, E., 291
Leloir, L. F., 162
Leon, A. S., 175
Lepow, I. H., 374
Lester, R. L., 342
Levedahl, B. H., 112, 206
Lever, W. F., 205
Levinthal, C., 356
Levy, A. L., 188, 260
Lewis, U. J., 419
Li, C. H., 254, 260, 261, 262, 264
Lindley, H., 259
Linderstrom-Lang, K., 41, 191, 201, 256, 258
Lineweaver, H., 160, 243, 245

LINKER, A., 175, 177, 178, 420
LIPMANN, F., 364
LIPSHITZ, R., 303
LITT, M., 68, 304, 312
LITTAUER, U. Z., 311
LITTLEFIELD, J. W., 311
LIU, C. H., 205
LJUMIBOVA, M. N., 424
LOCKINGEN, L. S., 357
LOEB, L., 136
LOEWI, G., 175, 420
LOFTFIELD, R. B., 363
LOGAN, A. C., 210
LOHSS, F., 391
LONGSWORTH, L. G., 31
LORAND, L., 378
LOSEVA, A. L., 214
LOTMAR, W., 173
LOTZKAR, H., 157
LOUGHBOROUGH, D. L., 140
LOVRIEN, R. E., 252
LOW, B. W., 210
LOWEY, S., 286
LOWRY, O. H., 36
LOZAITYTE, I., 176
LUCAS, F., 269, 270
LUCK, J. M., 214, 290, 295
LUDWIG, N. H., 170
LUM, F. G., 214
LUMRY, R., 206
LUNDBERG, R. D., 110, 199, 202
LUNDGREN, H. P., 50, 52, 272, 274
LURIA, S. E., 317

MACDONNELL, L. R., 160
MACFARLANE, R. G., 377
MACHEBOEUF, M., 376
MACLAY, W. D., 157
MADISON, R. K., 174
MAGASINIK, B., 320
MAGAT, M., 121
MAGEE, L. A., 400
MALCOLM, B. R., 203
MANDELKERN, L., 54, 85, 86, 304
MANN, J., 130
MANNERS, D. J., 146
MANTELL, C. L., 162
MARBETH, R., 175
MARGARETHA, H., 81, 86
MARK, H., 10, 15, 94, 115, 118, 131, 136
MARKHAM, R., 246, 289, 319
MARKO, A. M., 412
MARKUS, G., 200, 212, 213, 219
MARLIES, C., 94
MARMUR, J., 363
MARRINAN, H. J., 130
MARSH, R. E., 271
MARSHAK, A., 349
MARSHALL, P. A., 45, 170
MARVIN, D. A., 310, 339, 435
MARX, M., 131, 132
MASSON, C. R., 168
MATHEWS, M. B., 88, 89, 176, 279, 420
MATSUSHIMA, T., 187
MAURITZEN, C. M., 295, 395
MAXFIELD, M., 433
MAYER, M. M., 374
MAZIA, D. ,290, 338, 356
MCCREADY, R. M., 153
MCELROY, W., D., 193, 232, 334, 337, 352, 357, 359, 360
MCFADDEN, M. L., 390
MCGILL, B. B., 15
MCILWAIN, H., 430
MCLAREN, A. D., 71, 199
MCNEELY, W. H., 168
MECHAM, D. K., 222
MEILMAN, E., 194 ,283
MEISENHELDER, J. H., 260
MELIN, M., 205
MELLORS, R., 336
MERCER, E. H., 274
MESELSON, M., 356
MEYER, K. H., 3, 10, 115, 116, 130, 145, 173, 180, 266
MEYER, KARL, 171, 174, 175, 177, 178, 420
MEYERHOFF, G., 377
MICON, J., 358
MIDER, G. B., 400
MILES, F. D., 135
MILLAR, E. C. P., 318
MILLAR, J., 402
MILLER, E. C., 396
MILLER, J. A., 396
MILLER, S. L., 436
MIRSKY, A. E., 69, 291, 294, 297, 336, 338
MISCH, L., 118
MITCHELL, E. R., 284
MITIDIERI, E., 34
MITTELMAN, D., 205
MIYAKE, A., 390
MIZUSHIMA, S., 266
MOFFITT, W., 112, 203
MOHR, R., 10, 131, 136
MONOD, J., 154
MONTGOMERY, J. A., 406
MONTGOMERY, R., 162, 180
MOORE, D. H., 145, 373

MOORE, S., 23, 37, 185, 206, 246, 247, 295
MOORE, W. R., 137
MORALES, M. F., 424
MORI, T., 167
MORRISON, K. C., 205
MORTON, J. I., 385, 400
MOSIMANN, H., 65, 136
MOSS, J. A., 282
MOUTON, R. F., 205
MOYER, A. W., 260
MOYER, L. S., 26
MÜHLETHALER, K., 126
MUIR, H. M., 412
MULFORD, D. J., 205, 371
MÜLLER-EBERHARD, H. J., 386
MYRBÄCK, K., 237

NACHMANSOHN, D., 430
NAGAI, Y., 292, 293
NAISMITH, W. E. F., 224
NAJJAR, V. A., 329, 375, 377
NAKAHARA, W., 402
NARITA, K., 322
NATTA, G., 121
NAUGHTON, M. A., 256
NEISH, A. C., 126
NEUBERGER, A., 18, 28, 185, 204, 206, 232, 245, 254, 258, 293, 322, 323, 410, 412
NEUKOM, H., 166
NEUMAN, R. E., 275
NEURATH, H., 19, 107, 185, 195, 197, 204, 215, 226, 238, 241, 242, 244, 245, 251, 266, 272, 283, 289, 319, 368, 410, 422
NEWMAN, S., 136
NEWTON, E. B, 120
NEWTON-HEARN., P. A., 28
NICHOLS, J. B., 16, 17
NICKERSON, R. F., 131
NIEDERGERKE, R., 423
NIEUWENHUIS, K. J., 133
NISHIHARA, T., 15., 87, 279, 280
NISSELBAUM, J. S, 35
NIU, C. I., 187
NORD, F. F., 137, 140
NORTHROP, J. H., 51, 238
NOWINSKI, W. W. 336
NUSSENBAUM, S., 153
NUTTING, G. C., 58, 62

OAKLEY, H. B., 163
OCHOA, S., 314, 359, 360
O'CONNOR, M., 181
ODIER, M. E., 180
O'DONNELL, I. J., 274
OGSTON, A. G., 178
OHASHI, H., 229
OHNO, K., 187
OKADA, Y., 187, 193
OKUYAMA, T., 229
OLCOTT, H. S., 222
OLOFSSON, B., 274
OLSON, E. J., 179, 419
ONCLEY, J. L., 54, 72, 216, 369
O'NEAL, M. A., 263, 398
ONO, K., 193
OPARIN, A. I., 236, 259, 350, 435, 438, 440
OREKHOVITCH, K. D., 277, 412
OREKHOVITCH, V. N., 277, 412
ORTIZ, M., 314
ORTIZ, P. J., 359
OSAWA, S., 297, 339
OSBORNE, T. B., 223
OSTER, G., 40, 59, 60, 105, 336
OSTERBERG, H., 336
OTT, E., 129
OVERBEEK, J. T., 26
OWEN, J. A., 369, 383
OWENS, H. S., 157
OZAWA, H., 229

PAGE, I. H., 419, 433
PALADE, G. E., 340, 342, 345, 346
PALETTA, B., 216
PALEUS, S., 253
PALMER, K. J., 157, 168
PANKOW, G. W., 173
PAPKOFF, H., 264
PAPPAS, G. D., 413
PAPPENHEIMER, A. M., 374
PARRISH, R. G., 102
PARTRIDGE, S. M., 25, 418
PASYNSKII, A., 72, 87, 122
PATTERSON, A. L., 101
PAULING, L., 192, 266, 268, 271, 375
PEACOCKE, A. R., 307
PEARCE, R. H., 177
PEARSON, C. M., 429
PEAT, S., 153
PECHÉRE, J. F., 242
PEDERSEN, K. O., 10, 17, 52, 227, 235
PEISER, H. S., 96
PERCIVAL, E. G. V., 168
PEREVOSHCHIKOVA, K. A., 297
PERLMANN, G. E., 239, 240
PERLMUTTER, R., 206
PERONNE, I. C., 412
PERRIN, F., 54
PERRINGS, J. D., 210

Perry, S. V., 284
Perutz, M. F., 3, 102, 227
Peters, T., 210
Peterson, E. A., 25, 134, 161, 205, 217
Petre, A. W., 318
Petrova, A. N., 154
Philips, M., 381
Phillippoff, W., 78
Phillips, D. C., 103
Pickels, E. G., 55
Picken, L. E. R., 173
Piez, K. A., 276
Pigman, W., 145, 162
Pillemer, L., 374
Pinkel, D., 406
Pippen, E. L., 158
Pirie, N. W., 178
Piroue, R. P., 180
Platzman, R. L., 363
Plaut, W. S., 356, 358
Plescia, O. J., 26, 216
Plockl, M., 276
Plotnikova, N. E., 277, 412
Polglase, W. J., 219
Pollard, E. C., 318
Pollister, A. W., 40, 105, 336
Polson, A., 27
Pon, N. G., 260
Popenhoe, E. A., 255
Porath, J. O., 260
Porod, G., 216
Porter, K. R., 413
Porter, R. R., 232, 412
Portzehl, H., 283, 422
Potter, A. L., 145
Potter, V. R., 419
Pouradier, J., 281
Povoledo, D., 233
Prescott, D. M., 358
Priester, L. I., 369
Prince, W. C., 318
Prokofiev, A. A., 116
Psychoyos, S., 433
Putnam, F. W., 195, 197, 204, 215, 219, 382, 384, 386, 390
Putzeys, P., 58

Quastel, J. H., 433
Quastler, H., 363

Raacke, I. D., 261, 345
Race, R. R., 366
Radley, J. A., 142
Ragan, C., 420
Ramachandran, G. N., 279
Ramasarma, G. B., 418
Ramsdell, G. A., 57
Randall, J. T., 275, 281, 412
Randall, R. J., 36
Rands, D. G., 211
Rapport, M., 177, 420
Rasmussen, P. S., 295
Rasper, J., 198
Rathgeb, P., 180
Ratner, S., 376, 412
Redfield, A. C., 231
Redfield, R. R., 95, 194, 221, 240
Rees, E. D., 386
Reichmann, M. E., 61, 86, 90, 304, 338
Reiner, M., 368
Reinhart, M. A., 120
Reis, P. J., 348
Resner, R., 386
Ressler, Ch., 40, 255
Rhoads, C. P., 406
Ribeiro, L. P., 34
Rice, R. G., 214
Rice, S. A., 15, 86, 304, 306, 338
Rich, A., 279, 314, 440
Richards, E. G., 307
Richards, F. M., 249
Richards, O. W., 336
Richardson, H. L., 263
Richter, D., 430
Riggs, A. F., 229
Riley, D. P., 69
Ripa, O., 274
Ris, H., 294, 297, 337, 338
Rittenberg, D., 412
Rittenberg, S., 376
Robbins, F. C., 327
Robbins, W. C., 413
Robertis, E. D. P., 336
Roberts, C. W., 40
Roberts, E., 418
Roberts, R. B., 344
Roberts, R. R., 345
Robertson, C. H., 263
Robertson, J. M., 96
Robertson, W. van B., 412, 416, 420
Robins, A. B., 304
Robinson, B. C., 72
Robinson, C., 281
Roche, J., 233
Roe, C. P., 117
Roeske, R., 40, 255
Rogovin, Z. A., 134
Rollett, J. S., 259

Romano, D. V., 433
Romanoff, A. J., 220
Romanoff, A. L., 220
Rooksby, H. P., 96
Rosebrough, N. J., 36
Rosenfeld, L., 419
Rosenkranz, H. S., 303
Rosenthal, T. B., 418
Ross, A. G., 168
Ross, O. A., 374
Rossi-Fanelli, A., 228, 232, 233
Roswall, S., 72
Roughton, F. J. W., 231
Rougvie, M. A., 414
Rowe, D. S., 48
Rowen, J. W., 71, 178
Rudall, K. M., 171, 274
Rudolph, H., 107
Rundle, R. E., 144
Runnicles, D. F., 51
Rupley, J. A., 242, 244
Ruska, H., 67
Rusch, H. P., 394
Russell, A., 140
Ryle, A. P., 41, 185, 254

Saez, F. A., 336
Salk, J. E., 328
Samuels, L. T., 206
Sandegren, E., 223
Sanders, B. E., 369
Sanford, C. A., 210
Sanger, F., 11, 41, 95, 185, 186, 232, 254, 256, 266
Sanger, R., 366
Sasagawa, S., 229
Satake, K., 229. 295,
Sato, H., 402
Sato, M., 292
Saunders, W. M., 281
Säverborn, S., 157, 163
Sawada, F., 292
Scatchard, G., 48, 216
Schachman, H. K., 52, 56, 86, 307, 357
Schaffer, F. L., 327
Schauenstein, E., 379
Schellman, Ch., 111, 199, 201
Schellman, J. A., 107, 111, 193, 199, 206, 258, 259
Scheraga, H. A., 54, 66, 85, 86, 281, 304, 371, 377, 384
Schiller, S., 420
Schmid, K., 205, 369
Schmidt, A., 94
Schmidt, K., 232
Schmidtberger, R., 372, 373
Schmitt, F. O., 277, 278, 414, 431
Schneider, J. W., 322
Schneider, N. S., 379
Schoch, T. J., 143
Schoenheimer, R., 376, 411, 412
Schönenberger, M., 370, 372, 373
Schramm, G., 321, 322, 324
Schroeder, W. A., 241
Schubert, M., 174
Schubert, W. J., 140
Schultz, T. H., 157, 158
Schultze, H. E., 370, 372, 373
Schulz, G. V., 20, 46, 78, 122, 131, 132, 377
Schumaker, G., 321
Schumaker, V, N., 307
Schwander, H., 289
Schwartz, B., 416
Schwert, C. E., 327, 328
Schwert, W., 241
Schwick, G., 370, 373
Scott, J. F., 347
Scott, R. L., 121
Sears, E. M., 406
Seeds, W. E., 310
Seegers, W. H., 377, 378
Seifter, S., 194, 283
Sekora, A., 216
Sela, M., 191, 251
Senti, F. R., 148, 170
Shafizadeh, F., 175
Shapiro, H. S., 303
Shaw, J. T. B., 269, 270
Shedlovsky, T., 430
Shepherd, R. G., 260
Sherry, S., 381
Shipman, J. J., 120
Shooter, E. M., 224
Shooter, K. V., 304
Shore, V. C., 103
Shulman, S., 69, 380, 381
Signer, R., 22, 66, 76, 289
Simha, R., 86
Simmons, N. S., 310, 339, 435
Simms, E. S., 360
Simpson, M. V., 348
Singer, B., 313, 317
Singer, M. F., 359
Singer, S. J., 290, 376, 377
Singer, T. P., 251
Sinsheimer, R. L., 307, 313, 33[illegible]
Siu, R. G. H., 137

SKAU, E. L., 20, 118
SLACK, H. G. B., 412
SLAYTER, H. S., 379
SLEIN, M. W., 252
SMART, Ch. L., 125, 142, 155, 162, 167, 172
SMITH, A. F., 173
SMITH, D. B., 30, 169
SMITH, E. L., 219, 238, 239, 245, 366, 390
SMITH, E. N., 284
SMITH, E. V. C., 369
SMITH, F., 162
SMITH, J. D., 246, 289, 319, 327
SMITH, L. F., 41, 185
SMITH, R. H., 410, 412, 413
SMITH, S. G., 269, 270
SMITHIES, O., 35, 373
SNELL, E., 220
SNELLMAN, O., 181
SOBER, H. A., 25, 134, 205, 217
SOLLNER, K., 18
SOLMS, J., 158
SORENSEN, S. P. L., 10
SORM, F., 206
SOTELO, J. R., 353
SPEISER, R., 157
SPICER, D. S., 369
SPIRIN, A. S., 362
SPRINGALL, H. D., 185, 266
SPURLIN, H. M., 129
SPURR, JR, O. K., 137
STABIN, J. V., 48
STACEY, K., 59, 306
STACEY, M., 28, 153, 174,
STAHL, F. W., 356
STAHMANN, M. A., 94
STAINSBY, G., 279
STAMM, A. T., 140
STANIER, J. E., 178
STANIER, W. M., 417
STANLEY, W. M., 317, 319, 399
STAUDINGER, H., 4, 7, 9, 10, 15, 41, 76, 81, 92, 121, 131, 132, 135, 136, 148, 416
STAUFF, J., 46, 198
STAVITSKY, A. B., 376
STEDMAN, E., 295, 395
STEDMAN, R. J., 40, 255
STEIN, W. H., 23, 37, 185, 206, 246, 247, 295
STEINER, A. B., 168,
STEINER, R. F., 215, 314
STENT, G. S., 356, 359
STEPANENKO, B. N., 145
STEPHENSON, M. L., 347, 364
STERLING, C., 157
STERMAN, M. D., 144, 195
STERN, H., 291, 336, 338
STERN, K. G., 368
STERN, M. D., 93, 148
STERNBERG, H., 233
STETTEN, D., 366
STETTEN, M. R., 144
STEWARD, F. C., 225
STEWART, F. H. C., 40, 255
STEWART, S. E., 400
STOCKELL, A., 239
STOKES, A. R., 310
STOOPS, R., 289
STRACHER, A., 18, 293
STRACHITSKII, K., 195
STRANDBERG, B. E., 103
STRAUMANIS, M., 6, 17, 217
STROMINGER, J. L., 419
STRONG, L. E., 205, 371
STROSS, F. H., 43
STUMPF, P. K., 237
STUPEL, H., 133
STUTZ, E., 160
SUEOKA, N., 363
SUGAE, K., 187, 193
SUMNER, J. B., 237
SURGENOR, D. M., 205, 367, 377, 378
SUSICH, von, G., 115
SVEDBERG, T., 10, 16, 17, 31, 52, 131, 227, 234, 235
SVENSSON, H., 26, 368
SWAN, J. M., 40
SWANSON, M. A., 153, 211
SWIFT, H., 336
SYLVEN, B., 181
SYMONDS, P., 285, 378
SZENT-GYORGYI, A. G., 201, 283, 421, 422, 425

TAKATA, K., 339
TALMAGE, D. W., 377
TANFORD, CH., 78, 87, 183, 211, 232, 246, 252, 257, 258
TAPLEY, D. F., 210
TARVER, H., 245
TATUM, E. L., 396, 397
TAVEL, von P., 22
TAYLOR, H. L., 205, 356, 371
TAYLOR, J. F., 19, 252
TAYLOR, J. H., 336
TEMPLE, R. B., 105
TERESI, J. D., 214
THEORELL, H., 26, 236, 252
THOMAS, C. A., 86, 304, 338

Thompson, E. O. P., 210, 244
Thompson, J. F., 225
Tidswell, B. M., 137
Tinoco, I., 110, 380
Tiselius, A., 28, 31, 34, 204
Tobias, J. M., 430
Tobin, R., 170
Tobita, T., 292
Tobolsky, A. V., 15, 115
Toch, R., 406
Todd, A. R., 180, 203, 310
Todd, Audrey, 303
Todd, E. W., 374
Tondo, C. V., 369
Torriani, A. M., 154
Toth, G., 172
Trautman, R., 371
Trippett, S., 255
Tristram, G. R., 117, 218, 228, 272
Tsao, T. C., 284
Tsugita, A., 187
Tsvetkov, V. N., 66, 295
Tsyperovich, A. S., 214
Tu, C. C., 139
Tullis, J. L., 366, 377
Tuppy, H., 189, 253, 254
Turner, A. F., 361
Turner, J. E., 200
Tustanowski, A. A., 277, 412

Uber, F., 55, 80
Uhlig, H., 322
Ungar, G., 433
Unkauf, H., 161
Urey, H. C., 436
Uroma, E., 205
Usmanov, H. U., 127

Valkó, E., 115
Vallee, B. L., 244
Van de Hulst, H. C., 59
Van der Schaaf, P. C., 228
Van der Scheer, J., 260
Van der Wyk, 118
Van Iterson, G., 173
Veiss, A., 163
Velick, S. F., 252
Velluz, L., 179
Venet, A. M., 281
Vickery, H. B., 223
Vinograd, J., 345, 367
Virtanen, A., 233
Vis, H., 391
Vithayathil, P. J., 249
Vitucci, J. C., 137
Volkin, E., 310
Vollmert, B., 156, 157
Volman, D. H., 157

Waelch, H., 431
Wagner, R. H., 48
Waldenström, J., 385
Wales, M., 45, 170
Wallenius, G., 371
Waller, J. P., 261
Warburg, O., 252
Ward, D. N., 40, 255
Ward, K., 129
Ward, W. H., 50, 52, 227
Wardlaw, A. C., 374
Warner, R. C., 220, 314
Watson, F. R., 413
Watson, J. D., 302, 309, 318, 354, 356
Waugh, D. F., 257, 378, 379
Webb, E. C., 237
Weber, H. H., 283, 422
Weissberg, S. G., 45, 170
Weissberger, 15, 17, 48, 50, 66
Weissman, B., 177
Weller, T. H., 327
Wertheim, M., 145
Whistler, R. L., 125, 139, 142, 155, 162, 165, 167, 172, 179, 419
Whitby, G. S., 118
White, A., 366
White, F. H., 191
White, J. C., 231
White, W. F., 260, 261
Widmer, C., 342
Wildman, S. G., 290
Wilkins, M. F. H., 308, 309, 310, 339, 435
Wilkinson, I. A., 153
Williams, C. A., 373, 382
Williams, D. E., 419
Williams, J. W., 281
Williams, R. C., 40, 318, 320
Williams, R. J., 220, 365
Willson, E. A., 120
Wilson, A. J. C., 96
Wilson, H. R., 310, 339, 435
Wilson, I. B., 430
Winterstein, A., 175
Wintrobe, M. M., 366
Winzler, R. J., 400
Wise, L. E., 140, 161
Witnauer, L. P., 93, 148
Wolbach, R. A., 229
Wolf, B., 376

WOLFF, D., 271
WOLFROM, M. L., 174, 175, 180
WOLLENSAK, J., 391
WOLSTENHOLME, G. E. W., 181, 187, 318
WOOD, B. J., 117
WOOD, D. L., 105
WOODIN, A. M., 274
WOODS, E. F., 274
WOODS, P. S., 356
WORK, T. S., 348
WUHRMANN, F., 368, 382
WUNDERLY, CH., 34, 368, 382
WURMSER, R., 216
WYATT, G. R., 301, 327
WYCKOFF, M. M., 25, 205, 217
WYCKOFF, R. W., G. 66, 69, 102, 318
WYMAN, J., 20

YAMASAKI, M., 292, 293
YANG, J. T., 110, 111, 202, 211, 212, 282
YCAS, M., 362
YOCKEY, H. P., 363
YOUNG, R., 400
YUNOKI, K., 402

ZAHN, H., 272
ZAMECNIK, P. C., 311, 347, 364
ZAMENHOF, S., 307, 352
ZBARSKY, I. B., 297
ZECHMEISTER, L., 140, 172
ZERNIKE, F., 336
ZIFF, M., 373
ZILLIG, W., 321
ZIMM, B. H., 60, 61
ZIMMERMAN, S. B., 360
ZIRKLE, R. E., 291, 307, 331, 336, 347, 360 362, 364, 377
ZUBAY, G., 291
ZWEIG, G., 34
ZYDOWO, M., 284

SUBJECT-INDEX

Absorption of ultraviolet light 105, 398
Accelerator globulin 380
Acetate rayon 134
Acetyl cellulose 134
Acetylcholine 430
  esterase 430
Actin 283ff, 423ff
Activation of enzymes 237
Activator in blood clotting 378, 381
Actomyosin 283ff
Adaptation of cells 408
Adenocorticotropic hormone, ACTH, 260—261
Adenosine
  triphosphatase 424
  triphosphate, ATP, 341, 424, 427, 428
Adhesives 163, 169
Adsorption 13, 18, 35, 38, 70ff.
  chromatography 21ff
Agar, Agar-agar, 167ff
Aging 416
Agglomeration 366
Agglutination 366
Aggregation, aggregates, 9, 176, 257, 424, 427
Albumin
  egg (ovalbumin), 57, 70, 193, 196, 201, 202, 220—222
  plant, 223
  serum, plasma, 37, 82, 88, 109, 111, 196, 200—202, 204ff, 368ff, 383, 401, 403, 404, 405
Alcohol dehydrogenase 252
Aldolase 202
Alginic acid, algin, 168
Alkaline phosphatase 68
Amberlite 24
Amino acid
  content in proteins 207, 208, 219, 222, 224, 228, 239, 262, 270, 272, 273, 276, 285, 292, 296, 321, 375, 390, 416
  sequence in proteins 184ff, 230, 28,4 249, 253, 255, 256, 260, 262, 264, 293, 322
Amino acids, terminal, 184ff, 210, 230, 248—249, 253, 255—256, 260, 262, 264, 293, 322, 384, 386, 389
Amylases 150ff, 201, 202, 237
Amylopectin 93, 142ff
Amylose 142ff
  isomerase 154
Angular velocity 17
Anion exchange 24ff
Antibodies 216, 374, 391
  imperfect, 385
Anti-clotting agents, 381
Anticoagulants 179, 381
Antigens 374ff
Antihemophilic globulin 380
Antimetabolites 406ff
Antioxidants 15, 123
Antithrombin 381
Antithromboplastin 381
Antitoxins 374
Anti-tumor agents 406ff
Aortas 410
Apoenzyme 252
Apple pectin 156ff
Araban 138, 160, 161
Arabogalactans 138
Arachin 224
Arrowroot 143
Arteriosclerosis 418
Arthritis 383, 417
Ascorbic acid oxidase 2151
Association of macromolecules 42, 235
Asymmetric macromolecules 86
Autocatalytic reactions 242, 263
Autodigestion of enzymes 239
Avidin 220
Axial ratio 86, 281
Axon (nerve) 431—432

Bacteria 331ff
Bacterial amylase 193
Bacteriophages 317ff
Balata 116
Barley malt 150
Bassorin 164

Bence-Jones protein 38, 201—202, 391—393
Biosynthesis
  of cellulose 126ff
  of macromolecules 434ff
  of nucleic acids 360ff, 396, 406ff
  of polysaccharides 150ff, 179
  of proteins 320, 344ff, 363—364, 396, 403
  of rubber 117
Birefringence, streaming, see double refraction of flow
Bleaching of cellusole 132
Blood 365ff
  clotting 377ff
  corpuscles 366
  -group substances 181—182, 367
  pigments 226ff, 366ff
  plasma proteins 367ff, 382ff
  plasma substitutes 169
  vessels 173, 377
Bond strength 13
Bone 100, 173, 275, 410
Bound water 70ff
Branching
  factor 153
  of polymer chains 42—43, 94
Brownian movement 16, 73
Buna rubber 120
Bushy stunt virus 319ff

Cancer 394ff
Capillary viscometer 76ff
Carbohydrases 237
Carboxymethyl cellulose 133
Carboxypeptidase 188, 202, 237, 239, 243—244
Carcinogens 395ff
Carrageenin 176ff
Cartilage 173, 275, 420
Casein 184
Catalase 252, 401
Cation exchange 24
Cell membranes, walls, 125, 155
Cellobiose 129
Cellophane 18, 48, 132ff
Cells 4, 335ff, 395ff
Cellulase 237
Cellulose 15, 99, 112, 125ff
  acetate 134, 135
  bacterial 128
  carboxymethyl 133
  derivatives 132ff
  diethylaminoethyl (DEAE) 134
  enzymic degradation 137
  esters 134ff
  ethers 133
  methyl 133
  nitrate 134ff
  regenerated 133
  xanthate 133
Centrifugation 15ff
Ceruloplasmin 370
Chain
  configuration (conformation) 115, 119, 147, 194, 199
  flexibility 115
  growth 153
  length 146
Charge
  density 38, 88, 174, 180
  electrical, on macromolecules 38, 87ff, 424
Chemical analysis of polymers 39, 42
Chemotherapy 406—409
Cherry gum 165
Chitin 171—173
Chlorocruorin 234
Chlorophyll 233
Cholinesterase 430
Chondroitinsulfuric acid 88, 89, 173ff, 419
Chromatography
  analytical 36ff
  ion exchange 21, 24ff, 206
  partition 21
  preparative 21ff, 205, 206, 216
Chromosomes 336ff, 397
Chymotrypsin 188—189, 201—202, 241ff
Chymotrypsinogen 109, 201—202, 241ff
Cilia 428
Citrus petin 156ff
Classification of macromolecules 6
Clogging blood vessels 380
Clot, clotting, 179, 377ff
Clupeine 292
Coacervation 437
Coagulation see Clotting flocculation
Coenzyme 236, 252
Cohesion 125, 307
Coiling, degree of, 84—85
Collagen 87, 275ff, 410ff
Collodion 18, 69
Colloid chemistry 9
Colloidal particles 18, 97
Colloidal solutions 9
Colloids 6, 318

Complex macromolecules 176
Compressibility 72
Conalbumin 196, 220
Configuration (conformation) of macromolecules 6, 8, 85, 107ff, 259, 266ff, 279, 375,
Connective tissue 171, 410ff
Consistency 75, 91
Constitution of macromolecules, see structure
Contraction, muscular 421ff
Corn cobs 139
Corn starch 143
Cornea 420
Cotton 126ff
Couette viscometer 78ff
Counter current distribution 21
Creams 164
Creatin kinase 424
Cross-linking of macromolecules 42, 95, 115, 123ff, 192ff
Cryoglobulins 371, 384ff
Crystal structure 96ff
Crystallized polymers 39
Cytochromes, cytochrome-c, 253
Cytoplasm 338ff

Damson gum 165
Deformation of gels 91
Degradation of macromolecules 13ff, 137, 150ff
Degree of polymerization 7, 45
Dehydrogenases 252
Deionization of proteins 206
Denaturation
  of macromolecules 8, 25, 69, 289, 306, 398
  of proteins 194ff, 214, 240, 388
Deoxyribonuclease 361
Deoxyribonucleates, deoxyribonucleic acid, DNA, 68, 83, 87, 109, 112, 301ff, 337ff, 352ff, 360ff, 396ff
Detergents 214, 215
Deuterium exchange method 258
Dextran 45, 169—170
Dextrin 144ff
Dialysis 17ff
Dielectric constant 72
Dielectric dispersion 72
Diethylaminoethyl DEAE, cellulose, 25, 38, 134, 205
Differentiation of cells 429
Diffraction of X-rays 96
Diffusion 50ff
  constant (coefficient) 50, 182, 223, 234, 263
Dimensions of macromolecules 61, 85, 286
Dinitrophenylation of proteins 186, 255
Diphosphopyridine nucleotide (DPN) 252
Disaggregation 427
Dispersion constant, rotatory, 111, 201—202, 240, 259
Dissolution of polymers 19, 73
Dissymmetry of scattered light 59ff
Disulfide bonds, bridges, 190ff, 240, 248, 255, 256, 262, 264, 274, 385
Donnan effect 48
Double helix 302ff, 354ff
Double refraction of flow 64ff
Dowex 24
Drilling muds 161
Drude equation 110
Drugs 164
Dystrophy, muscular, 429

Edema 420
Edestin 223
Egg albumin, see albumin, egg
Egg
  -white proteins 220
  -yolk 222
Einstein's viscosity equation 81
Elastase 418
Elastic polymers 115
Elastic tissue 275, 410, 418ff
Elastin 275ff, 418ff
Electrical charge on macromolecules 26, 48, 87ff
Electrodialysis 18
Electrolytes, macromolecular 48
Electron density in crystals 101ff
Electron micrographs 68, 128, 278, 280, 322, 325, 326, 332, 340, 346, 379, 426, 428, 432
Electron microscope 66ff
Electro-osmosis 35
Electrophoresis
  analytical 31ff, 388
  convection 26, 215
  free boundary 26ff
  in gels 35
  on paper 27, 33ff, 369
  preparative 26ff
Electroviscous effect 87
Emulsions, emulsifying agents 164
End group analysis 43, 94—95, 184ff

Endopeptidase 244
Entropy 73—74, 116, 137, 197
Enzyme systems 334, 341
Enzymes 39, 236ff, 338ff
  classification 236—237
  hydrolytic 237
  proteolytic 237, 238ff
  redox 237, 251ff
Epidermin 272ff
Epidermis 273
Erythrocruorin 234
Erythrocytes 337
Esterases 237
Euglobulins 184, 216
Evolution
  ontogenic 236, 442
  phylogenic 172, 233, 334, 350, 421, 435ff
Excelsin 223
Exopeptidase 244
Expansion of macromolecules 213

Fats, fatty acids, 19
Feather keratin 272
Ferrihemoglobin (methemoglobin) 231
Ferroporphyrin 226, 231
Fiber diagram, X-ray 98ff
Fibers 125ff, 265ff, 412, 413, 418
Fibrillar structures 348, 411
Fibrin 378ff
Fibrinogen 65, 370, 378ff, 401
Fibrinolysis, fibrinolysin 381
Fibroblasts 412
Fibroin 269ff
Fibrous macromolecules 7, 13ff, 125ff, 265ff
Fibrous proteins 184, 265ff, 410ff, 423ff
Fick's diffusion law 50
Fillers in rubber 123
Filtration 17ff
Flagellae, bacterial 428
Flax fiber 132
Flax pectin 157
Flax seed mucilage 166, 167
Flexibility of macromolecules 66, 85
Flocculation 375, 392, 416
Flow
  anomalous 90
  birefingence 64, 65
  gradient 75, 90
  trough capillaries 76ff
Fluidity 75
Foams 168
Folding of chains in macromolecules 192ff, 249ff, 427
Food products 164, 167, 168, 221, 224
Fore-nucleic acids 437
Fore-proteins 436, 437
Fowl plague virus 319
Fractionation 21
Free energy 73, 197
Freeze drying 14
Friction, internal, see viscosity
Frictional force 52
Frictional ratio 53, 263
Fungi 137

Galactan 160, 161
Galactomannan 165
Gelatin 280ff
Gelation (setting) 158, 159
Gels 155ff, 167, 378
Genes, genetic factors 299, 336, 403
Gliadin 223, 224
Globin 227, 228
Globular macromolecules 7, 13, 81ff
Globular proteins 184
Globulins
  plant 223—225
  serum, plasma, 83, 109, 184, 196, 201, 202, 215ff, 368ff, 383, 389, 401
  various 184, 220
Glucosidases 237
Glue 417
Glyceraldehyde-3-phosphate dehydrogenase 252
Glycogens 82, 142ff
Glycoproteins 369ff
Golgi "apparatus" 349
Grinding 13, 14
Ground substance 177, 410ff, 419
Growth
  hormones 263—264
  malignant, 394ff
Guanosine triphosphate, GTP 347
Guar, guaran, 165
Guayule 116
Gum
  arabic 162ff
  karaya 164
  tragacanth 164—165
Gums, plant 162ff
Gutta-percha 116, 119
Gyration, radius of, see radius of gyration

Hair, see keratin
Heart tissue 337
Heat of dissolution 73
Helical macramolecules 258, 268ff, 354f

Hem 226
Hemerythrin 234
Hemicellulose 26, 138ff
Hemocyanins 65, 234—235
Hemoglobin 226ff
  fetal 228ff
Hemoglobins, abnormal 230
Hemolysis 227
Hemp 128
Heparin 179ff, 381
Heterogeneity of polymers 7, 45
Hide 417
High polymers 3ff
Histones 201, 294ff
Hoeppler viscometer 79
Holoenzyme 252
Homogeneity of polymers 7, 28ff, 39
Hormones 254ff
Horn, see keratin
Huggin's equation (and constant) 82
Hulls 128
Hyaluronic acid 177ff, 419—420
Hyaluronidase 177, 420
Hydration of macromolecules 70ff, 198
Hydrazinolysis of proteins 187
Hydrocarbons, polymeric 4, 115ff
Hydrogen bonds 13, 14, 71, 125, 307
Hydrophobic bonds 193, 307
Hydrophobic groups 193
Hydro-rubber 10

Ichthyocol (fish collagen) 277—278
Immobilization of solvent 71
Immunochemical reactions 216, 376
Immunoelectrophoresis 382
Individuality, biochemical, 365, 390, 408
Influenza virus 319, 329ff
Infrared dichroism 106
Infrared spectroscopy 105, 106
Inhibitors 237
Insulin 11, 41, 201, 202, 254ff
Intermelocular attraction 13ff
Interphase boundaries 439
Intrinsic viscosity 76
Inulin 162
Ion exchange chromatography 21
Ionization of polyelectrolytes 87ff
Irish moss 168
Isoelectric point 20, 211, 263, 370, 389
Isolation of macromolecules 12ff
Isomerization of albumin 212—213
Isomers 4
Isomorphous replacement method 102—103

Jellies 156

Karaya gum 164
Kelp 168
Keratins 272ff
Keratosulfates 171, 419
Kidney tissue 337
Kinematic viscosity 75
Koksaghyz 116

Lactic dehydrogenase 202, 252
Lactogenic hormone (prolactin) 261—262
Lactoglobulins 59, 64, 70, 196, 201—202
Latex 117ff
Leather 417
Legumin 223
Leukocytes 366
Life, origin of, 434 ff
Light scattering 57ff
Lignin 128, 140
Limit dextrin 152
Lipases 237
Lipids 19, 329, 341, 432
Lipophilic groups, see hydrophobic groups
Lipoproteins 369, 370
Liver tissue 337
Livetin 222
Locust beans 165
Low angle scattering 69, 216
Lymphosarcoma 384
Lyophilization 14
Lysozyme 59, 64, 70, 200—202, 220

Macroglobulins 370, 385—388, 402
Macromolecules 3ff
  fibrous 7ff, 80ff
  globular 7ff, 80ff
  organic, natural 4ff
  synthetic 10
Macroradical 93
Mannan 138ff
Mastication of rubber 122
Maxwell device 64
Membranes 48, 335, 337, 423, 430, 431—432
Mer 7
Mercaptalbumin 209
Mercerization 132
Meromyosins 284ff
Metabolic activity 411—412
Metabolic pathways 399, 407
Metal binding globulin 370
Methemoglobin 70, 231
Methyl cellulose 133

Micelles 9
Micromolecular substances 3
Microsomes 335, 344ff, 396, 397, 413
  degenerated 399
Milling of solids 14, 122
Mincing of tissues 13, 290
Mitochondria 335, 339ff, 397, 413, 422
Mitotic division 422
Mobility, electrophoretic 26, 372, 386, 389
Molecular
  dimensions 61, 65
  shape 64, 69, 80ff
  weight
    averages 7, 43ff
    chemical 4, 41
    determination, 41ff
    number average 43
    physical 41ff
    viscosity average 84
    weight average 44
    Z-average 53
Molecules, large 3
Monomers 94
Monophosphorylase 240
Mucilages 162ff, 165, 166
Mucopolysaccharides 171ff, 419
Mucoproteins 370
Multiple myeloma 389
Muscle
  anatomy 422ff
  contraction 421ff
  development 422
  diseases 429
  proteins 283ff, 421ff
Muscular dystrophy 429
Myelin sheath 431
Myoblasts 422
Myofibril 423
Myoglobin 99, 102ff, 196, 201, 228, 231—233
Myosin 283ff, 423ff
Myotomes 429

Nails (keratin) 273
Nalcite 24
Nativity of macromolecules 12ff
Natural selection 438—440
Neoplastic tissue 383, 395ff
Nerves
  anatomy 430ff
  physiology 430ff
Neurokeratin 273
Nitrocellulose 65, 135ff
Non-Newtonian solutions 90
Nucleases 237
Nucleic acids 4, 5, 15, 82, 90, 288ff, 299ff, 396ff, 429, 433
  biosynthesis 360ff
  chemical composition 301ff
  heterogeneity 303
  molecular weight 61, 304ff
  structure 302ff
Nucleolus 337ff
Nucleoproteins 4, 289ff, 318ff
Nucleosides 300, 360
Nucleotides 300ff, 320, 330, 360, 409, 419
Nucleotide sequence 303, 321, 357
Nucleus of cells 336ff, 397
Number average molecular weight 43
Nutrition 221

Oat hulls 139
Occlusion 71
Ointments 169
Okra 167
Opalescence 58
Optical rotation 106ff, 201—201, 213, 218, 403, 405
Optical rotary dispersion 110—111, 201—202, 220, 240
Organic macromolecules 3
Orientation
  in flow 64
  on stretching 115ff
Origin of life 434ff
Osmometry 54ff
Osmotic pressure 45ff
Ostwald's viscometer 77
Ovalbumin, see albumin, egg
Ovomucin 220
Ovomucoid 220
Oxyhemoglobin 230
Oxytocin 40, 256

Pancreas tissue 337
Papain 202, 239, 245
Paper
  electrophoresis 33ff
  manufacture 139
Papilloma virus 329
Paraffins 4
Paramyosin 283
Partial specific volume 52, 263
Partition chromatography 21
Pathological sera 371, 382ff
Paucidisperse solutions 235
Pectinesterase 160
Pectins, pectinic acids, 155ff
Pentosans 128, 138ff

Pepsin 189, 196, 200—202, 239ff
Pepsinogen 238
Peptide chains, folding 192ff
Permanent waving of hair 274
Permeability 293
Perioxdase 253
Phages (bacteriophages) 317ff, 331ff
Phenol oxidase 251
Phenylthiocarbamyl (PTC) method 187
Phosphate-diester bridge 240
Phosphatases 237
Phosphorylases 152
Phosvitin 200, 222
Phylogenesis 172, 233, 334, 350, 434ff
Plant proteins 223
Plasma, blood 204, 368, 382
Plasmin 381
Plasminogen 381
Platelets in blood 378
Pleated sheet configuration 267ff
Poise 75
Poiseuilles' law 76
Poliomyelitis virus (poliovirus) 319, 327ff
Polydisperse solutions 21
Poly-γ-benzyl-L-glutamate 111, 202
Polyelectrolytes 88, 89, 163, 167, 427
Polygalacturonase 160
Polygalacturonic acid 138ff, 156ff
Polyglucuronic acid 138ff
Polyglycine 436
Polyhedral virus 327
Polyisoprenes 115ff
Polymer
  analogous reactions (conversions) 10, 93
  homologous macromolecules 7, 21, 30, 81
Polymerase 361
Polymers 3ff
  ionized 87ff
Polymolecular solutions 7, 43, 137
Polynucleotides 314
Polyoma viruses 400
Polypeptide chains 5, 185ff
Polypeptides 185ff
Polypyrene chain 5
Polysaccharides 4, 5, 125ff, 419
Pore size 17
Potato
  protein 225
  starch 143
  virus X, 319—320
Prealbumin 373
Precipitability 21
Precipitation
  fractional 19ff
  titration 21
Primer 153
Printing inks 169
Proactivator 381
Procarboxypeptidase 244
Procollagen 412
Prohormone 261
Prolactin 261—262
Prolamines 223
Properdin 370, 374
Prophage 331
Prosthetic group 237
Protamines 291, ff
Proteins 4, 5, 183ff
  abnormal 382ff
  biosynthesis 320, 344ff, 363—364, 396, 403
  in blood 204, 215, 226, 367ff
  configuration (conformation) 183ff, 199ff, 266ff
  crystals 70, 102
  denaturation 194ff, 388
  in disease 382ff
  dissociation (disaggregation) 11, 235, 425, 433
  fibrous 182—182, 265ff, 410ff, 421ff
  flocculation 392
  globular (corpuscular) 182—183
  homogeneity 28ff, 190, 204, 209
  hydration 198
  isolation 12ff
  molecular weight 41, 70, 196, 223, 234, 370
  optical rotation 199ff, 213, 218, 281, 403, 405
  purity 28ff
  residual 296ff
  in seeds 223
  of serum, plasma 368ff, 400ff
  solubility 35, 36, 39, 392
  structure 10, 11, 183ff, 266ff, see also amino acid sequence, disulfide bonds
  subunits 284ff, 322ff, 385
  tissue 352ff
  viscosity 196, 212, 217—218, 281
Prothrombin 370, 378ff
Protofibrinolysin 381
Protopectin 155
Protoplasma 421
Pseudoglobulin 184, 216

Pseudokeratins 273
Pulp 139
Purity of polymers 12ff, 28ff

Quills 273

Radius of gyration 61, 148, 305
Ramie 132
Rayon 132ff
Red cells 227, 366, 367
Redox enzymes 251ff
Regeneration 417
Rennin 202
Replication, reduplication 351ff
Residual protein 296ff
Respiratory proteins 226ff
Retrogradation of starch 144
Rheology 75
Rheumatic fever 417
Rheumatoid arthritis 383, 417
Ribonuclease 196, 200—202, 246ff
Ribonucleic acid (RNA) 112, 310ff, 337ff, 352ff
Ribosomes 345, see also microsomes
Rotating cylinder viscometer 78ff
Rotatory diffusion 64
Rubber
  natural 9, 10, 73, 115ff
  synthetic 120
  vulcanization 122—124

Salmine 292
Sanger's method 186, 255
Sarcolemma 422
Scar tissue 417
Scattering of light 57ff
Schardinger dextrin 154
Seaweeds 162ff
Sedimentation
  constant 52, 182, 223, 234, 263, 305, 370, 384, 389
  diagrams 57, 387, 404
  equilibrium 53ff
  velocity 15, 16, 52ff
Seed proteins 223ff
Semi-colloids 26, 293
Semipermeable membranes 293
Sericin 269ff
Serum
  albumin, see albumin, serum
  globulins, see globulins, serum
  protein fractionation 204ff
Shape of macromolecules 7, 8, 13, 14, 38, 60, 64, 80ff
Shear stress 90
Silk 100, 269ff
Sinews 417
Size of macromolecules 41ff
Skin 173, 175, 275, 410ff
Small angle scattering 69
Smallpox vaccinia virus 330
Solubility of polymers 20, 35
Solvation 73, 137
Somatotropin 263—264
Southern bean mosaic virus 319ff
Species differences, molecular, 116, 143, 149, 156, 157, 172, 208, 210, 228, 230, 233, 255, 263—264, 270, 276, 296, 301, 337
Specific viscosity 76
Sperm, spermatozoids, 420, 428
Spermatogenesis 294
Spheroproteins, see globular proteins
Spider web 270
Spreading in tissues 177, 420
Stabilizers 168
Staining 35
Stalks 128
Starch 93, 142ff
Staudinger's law 84
Stokes' law 15, 53, 79
Stereospecific polymerization 120
Straws 128
Streaming birefringence (double refraction of flow) 64ff
Stretching of polymers 97, 116
Stroma 227
Structural analysis by X-rays 96ff
Structure
  of macromolecules 92ff
  of nucleic acids 300ff
  of polysaccharides 93, 129ff, 145ff, 156ff, 163ff, 173ff
  of proteins 104, 184ff, 241, 247ff, 253, 254ff, 266ff, 293
  of rubber 118ff
Substrate 237
Subunits in macromolecules 11, 284ff, 322ff, 385, 425
Sulfatases 237
Sulfur bridges, see disulfide bridges
Surface denaturation 199
Svedberg unit 52
Swelling, 197, 339
Syneresis 417

Synovial fluid 178
Synthetic rubber 120

Tannic acid 4, 128, 417
Tanning 417
Tapioca 143
Template concept 354, 364
Tendons 173, 275, 414, 417, 422
Terminal amino acids, see amino acids, terminal
Terminal groups
 in nucleic acids 303
 in polysaccharides 94, 130
 in rubber 94
Thermodynamic properties 73
Thickening agents 161, 163, 164, 168
Thixotropy 91
Thrombin 378ff
Thrombocytes 366
Thromboplastin 378ff
Thrombosis 380
Thymus tissue 337
Tissues 290, 337, 397, 410ff, 421ff
Tobacco
 mosaic virus 40, 60, 65, 319ff
 necrosis virus 319ff
 ringspot virus 319ff
Toxins 401ff, 407
Tragacanth gum 164
Transglucosidases 154
Tropocollagen 416
Tropomyosin 201, 283ff, 426
Trypsin 188, 189, 202, 241ff
 inhibitors 202
Trypsinogen 241ff
Tuberculosis 383
Tumors 394ff
Turbidity 58
Turnip yellow mosaic virus 319ff
Tussah silk 270, 271

Ultracentrifuge 54ff
Ultrafiltration 17
Ultrasonic irradiation 15, 280—281, 305
Ultraviolet light, absorption, 105
Unfolding of chain molecules 196ff
Unit cell 98ff

Vaccinia virus 330
Van der Waals forces, see cohesion, hydrophobic bonds
Van't Hoff's equation 46
Vasopressin 256
Velocity gradient 64
Venoms 420
Vicilin 223
Viruses
 animal, 327ff, 399
 plant, 40, 317ff
Viscometry 76ff
Viscose 133
Viscosity 75ff
 absolute 75
 anomalous 90—91
 intrinsic 76, 132, 135, 136, 196, 212, 218, 281, 305
 kinematic 75
 of fibrous macromolecules 132, 135, 136, 159, 176
 of globular macromolecules 80ff, 196, 212, 218
 and molecular shape 83ff
 and molecular weight 84ff, 136, 196, 281, 305
 molecular weight average 84
 reduced 76
 relative 76
 specific 76
Vitellenin 222
Vitellin 222
Volume of macromolecules 61, 85
Vulcanization of rubber 122—123

Water
 bound 70ff
 immobilized 71
Weight average molecular weight 44
Wheat starch 143
White cells 366
Wood 128ff, 137ff, 161
Wool 272ff

Xanthates of cellulose 132—133
X-ray diffraction 69, 96ff, 118, 130, 266ff, 274, 308, 414, 415
Xylan 138—139

Yellow enzyme 252

Zein 223, 224
Zeta potential 26
Zimm plot 61, 62
Zone electrophoresis 26ff
Zymogen 238